# CHEMISTRY
# PROBLEMS

■ *Indicates problem for homework*
■ ■ *Indicates extra-hard problem for homework*

# CHEMISTRY PROBLEMS

*M. J. Sienko*

CORNELL UNIVERSITY

W. A. BENJAMIN, INC.

NEW YORK   AMSTERDAM   1967

# STOICHIOMETRY AND STRUCTURE

W. A. BENJAMIN, INC.
*New York, New York*

# PREFACE

DURING THE PAST DECADE there has occurred, particularly in the U.S., a magnificent surge of self-improvement in the teaching of introductory chemistry. However, as the level of sophistication has risen, with beginning students introduced more and more to the elegant and profound aspects of chemistry, there has appeared an increasing tendency to neglect the old-fashioned aspects of chemical calculation. Still, chemical problem-solving, especially that devoted to stoichiometry and chemical equilibrium, remains the heart of a successful introduction to chemistry.

This book is written in response to a specific demand from teachers and students for a comprehensive introduction to problem-solving. It is intended primarily for self-study either by high school or by college students who wish to develop their skills in chemical calculation to match their mastery of fundamental principles. It can also be used as a classroom text from which study and work assignments can be given. The device I have adopted is to pose 801 problems such as may be encountered in a first-year chemistry course. These problems range from simple mensuration conversions to computations involving complex simultaneous equilibria. About half of the problems are shown with detailed solutions; a considerable number are provided only with directions by which the solution can be achieved. Some (marked with squares— ■ ) are not solved at all, but only an acceptable answer is given. A few, extra-tough ones, have been included for the tyro; these are designated by double squares— ■■. The squared and double-squared problems are intended for self-testing and can conveniently be used as the basis for homework assignments.

Any good this book achieves must be attributed to the stimulus afforded by my students at Cornell; any clarity it possesses must be assigned to the happy circumstance that it was Professors W. C. Bray, H. S. Frank, and J. H. Hildebrand who taught me as a graduate student at Berkeley how to solve freshman chemistry problems. Last but not least, I should like to acknowledge here the enormous stimulation I have received from my esteemed friend and colleague, Professor Robert A. Plane.

M. J. SIENKO

# CONTENTS

# CHEMISTRY
# PROBLEMS

# 1

# THE GRAM-ATOM

A GRAM-ATOM of an element corresponds to the Avogadro number ($6.02 \times 10^{23}$) of atoms of the element. How much a gram-atom weighs depends on what element we are talking about. We need to know the atomic weight of the element. If we take a weight in grams equal numerically to the atomic weight, we have one gram-atom of that element. Thus, for example, since 47.90 is the atomic weight of titanium, *47.90 grams* of titanium constitutes one gram-atom of titanium and contains $6.02 \times 10^{23}$ titanium atoms. Similarly, since 1.008 is the atomic weight of hydrogen, *1.008 grams* of hydrogen constitutes one gram-atom of hydrogen and contains $6.02 \times 10^{23}$ hydrogen atoms.

In recent years there has been some agitation to get rid of the term gram-atom, based on the claim that it is an unnecessary, confusing term which duplicates mole (see Chapter 3). This contention is not true, for the following reasons: (1) gram-atom and mole are not identical except in a few favorable cases (e.g., helium); (2) gram-atom has a long, honorable history in the scientific literature and continues to appear, so that you might as well learn what it is; (3) gram-atom has a specific, invariable meaning for a given element and there is no tricky mumbo-jumbo with formulas as to whether, for example, one gram-atom of sulfur means S or $S_2$ or $S_4$ or $S_6$ or $S_8$ or $S_n$. "One gram-atom

2

of sulfur" means 32.064 grams of sulfur and contains $6.02 \times 10^{23}$ atoms of sulfur no matter what formula you write for it. "One mole of sulfur," on the other hand, is an undefined term, and if you were sent to the stockroom to get a mole of sulfur you could make a case for bringing back almost any quantity from 32.064 grams to several kilograms.

However, this chapter is not meant to be a defense of gram-atoms. What we want to do is to learn by calculation what a gram-atom is and how it fits into chemical problems. To set the stage, we need to review first some of the concepts regarding atomic weight. Atomic weights are simply numbers that tell us something about the relative weights of different atoms. Complications come in because a given element frequently consists of several different kinds of atoms (isotopes) and because the choice of a standard atom for reference is arbitrary.

At the present time, the standard is the so-called "carbon-twelve" atom, frequently designated $C^{12}$. Natural carbon consists almost exclusively of two kinds of isotopes—carbon-twelve and carbon-thirteen. These differ from each other in the make-up of their nuclei: $C^{12}$ has 6 protons and 6 neutrons, $C^{13}$ has 6 protons and 7 neutrons. As might be expected, the $C^{13}$ atom is heavier than the $C^{12}$ atom. In fact, it is found experimentally that the $C^{13}$ atom is 1.08362 times as heavy as the $C^{12}$ atom. If we say—and this is what is done in setting up the present scale of standards—that the $C^{12}$ atom will be assigned a weight (or mass) of exactly twelve units (i.e., 12.0000000 . . .), then the $C^{13}$ atom, being 1.08362 times as heavy, will have to be considered to have a mass of (12)(1.08362), or 13.0034, of these same units. What we are doing, in effect, is defining a unit of mass such that a $C^{12}$ atom has exactly twelve of these units. Then we proceed to describe all other atoms in terms of these units. The unit is sometimes called the atomic mass unit and may be abbreviated a.m.u. In summary, then, the atomic mass unit is one-twelfth of the mass of a carbon-twelve atom, and in terms of this unit the $C^{13}$ atom is said to have a mass of 13.0034 atomic mass units.

Instead of working with individual atoms, the chemist normally works with large numbers of them. In such case, the chances are very good that his atoms will not all be exactly the same but will represent a distribution corresponding to the natural abundance. Consequently, the chemist is interested in an *average* atomic weight that reflects the different isotopes and their relative abundances. For example, in the case of carbon, a randomly selected natural sample will contain 98.892% of the $C^{12}$ variety and 1.108% of the $C^{13}$ variety. The weighted average mass is what is called the chemical atomic weight of the element.

PROBLEM 1    Given a sample of carbon in which the relative abundance of isotopes is 98.892% of $C^{12}$ (mass 12 a.m.u.) and 1.108% of $C^{13}$ (mass 13.0034 a.m.u.), what is the average mass of these atoms when weighted according to their abundance?

SOLUTION: Imagine you have 100,000 atoms total.
98,892 will have a mass of 12 a.m.u. each.
 1,108 will have a mass of 13.0034 a.m.u. each.
The total mass will be $(98,892)(12) + (1,108)(13.0034)$, or 1,201,100 a.m.u.
Divided 100,000 ways, this comes out to be **12.011** a.m.u. as the average weight of each atom.
[*Note:* In the above calculation, the 12 is an exact number, since it is so defined. This means that the number of significant figures in the answer is decided by the number of significant figures given for the abundance.]

On the basis of the calculation given in this problem, we can see why the chemical atomic weight listed in the tables is given as 12.011 for carbon. The atomic weights of all the elements are listed on the next page and also appear on the back of the cover. (Those values given in parentheses are *not* weighted averages over all the isotopes but represent only the mass numbers of the most stable isotopes. In all these cases, the elements are highly radioactive.)

PROBLEM 2    Natural oxygen consists 99.759% of $O^{16}$ with mass 15.9949 a.m.u., 0.037% of $O^{17}$ with mass 16.9991 a.m.u., and 0.204% of $O^{18}$ with mass 17.9991 a.m.u. With this distribution, calculate the chemical atomic weight of natural oxygen.

## Atomic Weights of Elements Referred to $C^{12} = 12.0000$

| Element | Symbol | Atomic weight | Element | Symbol | Atomic weight |
|---------|--------|---------------|---------|--------|---------------|
| Actinium | Ac | (227) | Mercury | Hg | 200.59 |
| Aluminum | Al | 26.9815 | Molybdenum | Mo | 95.94 |
| Americium | Am | (243) | Neodymium | Nd | 144.24 |
| Antimony | Sb | 121.75 | Neon | Ne | 20.183 |
| Argon | Ar | 39.948 | Neptunium | Np | (237) |
| Arsenic | As | 74.9216 | Nickel | Ni | 58.71 |
| Astatine | At | (210) | Niobium | Nb | 92.906 |
| Barium | Ba | 137.34 | Nitrogen | N | 14.0067 |
| Berkelium | Bk | (249) | Osmium | Os | 190.2 |
| Beryllium | Be | 9.0122 | Oxygen | O | 15.9994 |
| Bismuth | Bi | 208.980 | Palladium | Pd | 106.4 |
| Boron | B | 10.811 | Phosphorus | P | 30.9738 |
| Bromine | Br | 79.909 | Platinum | Pt | 195.09 |
| Cadmium | Cd | 112.40 | Plutonium | Pu | (242) |
| Calcium | Ca | 40.08 | Polonium | Po | (210) |
| Californium | Cf | (251) | Potassium | K | 39.102 |
| Carbon | C | 12.01115 | Praseodymium | Pr | 140.907 |
| Cerium | Ce | 140.12 | Promethium | Pm | (145) |
| Cesium | Cs | 132.905 | Protactinium | Pa | (231) |
| Chlorine | Cl | 35.453 | Radium | Ra | (226) |
| Chromium | Cr | 51.996 | Radon | Rn | (222) |
| Cobalt | Co | 58.9332 | Rhenium | Re | 186.2 |
| Copper | Cu | 63.54 | Rhodium | Rh | 102.905 |
| Curium | Cm | (247) | Rubidium | Rb | 85.47 |
| Dysprosium | Dy | 162.50 | Ruthenium | Ru | 101.07 |
| Einsteinium | Es | (254) | Samarium | Sm | 150.35 |
| Erbium | Er | 167.26 | Scandium | Sc | 44.956 |
| Europium | Eu | 151.96 | Selenium | Se | 78.96 |
| Fermium | Fm | (253) | Silicon | Si | 28.086 |
| Fluorine | F | 18.9984 | Silver | Ag | 107.870 |
| Francium | Fr | (223) | Sodium | Na | 22.9898 |
| Gadolinium | Gd | 157.25 | Strontium | Sr | 87.62 |
| Gallium | Ga | 69.72 | Sulfur | S | 32.064 |
| Germanium | Ge | 72.59 | Tantalum | Ta | 180.948 |
| Gold | Au | 196.967 | Technetium | Tc | (99) |
| Hafnium | Hf | 178.49 | Tellurium | Te | 127.60 |
| Helium | He | 4.0026 | Terbium | Tb | 158.924 |
| Holmium | Ho | 164.930 | Thallium | Tl | 204.37 |
| Hydrogen | H | 1.00797 | Thorium | Th | 232.038 |
| Indium | In | 114.82 | Thulium | Tm | 168.934 |
| Iodine | I | 126.9044 | Tin | Sn | 118.69 |
| Iridium | Ir | 192.2 | Titanium | Ti | 47.90 |
| Iron | Fe | 55.847 | Tungsten | W | 183.85 |
| Krypton | Kr | 83.80 | Uranium | U | 238.03 |
| Lanthanum | La | 138.91 | Vanadium | V | 50.942 |
| Lead | Pb | 207.19 | Xenon | Xe | 131.30 |
| Lithium | Li | 6.939 | Ytterbium | Yb | 173.04 |
| Lutetium | Lu | 174.97 | Yttrium | Y | 88.905 |
| Magnesium | Mg | 24.312 | Zinc | Zn | 65.37 |
| Manganese | Mn | 54.9380 | Zirconium | Zr | 91.22 |
| Mendelevium | Md | (256) | | | |

SOLUTION: Out of 100,000 atoms

99,759 will have mass 15.9949 a.m.u. = 1,595,635
37 will have mass 16.9991 a.m.u. = 630
204 will have mass 17.9991 a.m.u. = 3,670
────────                           ───────────
100,000                          = 1,599,935

The average weight is $\dfrac{1,599,935}{100,000}$ , or **15.999** .

Our doubtful digits have been underlined.

■ **PROBLEM 3**     Natural silicon has the following distribution of isotopes: 92.28% $Si^{28}$ with mass 27.9776 a.m.u., 4.67% $Si^{29}$ with mass 28.9773 a.m.u., and 3.05% $Si^{30}$ with mass 29.9735 a.m.u.   What is its chemical atomic weight?
     ANSWER: **28.09**

**PROBLEM 4**     Natural boron consists only of the isotopes $B^{10}$ (mass 10.0130) and $B^{11}$ (mass 11.0093).   If natural boron has an atomic weight of 10.811, what can you conclude about the relative abundance of $B^{10}$ and $B^{11}$ atoms?

SOLUTION: Take 1000 atoms of boron at random.
Let $x$ represent the number that are $B^{10}$ and $y$ the number that are $B^{11}$:

$x + y = 1000$

Each $B^{10}$ atom weighs 10.0130 a.m.u.   $x$ of these $B^{10}$ atoms weigh (10.0130)$(x)$ a.m.u.
Each $B^{11}$ atom weighs 11.0093 a.m.u.   $y$ of these $B^{11}$ atoms weigh (11.0093)$(y)$ a.m.u.
The average weight of the boron atoms is 10.811.   So, 1000 of them would weigh (1000)(10.811) a.m.u.
Since the weight of the $B^{10}$ atoms plus the weight of the $B^{11}$ atoms must add up to the total weight of the 1000, we can write

$(10.0130)(x) + (11.0093)(y) = (10.811)(1000)$

We know $x = 1000 - y$, so we can substitute $(1000 - y)$ in place of $x$ and get

$(10.0130)(1000 - y) + (11.0093)(y) = (10.811)(1000)$

The solution of this equation is $y = 801$.

Therefore, we conclude that **80.1%** of the boron atoms are $B^{11}$ and the remaining **19.9%** are $B^{10}$.

■ **PROBLEM 5**    Natural copper is composed only of $Cu^{63}$ and $Cu^{65}$. The first of these isotopes has a mass of 62.929 a.m.u. and the second, 64.928 a.m.u. Seeing that the atomic weight of copper is 63.54 a.m.u., what can you conclude as to the relative abundance of the two isotopes?

ANSWER: **69.4%** $Cu^{63}$ and **30.6%** $Cu^{65}$

For most chemical considerations, we couldn't care less for the fact that elements frequently consist of several isotopes. For one thing, the chemical behavior of an atom depends very little on small differences in mass such as normally exist between isotopes. For another thing, almost invariably we are dealing with such astronomically large numbers of atoms when we have a finite sample of element that we are justified in working with an average value for the weight of the atoms. For these reasons, the table of atomic weights, where the values for the different elements already take into account the various isotope distributions, is the most useful and the most convenient for carrying out chemical calculations involving weights of atoms. In this sense, when we talk about a gram-atom of an element, we mean a sample of element that weighs as many grams as the number appearing in the atomic weight table. We mean also that this sample contains a total of $6.02 \times 10^{23}$ atoms of the element, some of this isotope and some of that, according to the relative abundance. The number in the atomic weight table tells us directly what average weight we can assign to each atom so as to be able to describe the whole sample as consisting of $6.02 \times 10^{23}$ such average atoms.

**PROBLEM 6**    Given that the atomic weight of copper is 63.54, what is the weight in grams of one average copper atom?

SOLUTION: One gram-atom of copper weighs 63.54 g.
One gram-atom of copper contains $6.02 \times 10^{23}$ atoms.
If $6.02 \times 10^{23}$ atoms weigh 63.54 g, then one atom weighs

$$\frac{63.54 \text{ g}}{6.02 \times 10^{23} \text{ atoms}}, \quad \text{or} \quad \mathbf{1.06 \times 10^{-22} \text{ g per atom.}}$$

■ PROBLEM 7    Given that the atomic weight of chlorine is 35.453, what is the weight in grams of one average chlorine atom?

ANSWER: $5.89 \times 10^{-23}$ g per atom

PROBLEM 8    The isotopic distribution of copper is 69.4% $Cu^{63}$ and 30.6% $Cu^{65}$. How many $Cu^{63}$ atoms are there in one gram-atom?

SOLUTION: One gram-atom contains $6.02 \times 10^{23}$ atoms.
69.4% of these will be $Cu^{63}$.
69.4% of $6.02 \times 10^{23}$ is $4.18 \times 10^{23}$.

PROBLEM 9    What is the weight in grams of one $Cu^{65}$ atom?

SOLUTION: From Problem 5 we learn that the $Cu^{65}$ atom has a mass of 64.928 a.m.u. This means that, if we took one gram-atom of only $Cu^{65}$ atoms, the sample would weigh 64.928 g. It would contain $6.02 \times 10^{23}$ atoms.
If $6.02 \times 10^{23}$ $Cu^{65}$ atoms weigh 64.928 g, one $Cu^{65}$ atom weighs

$$\frac{64.928 \text{ g}}{6.02 \times 10^{23} \text{ atoms}}, \text{ or } 1.08 \times 10^{-22} \text{ g per atom.}$$

PROBLEM 10    How many atoms are there in 1.00 g of copper?

SOLUTION: We know there are always $6.02 \times 10^{23}$ atoms of any element in one gram-atom of that element.
Therefore, if we can calculate what fraction of a gram-atom we have, we know what fraction of $6.02 \times 10^{23}$ we have.
One gram-atom of copper weighs 63.54 g.

One g of copper is $\dfrac{1.00 \cancel{g}}{63.54 \cancel{g}/\text{gram-atom}}$, or 0.0157 gram-atom.

One gram-atom contains $6.02 \times 10^{23}$ atoms.
0.0157 gram-atom contains

$$(0.0157 \cancel{\text{gram-atom}}) \left( 6.02 \times 10^{23} \frac{\text{atoms}}{\cancel{\text{gram-atom}}} \right),$$

or $9.45 \times 10^{21}$ atoms.

PROBLEM 11    How many atoms are there in 3.80 g of fluorine?

SOLUTION: The atomic weight of fluorine is 18.9984 a.m.u.
One gram-atom of fluorine weighs 18.9984 g.

3.80 g fluorine is $\dfrac{3.80 \text{ g}}{18.9984 \text{ g/gram-atom}}$ , or 0.200 gram-atom.

One gram-atom of any element contains $6.02 \times 10^{23}$ atoms.
0.200 gram-atom contains

$$(0.200 \text{ gram-atom}) \left( 6.02 \times 10^{23} \ \dfrac{\text{atoms}}{\text{gram-atom}} \right),$$

or $1.20 \times 10^{23}$ atoms.

PROBLEM 12    Given that the atomic weight of bromine is 79.909, what would be the weight of $4.63 \times 10^{20}$ bromine atoms?

SOLUTION: One gram-atom contains $6.02 \times 10^{23}$ atoms.

$4.63 \times 10^{20}$ atoms is $\dfrac{4.63 \times 10^{20} \text{ atoms}}{6.02 \times 10^{23} \text{ atoms/gram-atom}}$ ,

or $7.69 \times 10^{-4}$ gram-atom.
One gram-atom of bromine weighs 79.909 g.
$7.69 \times 10^{-4}$ gram-atom of bromine weighs

$$(7.69 \times 10^{-4} \text{ gram-atom}) \left( 79.909 \ \dfrac{\text{g}}{\text{gram-atom}} \right), \text{ or } 0.0614 \text{ g.}$$

PROBLEM 13    Which of the following samples contains the largest number of atoms: (a) 6.70 g iron; (b) 0.11 gram-atom iron; (c) $7.83 \times 10^{22}$ atoms iron?

SOLUTION: We need to convert all these samples to the same units in order to make comparison. In general, both from the standpoint of instant recognition and greatest general utility in making calculations, gram-atoms is preferred over grams and over atoms. The instant recognition comes from the fact that we always know that one gram-atom of anything has $6.02 \times 10^{23}$ atoms; the utility comes from the fact that, in specifying the number of gram-atoms, we are really saying something about the numbers of atoms without getting involved with large exponents and huge numbers.

(a) Atomic weight of iron is 55.847 a.m.u.

$$6.70 \text{ g} = \frac{6.70 \text{ g}}{55.847 \text{ g/gram-atom}} = 0.120 \text{ gram-atom}$$

(b) 0.11 gram-atom                = 0.11 gram-atom

(c) One gram-atom contains $6.02 \times 10^{23}$ atoms.

$$\frac{7.83 \times 10^{22} \text{ atoms}}{6.02 \times 10^{23} \text{ atoms/gram-atom}} = 0.130 \text{ gram-atom}$$

Comparing these by the same measure, (c) represents the largest number of gram-atoms and, therefore, the largest number of atoms.

So far in this chapter the emphasis has been on conversions involving grams, atoms, and gram-atoms. The purpose of the calculations has been to show that, given the atomic weight table and the fact that one gram-atom contains $6.02 \times 10^{23}$ atoms, we can translate information given to us in measurable quantities (e.g., weight) to quantities that are useful for monitoring chemical reaction (e.g., number of atoms). In the following problems we shall see how the latter is done. At this stage, the point to be made is that the concept of gram-atom has an importance that cannot be overemphasized. It is *the* way by which we keep tabs on the number of atoms involved in chemical change. If by now you are still uncertain what a gram-atom is, you should carefully review the material we have just gone through. Otherwise, the going from here on is slippery indeed.

There are other methods for solving the following problems using chemical equations, as discussed in Chapter 4, but our main purpose at this point is to get a feeling for manipulating gram-atoms. Consequently, you should work out the following problems without recourse to chemical equations or to tricky substitution-in-formula methods. If needed atomic weights are not stated in the problem, look them up in the back of the book.

PROBLEM 14    You wish to carry out a chemical reaction in which four atoms of cerium (atomic weight 140.12) combine with three atoms of sulfur (atomic weight 32.064). You have 2.50 g cerium. How many grams of sulfur must you take to satisfy all the cerium atoms?

SOLUTION: Weights tell us little about numbers of atoms unless we put some information in to take care of the different atomic weights. By converting data given in grams to gram-atoms we are effectively counting the numbers of atoms.

Atomic weight of cerium is 140.12.

One gram-atom of cerium is 140.12 g.

$$2.50 \text{ g cerium} = \frac{2.50 \text{ g}}{140.12 \text{ g/gram-atom}} = 0.0178 \text{ gram-atom}$$

Our reaction demands three atoms of sulfur per four atoms of cerium. This is the same as requiring three gram-atoms of sulfur per four gram-atoms of cerium.

One gram-atom of cerium requires $\frac{3}{4}$ gram-atom of sulfur.

0.0178 gram-atom of cerium requires $\frac{3}{4}(0.0178)$, or 0.0134, gram-atom of sulfur.

Atomic weight of sulfur is 32.064.

One gram-atom of sulfur weighs 32.064 g.

0.0134 gram-atom of sulfur weighs (0.0134 gram-atom)(32.064 g/gram-atom), or **0.430 g.**

**PROBLEM 15**   When iron is heated in air, it picks up oxygen to the extent of three atoms of oxygen for each two atoms of iron.  If 1.50 g of iron is so heated, what will the total weight of product be?

SOLUTION:

$$1.50 \text{ g iron} = \frac{1.50 \text{ g}}{55.847 \text{ g/gram-atom}} = 0.0269 \text{ gram-atom.}$$

Two atoms of iron require three atoms of oxygen.

Two gram-atoms of iron require three gram-atoms of oxygen.

0.0269 gram-atom of iron requires $(0.0269)(\frac{3}{2})$ gram-atom of oxygen.

One gram-atom of oxygen equals 15.9994 g.

$(0.0269)(\frac{3}{2})$ gram-atom of oxygen equals $(0.0269)(\frac{3}{2})(15.9994)$, or 0.646 g.

Total weight of product = iron + oxygen

$$= 1.50 + 0.646 = \textbf{2.15 g}$$

**PROBLEM 16**   When silver and sulfur are heated together, they combine in such a way that two atoms of silver match each atom of sulfur.  If you start with 10.0 g of silver and 1.00 g of sulfur, what is the maximum amount of desired product you can get?

SOLUTION: This is a very common type of problem—sometimes called "excess problem"—where two reagents are mixed in more or less arbitrary amounts, but for which the combination requirement is rigidly fixed by the chemistry. In this case, we require two atoms of silver per atom of sulfur even though this may not be the ratio in which the atoms are made available. In such an event, one of the reagents limits the amount of reaction product, and the other reagent is left over in excess.

The atomic weight of silver is 107.870.

One gram-atom of silver weighs 107.870 g.

10.0 g silver is $\dfrac{10.0 \text{ g}}{107.87 \text{ g/gram-atom}}$, or 0.0927 gram-atom.

The atomic weight of sulfur is 32.064.

One gram-atom of sulfur weighs 32.064 g.

1.00 g sulfur is $\dfrac{1.00 \text{ g}}{32.064 \text{ g/gram-atom}}$, or 0.0312 gram-atom.

If we are going to match two silver atoms for each sulfur atom, we will need two gram-atoms of silver for each gram-atom of sulfur. For 0.0312 gram-atom of sulfur, we need (2)(0.0312), or 0.0624, gram-atom of silver. We have more than enough silver, so some of the silver atoms will remain uncombined. The product is thus limited by the sulfur available.

To use all the 0.0312 gram-atom of sulfur, we need to use 0.0624 gram-atom of silver.

The product will be made up, then, of 0.0312 gram-atom of sulfur plus 0.0624 gram-atom of silver.

0.0312 gram-atom of sulfur

$$= (0.0312 \text{ gram-atom}) \left( 32.064 \ \frac{\text{g}}{\text{gram-atom}} \right) = 1.00 \text{ g}.$$

0.0624 gram-atom of silver

$$= (0.0624 \text{ gram-atom}) \left( 107.870 \ \frac{\text{g}}{\text{gram-atom}} \right) = 6.73 \text{ g}.$$

Total product = 1.00 + 6.73 = 7.73 g .

PROBLEM 17    Analysis of chlorophyll shows that it consists 2.68% of magnesium. Given 1.00 g chlorophyll, how many magnesium atoms does it contain?

SOLUTION: 2.68% of 1.00 g is 0.0268 g.
Thus, the sample contains 0.0268 g of magnesium.
Atomic weight of magnesium is 24.312.
One gram-atom of magnesium weighs 24.312 g.

$$0.0268 \text{ g magnesium} = \frac{0.0268 \text{ g}}{24.312 \text{ g/gram-atom}} = 0.00110 \text{ gram-atom.}$$

One gram-atom contains $6.02 \times 10^{23}$ atoms.
0.00110 gram-atom contains (0.00110 gram-atom) $\times$

$$\left( 6.02 \times 10^{23} \frac{\text{atoms}}{\text{gram-atom}} \right), \text{ or } \mathbf{6.62 \times 10^{20} \text{ atoms.}}$$

PROBLEM 18    Morphine is a complex
compound which contains, besides other constituents, 67.3% carbon
and 4.6% nitrogen. What would be the relative number of carbon and
nitrogen atoms in this compound?

SOLUTION: Take 100 g morphine.
67.3%, or 67.3 g, will be carbon.
4.6%, or 4.6 g, will be nitrogen.
The atomic weight of carbon is 12.011.

$$67.3 \text{ g carbon} = \frac{67.3 \text{ g}}{12.011 \text{ g/gram-atom}} = 5.60 \text{ gram-atoms.}$$

The atomic weight of nitrogen is 14.0067.

$$4.6 \text{ g nitrogen} = \frac{4.6 \text{ g}}{14.0067 \text{ g/gram-atom}} = 0.33 \text{ gram-atom.}$$

The relative number of gram-atoms tells us directly the relative number
    of atoms.   (If you don't believe it, multiply each by $6.02 \times 10^{23}$
    atoms per gram-atom.)
5.60 gram-atoms of carbon per 0.33 gram-atom of nitrogen is the same
    as 5.60 atoms of carbon per 0.33 atom of nitrogen, or **17**.

PROBLEM 19    In making transistors,
one needs to control the concentration of impurity very carefully.
Suppose you wanted to make a germanium transistor containing $1.0 \times 10^{18}$ boron atoms per cc as impurity.  If the density of germanium is
5.35 g per cc, what relative weights of germanium and boron need to be
mixed?

SOLUTION: Let us make 1 cc of product. For this, we need 5.35 g germanium. (We can safely ignore the tiny effect of the boron impurity on the density.)

We also need $1.0 \times 10^{18}$ boron atoms.

We know $6.02 \times 10^{23}$ atoms is one gram-atom of anything.

$1.0 \times 10^{18}$ atoms must be $\dfrac{1.0 \times 10^{18} \text{ atoms}}{6.02 \times 10^{23} \text{ atoms/gram-atom}}$

$= 1.7 \times 10^{-6}$ gram-atom.

One gram-atom of boron is 10.821 g.

$1.7 \times 10^{-6}$ gram-atom of boron is $(1.7 \times 10^{-6}$ gram-atom) $\times$

$\left(10.821 \dfrac{\text{g}}{\text{gram-atom}}\right)$, or $1.8 \times 10^{-5}$ g.

To get the desired product, we need to mix **5.35 g** germanium and **$1.8 \times 10^{-5}$ g** boron.

■ PROBLEM 20    The "solar wind" bombards the lunar surface with about $1 \times 10^{11}$ hydrogen atoms per cm$^2$ per sec. What weight of hydrogen would thus be deposited on 1 cm$^2$ of lunar surface in $5 \times 10^9$ years?

ANSWER: **30 kg**

■ PROBLEM 21    A dab of mercury about the size of a fly speck would have a weight of $1 \times 10^{-5}$ g. How many mercury atoms in such a sample?

ANSWER: **$3 \times 10^{16}$**

■ PROBLEM 22    Given that the atomic weight of hydrogen is 1.00797 a.m.u., what is the weight in grams of one average hydrogen atom?

ANSWER: **$1.67 \times 10^{-24}$**

■ PROBLEM 23    Natural hydrogen consists of protium (H$^1$) and deuterium (H$^2$) isotopes. If the respective masses of these isotopes are 1.00781 and 2.01406 a.m.u., what can you conclude about the relative abundance of H$^1$ and H$^2$ in natural hydrogen (atomic weight 1.00797)?

ANSWER: **99,984 H$^1$ atoms for each 16 H$^2$ atoms**

■ PROBLEM 24    The element chromium has the following naturally occurring isotope distribution: 4.31% Cr$^{50}$ (49.946 a.m.u.); 83.76% Cr$^{52}$(51.940 a.m.u.); 9.55% Cr$^{53}$(52.941

a.m.u.);  2.38% $Cr^{54}$(53.939 a.m.u.).   Calculate the atomic weight
that corresponds to this distribution.
ANSWER: **52.00**


■ **PROBLEM 25**   You wish to make a
compound in which there are two chromium atoms for each three sulfur atoms.  If you have only 5.00 g sulfur available, how many grams
of chromium should you take?
ANSWER: **5.40 g**


■ **PROBLEM 26**   You want to make
some gallium arsenide, in which the atomic ratio must be one gallium
to one arsenic atom.  Starting with 1.00 g gallium and 1.00 g arsenic
and forming the maximum amount of product, which element will be
left over and how much?
ANSWER: **0.070 g of gallium**


■ **PROBLEM 27**   Nicotine is a complex
compound whose weight is made up of 74.0% carbon, 8.7% hydrogen,
and 17.3% nitrogen.  In terms of atoms, what per cent of all the atoms
in the compound are carbon atoms?
ANSWER: **38.5%**


■ **PROBLEM 28**   In igneous rocks, the
four most numerous atoms are those of oxygen, silicon, aluminum, and
sodium.  For every 100 silicon atoms, there are 296 oxygen atoms,
30.5 aluminum atoms, and 12.4 sodium atoms.  Suppose you had an
igneous rock that consisted only of those atoms in this ratio.  What per
cent of the rock's weight would be contributed by the aluminum?
ANSWER: **9.51%**


■ **PROBLEM 29**   Pure silicon is a poor
conductor of electricity, but if it has the right impurity it can be very
good as a conductor.  Suppose you want to have $3.60 \times 10^{18}$ arsenic
atoms per cc present as impurity in the silicon.  If the density of silicon is 2.42 g per cc, what weights of silicon and arsenic must you take
to make up 1.00 cc of arsenic-doped silicon?
ANSWER: **2.42 g silicon and 0.000448 g arsenic**


■ **PROBLEM 30**   A curie is defined as
the quantity of radioactive material that undergoes $3.7 \times 10^{10}$ disin-

tegrations per second.  Suppose you have 1 curie of radium.  What would be its weight loss per second, assuming that the radium atoms are undergoing disintegration to produce helium atoms (that go off as a gas) and other atoms which stay in the solid?

ANSWER: $2.5 \times 10^{-13}$ g per second

■ PROBLEM 31   Solid  palladium  can swallow up hydrogen so that on the average each palladium atom picks up 0.60 hydrogen atom.  On this basis, what gain in weight would you expect for 1.00 g palladium when it picks up hydrogen?

ANSWER: $5.6 \times 10^{-3}$ g

■ PROBLEM 32   Suppose  you  want  to synthesize a compound in which there are two indium atoms and four sulfur atoms for every magnesium atom.  Your starting resources are 1.00 g each of magnesium, indium, and sulfur.  What is the maximum weight of compound you can synthesize?

ANSWER: 1.66 g

■ PROBLEM 33   What is the total weight of the following mixture: 0.150 gram-atom of mercury plus 0.150 g of mercury plus $4.53 \times 10^{22}$ atoms of mercury?

ANSWER: 45.3 g

■ PROBLEM 34   How many gram-atoms in one atom of mercury?

ANSWER: $1.66 \times 10^{-23}$ gram-atom

■ PROBLEM 35   If the density of liquid mercury is 13.546 g per cc, what average volume can be assigned to each mercury atom?  Assuming it to be a sphere, what would be its radius?

ANSWER: $2.46 \times 10^{-23}$ cc; $1.80 \times 10^{-8}$ cm

■ PROBLEM 36   Copper atoms pack in the solid state so that atom centers fall on the vertices of a cube and at the centers of the cube faces.    Assuming that copper atoms are hard spheres and noting that the density of solid copper is 8.92 g per cc, calculate the radius of the copper atom, making due allowance for the empty space.

ANSWER: $1.28 \times 10^{-8}$ cm

# 2

## CHEMICAL FORMULAS

THERE ARE three major kinds of chemical formulas: (1) the *simplest* (also called *empirical*); (2) the *molecular;* and (3) the *structural.* The structural formula tells which atoms are connected to which atoms and how these are arranged in space; the molecular formula tells us how many atoms of the various kinds exist in the individual entity we call a molecule, but it doesn't say anything about how they are arranged; the simplest formula tells us only the relative number of atoms of the different sorts in the compound. As a specific example, CH is the simplest formula for benzene, $C_6H_6$ is its molecular formula, and the picture in Figure 56 is its structural formula. All three—CH, $C_6H_6$, and Figure 56—represent the same material, but they give varying degrees of information about it. The structural formula is the most informative because, from it, both the molecular and the simplest formulas can be deduced.

In chemistry, it is usually the simplest formula that is discovered first, since it comes directly out of the chemical analysis of the compound. For the molecular and structural formulas, other data are needed—specifically, what the behavior properties of the material are.

The simplest formula specifies the relative number of atoms of different kinds in the compound. It does this by means of subscripts affixed to the symbols of the various elements. For example, $A_xB_y$

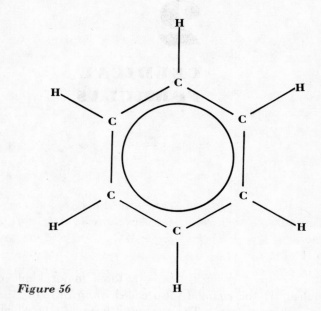

*Figure 56*

would represent a compound of elements A and B in which there are $x$ atoms of A for every $y$ atoms of B.   Because the gram-atom is just another way of counting atoms, the simplest formula also tells us the relative number of gram-atoms in the compound.   Thus, $A_xB_y$ means there are $x$ gram-atoms of element A per $y$ gram-atoms of B in this compound.   In practice, the setting up of simplest formulas usually goes the other way: from the analysis data (which are usually per cent by weight) we first figure out the relative number of gram-atoms and use this same ratio to give the relative number of atoms.

PROBLEM 37   Given a compound which contains one atom of magnesium for each two atoms of indium for each four atoms of sulfur.   What is its simplest formula?

SOLUTION: The symbols of the elements are Mg, In, and S.
One atom of magnesium would be indicated by subscript 1 on Mg.
Two atoms of indium would be indicated by subscript 2 on In.
Four atoms of sulfur would be indicated by subscript 4 on S.
The result is $Mg_1In_2S_4$, or $\mathbf{MgIn_2S_4}$, since the subscript "one" is understood when none is written.

**PROBLEM 38** What is the simplest formula of a compound which consists of 0.25 gram-atom cobalt per 0.50 gram-atom silicon?

SOLUTION: The symbols for cobalt and silicon are Co and Si.

We could designate the compound as $Co_{0.25}Si_{0.50}$, since we are thereby indicating the relative number of gram-atoms of cobalt and silicon in the compound.

Because of the desire to avoid decimals in the subscripts, we usually clear fractions—in this case, by dividing through by 0.25.

The result is $Co_{\frac{0.25}{0.25}}Si_{\frac{0.50}{0.25}}$, or $Co_1Si_2$, or **$CoSi_2$** .

[*Note:* This business of clearing fractions is not invariably followed. For example, as we learn more about the solid state, we get more used to formulas such as $Na_{0.31}V_2O_5$ or $WO_{2.90}$. These may have shocked John Dalton in 1805, but they are perfectly acceptable nowadays. The point is we try to have only whole numbers as subscripts, but not if it means getting into ridiculously large values for some of the subscripts.]

**PROBLEM 39** What is the simplest formula of a compound which consists of 7.0 g nitrogen for each gram of hydrogen?

SOLUTION: The data are given as weights. For the formula, we need to know about atoms; so the first thing to do is to translate weights to gram-atoms.

$$7.0 \text{ g nitrogen} = \frac{7.0 \text{ g}}{14.0 \text{ g/gram-atom}} = 0.50 \text{ gram-atom.}$$

$$1.0 \text{ g hydrogen} = \frac{1.0 \text{ g}}{1.008 \text{ g/gram-atom}} = 1.0 \text{ gram-atom.}$$

Therefore, the simplest formula is $N_{0.50}H_{1.0}$, or **$NH_2$** .

(We have cleared fractions by dividing both subscripts by 0.50. Since we are talking relative numbers, the ratio 0.50 to 1.0 is just as informative as the ratio 1 to 2.)

**PROBLEM 40** What is the simplest formula of a compound that shows the following analysis: 76.86% carbon, 12.90% hydrogen, 10.24% oxygen?

SOLUTION: Assume we have 100 g compound.

76.86% carbon would mean 76.86 g carbon.

12.90% hydrogen would mean 12.90 g hydrogen.

10.24% oxygen would mean 10.24 g oxygen.

Atomic weight of carbon is 12.011 a.m.u.  This means one gram-atom
carbon weighs 12.011 g.

$$76.86 \text{ g carbon} = \frac{76.86 \text{ g}}{12.011 \text{ g/gram-atom}} = 6.399 \text{ gram-atoms C.}$$

Atomic weight of hydrogen is 1.00797 a.m.u.  This means one gram-atom hydrogen weighs 1.00797 g.

$$12.90 \text{ g hydrogen} = \frac{12.90 \text{ g}}{1.00797 \text{ g/gram-atom}} = 12.80 \text{ gram-atoms H.}$$

Atomic weight of oxygen is 15.9994 a.m.u.  This means one gram-atom oxygen weighs 15.9994 g.

$$10.24 \text{ g oxygen} = \frac{10.24 \text{ g}}{15.9994 \text{ g/gram-atom}} = 0.6400 \text{ gram-atom O.}$$

The formula can be written $C_{6.399}H_{12.80}O_{0.6400}$.

If we divide all the subscripts by 0.6400, we get $C_{10}H_{20}O$ as the simplest formula.

PROBLEM 41    A given compound consists of $1.20 \times 10^{23}$ atoms carbon, $3.61 \times 10^{23}$ atoms hydrogen, and $6.02 \times 10^{22}$ atoms oxygen.  What is its simplest formula?

SOLUTION: For the simplest formula, we need to know the relative number of atoms.  As the basis of reference, it is usually most efficient to consider the smallest number—i.e., $6.02 \times 10^{22}$ atoms oxygen:

$$\frac{1.20 \times 10^{23} \text{ atoms C}}{6.02 \times 10^{22} \text{ atoms O}} = 2 \text{ atoms C per atom O}$$

$$\frac{3.61 \times 10^{23} \text{ atoms H}}{6.02 \times 10^{22} \text{ atoms O}} = 6 \text{ atoms H per atom O}$$

$$\frac{6.02 \times 10^{22} \text{ atoms O}}{6.02 \times 10^{22} \text{ atoms O}} = 1 \text{ atom O per atom O}$$

Thus, we have two carbon atoms and six hydrogen atoms per atom of oxygen.  Consequently, the simplest formula is $C_2H_6O$.

PROBLEM 42   A given bottle which contains only one pure compound can be described as containing the following ingredients: 0.90 gram-atom carbon plus $1.445 \times 10^{24}$ atoms hydrogen plus 4.8 g oxygen.   What is the compound's simplest formula?

SOLUTION: Translate all the data into gram-atoms.

0.90 gram-atom carbon = **0.90 gram-atom carbon**

$$1.445 \times 10^{24} \text{ atoms hydrogen} = \frac{1.445 \times 10^{24} \text{ atoms}}{6.02 \times 10^{23} \text{ atoms/gram-atom}}$$

$$= \textbf{2.40 gram-atoms hydrogen}$$

$$4.8 \text{ g oxygen} = \frac{4.8 \text{ g}}{15.9994 \text{ g/gram-atom}}$$

$$= \textbf{0.30 gram-atom oxygen}$$

Thus, the gram-atoms of C, H, and O in the compound are in the ratio of 0.90 to 2.40 to 0.30.

We can write $C_{0.90}H_{2.40}O_{0.30}$, or, clearing the decimals by division through with 0.30, $\textbf{C}_3\textbf{H}_8\textbf{O}$.

In all the above problems, we start with data on the composition of a material and end up writing the simplest formula.   This is a typical operation that is routinely performed, for example, when a new compound is first discovered.   The reason for making such a fuss over writing the simplest formula is that, once it is obtained, various pieces of information can be drawn from it.   Not only is the relative number of atoms immediately obvious, but also by plugging in atomic weight information we get data on weight relations as well.   Specifically, we can easily determine what per cent of the total weight is contributed by each of the several elements.   This might be useful, for example, in evaluating analytical results.

PROBLEM 43   Given the material copper sulfide, for which the simplest formula is $Cu_2S$.   What can you say about the per cent (by weight) composition of the sample?

SOLUTION: The simplest formula $Cu_2S$ tells us that the compound contains 2 atoms copper per atom of sulfur, or, stated alternatively, 2 gram-atoms copper per gram-atom of sulfur.

$$2 \text{ gram-atoms copper} = (2 \text{ gram-atoms}) \left( 63.54 \ \frac{g}{\text{gram-atom}} \right)$$
$$= 127.1 \text{ g}$$
$$1 \text{ gram-atom sulfur} = (1 \text{ gram-atom}) \left( 32.064 \ \frac{g}{\text{gram-atom}} \right)$$
$$= 32.064 \text{ g}$$

In other words, a representative sample would contain 127.1 g copper for each 32.064 g sulfur. The total weight of this sample would be $127.1 + 32.064 = 159.2$ g.

$$\% \text{ copper} = \frac{127.1 \text{ g copper}}{159.2 \text{ g total sample}} \times 100 = \mathbf{79.84\%.}$$

$$\% \text{ sulfur} = \frac{32.064 \text{ g sulfur}}{159.2 \text{ g total sample}} \times 100 = \mathbf{20.14\%.}$$

PROBLEM 44    Given a sample of compound for which the simplest formula is $Sc_2O_3$. If the sample weighs 5.00 g, how many atoms of scandium does it contain?

SOLUTION: The compound contains 2 gram-atoms Sc per 3 gram-atoms O.

$$2 \text{ gram-atoms Sc} = (2 \text{ gram-atoms}) \left( 44.956 \ \frac{g}{\text{gram-atom}} \right)$$
$$= 89.912 \text{ g}$$
$$3 \text{ gram-atoms O} = (3 \text{ gram-atoms}) \left( 15.9994 \ \frac{g}{\text{gram-atom}} \right)$$
$$= 47.998 \text{ g}$$

Thus, the weight composition of the sample is 89.912 g scandium per 47.998 g oxygen.

$$\% \text{ scandium} = \frac{89.912 \text{ g Sc}}{(89.912 + 47.998) \text{ g total}} \times 100 = 65.2\%.$$

Given the 5.00-g sample of $Sc_2O_3$, we know now that 65.2% of it, or $(0.652)(5.00)$ g, is scandium. Once we know how many grams of scandium we have, we can divide by the atomic weight to get the number of gram-atoms, and then multiply by $6.02 \times 10^{23}$ to get the number of atoms.

$$\frac{(5.00)(0.652) \text{ g}}{44.956 \text{ g/gram-atom}} \times 6.02 \times 10^{23} \ \frac{\text{atoms}}{\text{gram-atom}} = \mathbf{4.37 \times 10^{22} \text{ atoms.}}$$

PROBLEM 45    Given two minerals of copper for which the simplest formulas are $Cu_5FeS_4$ and $Cu_2S$. Which of these, on a per-cent-by-weight-of-copper basis, can be considered a richer mineral for copper?

SOLUTION: In $Cu_5FeS_4$ we have

$$5 \text{ gram-atoms Cu} = (5 \text{ gram-atoms}) \left( 63.54 \, \frac{g}{\text{gram-atom}} \right) = 317.7 \text{ g.}$$

$$1 \text{ gram-atom Fe} = (1 \text{ gram-atom}) \left( 55.85 \, \frac{g}{\text{gram-atom}} \right) = 55.85 \text{ g.}$$

$$4 \text{ gram-atoms S} = (4 \text{ gram-atoms}) \left( 32.064 \, \frac{g}{\text{gram-atom}} \right) = 128.26 \text{ g.}$$

Out of a total weight of $(317.7 + 55.85 + 128.26)$ g, or 501.8 g, we have 317.7 g copper.

$$\% \text{ Cu} = \frac{317.7 \text{ g Cu}}{501.8 \text{ g total}} \times 100 = 63.31\%.$$

In $Cu_2S$ we have

$$2 \text{ gram-atoms Cu} = (2 \text{ gram-atoms}) \left( 63.54 \, \frac{g}{\text{gram-atom}} \right) = 127.1 \text{ g.}$$

$$1 \text{ gram-atom S} = (1 \text{ gram-atom}) \left( 32.064 \, \frac{g}{\text{gram-atom}} \right) = 32.064 \text{ g.}$$

Out of a total weight of $(127.1 + 32.064)$ g, or 159.2 g, we have 127.1 g copper.

$$\% \text{ Cu} = \frac{127.1 \text{ g Cu}}{159.2 \text{ g total}} \times 100 = 79.84\%.$$

Evidently, $Cu_2S$ is a richer source of Cu than is $Cu_5FeS_4$.

In this chapter we cannot take up the deduction of *molecular* formulas, since we do not yet have the proper background in properties of materials—specifically, those of gases and solutions. However, once a molecular formula has been determined, per cent composition by weight can be calculated from it in the same way we have done for simplest formulas. This is done in the following problems, where the tip-off that we are dealing with molecular formulas instead of simplest formulas comes from the fact that the subscripts have a common divisor (e.g., $C_6H_6$ could be written as CH).

PROBLEM 46 What is the per cent composition by weight of benzene, $C_6H_6$?

SOLUTION: The formula says there are 6 gram-atoms carbon for each 6 gram-atoms hydrogen.

$$6 \text{ gram-atoms C} = (6 \text{ gram-atoms}) \left( 12.011 \frac{g}{\text{gram-atom}} \right) = 72.066 \text{ g}.$$

$$6 \text{ gram-atoms H} = (6 \text{ gram-atoms}) \left( 1.00797 \frac{g}{\text{gram-atom}} \right) = 6.0478 \text{ g}.$$

Total weight is $72.066 + 6.0478 = 78.114$ g.

$$\% \text{ C} = \frac{72.066 \text{ g C}}{78.114 \text{ g total}} \times 100 = 92.257\%.$$

$$\% \text{ H} = \frac{6.0478 \text{ g H}}{78.114 \text{ g total}} \times 100 = 7.7423\%.$$

■ PROBLEM 47    In a given reaction 2.04 g vanadium combines with 1.93 g sulfur to give a pure compound. What is the simplest formula of the product?

ANSWER: $V_2S_3$

■ PROBLEM 48    Under appropriate conditions, vanadium and sulfur can combine to form different compounds. What would be the simplest formulas of the compounds corresponding to the following combinations: (a) 0.15 gram-atom vanadium and $9.03 \times 10^{22}$ atoms sulfur; (b) 38.9% by weight vanadium and 61.1% sulfur; (c) 5.094 g vanadium and 0.15 gram-atom sulfur?

ANSWER: (a) $VS$; (b) $V_2S_5$; (c) $V_2S_3$

■ PROBLEM 49    Given that the simplest formula of nicotine is $C_5H_7N$, calculate its per cent composition by weight.

ANSWER: 74.03% carbon, 8.70% hydrogen, 17.27% nitrogen

■ PROBLEM 50    What would be the simplest formula of a compound having the following composition: 75.42% (by weight) carbon, 6.63% hydrogen, 8.38% nitrogen, and 9.57% oxygen?

ANSWER: $C_{21}H_{22}N_2O_2$

■ PROBLEM 51    The elements silver, molybdenum, and sulfur are brought together so only the compound $Ag_2MoS_4$ can be formed. Starting with 8.63 g silver, 3.36 g molybdenum, and 4.81 g sulfur, what is the maximum amount of $Ag_2MoS_4$ that can be formed?

ANSWER: **15.41 g**

■ PROBLEM 52    A given solid oxide $TiO_2$ is heated in hydrogen with the result that some of the oxygen is pulled out of the material.  If after the heating 1.5980 g $TiO_2$ is found to show a weight of 1.4380 g, what would be the simplest formula of the product?

ANSWER: **$Ti_2O_3$**

■ PROBLEM 53    A mixture is made up of substance A and substance B only.  Pure substance A has the simplest formula $CH_4O$, and pure substance B has the simplest formula $C_2H_6O$.  If analysis of the final mixture shows 37.0% oxygen, in what ratio of weights were A and B mixed?

ANSWER: **5.69 g B per 1.00 g A**

■ PROBLEM 54    When a perfectly pure crystal of NaCl is heated in sodium vapor, the crystal picks up some extra sodium atoms and fits them into its structure.  How many sodium atoms would a 1.00-g crystal of NaCl need to pick up in order to be converted from NaCl to $Na_{1.001}Cl$?

ANSWER: **$1 \times 10^{19}$**

■ PROBLEM 55    A classic freshman experiment is to heat a piece of copper wire in the presence of excess sulfur until the copper combines with sulfur to its maximum extent. Any sulfur left uncombined boils off, so the increase in weight suffered by the copper tells directly how much sulfur has combined with the given weight of copper.  In a typical experiment, it is observed that 1.2517 g Cu goes to 1.5723 g product.  What is the precise simplest formula of the product obtained?  What would have been the weight of final product if it really had gone to pure $Cu_2S$?

ANSWER: **$Cu_{1.970}S$; 1.5675 g**

■ PROBLEM 56    When tin is heated in concentrated nitric acid, the tin is converted from Sn to $SnO_2$.  What increase in weight would you expect for a piece of tin weighing 0.356 g if it were so converted?

ANSWER: **0.0960 g**

■ PROBLEM 57    For a long time the term "pure boron" was applied to something which was really $AlB_{12}$. What per cent of "pure boron" was boron?

ANSWER: 82.8%

■■ PROBLEM 58    A mixture is made up of components A, B, and C.   A has the simplest formula $CH_4O$; B has the simplest formula $C_2H_6O$; C has the simplest formula $C_3H_8$.   If the final mixture analyzes to 68.110% carbon, 16.125% hydrogen, and 15.765% oxygen (by weight), what would be the recipe for the mixture in terms of weight per cent of A, of B, and of C?

ANSWER: 10.5% A, 30.3% B, 59.2% C

■ PROBLEM 59    Element X reacts with oxygen to form a compound whose simplest formula is $X_3O_5$.   If 0.359 g of X reacts to give 0.559 g of the compound, what is the atomic weight of X?

ANSWER: 47.9 a.m.u.

■ PROBLEM 60    Elements A and B react with oxygen to form either $ABO_3$ or $AB_2O_5$.   The first of these compounds is 17.36% oxygen by weight; the second is 20.01% oxygen by weight.   What are the atomic weights of A and of B?

ANSWER: 137.2 a.m.u. for A and 91.3 a.m.u. for B

# 3

# THE MOLE

IT MAKES a great deal of sense to think of a mole as the Avogadro number of objects. In this respect, we can speak of a mole of H atoms, a mole of $H_2$ molecules, a mole of electrons, or a mole of ballet dancers—in each case having in mind $6.02 \times 10^{23}$ of the described articles. However, it is imperative that the nature of the numbered article be clearly specified. Otherwise, the meaning is uncertain. For example, to say a "mole of hydrogen" is ambiguous. It makes a king-size difference whether we have in mind a mole of *hydrogen atoms*, a mole of *hydrogen molecules*, or a mole of *hydrogen bombs*. In the same way, a "mole of sulfur" could mean different things depending on whether we were counting $S_2$, $S_4$, $S_6$, or $S_8$ molecules. So, when using the term mole in this simple counting sense, the first rule is to make sure you specify what you are counting.

In chemistry, the mole takes on a very special importance because numerous properties depend on the number of particles present in a sample (instead of, say, on the total mass of the sample). Furthermore, when one material is dissolved in another, the observed properties of the resulting solution depend in great measure on the relative number of particles present. Thus, the mole is an extremely useful concept for counting particles. It counts particles in groups of $6.02 \times 10^{23}$ in much the same way that the gram-atom counts atoms in groups of $6.02 \times 10^{23}$ or fractions thereof. The difference is that the mole can be used for counting complex objects (e.g., ballet dancers, nicotine molecules), whereas the gram-atom is reserved for counting atoms.

PROBLEM 61    Given that the U.S. population is 190 million people, how many moles of people in the U.S.?

SOLUTION: One mole is $6.02 \times 10^{23}$ objects.

$$\frac{190 \text{ million people}}{6.02 \times 10^{23} \text{ people/mole}} = 3.2 \times 10^{-16} \text{ mole of people.}$$

Actually, there is little reason to count people in terms of moles, since the mole is such an enormously large number that we would never have enough people to make up an appreciable fraction of even one mole. However, on the atomic and molecular scale we routinely work with quantities of the order of one mole of particles.

PROBLEM 62    Given $1.0 \times 10^{23}$ sulfur atoms in a sample. (a) How many moles of sulfur atoms do you have? (b) If the sulfur atoms were all grouped in the form of rings containing eight sulfur atoms per ring (molecule), how many moles of $S_8$ molecules would you have?

SOLUTION: (a) One mole is $6.02 \times 10^{23}$ particles. If we divide the number of sulfur atoms by the number required to give one mole, we will have the number of moles.

$$\frac{1.0 \times 10^{23} \text{ S atoms}}{6.02 \times 10^{23} \text{ S atoms/mole}} = 0.17 \text{ mole S atoms.}$$

(b) There are 8 sulfur atoms per $S_8$ molecule. If we divide the number of sulfur atoms by the number required to make one molecule, then we will know how many molecules we have.

$$\frac{1.0 \times 10^{23} \text{ S atoms}}{8 \text{ S atoms/} S_8 \text{ molecule}} = 0.12 \times 10^{23} \text{ } S_8 \text{ molecules.}$$

If now we divide the number of $S_8$ molecules by the number required to make one mole, we will have the number of moles.

$$\frac{0.12 \times 10^{23} \text{ } S_8 \text{ molecules}}{6.02 \times 10^{23} \text{ } S_8 \text{ molecules/mole}} = 0.020 \text{ mole } S_8 \text{ molecules.}$$

PROBLEM 63    Given 0.15 mole $P_4$ molecules.  (a) How many $P_4$ molecules is this?  (b) How many P atoms is this?  (c) How many moles of P atoms do you have?

SOLUTION: (a) One mole is $6.02 \times 10^{23}$ particles.

0.15 mole is $(0.15 \text{ mole}) \left( 6.02 \times 10^{23} \dfrac{\text{particles}}{\text{mole}} \right)$.

0.15 mole $P_4$ molecules is **$9.0 \times 10^{22}$ $P_4$ molecules.**

(b) One $P_4$ molecule contains four atoms.

$9.0 \times 10^{22}$ $P_4$ molecules contain $(9.0 \times 10^{22}$ $P_4$ molecules) $\times$

$\left( \dfrac{4 \text{ P atoms}}{P_4 \text{ molecule}} \right) =$ **$3.6 \times 10^{23}$ P atoms.**

(c) One mole is $6.02 \times 10^{23}$ particles.

$3.6 \times 10^{23}$ P atoms is $\left( \dfrac{3.6 \times 10^{23} \text{ P atoms}}{6.02 \times 10^{23} \text{ P atoms/mole}} \right)$

**= 0.60 mole P atoms.**

Unfortunately, the business on moles is nowhere near so simple as the above discussion implies.  However, we start our discussion of moles in the above fashion because it turns out to be helpful to get quickly into your mind the idea that the mole is a concept for counting particles.  Complications appear once we realize that in certain cases it may not be so easy to specify what the "particles" are, either because one merges its identity with another by overlapping it or, in many cases, because the "particle" does not have a unique size but continues on and on depending upon how big the sample is.  Another complication comes in because, frequently, we may not know what the "particle" consists of.  For example, the compound phosphorus pentoxide was assumed to consist of $P_2O_5$ "particles" until structure studies showed conclusively that the "particle" was $P_4O_{10}$.  Obviously, one mole of $P_2O_5$ is not the same as one mole of $P_4O_{10}$.  Because of the above complications (and other more sophisticated ones) we shall have to consider some more-difficult-to-visualize aspects of the mole.  Still, you should keep in mind that we are counting particles in one way or another.

The strict definition of mole is that it is equal to the *gram-formula-weight*. What is a gram-formula-weight? Take the atomic weights of the elements as they appear in the formula, multiply each atomic weight by the subscript of the corresponding element in the formula, add the works up, and you have the formula-weight. This number is in atomic mass units. If you take it in grams, you have the gram-formula-weight. The procedure is the same no matter whether you have a simplest formula or a molecular formula. Once you can write a formula down in terms of symbols and subscripts and once you have the table of atomic weights available, you can calculate formula-weights.

PROBLEM 64    What is the formula-weight of $H_2O$?

SOLUTION: Atomic weight of hydrogen is 1.00797 a.m.u.
You take twice it because of the subscript 2 on H in the formula:

$(2)(1.00797$ a.m.u.$) = 2.01594$ a.m.u.

Atomic weight of oxygen is 15.9994 a.m.u.
You take one times it because the subscript on O in $H_2O$ is "one" understood:

$(1)(15.9994$ a.m.u.$) = 15.9994$ a.m.u.

Formula-weight of $H_2O$

$= (2)$(atomic weight of H)$ + (1)$(atomic weight of O)

$= (2)(1.00797$ a.m.u.$) + 15.9994$ a.m.u.

$= 18.0153$ a.m.u.

PROBLEM 65    What is the formula-weight of $Ca(NO_3)_2$?

SOLUTION: The parentheses with the subscript 2 means that everything inside the parentheses gets multiplied by two.
Formula-weight of $Ca(NO_3)_2$

$= (1)$(atomic weight of Ca)$ + (2)$[atomic weight of N $+ (3)$(atomic weight of O)]

$= 40.08 + (2)[14.007 + (3)(15.999)]$

$= 164.09$ a.m.u.

Once you have the formula-weight in atomic mass units (a.m.u.), you can easily think of taking that many grams of the material—e.g., 18.0153 g $H_2O$ or 164.09 g $Ca(NO_3)_2$. In either case, you would be providing yourself with one gram-formula-weight of the material. This is what we call one *mole*. Thus, one mole of $H_2O$ is 18.0153 g; one mole of $Ca(NO_3)_2$ is 164.09 g. Note what you need to work with: You must be able to write down a formula; you must put in the atomic weights multiplied by the subscripts; you must choose grams as your weight unit.

(Although we shall not fuss with this, it is often convenient to work with weight units other than grams, as, for example, pounds or tons. In such cases it is efficient to introduce pound-formula-weight or ton-formula-weight, these being, respectively, the formula-weight in pounds or tons. Specifically, one pound-formula-weight of $H_2O$ is 18.0153 pounds; one pound-formula-weight of $Ca(NO_3)_2$ is 164.09 pounds. Furthermore, we could speak of these as one pound-mole of $H_2O$ (18.0153 pounds) or one pound-mole of $Ca(NO_3)_2$ (164.09 pounds). Because of this complication, the purist will insist that *formula-weight* should be taken only as being expressed in *a.m.u.* When he means it in *grams*, he will say *gram-formula-weight*. Furthermore, he will insist on saying *gram-mole* instead of *mole* for *gram-formula-weight*, claiming that so far as weight is concerned, the mole can be expressed in any weight unit. We have enough problems as it is and life is too short to worry about getting a vocabulary which most chemists do not use in practice. We shall confine practically all our work to grams, so we shall be dealing almost exclusively with the *gram-mole*. Therefore, it will be safe to assume that when we say *mole* we mean *gram-mole*. If occasionally it becomes necessary to refer to ton-moles or the like, then we shall specify the units.)

PROBLEM 66   What is the weight in grams of one mole NaCl?

SOLUTION: One mole NaCl is one gram-formula-weight.
Formula-weight of NaCl = atomic weight Na + atomic weight Cl

$$= 22.9898 \text{ a.m.u.} + 35.453 \text{ a.m.u.}$$

$$= 58.443 \text{ a.m.u.}$$

One mole NaCl = **58.443 g.**

PROBLEM 67    What is the weight in pounds of one pound-mole NaCl?

SOLUTION: One pound-mole NaCl is one pound-formula-weight.
Formula-weight of NaCl = 22.9898 a.m.u. + 35.453 a.m.u.

$$= 58.443 \text{ a.m.u.}$$

One pound-mole NaCl = **58.443 pounds.**

PROBLEM 68    What is the weight in grams of one pound-mole NaCl?

SOLUTION: Problem 257 tells us that one pound-mole NaCl = 58.443 pounds.
1 pound = 454 g.

$$\text{One pound-mole NaCl} = (58.443 \text{ pounds}) \left( 454 \, \frac{g}{\text{pound}} \right)$$

$$= 2.65 \times 10^4 \text{ g.}$$

What now is the connection between a mole, defined as one gram-formula-weight, and the Avogadro number of particles? We could say one mole consists of the Avogadro number of "particles" provided we interpret "particle" to mean an entity composed of as many atoms as are shown in the given formula. Such an entity does not necessarily have a real, separate existence. It may have to be invented purely for the sake of counting particles. For example, the material sodium chloride has the simplest formula NaCl. We can easily imagine a unit consisting of one sodium atom and one chlorine atom, even though in solid sodium chloride no particular sodium atom goes with any specific chlorine atom. Instead, each sodium belongs equally to six chlorine neighbors, which in turn belong equally to six sodium neighbors, and so on. The result is a huge, extended structure in which separate pairs—one sodium atom plus one chlorine atom—do not exist. However, for counting purposes, we can imagine that such pairs do exist and we will get away with it, because once a sodium is counted with one chlorine neighbor it will not need to be counted again. To make our reasoning a bit easier to follow we shall introduce a term—the "formula-unit"—to mean specifically this entity (hypothetical or not) which contains as many atoms as are shown in the chemical formula. We thus put a double burden on the formula. In it, a symbol not only stands for an *element* but it also stands for *one atom* of the element; furthermore, the subscript not only stands for the relative number of gram-atoms in the compound but also the number of atoms in the "formula-unit."

As specific examples of what the above means, let us look at some typical formulas: $H_2O$, $S_8$, $CaCl_2$, $P_4O_{10}$, $C_{19}H_{22}N_2O$. For $H_2O$, the formula-unit consists of two hydrogen atoms and one oxygen atom; this entity actually exists and constitutes the water molecule as found in water vapor. For $S_8$, the formula-unit consists of eight sulfur atoms; this entity also exists and, in fact, is the molecule that makes up solid, rhombic sulfur. For $CaCl_2$, the formula-unit consists of one calcium atom and two chlorine atoms; it does *not* exist as a separate unit in solid calcium chloride (although it may exist as a real entity in alcoholic solutions of calcium chloride). The formula-unit $P_4O_{10}$ consists of four P atoms and ten oxygen atoms; it is the molecule that makes up the white solid called phosphoric anhydride. The formula-unit $C_{19}H_{22}N_2O$ consists of 19 carbon atoms, 22 hydrogen atoms, 2 nitrogen atoms, and 1 oxygen atom; it has a real identity as the molecule of the substance cinchonine (closely related to strychnine).

From all these examples, the point to be learned is that just looking at the chemical formula will not tell us whether there is a real entity consisting only of the atoms shown in the formula. We need to *know* that the chemical formula given is truly a *molecular formula* if we want to attach the label "molecule" to the aggregate represented by the formula. If we have only the *simplest* formula, then we are uncertain. The whole purpose of introducing "formula-unit" is to bypass this ambiguity. In terms of "formula-units," no matter whether they are molecules or not, we can always say correctly that "one mole contains the Avogadro number of formula-units." Only in special cases can we say correctly that "one mole contains the Avogadro number of molecules."

The above, somewhat lengthy, discussion has been introduced because beginners in chemistry are often enticed into making incorrect use of terms, especially when current practice amongst chemists is not standardized. This, unfortunately, is true for the terms "molecule" and "mole," which frequently are imprecisely defined and imprecisely used. The safest procedure (it is the one we shall follow from here on) is to give the formula for which the formula-weight is being calculated and also the formula of the "particle" which is being counted. In some cases, we shall use the term "molecule" instead of "formula-unit," but only in those cases where the identity of the molecule has been established by other evidence. To the beginner, the advice is to use the term "formula-unit" except in those cases where he has accumulated enough chemical "know-how" to be able to say "molecule." For example, there is no point to saying "the formula-unit $H_2$" when it is generally known that "the molecule $H_2$" is correct. In any case, the other piece of advice is to use the symbols and subscripts to a maximum when ambiguity is likely to occur.

The following summary may be useful in setting the stage for practical calculations involving the mole:

One mole = one gram-formula-weight.

One mole = $6.02 \times 10^{23}$ formula-units.

One formula-unit contains as many atoms as are shown in the formula.

A formula-unit is the same as a molecule in those cases where we are working with the molecular formula.

**PROBLEM 69** How many formula-units are there in 0.10 mole $Ba(NO_3)_2$? [*Note:* Like most salts, $Ba(NO_3)_2$ is not a molecular material.]

SOLUTION: One mole contains $6.02 \times 10^{23}$ formula-units.

0.10 mole contains (0.10 mole) $\left( 6.02 \times 10^{23} \dfrac{\text{formula-units}}{\text{mole}} \right)$.

0.10 mole contains $6.0 \times 10^{22}$ **formula-units.**

**PROBLEM 70** How many atoms of barium are there in 0.10 mole $Ba(NO_3)_2$?

SOLUTION: One mole contains $6.02 \times 10^{23}$ formula-units.

0.10 mole contains $6.0 \times 10^{22}$ formula-units.

One formula-unit of $Ba(NO_3)_2$ contains one barium atom.

$6.0 \times 10^{22}$ formula-units contain $(6.0 \times 10^{22}$ formula-units) $\times$

$\left( 1 \dfrac{\text{Ba atom}}{\text{formula-unit}} \right) = 6.0 \times 10^{22}$ **Ba atoms.**

PROBLEM 71 How many atoms of oxygen in 0.10 mole $Ba(NO_3)_2$?

SOLUTION: 0.10 mole $Ba(NO_3)_2$ contains $6.0 \times 10^{22}$ formula-units of $Ba(NO_3)_2$.

One formula-unit of $Ba(NO_3)_2$ contains six atoms of oxygen.

0.10 mole $Ba(NO_3)_2$ contains $\left(6 \dfrac{\text{atoms oxygen}}{\text{formula-unit}}\right)$ $(6.0 \times 10^{22}$ formula-units$) = 3.6 \times 10^{23}$ **atoms oxygen.**

PROBLEM 72 How many gram-atoms nitrogen in 0.10 mole $Ba(NO_3)_2$?

SOLUTION: One mole contains $6.02 \times 10^{23}$ formula-units.
0.10 mole contains $6.0 \times 10^{22}$ formula-units.
One formula-unit of $Ba(NO_3)_2$ contains two nitrogen atoms.
0.10 mole $Ba(NO_3)_2$ contains $(6.0 \times 10^{22}$ formula-units$) \times$

$\left(2 \dfrac{\text{N atoms}}{\text{formula-unit}}\right) = 1.2 \times 10^{23}$ N atoms.

One gram-atom N $= 6.02 \times 10^{23}$ N atoms.

$$\frac{1.2 \times 10^{23} \text{ N atoms}}{6.02 \times 10^{23} \text{ N atoms/gram-atom}} = 0.20 \text{ gram-atom N.}$$

The above problem is an important one because we shall find it frequently convenient to go directly from moles to gram-atoms. As the preceding problem shows, the number of gram-atoms is equal to the number of moles of material times the number of gram-atoms per mole. In the case of $Ba(NO_3)_2$, there are two gram-atoms of N per mole of $Ba(NO_3)_2$. In the general case, we simply note that the subscripts not only tell the number of atoms per formula-unit but also the number of gram-atoms per mole. Thus, one mole of $Ba(NO_3)_2$ contains one gram-atom of barium plus two gram-atoms of nitrogen plus six gram-atoms of oxygen. Recall that a subscript outside a parenthesis multiplies all subscripts inside the parentheses.

PROBLEM 73 How many gram-atoms oxygen are there in 0.15 mole $Ba(NO_3)_2$?

SOLUTION: 1 mole $Ba(NO_3)_2$ contains 6 gram-atoms oxygen.

0.15 mole $Ba(NO_3)_2$ contains (0.15 mole) $\left( 6 \dfrac{\text{gram-atoms O}}{\text{mole of Ba } (NO_3)_2} \right)$
   = **0.90 gram-atom oxygen.**

PROBLEM 74    How many atoms of oxygen are there in 5.22 g $Ba(NO_3)_2$?

SOLUTION: Formula-weight of $Ba(NO_3)_2$ = atomic weight Ba + (2) × (atomic weight of N) + (6)(atomic weight of O) = 137.34 + (2)(14.0067) + (6)(15.9994) = 261.35 a.m.u.

One mole $Ba(NO_3)_2$ = 261.35 g.

5.22 g $Ba(NO_3)_2$ = $\dfrac{5.22 \text{ g}}{261.35 \text{ g/mole}}$ = 0.0200 mole.

One mole $Ba(NO_3)_2$ contains 6 gram-atoms oxygen.

0.0200 mole $Ba(NO_3)_2$ contains (0.0200 mole) $\left( 6 \dfrac{\text{gram-atoms O}}{\text{mole}} \right)$
   = 0.120 gram-atom O.

One gram-atom oxygen contains $6.02 \times 10^{23}$ atoms.

0.120 gram-atom oxygen contains (0.120 gram-atom) ×
$\left( 6.02 \times 10^{23} \dfrac{\text{atoms}}{\text{gram-atom}} \right)$ = **$7.22 \times 10^{22}$ oxygen atoms.**

PROBLEM 75    How many grams $Ba(NO_3)_2$ would you need to take to get 1.00 g barium?

SOLUTION:

1.00 g barium = $\dfrac{1.00 \text{ g}}{137.34 \text{ g/gram-atom}}$ = 0.00728 gram-atom.

Formula $Ba(NO_3)_2$ shows 1 gram-atom of Ba per mole of $Ba(NO_3)_2$. To get 0.00728 gram-atom Ba, you need to take 0.00728 mole $Ba(NO_3)_2$. One mole $Ba(NO_3)_2$ equals 261.35 g.

0.00728 mole $Ba(NO_3)_2$ equals (0.00728 mole) $\left( 261.35 \dfrac{\text{g}}{\text{mole}} \right)$ = **1.90 g.**

PROBLEM 76    Suppose for a given reaction you need $3.0 \times 10^{21}$ formula-units of $NO_3^-$. You propose to get this by using $Ba(NO_3)_2$ as the source. What weight of $Ba(NO_3)_2$ is needed?

SOLUTION: One formula-unit of $Ba(NO_3)_2$ provides two formula-units of $NO_3^-$.

To get $3.0 \times 10^{21}$ formula-units of $NO_3^-$, we need

$$\left( \frac{3.0 \times 10^{21} \text{ formula-units } NO_3^-}{2 \text{ formula-units } NO_3^-/\text{formula-unit } Ba(NO_3)_2} \right)$$

$$= 1.5 \times 10^{21} \text{ formula-units of } Ba(NO_3)_2.$$

One mole $Ba(NO_3)_2$ contains $6.02 \times 10^{23}$ formula-units of $Ba(NO_3)_2$.
To get $1.5 \times 10^{21}$ formula-units of $Ba(NO_3)_2$, you need

$$\left( \frac{1.5 \times 10^{21} \text{ formula-units } Ba(NO_3)_2}{6.02 \times 10^{23} \text{ formula-units/mole}} \right)$$

$$= 2.5 \times 10^{-3} \text{ mole } Ba(NO_3)_2.$$

One mole $Ba(NO_3)_2$ equals 261.35 g.

$$2.5 \times 10^{-3} \text{ mole } Ba(NO_3)_2 = (2.5 \times 10^{-3} \text{ mole}) \left( 261.35 \frac{g}{\text{mole}} \right)$$

$$= \mathbf{0.65\ g.}$$

[*Note:* In this case, it would make sense to replace the term "formula-unit $NO_3^-$" by "ion $NO_3^-$," or "nitrate ion," since that is what it is. More on this when we discuss dissociation in Chapter 13.]

**PROBLEM 77**    Given 1.08 g quinine, $C_{20}H_{24}N_2O_2$. How many molecules is this?

SOLUTION: The fact that the formula is not the simplest that could be written with this ratio of atoms is a good indication that we are dealing with a molecular material for which the make-up of the molecule is known. In other words, in this case, the formula-unit is a *bona fide* molecule.

Formula-weight of quinine = (20)(atomic weight of carbon) + (24) $\times$ (atomic weight of hydrogen) + (2)(atomic weight of nitrogen) + (2)(atomic weight of oxygen) = (20)(12.011) + (24)(1.008) + (2)(14.007) + (2)(15.999) = 324.424 a.m.u.

One mole quinine = 324.424 g.

$$1.08 \text{ g quinine} = \frac{1.08 \text{ g}}{324.424 \text{ g/mole}} = 0.00333 \text{ mole.}$$

One mole contains $6.02 \times 10^{23}$ molecules.

$$0.00333 \text{ mole contains } (0.00333 \text{ mole}) \left( 6.02 \times 10^{23} \frac{\text{molecules}}{\text{mole}} \right)$$

$$= \mathbf{2.00 \times 10^{21} \text{ molecules.}}$$

**PROBLEM 78**    How many atoms of hydrogen are there in 1.08 g quinine, $C_{20}H_{24}N_2O_2$?

SOLUTION: One mole quinine = 324.424 g.

$$1.08 \text{ g quinine} = \frac{1.08 \text{ g}}{324.424 \text{ g/mole}} = 0.00333 \text{ mole.}$$

One mole contains $6.02 \times 10^{23}$ molecules.

$0.00333$ mole contains $(0.00333 \text{ mole}) \left( 6.02 \times 10^{23} \dfrac{\text{molecules}}{\text{mole}} \right)$

$\qquad = 2.00 \times 10^{21}$ molecules.

Each molecule of quinine contains 24 hydrogen atoms.

$2.00 \times 10^{21}$ molecules contain $(2.00 \times 10^{21} \text{ molecules}) \times$

$\qquad \left( 24 \dfrac{\text{hydrogen atoms}}{\text{molecule}} \right) = 4.80 \times 10^{22}$ **H atoms.**

PROBLEM 79    Suppose you have 0.14 g radioactive nitrogen. How many molecules of quinine can you make in which all the nitrogen atoms are tagged as radioactive?

SOLUTION: (Given the weight of nitrogen, you can easily find the number of gram-atoms of nitrogen. Then find the number of moles of quinine this corresponds to, and finally convert to molecules. It is almost always best to work through moles, since the molar relations are usually the easiest to establish.)

Atomic weight of nitrogen is 14.007 a.m.u.

One gram-atom nitrogen weighs 14.007 g.

$$0.14 \text{ g nitrogen} = \frac{0.14 \text{ g}}{14.007 \text{ g/gram-atom}} = 0.010 \text{ gram-atom N.}$$

For $C_{20}H_{24}N_2O_2$, there are two gram-atoms N per mole $C_{20}H_{24}N_2O_2$.

$0.010$ gram-atom N corresponds to

$$\left( \frac{0.010 \text{ gram-atom N}}{2 \text{ gram-atoms N/mole } C_{20}H_{24}N_2O_2} \right)$$

$\qquad = 0.0050$ mole $C_{20}H_{24}N_2O_2$.

One mole contains $6.02 \times 10^{23}$ molecules.

$0.0050$ mole contains $(0.0050 \text{ mole}) \left( 6.02 \times 10^{23} \dfrac{\text{molecules}}{\text{mole}} \right)$

$\qquad = 3.0 \times 10^{21}$ **molecules.**

PROBLEM 80    How many gram-atoms radioactive carbon would you need in order to make $1.0 \times 10^{-6}$ g of fully tagged quinine? "Fully tagged" means all the carbon atoms would need to be of the radioactive type.

SOLUTION: One mole $C_{20}H_{24}N_2O_2$ weighs 324 g.

$$1.0 \times 10^{-6} \text{ g quinine} = \frac{1.0 \times 10^{-6} \text{ g}}{324 \text{ g/mole}} = 3.1 \times 10^{-9} \text{ mole.}$$

One mole $C_{20}H_{24}N_2O_2$ contains 20 gram-atoms carbon.

$$3.1 \times 10^{-9} \text{ mole contains } (3.1 \times 10^{-9} \text{ mole}) \left( 20 \, \frac{\text{gram-atoms C}}{\text{mole}} \right)$$

$$= 6.2 \times 10^{-8} \textbf{ gram-atom carbon.}$$

**PROBLEM 81** How many formula-units in 0.15 mole $P_2O_5$?

SOLUTION: One mole of anything contains $6.02 \times 10^{23}$ formula-units.

$$0.15 \text{ mole } P_2O_5 \text{ contains } (0.15 \text{ mole}) \left( 6.02 \times 10^{23} \, \frac{\text{formula-units}}{\text{mole}} \right)$$

$$= 9.0 \times 10^{22} \textbf{ formula-units.}$$

**PROBLEM 82** How many molecules in 0.15 mole $P_2O_5$?

SOLUTION: (This is a trick question. Compare it carefully with Problem 271. As a matter of fact, you cannot answer it—not without putting in the additional information that $P_2O_5$ is actually composed of the molecules $P_4O_{10}$. Once you know this, you can see that it takes two of the formula-units $P_2O_5$ to make one molecule of $P_4O_{10}$.)

One mole $P_2O_5$ contains $6.02 \times 10^{23}$ $P_2O_5$ units.
0.15 mole $P_2O_5$ contains $9.0 \times 10^{22}$ $P_2O_5$ units.
It takes two $P_2O_5$ units to make one $P_4O_{10}$ molecule.

$$9.0 \times 10^{22} \text{ } P_2O_5 \text{ units will make } \frac{9.0 \times 10^{22} \text{ } P_2O_5 \text{ units}}{2 \text{ } P_2O_5 \text{ units}/P_4O_{10} \text{ molecule}}$$

$$= 4.5 \times 10^{22} \textbf{ } P_4O_{10} \textbf{ molecules.}$$

**PROBLEM 83** How many $P_4O_{10}$ molecules in 0.150 g $P_4O_{10}$?

SOLUTION: Formula-weight of $P_4O_{10}$ = (4)(atomic weight of P) + (10)(atomic weight of O) = (4)(30.974) + (10)(15.999) = 283.89 a.m.u.

One mole $P_4O_{10}$ = 283.89 g.

$$0.150 \text{ g } P_4O_{10} = \frac{0.150 \text{ g}}{283.89 \text{ g/mole}} = 5.28 \times 10^{-4} \text{ mole } P_4O_{10}.$$

One mole of anything contains $6.02 \times 10^{23}$ formula-units.

$5.28 \times 10^{-4}$ mole contains $(5.28 \times 10^{-4}$ mole$) \times$

$$\left( 6.02 \times 10^{23} \frac{\text{formula-units}}{\text{mole}} \right)$$

$$= 3.18 \times 10^{20} \text{ formula-units } P_4O_{10}$$

$$= \mathbf{3.18 \times 10^{20} \text{ molecules of } P_4O_{10}}$$

(because one formula-unit of $P_4O_{10}$ is the same as one molecule of $P_4O_{10}$).

**PROBLEM 84**    How many $P_4O_{10}$ molecules in 0.150 g $P_2O_5$?

SOLUTION: [*Note:* If you are clever enough, you can figure out without additional pencil-pushing that the answer to this question should be the same as the answer to Problem 273.   The reasoning goes like this: If the formula-weight is half as great, you have twice as many formula-units; but it takes two formula-units to make a molecule, so you end up with the same number of molecules.]

Formula-weight of $P_2O_5$ = (2)(atomic weight of P) + (5)(atomic weight of O) = (2)(30.974) + (5)(15.999) = 141.94 a.m.u.

One mole $P_2O_5$ = 141.94 g.

$$0.150 \text{ g } P_2O_5 = \frac{0.150 \text{ g}}{141.94 \text{ g/mole}} = 1.06 \times 10^{-3} \text{ mole } P_2O_5.$$

One mole of anything contains $6.02 \times 10^{23}$ formula-units.

$1.06 \times 10^{-3}$ mole $P_2O_5$ contains $(1.06 \times 10^{-3}$ mole$) \times$

$$\left( 6.02 \times 10^{23} \frac{\text{formula-units of } P_2O_5}{\text{mole}} \right)$$

$$= 6.38 \times 10^{20} \text{ formula-units of } P_2O_5.$$

But, it takes two formula-units of $P_2O_5$ to make one molecule of $P_4O_{10}$.

$$\frac{6.38 \times 10^{20} \text{ formula-units of } P_2O_5}{2 \text{ formula-units of } P_2O_5/\text{molecule of } P_4O_{10}}$$

$$= \mathbf{3.19 \times 10^{20} \text{ molecules of } P_4O_{10}.}$$

**PROBLEM 85**    How many atoms of phosphorus in 0.150 mole $P_2O_5$?

SOLUTION: One mole $P_2O_5$ contains 2 gram-atoms phosphorus.

0.150 mole $P_2O_5$ contains (0.150 mole) $\left( 2 \dfrac{\text{gram-atoms P}}{\text{mole } P_2O_5} \right)$

   $= 0.300$ gram-atom P.

One gram-atom of anything contains $6.02 \times 10^{23}$ atoms.

0.300 gram-atom P $= (0.300 \text{ gram-atom}) \left( 6.02 \times 10^{23} \dfrac{\text{atoms}}{\text{gram-atom}} \right)$

   $= \mathbf{1.81 \times 10^{23}}$ **atoms P.**


**PROBLEM 86**   How many atoms of phosphorus in 0.150 mole $P_4O_{10}$?

SOLUTION: One mole $P_4O_{10}$ contains 4 gram-atoms phosphorus.

0.150 mole $P_4O_{10}$ contains (0.150 mole) $\left( 4 \dfrac{\text{gram-atoms P}}{\text{mole } P_4O_{10}} \right)$

   $= 0.600$ gram-atom P.

One gram-atom of anything contains $6.02 \times 10^{23}$ atoms.

0.600 gram-atom P $= (0.600 \text{ gram-atom}) \left( 6.02 \times 10^{23} \dfrac{\text{atoms}}{\text{gram-atom}} \right)$

   $= \mathbf{3.61 \times 10^{23}}$ **atoms P.**


**PROBLEM 87**   How many grams oxygen in 0.150 mole $P_2O_5$?

SOLUTION: One mole $P_2O_5$ contains 5 gram-atoms oxygen.

0.150 mole $P_2O_5$ contains (0.150 mole) $\left( 5 \dfrac{\text{gram-atoms O}}{\text{mole } P_2O_5} \right)$

   $= 0.750$ gram-atom O.

Atomic weight of oxygen is 15.999 a.m.u.

One gram-atom O $= 15.999$ g.

0.750 gram-atom O $= (0.750 \text{ gram-atom}) \left( 15.999 \dfrac{\text{g}}{\text{gram-atom}} \right)$

   $= \mathbf{12.0}$ **g oxygen** .


**PROBLEM 88**   How many grams oxygen in 0.150 mole $P_4O_{10}$?

SOLUTION: One mole $P_4O_{10}$ contains 10 gram-atoms oxygen.

0.150 mole $P_4O_{10}$ contains (0.150 mole) $\left( 10 \dfrac{\text{gram-atoms O}}{\text{mole } P_4O_{10}} \right)$

   $= 1.50$ gram-atom O.

One gram-atom O = 15.999 g.

1.50 gram-atoms O = (1.50 gram-atoms) $\left( 15.999 \dfrac{g}{gram\text{-}atom} \right)$

= 24.0 g oxygen.

PROBLEM 89    How many moles $P_2O_5$ can you make from 2.00 g phosphorus and 5.00 g oxygen?

SOLUTION: (Whenever you have weights given, convert to gram-atoms to see quickly which reagent is in excess. Then, it is just another step to figure out how much product will be formed.)

2.00 g phosphorus = $\dfrac{2.00\ g}{30.974\ g/gram\text{-}atom\ P}$ = 0.0646 gram-atom P.

5.00 g oxygen = $\dfrac{5.00\ g}{15.999\ g/gram\text{-}atom\ O}$ = 0.313 gram-atom O.

To get $P_2O_5$, the gram-atoms should be in the ratio 2 of P to 5 of O. However, the numbers above indicate that we have almost five times as many gram-atoms of O as of P, so the oxygen is evidently in excess. The reaction product is thus limited by the amount of phosphorus. We have to base our calculations on it.

From 2 gram-atoms P, we can get 1 mole $P_2O_5$.

From 0.0646 gram-atom P, we can get (0.0646 gram-atom P) $\times$

$\left( \dfrac{1\ mole\ P_2O_5}{2\ gram\text{-}atoms\ P} \right)$ = 0.0323 mole $P_2O_5$.

PROBLEM 90    How many moles $P_2O_5$ can you make from 5.00 g phosphorus and 2.00 g oxygen?

SOLUTION: 5.00 g P = $\dfrac{5.00\ g}{30.974\ g/gram\text{-}atom\ P}$ = 0.161 gram-atom P.

2.00 g O = $\dfrac{2.00\ g}{15.999\ g/gram\text{-}atom\ O}$ = 0.125 gram-atom O.

To get $P_2O_5$, we need oxygen-to-phosphorus in a gram-atom ratio of 5 to 2, or $2\frac{1}{2}$ times as many gram-atoms of O as of P.

The numbers above indicate that there is nowhere near enough oxygen to satisfy all the given phosphorus, so in this case it will be the oxygen that limits the amount of reaction product.

From 5 gram-atoms oxygen, we get 1 mole $P_2O_5$.

From 0.125 gram-atom O, we get (0.125 gram-atom O) $\times$

$$\left( \frac{1 \text{ mole } P_2O_5}{5 \text{ gram-atoms } O} \right) = 0.0250 \text{ mole } P_2O_5.$$

**PROBLEM 91** How many moles $MgIn_2S_4$ could you make from 1.00 g magnesium, 1.00 g indium, and 1.00 g sulfur?

SOLUTION: $1.00 \text{ g Mg} = \dfrac{1.00 \text{ g}}{24.312 \text{ g/gram-atom Mg}}$

$= 0.0411$ gram-atom Mg.

$1.00 \text{ g In} = \dfrac{1.00 \text{ g}}{114.82 \text{ g/gram-atom In}} = 0.00871$ gram-atom In.

$1.00 \text{ g S} = \dfrac{1.00 \text{ g}}{32.064 \text{ g/gram-atom S}} = 0.0312$ gram-atom S.

So far as gram-atoms are concerned, we need Mg:In:S in the ratio 1:2:4.

Based on 0.0411 gram-atom Mg this would mean 0.0822 gram-atom In and 0.164 gram-atom S. We don't have that much In nor that much S, so we cannot base our calculation on Mg.

Based on 0.00871 gram-atom In, this would mean 0.00436 gram-atom Mg and 0.0174 gram-atom S. We have more than enough Mg and S to satisfy these requirements, so this looks OK.

(Just to be sure, look at the needs based on 0.0312 gram-atom S. We would need 0.00780 gram-atom Mg and 0.0156 gram-atom In. We have the Mg but not the In, so we cannot base the calculation on the S.)

Once we decide that the In is the limiting reagent, the rest is easy.

To get 1 mole $MgIn_2S_4$, we need 2 gram-atoms In.

Therefore, if we have 0.00871 gram-atom In, we can only get

$$(0.00871 \text{ gram-atom In}) \left( \frac{1 \text{ mole } MgIn_2S_4}{2 \text{ gram-atoms In}} \right)$$

$= 0.00436 \text{ mole } MgIn_2S_4.$

**PROBLEM 92** What is the weight of one molecule of quinine, $C_{20}H_{24}N_2O_2$?

SOLUTION: Formula-weight of $C_{20}H_{24}N_2O_2$ equals 324.424 a.m.u.

One mole $C_{20}H_{24}N_2O_2$ weighs 324.424 g.

One mole contains $6.02 \times 10^{23}$ molecules.

One molecule weighs $\dfrac{324.424 \text{ g/mole}}{6.02 \times 10^{23} \text{ molecules/mole}}$

$= 5.39 \times 10^{-22}$ **g/molecule.**

**PROBLEM 93**    Suppose you make a mixture consisting of 1.00 g $N_2O$, 1.00 g CO, and 1.00 g $CO_2$. What fraction of the total number of molecules is represented by $N_2O$ molecules? (These are all molecular materials, as is true for most gases.)

SOLUTION: Since the mole gives us a way of counting particles, all we need to do is to determine the fraction of total moles that is $N_2O$.

$1.00 \text{ g } N_2O = \dfrac{1.00 \text{ g}}{44.0 \text{ g/mole}} = 0.0227$ mole $N_2O$.

$1.00 \text{ g CO} = \dfrac{1.00 \text{ g}}{28.0 \text{ g/mole}} = 0.0357$ mole CO.

$1.00 \text{ g } CO_2 = \dfrac{1.00 \text{ g}}{44.0 \text{ g/mole}} = 0.0227$ mole $CO_2$.

Total moles in mixture $= 0.0227 + 0.0357 + 0.0227 = 0.0811$.

Fraction of total that is $N_2O = \dfrac{0.0227}{0.0811} = \mathbf{0.280.}$

**PROBLEM 94**    A drop of water is about 0.05 ml. The density of water at room temperature is about 1.0 g per ml. How many $H_2O$ molecules in a drop of water?

SOLUTION: Weight of $H_2O$ in 1 drop $= (0.05 \text{ ml}) \left( 1.0 \dfrac{\text{g}}{\text{ml}} \right) = 0.05$ g.

Formula-weight of $H_2O = (2)$(atomic weight of H) + atomic weight of O $= (2)(1.0) + 16.0 = 18.0$ a.m.u.

One mole $H_2O = 18.0$ g.

$0.05 \text{ g } H_2O = \dfrac{0.05 \text{ g}}{18.0 \text{ g/mole}} = 0.003$ mole.

One mole $H_2O$ contains $6.02 \times 10^{23}$ $H_2O$ molecules.

$0.003$ mole $H_2O$ contains $(0.003 \text{ mole}) \left( 6.02 \times 10^{23} \dfrac{\text{molecules}}{\text{mole}} \right)$

$= 2 \times 10^{21}$ **molecules $H_2O$.**

■ **PROBLEM 95** Tetraethyllead has the molecular formula $Pb(C_2H_5)_4$. How many molecules of $Pb(C_2H_5)_4$ in a 12.94-g sample?

ANSWER: $2.41 \times 10^{22}$ **molecules**

■ **PROBLEM 96** From 1.00 g lead, how many moles of $Pb(C_2H_5)_4$ can you make?

ANSWER: **0.00483 moles**

■ **PROBLEM 97** How many gram-atoms hydrogen are there in 2.33 g $Pb(C_2H_5)_4$?

ANSWER: **0.144 gram-atoms**

■ **PROBLEM 98** You are given a pure molecular material such that $1.8 \times 10^{18}$ molecules of the material weigh 1.11 mg. What is the formula-weight of the material?

ANSWER: $3.7 \times 10^2$ **a.m.u.**

■ **PROBLEM 99** You are given a sample of a pure molecular material. From the following information about the sample, deduce what its chemical formula must be: "The sample is 0.18 mole. It contains 1.08 gram-atoms oxygen, 2.18 g hydrogen, and $6.50 \times 10^{23}$ carbon atoms."

ANSWER: $O_6H_{12}C_6$

■ **PROBLEM 100** You have a sample consisting of a mixture of $N_2$ molecules and $O_2$ molecules. The total number of moles in the sample is $4.0 \times 10^{-3}$. The total weight of the sample is 0.124 g. What is the composition of the sample expressed as per cent nitrogen by weight?

ANSWER: **23% nitrogen by weight**

■ **PROBLEM 101** A given sample of xenon fluoride contains molecules of a single type $XeF_n$, where $n$ is some whole number. Given that $9.03 \times 10^{20}$ molecules weigh 0.311 g, what is $n$?

ANSWER: **four**

■■ PROBLEM 102   Given a mixture consisting of $C_2H_6$ and $C_3H_8$.   In a given sample, there is a total of 0.00480 mole weighing 0.187 g.   How many grams carbon are there in the sample?

ANSWER: **0.152 g**

■■ PROBLEM 103   A given white powder may be pure $Na_2SO_4$, pure $K_2SO_4$, or a mixture of $Na_2SO_4$ and $K_2SO_4$. If 1.000 g of the sample reacts with $BaCl_2$ solution to produce 0.00660 mole $BaSO_4$, then which of the three possibilities describes the identity of the white powder?

ANSWER: **mixture of $Na_2SO_4$ and $K_2SO_4$**

■ PROBLEM 104   A given mixture consists only of pure substance X and pure substance Y.   The total weight of the mixture is 3.72 g; the total number of moles is 0.0600.   If the weight of one mole Y is 48.0 g and if there is 0.0200 mole X in the mixture, what is the weight of one mole X?

ANSWER: **90.0 g**

■ PROBLEM 105   A   given   substance shows the following analysis by weight: 57.1% carbon, 4.79% hydrogen, and 38.1% sulfur.   If 5.0 g of this material produces the same effect on molar properties as $1.8 \times 10^{22}$ molecules, what is the molecular formula of the substance?

ANSWER: **$C_8H_8S_2$**

■ PROBLEM 106   What is the weight in grams of 0.15 mole $Li_{0.35}V_{1.98}O_5$?

ANSWER: **27 g**

■■ PROBLEM 107   A given mixture contains only $N_2$, $O_2$, and $CO_2$.   The total number of moles is 0.0108. The analysis shows 22.5% N and 65.2% O by weight.   What is the molar make-up of the mixture?

ANSWER: **0.00305 mole $N_2$,  0.00385 mole $O_2$,  and 0.00390 mole $CO_2$**

■PROBLEM 108   A mixture of 1.65 ×
$10^{21}$ molecules of X and 1.85 × $10^{21}$ molecules of Y weighs 0.688 g.
If the molecular weight of X is 42.0 a.m.u., what is the molecular
weight of Y?

ANSWER: **187 a.m.u.**

■PROBLEM 109   Suppose that P and Q
are two elements which form the compounds $P_2Q_3$ and $PQ_2$.   If 0.15
mole $P_2Q_3$ weighs 15.9 g and 0.15 mole $PQ_2$ weighs 9.3 g, what are the
atomic weights of P and Q?

ANSWER: **P is 26 a.m.u. and Q is 18 a.m.u.**

■■PROBLEM 110   Suppose that elements
A and B form the molecular compounds $AB_x$, $AB_y$, and $AB_z$, where $x$,
$y$, and $z$ are integers smaller than eight.   You are told that 0.00470
mole $AB_x$ weighs 0.512 g; that 4.70 × $10^{21}$ molecules of $AB_y$ weigh
1.15 g; and that one molecule of $AB_z$ weighs 3.08 × $10^{-22}$ g.   Given
the further information that the atomic weight of A is greater than that
of B and that both atomic weights lie between 10 and 60 a.m.u., figure
out the formulas of the three compounds and the atomic weights of A
and B.

ANSWER: **$AB_3$, $AB_5$, $AB_7$; A = 52 a.m.u., B = 19 a.m.u.**

# 4

# CHEMICAL REACTIONS
# AND CHEMICAL
# EQUATIONS

IN ADDITION to the symbols and formulas we
have just considered in detail, the other major shorthand device used
by the chemist is the chemical equation.

## Writing equations

A chemical equation is a way of describing a chemical reaction. It uses
formulas and symbols not only to represent the nature of the materials
that are used up and are formed but also to stand for specific molar
amounts of these materials. Coefficients, or numbers preceding the
formulas and symbols, tell how many moles of each material are involved. Thus, for example, in the chemical equation

$$C_3H_8 + 5O_2 \rightarrow 3CO_2 + 4H_2O$$

the formulas $C_3H_8$, $O_2$, $CO_2$, and $H_2O$ stand respectively for the substances propane, oxygen, carbon dioxide, and water; the coefficients 1
(understood to precede $C_3H_8$), 5 (preceding $O_2$), 3 (before $CO_2$), and 4
(before $H_2O$) indicate how many moles of these substances are involved
in the reaction. The arrow, which is read "reacts to give," is sometimes

replaced by an equal sign ($=$) or double arrows ($\rightleftharpoons$), but in any case what appears to the left of it is understood to be used up in the reaction and what appears to the right is formed in the course of the reaction. The single arrow ($\rightarrow$) is generally used when we wish to emphasize the change going from left to right—that is, the disappearance of the stuff on the left (the "reactants") and the appearance of the stuff on the right (the "products"). The equal sign ($=$) is preferred by some when the quantitative aspects of chemical reaction are being emphasized— viz., that the mass of starting material used up equals the mass of product material formed. The double arrows ($\rightleftharpoons$) call attention to the reversibility of the reaction and are particularly useful when we are considering the equilibrium state—i.e., the state where the forward chemical reaction is just offset by the reverse chemical reaction (see Chapter 12). In this chapter we shall use the single arrow, since we shall be concerned with 100% conversion from the state of affairs represented by the left of the equation to the state of affairs represented by the right of the equation.

For a chemical equation to represent correctly a chemical reaction, the following conditions must be met:

1. The formulas shown on the left and on the right of the equation must correctly correspond to the observed experimental facts as to what is used up in the reaction and what is produced in the reaction.

2. The coefficients shown on the left and right must correspond to a *balanced equation*—i.e., one that is consistent with conservation of mass and with conservation of charge. In special applications, which we shall take up in Chapter 9, it may be of interest to include in the balancing pertinent information on the energy changes in the reaction.

With these two conditions satisfied, the chemical equation gives us efficiently information as to what happens to atoms, molecules, and formula-units in a reaction, but, more important, enables us to deduce weight relations applying to the same reaction. First we take up the various methods for balancing equations and then the several kinds of calculations that can be done using balanced equations.

How do we write a balanced equation? First, get the observed facts—"so-and-so reacts with so-and-so to give" and so forth. Then write down the correct formulas of the materials, used-up substances

on the left and produced substances on the right.  Be particularly careful that the subscripts of the formulas are correctly written, also that
any superscript charges on ionic species are not omitted.  Supply any
missing species needed to give a complete reaction and insert properly
chosen coefficients to give a balanced equation.

How do we select the proper coefficients?  There are three general
methods: (1) hit-or-miss, sometimes more elegantly referred to as
"balancing by inspection"; (2) balancing via oxidation-number change
(what this is, we shall consider shortly); and (3) balancing via half-
reaction, sometimes referred to as the "ion-electron method."  Which
of these methods is best to use depends on the particular reaction, what
kind of reaction it is, and how complicated it is likely to be.  Some
chemical reactions are quite simple in that they involve only pairing
or unpairing of species or perhaps shifting of partners.  For example,
the combining of magnesium ion ($Mg^{++}$) and fluoride ion ($F^-$) to form
the insoluble salt magnesium fluoride ($MgF_2$) can be represented by
the equation

$$Mg^{++} + 2F^- \rightarrow MgF_{2(s)}$$

[The subscript $(s)$ means solid state; $(g)$ would stand for gaseous state;
$(l)$, liquid state.  No subscript on an ion is generally taken to mean
"in solution".]  Given the raw information that $Mg^{++} + F^- \rightarrow$
$MgF_{2(s)}$, the coefficient 2 for $F^-$ could be deduced by noting that two
fluorine atoms appear on the right, so two fluorine atoms ought to
appear on the left.  In other words, mass (or atoms) must be conserved.
Alternatively, we could note that $MgF_2$ on the right side of the equation is electrically neutral.  On the left, since $Mg^{++}$ is doubly positive,
we would need twice as many singly negative particles ($F^-$) to preserve
electrical neutrality.

Another example: Sodium sulfate ($Na_2SO_4$) dissolves in water to
give sodium ions ($Na^+$) and sulfate ions ($SO_4^=$).  Because the starting
material $Na_2SO_4$ contains two $Na^+$ per one $SO_4^=$, as indicated by the
subscript 2 in the formula $Na_2SO_4$, we can conclude that the dissolving
reaction liberates two $Na^+$ per $SO_4^=$.  Therefore, as a balanced equation, we can write

$$Na_2SO_{4(s)} \rightarrow 2Na^+ + SO_4^=$$

In both of these examples, the chemical change can be visualized, respectively, as the coming together or the going apart of ions. So-called "double-substitution," or metathesis reactions, can be similarly treated. For example, mixing silver sulfate ($Ag_2SO_4$) with barium chloride ($BaCl_2$) in water produces solid barium sulfate ($BaSO_4$) and solid silver chloride ($AgCl$). The balanced equation

$$Ag_2SO_4 + BaCl_2 \rightarrow BaSO_{4(s)} + 2AgCl_{(s)}$$

shows a coefficient 2 preceding the formula of the product $AgCl$. Since there are two silver atoms on the left of the equation, there must be two on the right; similarly, since there are two chlorine atoms on the left of the equation, there must be two on the right. The reaction can be visualized as one in which the two $Ag^+$ ions, originally paired with the $SO_4^=$ ion in $Ag_2SO_4$, have exchanged places with the $Ba^{++}$ that is originally paired with the two chloride ions. It would not be cricket to write the product as $Ag_2Cl_2$, since we are given the information that it is to be written $AgCl$. Therefore, we need the coefficient 2 to precede $AgCl$ to conserve the atomic balance.

PROBLEM 111 Write a balanced equation for the combining of aluminum ion ($Al^{+3}$) and sulfate ion ($SO_4^=$) to form solid aluminum sulfate, $Al_2(SO_4)_3$.

SOLUTION: First we write the given information in symbols:

$$Al^{+3} + SO_4^= \rightarrow Al_2(SO_4)_{3(s)}$$

Two Al atoms on the right means two Al atoms on the left, so put a 2 before $Al^{+3}$.

Three $SO_4^=$ groups on the right means three $SO_4^=$ groups on the left, so put a 3 before $SO_4^=$.

Balanced equation then reads

$$2Al^{+3} + 3SO_4^= \rightarrow Al_2(SO_4)_{3(s)}$$

To check, we can note that not only are the numbers of each kind of atom equal on both sides of the equation but also the net charge is the same on both sides. For the latter, two $Al^{+3}$ ions contribute (two times three) positive charges and the three $SO_4^=$ ions contribute (three times two) negative charges to the left-hand side of the equation. This makes $(2)(+3)$ plus $(3)(-2)$, or $+6 - 6 =$

0, or neutral, which agrees with the right-hand side of the equation.

PROBLEM 112    Write a balanced equation for the formation of ferrous ion ($Fe^{++}$), ammonium ion ($NH_4^+$), and sulfate ion ($SO_4^=$) from the dissolving of the solid, ferrous diammonium disulfate, $Fe(NH_4)_2(SO_4)_2$.

SOLUTION: The given information is expressed symbolically:

$$Fe(NH_4)_2(SO_4)_{2(s)} \rightarrow Fe^{++} + 2NH_4^+ + 2SO_4^=$$

Two $NH_4$ groups on the left mean two on the right, so put a 2 before $NH_4^+$.

Two $SO_4$ groups on the left mean two on the right, so put a 2 before $SO_4^=$.

The balanced equation reads

$$Fe(NH_4)_2(SO_4)_{2(s)} \rightarrow Fe^{++} + 2NH_4^+ + 2SO_4^=$$

It checks out OK, since the left side is neutral and the right side is $(+2) + (2)(+1) + (2)(-2) = 0$, corresponding to one dipositive ion plus two monopositive ions plus two dinegative ions, or zero, also.

PROBLEM 113    When $Al(OH)_3$ reacts with $H_2SO_4$ under the proper conditions, the products are $Al_2(SO_4)_3$ and $H_2O$. Write a balanced equation for the reaction.

SOLUTION: Write the raw information, noting that $H_2O$ can be written HOH:

$$Al(OH)_3 + H_2SO_4 \rightarrow Al_2(SO_4)_3 + HOH$$

The subscript 2 on Al on the right indicates two Al atoms in the product. There must be two Al atoms in the starting material, so put a 2 before $Al(OH)_3$. The subscript 3 on $SO_4$ on the right indicates three $SO_4$ groups in the product. There must be three $SO_4$ groups in the starting material, so put a 3 before $H_2SO_4$.

Note now that the $2Al(OH)_3$ on the left of the partially balanced equation says there are two times three OH groups (two, from the coefficient, times the subscript 3), or six OH groups, in the starting material. There must be six OH groups in the product, so on the right side stick a 6 before HOH.

The final equation reads

$$2Al(OH)_3 + 3H_2SO_4 \rightarrow Al_2(SO_4)_3 + 6HOH$$

■ P R O B L E M  114   Write a balanced equation for the reaction of $Ca(OH)_2$ with $H_3PO_4$ to produce $Ca_3(PO_4)_2$ and $H_2O$.

ANSWER: $3Ca(OH)_2 + 2H_3PO_4 \rightarrow Ca_3(PO_4)_2 + 6H_2O$

These are almost trivial cases of equation-balancing because they simply require proper counting of atoms and groups of atoms. They are typical of the equations that describe reactions in which no electron-shifting occurs. More likely to cause trouble are those reactions in which electrons are transferred or shifted from one atom to another, so-called "oxidation-reduction," or "redox," reactions. For these oxidation-reduction reactions, balancing by inspection is not only likely to be a hit-or-miss project but also may lead to a wrong answer. Therefore, it is advisable that a systematic approach be employed whenever an oxidation-reduction reaction needs to be balanced.

## *Oxidation numbers*

First we look at the oxidation-number method of balancing equations. For this, we need to define briefly what an oxidation number is and how it is used. (Sometimes "oxidation numbers" are referred to as "valence numbers" or "oxidation states," also.) An oxidation number is simply a number assigned to an atom in an element or in a compound, following quite specific rules, so as to keep tabs on electron shifts in chemical reactions. The oxidation number in a given case may turn out to be positive $(+)$, negative $(-)$, or zero; it may be a whole number, or a fraction. The rules are basically derived from an agreement to count shared electrons with more electronegative atoms unless the two sharing atoms are identical, in which case the shared electrons are split equally in the counting process. (See your textbook for a more complete discussion.) The rules are:

1. In the elemental, or uncombined, state the atoms are assigned an oxidation number of zero.

2. In compounds, the oxidation number of fluorine is always assigned to be $-1$.

3. In compounds, the group I elements (Li, Na, K, Rb, Cs, and Fr) have an oxidation number of $+1$.

4. In compounds, the group II elements (Be, Mg, Ca, Sr, Ba, and Ra) have an oxidation number of $+2$.

5. In compounds, hydrogen is generally assigned the oxidation number $+1$. The exception is in the hydrides, where hydrogen is given an oxidation number of $-1$.

6. In compounds, oxygen is generally assigned the oxidation number $-2$. The exceptions are the fluorine-oxygen compounds, where the fluorine assignment $-1$ takes precedence, and the peroxides, where oxygen is given an oxidation number of $-1$.

7. For neutral species, the sum of the oxidation numbers times the number of each kind of atom adds up to zero.

8. For charged species (ions), the sum of the oxidation numbers times the number of each kind of atom adds up to the net charge on the ion.

PROBLEM 115    What is the oxidation number of S in $H_2SO_4$?

SOLUTION: Oxidation number of H is $+1$.
Oxidation number of O is $-2$.
Two H's contribute $(2)(+1)$, or $+2$.
Four O's contribute $(4)(-2)$, or $-8$.
Net contribution by H's and O's is $+2 - 8$, or $-6$.
Compound $H_2SO_4$ is neutral, so we need a $+6$ to counteract the $-6$.
    This $+6$ must be contributed by the S. Since there is but one S atom, its oxidation number must be $+6$.

PROBLEM 116    What is the oxidation number of S in $H_2S_2O_7$?

SOLUTION: Two H's contribute $(2)(+1)$, or $+2$.
Seven O's contribute $(7)(-2)$, or $-14$.
Net contribution by H's and O's is $+2 - 14$, or $-12$.
We need a $+12$ contribution from the S's.
There are two S atoms per formula-unit, so each S atom contributes $\frac{1}{2}(+12)$, or $+6$.
Thus, the oxidation number of S in $H_2S_2O_7$ is $+6$.

PROBLEM 117    What is the oxidation number of S in $Na_2S_2O_3$?

SOLUTION: Oxidation number of Na is $+1$.

Two Na's contribute $(2)(+1)$, or $+2$.

Oxidation number of O is $-2$.

Three O's contribute $(3)(-2)$, or $-6$.

Net contribution by Na's and O's is $+2 - 6$, or $-4$.

We need a contribution of $+4$ from the S's to come out neutral.

There are two S's per formula-unit, so each S atom contributes $\frac{1}{2}(+4)$, or $+2$.

Thus, the oxidation number of S in $Na_2S_2O_3$ is $+2$.

**PROBLEM 118** What is the oxidation number of S in $S_4O_6^=$?

SOLUTION: Oxidation number of O is $-2$.

Six O's contribute $(6)(-2)$, or $-12$.

Net charge on the ion is $-2$.

What do we need to have with $-12$ to get a net of $-2$?

Obviously, we need a $+10$.

This $+10$ must be contributed by the four S's.

Each S atom contributes $\dfrac{+10}{4}$, or $+2\frac{1}{2}$.

Thus, the oxidation number of S in $S_4O_6^=$ is $+2\frac{1}{2}$.

**PROBLEM 119** What is the oxidation number of S in $Ca(HSO_3)_2$?

SOLUTION: Oxidation number of Ca is $+2$.

Since the compound is neutral, each $HSO_3$ must contribute a charge of $-1$.

In $HSO_3^-$, one H and the three O's contribute $(1)(+1)+(3)(-2)$, or $1 - 6$, or $-5$. To come out with a net charge of $-1$ on the whole complex ion $HSO_3^-$, the S must contribute $+4$. There is but one S atom per formula-unit, so the oxidation number of S in $Ca(HSO_3)_2$ is $+4$.

From the above examples, the procedure to follow is to assign first those oxidation numbers you know, using either the rules given above or knowledge of the group behavior in the periodic table (e.g., Ca is a group II element and forms $Ca^{++}$ ions), and then figure out what the other atom must be to be consistent with rules and electrical charge balance.

For shorthand convenience, it is frequently desirable to write the oxidation number just below the atom for which it applies. (Remember that oxidation number is a *per atom* deal.) Then, if necessary, under that you can write the apparent contribution to the charge by all the atoms of that type—in other words, oxidation number times the number of atoms. This notation, which is illustrated in the next problems, will be handy when we start balancing equations using oxidation numbers.

P R O B L E M  120  What is the oxidation number of C in $H_2C_2O_4$?

SOLUTION:

$H_2C_2O_4$
$+1$  ?  $-2$ ← oxidation numbers
$+2$    $-8$ ← apparent  charge  contribution = atoms $\times$ oxidation number

From the $+2$ and $-8$, we conclude that the contribution from the carbon must be $+6$. There are two carbons, so each is $+3$. Therefore, oxidation number of C in $H_2C_2O_4$ is $+3$.

■ P R O B L E M  121  What is the oxidation number of Mn in each of the following: $MnO$, $Mn(OH)_3$, $K_2MnO_4$, $KMnO_4$, $Mn_3O_4$?

ANSWER: $+2, +3, +6, +7, +8/3$

■ P R O B L E M  122  What is the oxidation number of P in each of the following: $PH_4^+$, $PO_2^{-3}$, $PO_4^{-3}$, $PO_3^{-3}$, $H_2P_2O_7^=$?

ANSWER: $-3, +1, +5, +3, +5$

■ P R O B L E M  123  What is the oxidation number of the underlined atom in each of the following compounds, all of which are either hydrides or peroxides: $\underline{U}H_3$, $Li\underline{B}H_4$, $\underline{Zn}O_2$, $Na_2\underline{O}_2$, $Na_2\underline{Mo}O_8$?

ANSWER: $+3, +3, +2, -1, +6$

At this point it should be evident that the oxidation number is only a formal way of keeping track of the electrical charge in compounds. In most cases, proper application of the rules leads to a unique assignment of oxidation number for each element in a compound. However, as Problem 313 suggests, this is not always the case. For example, in the compound $Na_2MoO_8$, a $+6$ assignment for Mo is obtainable only provided we know that this is a peroxide and, therefore, that the oxygen is to be regarded as $-1$.

Suppose we did not have this information. Then we would assume $-2$ for oxygen, eventually leading to an oxidation number of $+14$ for Mo. Now this is a ridiculous oxidation number for molybdenum, seeing where it is in the periodic table and knowing something about how oxidation numbers run. But how could *you* be expected to know this? The answer is you would not and, in fact, you could make a good case for choosing to assign Mo in $Na_2MoO_8$ an oxidation number of $+14$ instead of $+6$. The point is that in some cases, there is not a unique assignment possible and a choice may rest on some other point of information. The fortunate part is that *it does not matter which choice you make*, provided you are consistent in assigning the other atoms. Specifically, in $Na_2MoO_8$ if you say O is $-1$ then Mo has to be $+6$, but if you say O is $-2$, then Mo has to be $+14$. So far as balancing equations is concerned, either choice would work out.

PROBLEM 124 What is the oxidation number of C in NaSCN?

SOLUTION: The oxidation number of Na is $+1$.

Therefore, the sum of the oxidation numbers of S, C, and N must add up to $-1$.

But the number of possibilities for C appear unlimited, since our rules do not fix either the S or the N uniquely.

You might not know it, but oxidation numbers of S generally run from $-2$ to $+6$ and those of N from $-3$ to $+5$. Correspondingly, there are 81 possible combinations ranging from $-2$ for S and $-3$ for N (in which case, C would come out to be $+4$, which is quite reasonable) to the other extreme, where S is taken to be $+6$ and N is taken to be $+5$ (in which case C would come out to be $-12$, which most chemists would consider unreasonable). However, for balancing equations it does not matter which value of oxidation number is taken, $+4$ or $-12$ or anything in-between, so long as we are consistent with the other atoms and stick with them in the course of the reaction. This ambiguity in the choice of some oxidation numbers is one principal reason for preferring the half-reaction method of balancing equations, which, as we shall see later, dispenses with oxidation numbers completely.

## Balancing equations by use of oxidation numbers

The underlying principle here is that electrical charge must be conserved in the course of a chemical reaction, so any increase in oxidation number must be compensated by a decrease. To balance an equation, in the most favorable case where all the reactants and all the products are specified, all we need to do is to assign oxidation numbers to those atoms which undergo change in oxidation state and then match the increase against the decrease. Finally, the coefficients of all the other reactants and products must be adjusted to be consistent with conservation of mass and charge. In more sophisticated problems, only the oxidizing agent (substance in which oxidation number goes down) and the reducing agent (substance in which oxidation number goes up) are given along with their products, so in this case the equation may have to be completed—i.e., missing reactants and products supplied—as well as balanced. In the following problems, the oxidation numbers involved are written just below the symbol of the corresponding atom. Arrows are used to show how many units of electronic charge must be shifted in or out to account for the observed change in oxidation number.

**PROBLEM 125**  Balance the equation $?CH_4 + ?O_2 \rightarrow ?CO_2 + ?H_2O$ using oxidation numbers.

SOLUTION: The oxidation number of C changes from $-4$ in $CH_4$ to $+4$ in $CO_2$.

The oxidation number of O changes from 0 in $O_2$ to $-2$ in $CO_2$ and $H_2O$.

This can be summarized schematically as follows:

$$?CH_4 + ?O_2 \rightarrow ?CO_2 + ?H_2O$$
$$-4 \qquad 0 \qquad +4 \;\; -2 \qquad\;\; -2$$

The C atom, in going from $-4$ to $+4$, has to get rid of 8 units of negative charge. We can indicate this by showing an arrow going downward from the $-4$ carbon and labeling it $8e^-$ (which stands for eight electronic charges). The O atom, in going from 0 to $-2$, has to gain 2 units of negative charge. We can indicate this by an arrow going upward to the zero oxygen. The tableau looks like this:

$$?CH_4 + ?O_2 \rightarrow \quad ?CO_2 + ?H_2O$$
$$-4 \qquad 0 \qquad\quad +4 \ -2 \quad\ -2$$
$$\downarrow 8e^- \qquad \uparrow 2e^-$$

Next we note that, whereas only one carbon atom need be considered (the subscript of C being unity in $CH_4$), two oxygen atoms need to be considered (because the subscript is 2 in $O_2$). This means that, although each O atom goes from 0 to $-2$, two such changes need to be considered. We can indicate this by putting a "$\times 2$" next to the "$2e^-$."

$$?CH_4 + ?O_2 \rightarrow ?CO_2 \quad + ?H_2O$$
$$-4 \qquad 0 \qquad +4 \ -2 \qquad -2$$
$$\downarrow 8e^- \qquad \uparrow 2e^- \times 2$$

So now we have $8e^-$ moving out and $2e^- \times 2$ moving in, which is unsatisfactory if we want to keep electrical balance. We can correct the situation by taking twice as many of the $2e^- \times 2$ changes as of the $8e^-$ changes. This means multiplying the whole $O_2$ business by two:

$$CH_4 + 2O_2 \longrightarrow ?CO_2 \quad + ?H_2O$$
$$-4 \qquad 2\left(\begin{matrix}0\\ \uparrow 2e^- \times 2\end{matrix}\right) \quad +4 \ -2 \qquad -2$$
$$\downarrow 8e^-$$

At this stage, the problem is essentially solved because we have determined that $CH_4$ and $O_2$ react in the ratio 1 to 2. (One $CH_4$ gives up $8e^-$'s; two $O_2$'s pick up $2 \times 2 \times 2 = 8e^-$.) All we need to do now is to fix up the rest of the equation, being careful however not to disturb this 1-to-2 ratio.

For the conclusion of the problem, all the tableau involving oxidation numbers is to be ignored and we work only from

$$CH_4 + 2O_2 \rightarrow ?CO_2 + ?H_2O$$

One C on the left requires one C on the right, so we put a 1 (understood) before $CO_2$.

Four O atoms on the left require four O atoms on the right. Two of these are provided in the $1CO_2$; the other two can come from the $H_2O$ if we put a 2 before $H_2O$.

The final balanced equation is

$$CH_4 + 2O_2 \rightarrow CO_2 + 2H_2O$$

Actually, in this case, you probably could have balanced it by inspection more quickly.

PROBLEM 126   Balance the following by the oxidation-number method: $?C_3H_8 + ?O_2 \rightarrow ?CO + ?H_2O$.

SOLUTION:

$$?C_3 \quad\quad H_8 + ?O_2 \rightarrow ?CO \quad\quad + ?H_2O$$
$$(3)(-\tfrac{8}{3}) \quad\quad\quad 0 \quad (3)(+2) \quad\quad -2$$
$$\downarrow {\scriptstyle 14e^-} \quad\quad\quad \uparrow {\scriptstyle 2e^- \times 2}$$

Each carbon atom goes from $-\tfrac{8}{3}$ to $+2$. Because $\tfrac{8}{3}$ is such an awkward number to work with, we would be better off to consider three atoms as a group—in other words, multiply this particular oxidation-number change by 3. On the left of the equation, this will be done automatically for us when we take into account the subscript 3 on C in $C_3H_8$. These three carbons together are worth $(3)(-\tfrac{8}{3})$, or $-8$. On the right, we need to be careful to insert the same factor of three. We do this by putting a 3 before the CO, noting that three such carbon atoms are worth $(3)(+2)$, or $+6$. Thus, for $C_3H_8$ going to 3CO, the charge change would be from $-8$ to $+6$, corresponding to a loss of $14e^-$.

So, the problem is really

$$C_3H_8 + ?O_2 \rightarrow 3CO + ?H_2O$$
$$\downarrow {\scriptstyle 14e^-} \quad\quad \uparrow {\scriptstyle 4e^-}$$

We can square away the electron loss and electron gain if we take two of the $14e^-$ changes $(= 28e^-)$ for seven of the $4e^-$ changes $(= 28e^-)$—in other words, take $2C_3H_8$ for every $7O_2$. However, if we take $2C_3H_8$ on the left, we need to have 6CO on the right.

$$2C_3H_8 + 7O_2 \rightarrow 6CO + ?H_2O$$

To get the coefficient for $H_2O$, we can either count H atoms (16H on the left means 16H on the right) or count O atoms (14 oxygen on the left means 14 oxygen on the right, of which 6 are already furnished by 6CO). In either case, $8H_2$ comes out.

The final equation is

$$2C_3H_8 + 7O_2 \rightarrow 6CO + 8H_2O$$

■ P R O B L E M   127   Balance  the  following by the oxidation-number method: $?HN_3 + ?O_2 \rightarrow ?NO_2 + ?H_2O$.

ANSWER: $4HN_3 + 13O_2 \rightarrow 12NO_2 + 2H_2O$

P R O B L E M   128   Balance  the  following by the oxidation-number method: $?KMnO_4 + ?H_2C_2O_4 \rightarrow ?K_2CO_3 + ?MnO_2 + ?H_2O + ?CO_2$.

SOLUTION: The Mn goes from $+7$ in $KMnO_4$ to $+4$ in $MnO_2$.   This is a $3e^-$ change.

The C goes from $+3$ in $H_2C_2O_4$ to $+4$ in $K_2CO_3$ and in $CO_2$.   This looks like a $1e^-$ change, but it needs to be taken twice, because of the subscript 2 on C in $H_2C_2O_4$.

To balance a $3e^-$ gain against a $2e^-$ loss, we need to take two of the former with three of the latter.   This gives us

$$2KMnO_4 + 3H_2C_2O_4 \rightarrow ?K_2CO_3 + ?MnO_2 + ?H_2O + ?CO_2$$

Since there are two K atoms on the left, we need to put a 1 before $K_2CO_3$ on the right.

Since there are two Mn atoms on the left, we need to put a 2 before $MnO_2$ on the right.

Since there are six H atoms on the left (in $3H_2C_2O_4$), we need to put a 3 before $H_2O$ on the right.

Finally, the six C atoms on the left (in $3H_2C_2O_4$) require six C atoms on the right, one of which is already accounted for in the $1K_2CO_3$; so, we need to put a 5 before the $CO_2$ on the right.

The final equation is

$$2KMnO_4 + 3H_2C_2O_4 \rightarrow K_2CO_3 + 2MnO_2 + 3H_2O + 5CO_2$$

It can be checked out by counting oxygen atoms ($2 \times 4$ plus $3 \times 4 = 20$ on the left; 3 plus $2 \times 2$ plus 3 plus $5 \times 2 = 20$ on the right), which we have not used in establishing the balanced equation.

The great majority of chemical equations encountered in freshman chemistry describe reactions in aqueous solutions.   In these cases, usually the given information is not complete as to all reactants and all products.   What is usually specified is the oxidizing and the reducing agent, what they go to in the course of the reaction, and whether the solution is acidic or basic.   The rest of the information (whether the equation involves $H^+$ or $OH^-$ or $H_2O$ and on which side of the equation these need to be put) has to be figured out. The following systematic procedure is recommended:

1. Assign oxidation numbers to the atoms that change.

2. Choose the proper ratio of oxidizing to reducing agent so the oxidation-number-change is balanced.

3. Adjust the coefficients of the products to correspond to the coefficients selected in step 2.

4. Count up the oxygen atoms on both sides and add $H_2O$ to the side that is deficient in oxygen.

5. Count up the hydrogen atoms on both sides and add $H^+$ to the side that is deficient in hydrogen. It is important that step 4 precede step 5.

6. If the conditions are specified to be "acidic" solution, you are all done. If, however, the reaction is said to be for "basic" solution, you need to get rid of the $H^+$ as a species in the equation. You do this by adding a sufficient number of $OH^-$ ions to neutralize all the $H^+$ into $H_2O$, being careful to add an equal number of $OH^-$ ions to the other side of the equation to maintain balance.

7. Cancel any duplications that appear on both sides of the equation.

PROBLEM 129    Given the change $Cr_2O_7^= + H_2SO_3 \rightarrow Cr^{+3} + HSO_4^-$ occurring in acidic solution. Complete and balance the equation for the reaction, using the oxidation-number method.

SOLUTION: The Cr goes from $+6$ in $Cr_2O_7^=$ to $+3$ in $Cr^{+3}$. This is a $3e^-$ gain. There are two of them because of the subscript 2 on Cr in $Cr_2O_7^=$. In effect, this is a $6e^-$ change.
The S goes from $+4$ in $H_2SO_3$ to $+6$ in $HSO_4^-$. This is a $2e^-$ loss. To balance a $6e^-$ gain vs. a $2e^-$ loss, we need to take one of the former for three of the latter. Therefore, the ratio of $Cr_2O_7^=$ to $H_2SO_3$ must be taken 1 to 3. We thus have

$$Cr_2O_7^= + 3H_2SO_3 \rightarrow ?Cr^{+3} + ?HSO_4^-$$

Two chromium atoms on the left require a coefficient of 2 to be placed before $Cr^{+3}$ on the right. Likewise, the three sulfur atoms on the left can be balanced by putting a 3 before the $HSO_4^-$ on the right.

We now have

$$Cr_2O_7^= + 3H_2SO_3 \rightarrow 2Cr^{+3} + 3HSO_4^-$$

Counting up the oxygen atoms gives $7 + (3)(3) = 16$ on the left and $(3)(4) = 12$ on the right. The fact that the right side has four less oxygen atoms than the left can be fixed up by adding $4H_2O$ to the right side of the equation. It now reads

$$Cr_2O_7^= + 3H_2SO_3 \rightarrow 2Cr^{+3} + 3HSO_4^- + 4H_2O$$

Counting up the hydrogen atoms, we have $(3)(2)$, or 6, on the left and $3 + (4)(2)$, or 11, on the right. The left side has five less hydrogen atoms, and we can fix it by adding $5H^+$ to the left. The result is the final balanced equation

$$5H^+ + Cr_2O_7^= + 3H_2SO_3 \rightarrow 2Cr^{+3} + 3HSO_4^- + 4H_2O$$

It can be checked by comparing the net charge on the left and the right. On the left we have 5 monopositive ions plus one dinegative plus 3 neutral species, which adds up to a net charge of $+3$; on the right side we have 2 tripositive plus 3 mononegative plus 4 neutral, which adds up to a net charge of $(2)(+3) + (3)(-1)$, or $+3$, also.

PROBLEM 130  The reaction $CrO_4^= + SO_3^= \rightarrow Cr(OH)_4^- + SO_4^=$ occurs in basic solution. Write a complete balanced equation for the reaction, using the oxidation-number method.

SOLUTION: The Cr goes from $+6$ in $CrO_4^=$ to $+3$ in $Cr(OH)_4^-$. This is a $3e^-$ gain.

The S goes from $+4$ in $SO_3^=$ to $+6$ in $SO_4^=$. This is a $2e^-$ loss.

To balance electron gain against electron loss, we take two of the former against three of the latter.

This gives us

$$2CrO_4^= + 3SO_3^= \rightarrow ?Cr(OH)_4^- + ?SO_4^=$$

Two Cr atoms on the left require a coefficient 2 before the $Cr(OH)_4^-$ on the right; three S atoms on the left require $3SO_4^=$ on the right. We now have

$$2CrO_4^= + 3SO_3^= \rightarrow 2Cr(OH)_4^- + 3SO_4^=$$

Counting up oxygens gives $(2)(4) + (3)(3) = 17$ on the left and $(2)(4) + (3)(4) = 20$ on the right. The left side is deficient by three oxygen atoms, so we stick $3H_2O$ on the left side of the equation.

It now reads

$$3H_2O + 2CrO_4^= + 3SO_3^= \rightarrow 2Cr(OH)_4^- + 3SO_4^=$$

Counting up hydrogens gives $(3)(2) = 6$ on the left and $(2)(4) = 8$ on the right. The left side is deficient by two hydrogen atoms, so we stick $2H^+$ on the left side of the equation. The result is

$$2H^+ + 3H_2O + 2CrO_4^= + 3SO_3^= \rightarrow 2Cr(OH)_4^- + 3SO_4^=$$

This equation is completely balanced but is *wrong* because it is not valid for basic solution. To make it right, we can add $2OH^-$ to the left to chew up the $2H^+$, but to leave the balancing undisturbed we must simultaneously add $2OH^-$ to the right. On the left, the $2H^+$ and $2OH^-$ give $2H_2O$, which can be combined with the $3H_2O$ to give $5H_2O$. On the right, two additional $OH^-$'s appear. The final equation, valid for basic solution, is

$$5H_2O + 2CrO_4^= + 3SO_3^= \rightarrow 2Cr(OH)_4^- + 3SO_4^= + 2OH^-$$

The net charge checks out: On the left, $(5)(0) + (2)(-2) + (3)(-2) = -10$; on the right, $(2)(-1) + (3)(-2) + (2)(-1) = -10$.

■ PROBLEM 131   Balance the following, using the oxidation-number method: $?KClO_3 + ?S \rightarrow ?KCl + ?SO_2$.
ANSWER: $2KClO_3 + 3S \rightarrow 2KCl + 3SO_2$

■ PROBLEM 132   Balance the following, using the oxidation-number method: $?KClO_3 + ?S + ?H_2O \rightarrow ?Cl_2 + ?K_2SO_4 + ?H_2SO_4$.
ANSWER: $6KClO_3 + 5S + 2H_2O \rightarrow 3Cl_2 + 3K_2SO_4 + 2H_2SO_4$

■ PROBLEM 133   Balance the following, using the oxidation-number method: $?KMnO_4 + ?C_6H_{12}O_6 \rightarrow ?CO_2 + ?MnO + ?H_2O + ?K_2CO_3$.
ANSWER: $24KMnO_4 + 5C_6H_{12}O_6 \rightarrow 18CO_2 + 24MnO + 30H_2O + 12K_2CO_3$

■■ PROBLEM 134   Balance the following, using the oxidation-number method: $?KSCN + ?H_2Cr_2O_7 + ?K_2Cr_2O_7 \rightarrow ?CO_2 + ?NO_2 + ?Cr_2O_3 + ?K_2SO_4 + ?H_2O$.
ANSWER: $2KSCN + 4H_2Cr_2O_7 + K_2Cr_2O_7 \rightarrow 2CO_2 + 2NO_2 + 5Cr_2O_3 + 2K_2SO_4 + 4H_2O$

■ P R O B L E M 135 Given the change $H_2S$ $+ NO_3^- \to S + NO_2$ in acidic solution. Complete and balance the equation for the reaction, using the oxidation-number method.

ANSWER: $H_2S + 2NO_3^- + 2H^+ \to S + 2NO_2 + 2H_2O$

■ P R O B L E M 136 Given the change $HS^-$ $+ NO_3^- \to S + NO_2^-$ in basic solution. Write a complete balanced equation for the reaction, using the oxidation-number method.

ANSWER: $HS^- + NO_3^- \to S + NO_2^- + OH^-$

■ P R O B L E M 137 Given the change $Ag_2O + Co(OH)_2 \to Ag + Co(OH)_3$ in basic solution. Complete and balance the equation, using the oxidation-number method.

ANSWER: $H_2O + Ag_2O + 2Co(OH)_2 \to 2Ag + 2Co(OH)_3$

■ P R O B L E M 138 Given the change $H_2O_2$ (peroxide) $+ Br_2 \to BrO_3^- + H_2O$ in acidic solution. Complete and balance the equation, using the oxidation-number method.

ANSWER: $5H_2O_2 + Br_2 \to 2BrO_3^- + 4H_2O + 2H^+$

■ P R O B L E M 139 Given the change $HO_2^-$ (peroxide) $+ IO_3^- \to OH^- + H_3IO_6^=$ in basic solution. Complete and balance the equation, using the oxidation-number method.

ANSWER: $IO_3^- + HO_2^- + H_2O \to H_3IO_6^=$

■■ P R O B L E M 140 When washing soda is boiled in aluminum pans, the aluminum dissolves and hydrogen gas is liberated. The principal change can be written $Al + OH^- \to Al(OH)_4^- + H_2$. Complete and balance this equation, using the oxidation-number method.

ANSWER: $2Al + 2OH^- + 6H_2O \to 2Al(OH)_4^- + 3H_2$

## Balancing equations by use of half-reactions

As indicated, there is frequently ambiguity in choice of oxidation number to be assigned. Coupled with the problems involved in handling oxidation numbers, it would be desirable to get around the whole concept (which is an artificial one, anyhow, not necessarily showing any resemblance to reality). This is what the half-reaction method does. It separates the oxidizing and reducing agents from each other, shows each one going to its respective products, and writes a balanced half-reaction for each one separately.   The only unorthodox feature is that electrons appear as chemical species in each of the half-reactions. Normally, electrons cannot exist separately as a species in solutions, so in this sense we are using an artificiality. However, it does allow us to monitor charge changes in oxidation-reduction reactions, and it does so without making any use of oxidation numbers.

The procedure of half-reactions is particularly useful for solutions but it may be used also for reactions in the gas phase and in the solid state.   In such cases, the interpretation of the half-reaction as a real possible change going on may not be tenable, but still we can use it to balance equations and that, after all, is our purpose at this point.

The steps to follow are these:

1. Separate the oxidizing and the reducing agent.

2. Show the oxidizing agent going to its reduced form.

3. Show the reducing agent going to its oxidized form.

4. Make sure the atoms other than H and O are balanced on the two sides of each half-reaction.   If necessary, adjust coefficients.

5. Count up the number of oxygen atoms on the left and right of each half-reaction, and add $H_2O$ to the side deficient in oxygen.

6. Count up the number of hydrogen atoms on left and right and add $H^+$ to the side deficient in hydrogen.   (It is important that step 5 precede step 6.)

7. Count up the net charge on left and right and add electrons $(e^-)$ to the side deficient in negative charge.

8. If the reaction is specified to be in basic solution, add to each side of each half-reaction enough $OH^-$ to cancel the $H^+$ appearing in that half-reaction.   Combine $H^+$ and $OH^-$ and cancel $H_2O$ duplication.

At this stage you should have two half-reactions, each of which is completely balanced so far as atoms and charges are concerned, the only odd point being that $e^-$ appears on the right of one half-reaction and on the left of the other.

9. To get a balanced equation, multiply each half-reaction all the way through by an appropriate number so that when the two half-reactions are added up the electrons can be cancelled out.

10. Add up the half-reactions and cancel any duplication of species on the left and right sides.

**PROBLEM 141** Balance the equation $?C_3H_8 + ?O_2 \rightarrow ?CO + ?H_2O$ by the method of half-reactions.

SOLUTION: One half-reaction involves the change $C_3H_8 \rightarrow CO$. To write a balanced half-reaction for this change we note that 3 carbon atoms on the left require 3 carbon atoms on the right, so we put a 3 before the CO. This gives us

$$C_3H_8 \rightarrow 3CO$$

Counting up oxygen atoms, we find none on the left and three on the right, so the left side is deficient by three oxygen atoms. We can fix it up by putting $3H_2O$ on the left side. This gives us

$$C_3H_8 + 3H_2O \rightarrow 3CO$$

Counting up hydrogen atoms, we find $8 + (3)(2) = 14$ on the left and none on the right. We, therefore, add $14H^+$ to the right side, giving

$$C_3H_8 + 3H_2O \rightarrow 3CO + 14H^+$$

All the atoms are now balanced (so, mass is conserved) and all we have to worry about is the charge. If we add up the charge, we find 3 neutral $H_2O$ plus one neutral $C_3H_8$ on the left, which adds up to zero charge, and 3 neutral CO plus 14 monopositive $H^+$ on the right, which adds up to $+14$. To make sure that electrical charge is preserved when the reaction goes from left to right, we need to have the same net charge on both sides of the half-reaction. We achieve this by adding $14e^-$ to the right side. The final half-reaction looks like this:

$$C_3H_8 + 3H_2O \rightarrow 3CO + 14H^+ + 14e^-$$

The other half-reaction involves the change $O_2 \rightarrow H_2O$. To get a balanced half-reaction for this, we note first that there are two oxygen atoms on the left and one on the right. Therefore, we need to multiply the $H_2O$ by two, giving us

$$O_2 \rightarrow 2H_2O$$

Counting up oxygen atoms shows balance in this respect. Counting up hydrogen atoms shows a deficiency of four on the left, so we add $4H^+$ to the left side of the half-reaction. This gives us

$$O_2 + 4H^+ \rightarrow 2H_2O$$

To balance charge, we note that the left side has $0 + (4)(+1) = +4$, and the right side, zero. So, we add $4e^-$ to the left, getting

$$O_2 + 4H^+ + 4e^- \rightarrow 2H_2O$$

We now have two half-reactions, both balanced as to atoms and charge conservation. One is for the reducing agent ($C_3H_8$) and the other is for the oxidizing agent ($O_2$):

*reducing agent:* $C_3H_8 + 3H_2O \rightarrow 3CO + 14H^+ + 14e^-$

*oxidizing agent:* $O_2 + 4H^+ + 4e^- \rightarrow 2H_2O$

If these two half-reactions are to be part of the same over-all reaction, the electron production of the first one has to be matched by the electron consumption of the second one. This will be the case if seven of the second occur for every two of the first. So, we multiply the first all the way through by two and the second by seven. The result is

*reducing agent:* $2C_3H_8 + 6H_2O \rightarrow 6CO + 28H^+ + 28e^-$

*oxidizing agent:* $7O_2 + 28H^+ + 28e^- \rightarrow 14H_2O$

Now we can add these up keeping all terms to the left or right of the arrow as they occur. The sum is

$$2C_3H_8 + 6H_2O + 7O_2 + \cancel{28H^+} + \cancel{28e^-} \rightarrow$$
$$6CO + \cancel{28H^+} + \cancel{28e^-} + 14H_2O$$

Cancelling out duplications right and left, we strike out the 28 $e$'s and also the 28 $H^+$'s from each side. Furthermore, there are $6H_2O$ on the left and $14H_2O$ on the right. Six of these are duplicated and can be deducted from each side, leaving only $8H_2O$ on the right. The final result is

$$2C_3H_8 + 7O_2 \rightarrow 6CO + 8H_2O$$

Note that it has been obtained here without introducing oxidation numbers.

**PROBLEM** 142 Given the change $Cr_2O_7^= + H_2SO_3 \rightarrow Cr^{+3} + HSO_4^-$ occurring in acidic solution. Complete and balance the equation for the reaction, using the half-reaction method.

SOLUTION: In one half-reaction, the change is $Cr_2O_7^= \rightarrow Cr^{+3}$. Two chromium atoms on the left require a 2 before $Cr^{+3}$.

$$Cr_2O_7^= \rightarrow 2Cr^{+3}$$

There are seven oxygen atoms on the left, none on the right, so we add $7H_2O$ to the right, getting

$$Cr_2O_7^= \rightarrow 2Cr^{+3} + 7H_2O$$

There are 14 H atoms on the right, none on the left, so we add $14H^+$ to the left, leading to

$$Cr_2O_7^= + 14H^+ \rightarrow 2Cr^{+3} + 7H_2O$$

As to charge, the left side has 14 monopositive species plus one dinegative one, corresponding to $+14 - 2 = +12$; the right side, two tripositive plus 7 neutral $= (2)(+3) = +6$. The left side needs $6e^-$. We have finally

$$Cr_2O_7^= + 14H^+ + 6e^- \rightarrow 2Cr^{+3} + 7H_2O$$

for the completely balanced half-reaction, showing what happens to the oxidizing agent.

In the other half-reaction, the change is $H_2SO_3 \rightarrow HSO_4^-$. The sulfur atoms are already balanced. As to oxygen atoms, there are three on the left and four on the right, so we make up the deficit by adding $1H_2O$ to the left. This gives us

$$H_2SO_3 + H_2O \rightarrow HSO_4^-$$

As to hydrogen atoms, there are now four on the left and one on the right. To redress the balance, we add $3H^+$ to the right, getting

$$H_2SO_3 + H_2O \rightarrow HSO_4^- + 3H^+$$

For charge, the left side is neutral but the right side has a net charge of $(-1) + (+3) = +2$. We fix it up by adding $2e^-$ to the right side. The final half-reaction is

$$H_2SO_3 + H_2O \rightarrow HSO_4^- + 3H^+ + 2e^-$$

The $Cr_2O_7^=$ half-reaction uses up $6e^-$; the $H_2SO_3$ half-reaction produces $2e^-$. Therefore, we must take three of the latter for every one of the former. Multiplying the $Cr_2O_7^=$ half-reaction by one and the $H_2SO_3$ half-reaction by three gives us

$$Cr_2O_7^= + 14H^+ + 6e^- \rightarrow 2Cr^{+3} + 7H_2O$$

$$\underline{3H_2SO_3 + 3H_2O \rightarrow 3HSO_4^- + 9H^+ + 6e^-}$$

$$Cr_2O_7^= + 14H^+ + 6e^- + 3H_2SO_3 + 3H_2O \rightarrow$$

$$2Cr^{+3} + 7H_2O + 3HSO_4^- + 9H^+ + 6e^-$$

Duplications are $6e^-$, $3H_2O$, and $9H^+$. If we strike these out from both sides, we are left with

$$Cr_2O_7^= + 5H^+ + 3H_2SO_3 \rightarrow 2Cr^{+3} + 4H_2O + 3HSO_4^-$$

which agrees with what we got by the oxidation-number method.

P R O B L E M 143    Using half-reactions, deduce the balanced equation for the change $CrO_4^= + SO_3^= \rightarrow Cr(OH)_4^- + SO_4^=$ in basic solution.

SOLUTION: In one half-reaction, the change is $CrO_4^= \rightarrow Cr(OH)_4^-$.
The chromium atoms are balanced.
The oxygen atoms are balanced.
As to hydrogen, there are none on the left but four on the right, so we stick $4H^+$ on the left, getting

$$4H^+ + CrO_4^= \rightarrow Cr(OH)_4^-$$

As to charge, the left side is $(4)(+1) + (-2) = +2$ but the right side is $-1$. So we need to add $3e^-$ to the left. We get

$$3e^- + 4H^+ + CrO_4^= \rightarrow Cr(OH)_4^-$$

This is a completely balanced half-reaction but is no good for basic solution. We need to get rid of the $4H^+$. We can do this by adding $4OH^-$ to both sides and combining $4H^+$ and $4OH^-$ into $4H_2O$ on the left. The result is

$$3e^- + 4H_2O + CrO_4^= \rightarrow Cr(OH)_4^- + 4OH^-$$

which is not only balanced but also is valid for basic solution.

In the other half-reaction, the change is $SO_3^= \rightarrow SO_4^=$.
The sulfur atoms are balanced.

As to oxygen atoms, the left side is deficient by one oxygen, so we need
to add $1H_2O$ to the left.  The result is

$$H_2O + SO_3^= \rightarrow SO_4^=$$

As to hydrogen atoms, the right side is now deficient by two, so we stick
$2H^+$ on the right, getting

$$H_2O + SO_3^= \rightarrow SO_4^= + 2H^+$$

For balancing the charge, we note that the left side has two neutral
plus one dinegative, or $-2$, charge.  The right side has one dinegative plus two monopositive, or $0$, charge.  To square away $-2$
with $0$, we need to add $2e^-$ to the right.  The result

$$H_2O + SO_3^= \rightarrow SO_4^= + 2H^+ + 2e^-$$

is, however, not valid for basic solution.  We get rid of the $2H^+$
by adding $2OH^-$ to both sides and cancelling the $1H_2O$ on the left
against one of the $(H^+OH^-)$ combinations on the right.  The
final balanced half-reaction for basic solution is

$$2OH^- + SO_3^= \rightarrow SO_4^= + H_2O + 2e^-$$

To combine the two half-reactions:

*oxidizing agent:* $3e^- + 4H_2O + CrO_4^= \rightarrow Cr(OH)_4^- + 4OH^-$

*reducing agent:* $2OH^- + SO_3^= \rightarrow SO_4^= + H_2O + 2e^-$

we need to multiply the first by two and the second by three.  This
gives

$$6e^- + 8H_2O + 2CrO_4^= \rightarrow 2Cr(OH)_4^- + 8OH^-$$

$$6OH^- + 3SO_3^= \rightarrow 3SO_4^= + 3H_2O + 6e^-$$

which add up to the following:

$$6e^- + 8H_2O + 2CrO_4^= + 6OH^- + 3SO_3^= \rightarrow$$
$$2Cr(OH)_4^- + 8OH^- + 3SO_4^= + 3H_2O + 6e^-$$

Cancellation of $6e^-$, $3H_2O$, and $6OH^-$ from both sides leaves

$$5H_2O + 2CrO_4^= + 3SO_3^= \rightarrow 2Cr(OH)_4^- + 2OH^- + 3SO_4^=$$

The great advantage of the half-reaction method really shows up in those cases where oxidation numbers are difficult to assign (e.g., $SCN^-$) or where the changes in oxidation number are apt to be miscounted (e.g., $HO_2^-$ going to $H_2O$). If there are no false moves, the oxidation-number method of balancing equations is likely to be faster. However, the half-reaction method is less likely to lead to errors.  In the old days, people used to object to the half-reaction method on the grounds that a half-reaction by itself cannot occur and therefore has no physical reality.  This kind of objection is fast dying out under the impact of new electrochemical devices such as the fuel cell, in which an over-all reaction of the type $C_3H_8 + 5O_2 \rightarrow 3CO_2 + 4H_2O$ is made to occur so one half-reaction occurs at one electrode and the other half-reaction at the other electrode.

■ PROBLEM 144   Using the half-reaction method, complete and balance the equation for the change $MnO_4^- + H_2C_2O_4 \rightarrow Mn^{++} + CO_2$ in acidic solution.

ANSWER: $2MnO_4^- + 6H^+ + 5H_2C_2O_4 \rightarrow 2Mn^{++} + 8H_2O + 10CO_2$

■ PROBLEM 145   Using the half-reaction method, complete and balance the equation for the change $MnO_4^- + I^- \rightarrow MnO_4^= + IO_3^-$ in basic solution.

ANSWER: $6MnO_4^- + 6OH^- + I^- \rightarrow 6MnO_4^= + IO_3^- + 3H_2O$

■ PROBLEM 146   Using the half-reaction method, figure out the equation for the change $H_2O_2 + MnO_2 \rightarrow MnO_4^- + H_2O$ in acidic solution.

ANSWER: $3H_2O_2 + 2MnO_2 \rightarrow 2H_2O + 2MnO_4^- + 2H^+$

■ PROBLEM 147   Using the half-reaction method, figure out the equation for the change $H_2O_2 + MnO_4^- \rightarrow Mn^{++} + O_2$ in acidic solution.

ANSWER: $5H_2O_2 + 2MnO_4^- + 6H^+ \rightarrow 5O_2 + 2Mn^{++} + 8H_2O$

■ PROBLEM 148   Using the half-reaction method, figure out the equation for the change $HO_2^- + Ag_2O \rightarrow OH^- + AgO$ in basic solution.

ANSWER: $Ag_2O + HO_2^- \rightarrow 2AgO + OH^-$

■ P R O B L E M   149   In basic solution, green $Cr(OH)_4^-$ is oxidized to yellow $CrO_4^=$ by $HO_2^-$ as it goes to $OH^-$. Using half-reactions, figure out the equation for the net reaction.

ANSWER: $3HO_2^- + 2Cr(OH)_4^- \rightarrow 2CrO_4^= + OH^- + 5H_2O$

■ P R O B L E M   150   Suppose that $HO_2^- \rightarrow OH^-$ can oxidize $SCN^-$ to $CO_3^= + NO_3^- + SO_4^=$. Using the method of half-reactions, figure out the net equation in basic solution.

ANSWER: $8HO_2^- + SCN^- \rightarrow 4OH^- + 2H_2O + CO_3^=$
$+ NO_3^- + SO_4^=$

## Calculations involving equations

Once a balanced chemical equation has been written for a reaction, it can be used not only as a summary of the net atomic change in the course of the reaction but also (after atomic weight information has been put in) as a summary of the weight changes that occur when reactants are converted to products. This comes about because the coefficients in the balanced equation not only tell how many formula-units (atoms, molecules, or formula-units) are involved but also how many moles of each come into play. Thus, for the balanced equation

$$2C_3H_8 + 7O_2 \rightarrow 6CO + 8H_2O$$

the coefficients 2, 7, 6, and 8 tell us (a) that *two molecules* of $C_3H_8$ plus *seven molecules* of $O_2$ react to give *six molecules* of CO plus *eight molecules* of $H_2O$ or (b) that *two moles* of $C_3H_8$ plus *seven moles* of $O_2$ react to give *six moles* of CO plus *eight moles* of $H_2O$. The second part of the statement comes from the fact that once the coefficients in the equation are established, they fix once and for all the relative number of particles involved. If we multiply through by any number, the coefficients still have relative validity. Specifically, if we multiply through by the Avogadro number, we are converting the information of the chemical equation from individual particle numbers to large groups of particles, such as are of the order of magnitude encountered in typical samples in a laboratory. Because, at the present, our main emphasis is on weight calculations involving typical samples, we shall henceforth in this chapter concentrate on the molar aspects of chemical equations.

The two points that will be of use to us are these: (1) the coefficients in the balanced equation tell us the number of moles of each reactant and product when the reaction takes place as written, and (2) we need to consider only the relative number of moles of those reactants and products asked about in the calculation, assuming that the other reactants are available in needed amount and that other products than those asked about may also form. Thus, given

$$2C_3H_8 + 7O_2 \rightarrow 6CO + 8H_2O$$

we could calculate how much $O_2$ is needed for a given amount of $C_3H_8$, using the 7:2 molar ratio only, ignoring the rest of the equation. Similarly, we could calculate how much CO comes from a given amount of $C_3H_8$ using only the 6:2 molar ratio. Stated another way, you don't have to use *all* the information implicit in the equation to solve a particular problem.

Before we undertake typical problems we might summarize the way information is stored in a specific equation.

Given: $2C_3H_8 + 7O_2 \rightarrow 6CO + 8H_2O$

This means

$$\left(\begin{array}{c} 2 \text{ molecules} \\ C_3H_8 \end{array}\right) \text{react with} \left(\begin{array}{c} 7 \text{ molecules} \\ O_2 \end{array}\right) \text{to give} \left(\begin{array}{c} 6 \text{ molecules} \\ CO \end{array}\right)$$

$$\text{plus} \left(\begin{array}{c} 8 \text{ molecules} \\ H_2O \end{array}\right)$$

It also means

$$\left(\begin{array}{c} 2 \text{ moles} \\ C_3H_8 \end{array}\right) \text{react with} \left(\begin{array}{c} 7 \text{ moles} \\ O_2 \end{array}\right) \text{to give} \left(\begin{array}{c} 6 \text{ moles} \\ CO \end{array}\right) \text{plus} \left(\begin{array}{c} 8 \text{ moles} \\ H_2O \end{array}\right)$$

Furthermore,

$$2 \text{ moles } C_3H_8 = 2 \times \text{gram-formula-weight of } C_3H_8$$
$$= 2 \times (44.097 \text{ g}) = 88.194 \text{ g}$$
$$7 \text{ moles } O_2 = 7 \times \text{gram-formula-weight of } O_2$$
$$= 7 \times (31.999 \text{ g}) = 223.99 \text{ g}$$
$$6 \text{ moles } CO = 6 \times \text{gram-formula-weight of } CO$$
$$= 6 \times (28.010 \text{ g}) = 168.06 \text{ g}$$
$$8 \text{ moles } H_2O = 8 \times (18.015 \text{ g}) = 144.12 \text{ g.}$$

Putting this information into the above statement in moles, we can say

$$\left(\genfrac{}{}{0pt}{}{88.194 \text{ g}}{C_3H_8}\right) \text{ react with } \left(\genfrac{}{}{0pt}{}{223.99 \text{ g}}{O_2}\right) \text{ to give } \left(\genfrac{}{}{0pt}{}{168.06 \text{ g}}{CO}\right)$$

$$\text{plus } \left(\genfrac{}{}{0pt}{}{144.12 \text{ g}}{H_2O}\right)$$

Obviously, the latter numbers are harder to keep in your head and to manipulate. Because the molar numbers are easier to work with, most chemists carry out their calculations on a molar basis, even if it means converting given data in grams to number of moles first. For the novice, it is extremely important to get into the habit of thinking in terms of moles and setting up calculations in these terms.

**PROBLEM 151** How many grams $O_2$ are required to oxidize 1.00 g $C_3H_8$ to CO and $H_2O$?

SOLUTION: (Figure out how many moles $C_3H_8$ you are given. Then from the equation decide how many moles $O_2$ are required. Finally, compute how many grams $O_2$ this amounts to.)
One mole $C_3H_8$ weighs 44.097 g.

$$1.00 \text{ g } C_3H_8 = \frac{1.00 \text{ g}}{44.097 \text{ g/mole}} = 0.0227 \text{ mole } C_3H_8.$$

From the equation

$$2C_3H_8 + 7O_2 \rightarrow 6CO + 8H_2O$$

we note that 7 moles $O_2$ are required per 2 moles $C_3H_8$. Therefore, for 0.0227 mole $C_3H_8$ we need

$$(0.0227 \text{ mole } C_3H_8)\left(\frac{7 \text{ moles } O_2}{2 \text{ moles } C_3H_8}\right) = 0.0794 \text{ mole } O_2.$$

One mole $O_2 = 32.00$ g.

$$0.0794 \text{ mole } O_2 = (0.0794 \text{ mole})\left(\frac{32.00 \text{ g}}{\text{mole}}\right) = 2.54 \text{ g } O_2.$$

**PROBLEM 152** How many grams CO are produced when 3.42 g $C_3H_8$ is oxidized by $O_2$ to CO and $H_2O$?

SOLUTION: (Figure out how many moles $C_3H_8$ you have. Then from the equation decide how many moles of CO are produced. Finally, calculate how many grams CO this is.)

One mole $C_3H_8$ = 44.097 g.

$$3.42 \text{ g } C_3H_8 = \frac{3.42 \text{ g}}{44.097 \text{ g/mole}} = 0.0776 \text{ mole } C_3H_8.$$

From the equation

$$2C_3H_8 + 7O_2 \rightarrow 6CO + 8H_2O$$

we note that for each 2 moles $C_3H_8$ used up, 6 moles CO are produced. Therefore, if 0.0776 mole $C_3H_8$ is used up, there will be produced

$$(0.0776 \text{ mole } C_3H_8)\left(\frac{6 \text{ moles CO}}{2 \text{ moles } C_3H_8}\right) = 0.233 \text{ mole CO}.$$

One mole CO weighs 28.010 g.

$$0.233 \text{ mole CO} = (0.233 \text{ mole})\left(28.010 \frac{\text{g}}{\text{mole}}\right) = \textbf{6.53 g CO.}$$

PROBLEM 153    When $C_3H_8$ is oxidized by $O_2$ to CO and $H_2O$, how many grams $H_2O$ will be produced at the same time as 3.43 g CO?

SOLUTION: (Figure out how many moles CO are produced. From the equation decide how many moles $H_2O$ form at the same time. Convert to grams.)

One mole CO = 28.010 g.

$$3.43 \text{ g CO} = \frac{3.43 \text{ g}}{28.010 \text{ g/mole}} = 0.122 \text{ mole CO}.$$

From the equation

$$2C_3H_8 + 7O_2 \rightarrow 6CO + 8H_2O$$

we note that 8 moles $H_2O$ are produced every time 6 moles CO form. Therefore, when 0.122 mole CO is produced, we will get simultaneously

$$(0.122 \text{ mole CO})\left(\frac{8 \text{ moles } H_2O}{6 \text{ moles CO}}\right) = 0.163 \text{ mole } H_2O.$$

One mole $H_2O$ = 18.015 g.

$$0.163 \text{ mole } H_2O = (0.163 \text{ mole})\left(18.015 \frac{\text{g}}{\text{mole}}\right) = \textbf{2.94 g } H_2O.$$

PROBLEM 154 Suppose that 2.00 g $C_3H_8$ and 7.00 g $O_2$ are allowed to react to the maximum possible extent to form CO and $H_2O$. How many grams CO will be formed?

SOLUTION: (This is an excess problem where one of the reagents limits the extent of the reaction, the other one being present in excess. To solve it, convert the data given into moles. Then compare the given number of moles with that required in the equation. Decide which reagent is present in excess. Then work with the limiting one to determine how many moles CO can be formed. Convert to grams.)

One mole $C_3H_8$ = 44.097 g.

$$2.00 \text{ g } C_3H_8 = \frac{2.00 \text{ g}}{44.097 \text{ g/mole}} = 0.0454 \text{ mole } C_3H_8.$$

One mole $O_2$ = 32.00 g.

$$7.00 \text{ g } O_2 = \frac{7.00 \text{ g}}{32.00 \text{ g/mole}} = 0.219 \text{ mole } O_2.$$

The equation

$$2C_3H_8 + 7O_2 \rightarrow 6CO + 8H_2O$$

says that 7 moles $O_2$ are needed for 2 moles $C_3H_8$. For 0.0454 mole $C_3H_8$ we would then need

$$(0.0454 \text{ mole } C_3H_8) \left( \frac{7 \text{ moles } O_2}{2 \text{ moles } C_3H_8} \right) = 0.159 \text{ mole } O_2.$$

This is the minimum amount of $O_2$ needed. We actually are given 0.219 mole $O_2$, which is considerably in excess. Therefore, we conclude $O_2$ is more than sufficient. The amount of product is decided by the 0.0454 mole $C_3H_8$.

The equation

$$2C_3H_8 + 7O_2 \rightarrow 6CO + 8H_2O$$

tells us we get 6 moles CO for each 2 moles $C_3H_8$ used. Therefore, if we use up only 0.0454 mole $C_3H_8$, we would get

$$(0.0454 \text{ mole } C_3H_8) \left( \frac{6 \text{ moles } CO}{2 \text{ moles } C_3H_8} \right) = 0.136 \text{ mole } CO.$$

One mole CO = 28.010 g.

$$0.136 \text{ mole } CO = (0.136 \text{ mole}) \left( 28.010 \frac{g}{mole} \right) = 3.81 \text{ g CO}.$$

PROBLEM 155   Suppose that 2.00 g $C_3H_8$ and 7.00 g $O_2$ are allowed to react to the maximum possible extent to form $CO_2$ and $H_2O$. How many grams $CO_2$ will be formed?

SOLUTION: (The method is similar to that used in Problem 344 except do not overlook the important fact that one of the products is different, so the pertinent equation in this problem is different from the one used in Problem 344.)

One mole $C_3H_8$ = 44.097 g.

$$2.00 \text{ g } C_3H_8 = \frac{2.00 \text{ g}}{44.097 \text{ g/mole}} = 0.0454 \text{ mole } C_3H_8.$$

One mole $O_2$ = 32.00 g.

$$7.00 \text{ g } O_2 = \frac{7.00 \text{ g}}{32.00 \text{ g/mole}} = 0.219 \text{ mole } O_2.$$

The equation for the reaction is

$$C_3H_8 + 5O_2 \rightarrow 3CO_2 + 4H_2O$$

It tells us we need 5 moles $O_2$ per mole $C_3H_8$. For 0.0454 mole $C_3H_8$ we would have to use up

$$(0.0454 \text{ mole } C_3H_8) \left( \frac{5 \text{ moles } O_2}{1 \text{ mole } C_3H_8} \right) = 0.227 \text{ mole } O_2.$$

But we don't have this much $O_2$ available; we are given only 0.219 mole $O_2$. In other words, we do not have enough $O_2$ to chew up all the $C_3H_8$, so it must be the $C_3H_8$ which is now in excess. Any computations based on $C_3H_8$ would be incorrect, since the 0.219 mole $O_2$ is the limiting reagent.

Once we decide which reagent is limiting, the rest is easy. The equation

$$C_3H_8 + 5O_2 \rightarrow 3CO_2 + 4H_2O$$

says that for every 5 moles $O_2$ used up, 3 moles $CO_2$ form. If we use up only 0.219 mole $O_2$, we get

$$(0.219 \text{ mole } O_2) \left( \frac{3 \text{ moles } CO_2}{5 \text{ moles } O_2} \right) = 0.131 \text{ mole } CO_2.$$

One mole $CO_2$ = 44.010 g.

$$0.131 \text{ mole } CO_2 = (0.131 \text{ mole}) \left( \frac{44.010 \text{ g}}{\text{mole}} \right) = 5.77 \text{ g } CO_2.$$

PROBLEM 156 Suppose we mix $1.00 \times 10^{-3}$ mole $Ag^+$ and $1.00 \times 10^{-3}$ mole $CrO_4^=$. Suppose, further, they react as much as possible to precipitate $Ag_2CrO_4$. How many grams $Ag_2CrO_4$ could be formed?

SOLUTION: (Write the equation for the reaction. Figure out which reagent is limiting the product. Calculate moles of product consistent with limiting reagent. Convert to grams.)
The equation

$$2Ag^+ + CrO_4^= \rightarrow Ag_2CrO_4$$

says that we need to use twice as many moles of $Ag^+$ as of $CrO_4^=$. If we took $1.00 \times 10^{-3}$ mole $CrO_4^=$ to be limiting, we would need $2.00 \times 10^{-3}$ mole $Ag^+$. But we don't have that much, so that approach is wrong. It must be that the $1.00 \times 10^{-3}$ mole $Ag^+$ is limiting. It would require only $0.500 \times 10^{-3}$ mole $CrO_4^=$, which is easily there in excess.

The equation says we get 1 mole $Ag_2CrO_4$ for each 2 moles $Ag^+$ used up. If we use up all the $1.00 \times 10^{-3}$ mole $Ag^+$ provided, we would get

$$(1.00 \times 10^{-3} \text{ mole } Ag^+) \left( \frac{1 \text{ mole } Ag_2CrO_4}{2 \text{ moles } Ag^+} \right)$$
$$= 0.500 \times 10^{-3} \text{ mole } Ag_2CrO_4.$$

One mole $Ag_2CrO_4 = 331.73$ g.

$$0.500 \times 10^{-3} \text{ mole } Ag_2CrO_4 = (0.500 \times 10^{-3} \text{ mole}) \left( 331.73 \frac{g}{\text{mole}} \right)$$
$$= \mathbf{0.166 \text{ g } Ag_2CrO_4.}$$

PROBLEM 157 Suppose that $1.00$ g $Cr_2O_7^=$ is oxidized in acidic solution by excess $SO_2$ to form $HSO_4^-$ and $Cr^{+3}$. What is the minimum number of moles $H^+$ that must be provided?

SOLUTION: (Write the balanced equation for the reaction. Calculate how many moles of $Cr_2O_7^=$ you will use up. From the equation, decide how many moles of $H^+$ must be provided.)
For the change

$$SO_2 + Cr_2O_7^= \rightarrow HSO_4^- + Cr^{+3}$$

the balanced equation can be figured out by the methods discussed earlier in this chapter to be

$$5H^+ + 3SO_2 + Cr_2O_7^= \rightarrow 3HSO_4^- + 2Cr^{+3} + H_2O$$

We are given 1.00 g $Cr_2O_7^=$.
One mole $Cr_2O_7^=$ weighs 215.988 g.

$$1.00 \text{ g } Cr_2O_7^= = \frac{1.00 \text{ g}}{215.988 \text{ g/mole}} = 0.00463 \text{ mole } Cr_2O_7^=.$$

The equation tells us we use 5 moles $H^+$ for each mole $Cr_2O_7^=$. There-fore, if we use up $4.63 \times 10^{-3}$ mole $Cr_2O_7^=$ we will need to use up simultaneously:

$$(0.00463 \text{ mole } Cr_2O_7^=) \left( \frac{5 \text{ moles } H^+}{1 \text{ mole } Cr_2O_7^=} \right) = 0.0232 \text{ mole } H^+.$$

PROBLEM 158    Suppose that $H_2O_2$ is to be ozidized by $MnO_4^-$ in acidic solution to form $O_2$ and $Mn^{++}$. How many grams $O_2$ could you get from $1.50 \times 10^{-3}$ mole $MnO_4^-$ and $1.50 \times 10^{-3}$ g $H_2O_2$?

SOLUTION: (Convert the data "g $H_2O_2$" into moles. Compare with the balanced equation to see which reagent is in excess. Compute moles $O_2$ determined by the limiting reagent. Convert to grams.)
One mole $H_2O_2$ = 34.014 g.

$$1.50 \times 10^{-3} \text{ g } H_2O_2 = \frac{1.50 \times 10^{-3} \text{ g}}{34.014 \text{ g/mole}} = 4.41 \times 10^{-5} \text{ mole } H_2O_2.$$

For the change $H_2O_2 + MnO_4^- \rightarrow Mn^{++} + O_2$ in acidic solution, the balanced equation comes out to be

$$6H^+ + 5H_2O_2 + 2MnO_4^- \rightarrow 2Mn^{++} + 8H_2O + 5O_2.$$

It tells us that 5 moles $H_2O_2$ require 2 moles $MnO_4^-$ in the reaction. For $4.41 \times 10^{-5}$ mole $H_2O_2$, we would need

$$(4.41 \times 10^{-5} \text{ mole } H_2O_2) \left( \frac{2 \text{ moles } MnO_4^-}{5 \text{ moles } H_2O_2} \right)$$
$$= 1.76 \times 10^{-5} \text{ mole } MnO_4^-.$$

We are given $1.50 \times 10^{-3}$ mole $MnO_4^-$, so we have plenty of $MnO_4^-$ in excess over the $1.76 \times 10^{-5}$ mole required. The product $O_2$ is determined by the limiting reagent, $H_2O_2$.
The equation tells us 5 moles $H_2O_2$ lead to 5 moles $O_2$. If we use up the $4.41 \times 10^{-5}$ mole $H_2O_2$ that is available, then we should get

$$(4.41 \times 10^{-5} \text{ mole H}_2\text{O}_2) \left( \frac{5 \text{ moles O}_2}{5 \text{ moles H}_2\text{O}_2} \right) = 4.41 \times 10^{-5} \text{ mole O}_2.$$

One mole $O_2 = 31.999$ g.

$$4.41 \times 10^{-5} \text{ mole O}_2 = (4.41 \times 10^{-5} \text{ mole}) \left( 31.999 \frac{g}{\text{mole}} \right)$$
$$= 1.41 \times 10^{-3} \text{ g O}_2.$$

PROBLEM 159   When a basic solution of $I^-$ is exposed to air, the $I^-$ is gradually converted to $IO_3^-$ by the oxidizing action of $O_2$ going to $OH^-$.   Given a solution that initially contains $1.50 \times 10^{-3}$ mole $I^-$, what fraction of the $I^-$ could be converted to $IO_3^-$ by using $1.50 \times 10^{-3}$ mole $O_2$?

SOLUTION: (Write the balanced equation for the reaction.   From it, decide how many moles $I^-$ could be chewed up by $1.50 \times 10^{-3}$ mole $O_2$.   Figure out what fraction this is of the $I^-$ made available initially.)

For the change $I^- + O_2 \rightarrow IO_3^- + OH^-$ in basic solution, the net equation comes out to be

$$2I^- + 3O_2 \rightarrow 2IO_3^-$$

This tells us we need 3 moles $O_2$ per 2 moles $I^-$.   If we use $1.50 \times 10^{-3}$ mole $O_2$, we would need to use up

$$(1.50 \times 10^{-3} \text{ mole O}_2) \left( \frac{2 \text{ moles I}^-}{3 \text{ moles O}_2} \right) = 1.00 \times 10^{-3} \text{ mole I}^-.$$

We are given $1.50 \times 10^{-3}$ mole $I^-$.   Therefore, the fraction of $I^-$ used up is

$$\frac{1.00 \times 10^{-3} \text{ mole I}^- \text{ used}}{1.50 \times 10^{-3} \text{ mole I}^- \text{ available}} = 0.667.$$

■ PROBLEM 160   How many grams C are required to reduce 3.50 g $Fe_3O_4$ to Fe, assuming all the C is converted to CO?

ANSWER: **0.726 g**

■ PROBLEM 161   When Al goes to $Al_2O_3$ in reducing $TiO_2$ to Ti, how many grams Ti will be produced if 3.50 g Al is consumed?

ANSWER: **4.66 g**

■ PROBLEM 162   Consider the reaction in which $NH_3$ is oxidized by $O_2$ to give NO and $H_2O$. How many grams $H_2O$ are produced per gram NO in this reaction?
ANSWER: **0.901 g**

■ PROBLEM 163   When $Ca_3P_2$ is treated with $H_2O$, the products are $Ca(OH)_2$ and $PH_3$. What is the maximum weight of $PH_3$ that can be formed from 2.00 g $Ca_3P_2$ and 1.00 g $H_2O$?
ANSWER: **0.629 g**

■ PROBLEM 164   Consider the reaction in which tin reacts with $HNO_3$ to produce $SnO_2$, $NO_2$, and $H_2O$. How many moles $NO_2$ will be produced per gram $SnO_2$ formed?
ANSWER: **0.0265 mole**

■ PROBLEM 165   $Sn^{++}$ in acidic solution can reduce $Cr_2O_7^=$ to $Cr^{+3}$, forming $Sn^{+4}$ in the process. How many moles $Cr_2O_7^=$ could you thus reduce, using 1.00 g $Sn^{++}$?
ANSWER: **$2.81 \times 10^{-3}$ mole**

■ PROBLEM 166   In basic solution Sn can reduce $CrO_4^=$ to $Cr(OH)_4^-$, itself being converted to $Sn(OH)_6^=$. Starting with 1.00 g Sn and 1.00 g $CrO_4^=$ how many moles $OH^-$ would you need to provide for maximum reaction?
ANSWER: **$4.31 \times 10^{-3}$ mole**

■ PROBLEM 167   In acidic solution, $I^-$ going to $I_2$ can reduce $H_3AsO_4$ to $H_3AsO_3$. How many grams $I_2$ are produced if enough $H_3AsO_4$ is reduced to use up $1.5 \times 10^{22}$ electrons?
ANSWER: **3.2 g**

■ PROBLEM 168   Zn reacts with $H^+$ to give $Zn^{++}$ and $H_2$; Al reacts with $H^+$ to give $Al^{+3}$ and $H_2$. If 1.00 g of a mixture containing only Zn and Al reacts with $H^+$ to liberate 0.040 mole $H_2$, how many grams of Zn and of Al in the original mixture?
ANSWER: **0.39 g Zn and 0.61 g Al**

■ PROBLEM 169   You are given 0.640 kg of a mixture consisting only of $C_8H_{18}$ and $C_9H_{20}$. When the mixture is burned in excess $O_2$ so conversion to $CO_2$ and $H_2O$ is complete, the weight of water collected is 0.904 kg.   What per cent by weight of the original mixture must have been $C_8H_{18}$?

ANSWER: **53%**

■■ P R O B L E M   170   You are given a 1.000-g sample consisting only of a mixture of Zn, Mg, and Al.   When exactly half of the sample is treated with excess $H^+$ to convert it to $Zn^{++}$, $Mg^{++}$, and $Al^{+3}$, 0.0135 mole $H_2$ is released.   When the other half of the sample is burned in excess $O_2$ to convert it to ZnO, MgO, and $Al_2O_3$, the weight of product is 0.717 g.   What is the make-up of the original sample?   It had at the start $1.52 \times 10^{22}$ atoms.

ANSWER: **by weight 60.2% Zn, 30.1% Mg, 9.7% Al**

# 5

# THE GRAM-
# EQUIVALENT

THE TERM "gram-equivalent" comes up in two important senses. In acid-base theory, it denotes the amount of material which furnishes or uses up one mole of hydrogen ions (i.e., $6.02 \times 10^{23}$ $H^+$); in oxidation-reduction theory, it denotes the amount of material which furnishes or uses up one mole of electrons (i.e., $6.02 \times 10^{23}$ $e^-$). Although most stoichiometry calculations can be performed without introducing gram-equivalents, your work will be made so much easier and faster with gram-equivalents that you would be foolish not to take the time to master the concepts involved. The chief advantage of working with gram-equivalents is that generally you won't have to write the balanced equation for the problem, since much of the same information is embodied in the very definition of a gram-equivalent. The other point that argues for gram-equivalents is that much solution work is built around the concept; in fact, it is hard to walk into a chemistry laboratory without finding some bottles labeled in terms of gram-equivalents.

Strictly speaking, we should use the term "gram-equivalent-weight" instead of "gram-equivalent," but in common parlance the terms are equally acceptable, so we pick the simpler one. There is a tendency among some people to abbreviate further and use only "equivalent" as a synonymous expression. There is real possibility of confusion here, especially when other than gram units are involved or when individual particles are being discussed. For this reason, we shall stick to gram-equivalents and thereby avoid confusion. As you get more sophisticated in your calculations, you can easily drop the "gram-" part.

## Gram-equivalents of acids and bases

A gram-equivalent of an acid is defined as the amount of material which can furnish one mole of $H^+$; a gram-equivalent of a base is defined as the amount of material which can pick up one mole of $H^+$. Since $OH^-$ is the usual vehicle for picking up $H^+$, an alternate definition of a gram-equivalent of base would be the amount of material which can furnish one mole of $OH^-$. By the nature of the definitions, one gram-equivalent of any acid can neutralize one gram-equivalent of any base.

For the neutralization reaction

$$HCl + NaOH \rightarrow NaCl + H_2O$$

one mole HCl reacts with one mole NaOH. We can visualize this as coming about because the mole of $H^+$ (from HCl) combines with the mole of $OH^-$ (from NaOH). So, for the neutralization part, we are really interested in the fact that 1 mole HCl neutralizes 1 mole NaOH by virtue of matching 1 mole $H^+$ against 1 mole $OH^-$. Such matching of $H^+$ with $OH^-$ is assured when we require equal number of gram-equivalents of acid and base.

In the reaction

$$H_2SO_4 + 2NaOH \rightarrow Na_2SO_4 + 2H_2O$$

two moles NaOH are required per mole $H_2SO_4$, because each mole of $H_2SO_4$ furnishes 2 moles of $H^+$. Two moles of NaOH is the same as 2 gram-equivalents of base, so we need 2 gram-equivalents of acid to neutralize. These 2 gram-equivalents of acid are furnished in the 1 mole of $H_2SO_4$.

In the reaction

$$H_3PO_4 + 3NaOH \rightarrow Na_3PO_4 + 3H_2O$$

one mole $H_3PO_4$ is neutralized by 3 moles NaOH.  Three moles NaOH is the same as 3 gram-equivalents of base, so we need 3 gram-equivalents of acid to neutralize it.  These 3 gram-equivalents of acid are furnished in the 1 mole of $H_3PO_4$.

The only real trick in figuring out gram-equivalents of acids and bases is to know how many $H^+$ or $OH^-$ can be furnished by a given molecule.  In the vast majority of cases, this can be deduced from the chemical formula: HCl gives one $H^+$, $H_2SO_4$ gives $2H^+$, $H_3PO_4$ gives $3H^+$.  In these cases, we assume that all the $H^+$ available is actually used.  However, this need not always be the case.  For example, in the reaction

$$H_2SO_4 + NaOH \rightarrow NaHSO_4 + H_2O$$

only one of the H's of the $H_2SO_4$ is used up.  In terms of gram-equivalents *for this particular reaction*, the $H_2SO_4$ is worth only half as much as if both H's were used.  If only one H of $H_2SO_4$ is neutralized, we have to say that one mole $H_2SO_4$ furnishes one mole $H^+$—i.e., one mole $H_2SO_4$ is one gram-equivalent.  If both H's of $H_2SO_4$ are neutralized, we have to say that one mole $H_2SO_4$ furnishes two moles $H^+$— i.e., one mole $H_2SO_4$ is two gram-equivalents.  In most cases, we shall use up all the $H^+$ available, and we shall call this "full reaction" or "full neutralization."  Otherwise, we shall specify how many $H^+$ are used.  In case of doubt, it is safest to write the equation for the reaction in which the reagent is being used.

The other pitfall is that sometimes, even for full neutralization, the chemical formula may be misleading.  As an example, one mole $H_3PO_2$ looks like it could furnish three moles $H^+$.  Yet, if you try the experiment, you will find that only one mole $H^+$ can be pulled out.  Two of the three hydrogens are bound differently and cannot be neutralized by conventional acid-base reaction.  This can be indicated, as is sometimes done, by writing the formula as $H(H_2PO_2)$ instead of $H_3PO_2$.  Fortunately, most of the common acids and bases do not have this complication and we can deduce their gram-equivalent relations, at least for full reaction, directly from the chemical formula.

PROBLEM 171   How many grams HCl would there be in one gram-equivalent of HCl?

SOLUTION: By definition, one gram-equivalent furnishes one mole $H^+$.
To get one mole $H^+$ from HCl, we need to take one mole HCl.
One mole HCl weighs 36.461 g.
Therefore, to get one mole $H^+$ from HCl, we need to take 36.461 g HCl.
Thus, one gram-equivalent HCl = **36.461 g HCl**.

PROBLEM 172    You are given 0.15 mole $H_2SO_4$. How many gram-equivalents of $H_2SO_4$ do you have (for full reaction)?

SOLUTION: One mole $H_2SO_4$ gives 2 moles $H^+$.
By definition, this is two gram-equivalents.
So, one mole $H_2SO_4$ = 2 gram-equivalents.
0.15 mole $H_2SO_4$ = **0.30 gram-equivalent**.

PROBLEM 173    You are given 0.15 gram-equivalent of $H_3PO_4$ (full reaction). How many grams $H_3PO_4$ do you have?

SOLUTION: One mole $H_3PO_4$ gives 3 moles $H^+$.
Therefore, one mole $H_3PO_4$ is 3 gram-equivalents.

$$0.15 \text{ gram-equivalent} = (0.15 \text{ gram-equivalent}) \left( \frac{1 \text{ mole}}{3 \text{ gram-equivalents}} \right)$$
$$= 0.050 \text{ mole}.$$

One mole $H_3PO_4$ = 98.00 g.

$$0.050 \text{ mole } H_3PO_4 = (0.050 \text{ mole}) \left( 98.00 \frac{g}{\text{mole}} \right) = \textbf{4.9 g}.$$

PROBLEM 174    You are given 1.00 g HCl. How many gram-equivalents is this?

SOLUTION: One mole HCl gives one mole $H^+$.
Therefore, one mole HCl = one gram-equivalent.
One mole of HCl = 36.461 g = one gram-equivalent.

$$1.00 \text{ g HCl} = \frac{1.00 \text{ g}}{36.461 \text{ g/gram-equivalent}} = \textbf{0.0274 gram-equivalent}.$$

PROBLEM 175    You are given 3.65 g $H_2SO_4$. For full reaction, how many gram-equivalents of $H_2SO_4$ is this?

SOLUTION: One mole $H_2SO_4$ gives 2 moles $H^+$.
Therefore, one mole $H_2SO_4$ = 2 gram-equivalents.
One mole $H_2SO_4$ weighs 98.08 g.
Two gram-equivalents $H_2SO_4$ weigh 98.08 g.
One gram-equivalent $H_2SO_4$ weighs $\frac{1}{2}$(98.08 g) = 49.04 g.

$$3.65 \text{ g } H_2SO_4 = \frac{3.65 \text{ g}}{49.04 \text{ g/gram-equivalent}} = \textbf{0.0744 gram-equivalent.}$$

**PROBLEM 176**   How many gram-equivalents in $3.66 \times 10^{22}$ molecules HCl?

SOLUTION: One mole HCl contains $6.02 \times 10^{23}$ molecules.

$$3.66 \times 10^{22} \text{ molecules is } \frac{3.66 \times 10^{22} \text{ molecules}}{6.02 \times 10^{23} \text{ molecules/mole}} = 0.0608 \text{ mole.}$$

One mole HCl furnishes one mole $H^+$.
By definition, this is one gram-equivalent.
So, 0.0608 mole HCl is **0.0608 gram-equivalent.**

**PROBLEM 177**   You are given 20.5 g of an unknown acid with the statement that this amount of acid will furnish $2.05 \times 10^{22}$ $H^+$.   What is the weight of one gram-equivalent of your unknown acid?

SOLUTION: (Find out how many moles $H^+$ you have.   This defines how many gram-equivalents you have.   Divide the weight given by this number of gram-equivalents.)

$$2.05 \times 10^{22} \text{ H}^+ = \frac{2.05 \times 10^{22} \text{ H}^+}{6.02 \times 10^{23} \text{ H}^+/\text{mole}} = 0.0341 \text{ mole H}^+$$

To get 0.0341 mole $H^+$, you must have 0.0341 gram-equivalents acid in your sample.
0.0341 gram-equivalent acid = 20.5 g.

$$\text{Therefore, one gram-equivalent acid} = \frac{20.5 \text{ g}}{0.0341 \text{ equivalent}} = 601 \text{ g.}$$

**PROBLEM 178**   You are given 2.00 g NaOH.   How many gram-equivalents of base is this?

SOLUTION: One mole NaOH gives one mole $OH^-$.
By definition, this is one gram-equivalent of base.
One mole NaOH weighs 39.997 g.

One mole NaOH = 39.997 g = one gram-equivalent.

$$2.00 \text{ g NaOH} = \frac{2.00 \text{ g}}{39.997 \text{ g/gram-equivalent}}$$

$$= \textbf{0.0500 gram-equivalent.}$$

PROBLEM 179  You are given 2.00 g $Ca(OH)_2$. How many gram-equivalents of base is this (full reaction)?

SOLUTION: One mole $Ca(OH)_2$ gives two moles $OH^-$.
By definition, this is two gram-equivalents base.
One mole $Ca(OH)_2$ weighs 74.09 g.
74.09 g $Ca(OH)_2$ = 2 gram-equivalents.
37.04 g $Ca(OH)_2$ = 1 gram-equivalent.

$$2.00 \text{ g } Ca(OH)_2 = \frac{2.00 \text{ g}}{37.04 \text{ g/gram-equivalent}}$$

$$= \textbf{0.0540 gram-equivalent.}$$

PROBLEM 180  An unknown base gives 0.030 mole $OH^-$ per 0.78 g base. What is the gram-equivalent weight of the base?

SOLUTION: One gram-equivalent of any base gives one mole $OH^-$.
To get 0.030 mole $OH^-$, you must have present 0.030 gram-equivalent base.
Therefore, 0.78 g base = 0.030 gram-equivalent.

$$\text{The weight of 1 gram-equivalent} = \frac{0.78 \text{ g}}{0.030 \text{ gram-equivalent}} = \textbf{26 g.}$$

PROBLEM 181  You are given 0.032 gram-equivalent HCl. How many gram-equivalents of base X do you need to neutralize this?

SOLUTION: It takes one gram-equivalent of any acid to neutralize one gram-equivalent of any base. Therefore, if you have 0.032 gram-equivalent acid, you must get 0.032 gram-equivalent base.
In this case, you need **0.032 gram-equivalent** base X.

PROBLEM 182  You are given 2.00 g $HNO_3$. How many grams NaOH do you need to neutralize this?

SOLUTION: One mole $HNO_3$ = one gram-equivalent = 63.01 g.

$$2.00 \text{ g HNO}_3 = \frac{2.00 \text{ g}}{63.01 \text{ g/gram-equivalent}}$$

= 0.0317 gram-equivalent acid.

It takes 1 gram-equivalent base to neutralize 1 gram-equivalent acid. If you have 0.0317 gram-equivalent acid, you need 0.0317 gram-equivalent NaOH.

One mole NaOH = one gram-equivalent NaOH = 39.997 g.

0.0317 gram-equivalent NaOH

$$= (0.0317 \text{ gram-equivalent}) \left( 39.997 \frac{\text{g}}{\text{gram-equivalent}} \right) = \textbf{1.27 g.}$$

PROBLEM 183    A given sample contains 0.206 gram-equivalent $Ca(OH)_2$. Assuming complete reaction, how many grams $H_3PO_4$ would be required to neutralize the sample?

SOLUTION: You have 0.206 gram-equivalent base; therefore, you need 0.206 gram-equivalent acid.

For $H_3PO_4$, one mole gives 3 moles $H^+$. This means one mole $H_3PO_4$ is the same as 3 gram-equivalents.

To get 0.206 gram-equivalent $H_3PO_4$, we need

$$(0.206 \text{ gram-equivalent}) \left( \frac{1 \text{ mole}}{3 \text{ gram-equivalents}} \right) = 0.0687 \text{ mole } H_3PO_4.$$

One mole $H_3PO_4$ weighs 97.995 g.

$$0.0687 \text{ mole } H_3PO_4 \text{ weighs } (0.0687 \text{ mole}) \left( 97.995 \frac{\text{g}}{\text{mole}} \right) = \textbf{6.73 g.}$$

PROBLEM 184    What is the weight of one gram-equivalent of $H_3PO_4$ in each of the following reactions:

(I) $H_3PO_4 + NaOH \rightarrow NaH_2PO_4 + H_2O$

(II) $H_3PO_4 + 2NaOH \rightarrow Na_2HPO_4 + 2H_2O$

(III) $H_3PO_4 + 3NaOH \rightarrow Na_3PO_4 + 3H_2O$

SOLUTION: In reaction (I) only one H out of three of $H_3PO_4$ is neutralized. So, for reaction (I), one mole $H_3PO_4$ furnishes but one mole $H^+$ (to react with one mole NaOH). This means, so far as reaction (I) is concerned, one mole $H_3PO_4$ is the same as one gram-equivalent.

One mole $H_3PO_4$ = 97.995 g.

One gram-equivalent $H_3PO_4$ for reaction (I) = **97.995 g.**

In reaction (II), where two moles NaOH are used, each mole $H_3PO_4$ must furnish two moles $H^+$.  So, for reaction (II) one mole $H_3PO_4$ is the same as two gram-equivalents.

One mole $H_3PO_4$ = 97.995 g = 2 gram-equivalents.

One gram-equivalent = $\frac{1}{2}$(97.995) = **48.998 g.**

In reaction (III), three moles NaOH react per mole $H_3PO_4$, so each mole $H_3PO_4$ must furnish three moles $H^+$.  For reaction (III), one mole $H_3PO_4$ is the same as three gram-equivalents.

One mole $H_3PO_4$ = 97.995 g = 3 gram-equivalents.

One gram-equivalent = $\frac{1}{3}$(97.995) = **32.665 g.**

■ P R O B L E M  185   Given  1.00 g  $HClO_4$. How many gram-equivalents of acid is this?

ANSWER: **0.00995 gram-equivalent**

■ P R O B L E M  186   Given 1.00 g $Ba(OH)_2$. How many gram-equivalents base is this (assuming full neutralization)?

ANSWER: **0.0117 gram-equivalent**

■ P R O B L E M  187   Given 1.00 g $H_4P_2O_7$. For a neutralization reaction where only two of the four protons are used up, how many gram-equivalents of acid would there be in this sample?

ANSWER: **0.0112 gram-equivalent**

■ P R O B L E M  188   Given  0.169  mole $La(OH)_3$.  How many gram-equivalents of base are there in this sample, assuming full neutralization?

ANSWER: **0.507 gram-equivalent**

■ P R O B L E M  189   Assuming full neutralization, how many grams of which reagent will be left over when reaction occurs between 0.100 gram-equivalent of $H_2SO_4$ and 0.150 gram-equivalent of KOH?

ANSWER: **2.8 g KOH**

■ P R O B L E M  190   Assuming formation of $Ca_3(PO_4)_2$, how many grams $Ca(OH)_2$ would be needed to react with $2.85 \times 10^{-3}$ gram-equivalent of $H_3PO_4$?

ANSWER: **0.106 g**

■ PROBLEM 191    You are given a 1.00-g sample of an unknown acid X which may be A, or B, or something else. The gram-equivalent weights of A and B are 90.0 and 115.0 g, respectively. If it takes just 0.350 g KOH to neutralize the 1.00-g sample, which of the substances, A or B or something else, is it?

ANSWER: With gram-equivalent weight equal to 160 g, X must be **something other** than A or B

■ PROBLEM 192    You have just synthesized a new material X, which can act as an acid and also as a base. You find experimentally that 1.36 g X can neutralize 0.191 g NaOH and also that a separate 1.36-g sample of X can neutralize 0.522 g HCl. What is the gram-equivalent weight of X as an acid and as a base?

ANSWER: **285 g as an acid; 95.0 g as a base**

■ PROBLEM 193    To neutralize completely a mixture containing 0.069 gram-equivalent KOH and 0.030 gram-equivalent $Ba(OH)_2$, how many moles $H_2SO_4$ are required?

ANSWER: **0.050 mole**

■ PROBLEM 194    A mixture consisting only of KOH and $Ba(OH)_2$ weighs 2.00 g. If it takes 0.0281 gram-equivalent HCl to neutralize the mixture, what is its composition in per cent by weight?

ANSWER: **38.7% KOH and 61.3% $Ba(OH)_2$**

## Gram-equivalents in oxidation-reduction

An oxidizing agent picks up electrons; a reducing agent supplies them. One gram-equivalent of oxidizing agent is the weight of material required to pick up one mole of electrons; one gram-equivalent of reducing agent is the weight of material required to furnish one mole of electrons. One gram-equivalent of any oxidizing agent just matches one gram-equivalent of any reducing agent so far as electron transfer is concerned.

Consider the reaction

$$Zn + Cl_2 \rightarrow ZnCl_2$$

where one mole of Zn reacts with one mole of $Cl_2$. In this reaction, the Zn can be considered to go from the 0 oxidation state to the +2 oxidation state. In doing so, each Zn atom gives up two electrons. One mole of Zn atoms ($6.02 \times 10^{23}$ Zn atoms) must consequently give up two moles of electrons ($2 \times 6.02 \times 10^{23}$ electrons). We have defined one gram-equivalent as the amount that gives up one mole of electrons, so if we give up two moles of electrons we must have present two gram-equivalents of reducing agent. In other words, 1 mole of Zn equals 2 gram-equivalents of reducing agent.

Simultaneously, in the reaction, the chlorine can be considered to go from the 0 state to the $-1$ state. This means a gain of one electron. Since there are two chlorine atoms per $Cl_2$ molecule, each $Cl_2$ molecule effectively picks up 2 electrons. One mole of $Cl_2$ molecules ($6.02 \times 10^{23}$ $Cl_2$ molecules) must pick up two moles of electrons ($2 \times 6.02 \times 10^{23}$ electrons). By definition, this is two gram-equivalents of oxidizing agent. So, we have the result that when one mole of Zn reacts with one mole of $Cl_2$, two gram-equivalents of reducing agent (Zn) are reacting with two gram-equivalents of oxidizing agent ($Cl_2$).

Take a more complicated case—e.g., Zn reacting with $MnO_4^-$ to give $Zn^{++}$ plus $Mn^{++}$. Again the Zn goes from 0 to $+2$, so one mole of Zn equals 2 gram-equivalents   In $MnO_4^-$ the Mn goes from $+7$ to $+2$ in $Mn^{++}$. This is a gain of 5 electrons. So far as $MnO_4^- \rightarrow Mn^{++}$ is concerned, one mole of $MnO_4^-$ accepts 5 moles of electrons; consequently, one mole of $MnO_4^-$ is 5 gram-equivalents of oxidizing agent. To make sure that electron gain and electron loss are balanced, the number of gram-equivalents of oxidizing and reducing agent must be identical. If we take one mole of Zn ($= 2$ gram-equivalents), then we need to take 2 gram-equivalents of $MnO_4^-$. The latter is $\frac{2}{5}$ of a mole of $MnO_4^-$. So the molar ratio of Zn to $MnO_4^-$ is $1:\frac{2}{5}$, as can easily be checked by writing the balanced equation

$$5Zn + 2MnO_4^- + 16H^+ \rightarrow 5Zn^{++} + 8H_2O + 2Mn^{++}$$

From the above examples, it should be evident that in any oxidation-reduction reaction:

1. Total electron gain = total electron loss.
2. Number of gram-equivalents used of oxidizing agent = number of gram-equivalents used of reducing agent.
3. Weight of 1 gram-equivalent of reducing agent = weight of one mole divided by electron loss.

4. Weight of 1 gram-equivalent of oxidizing agent = weight of one mole divided by electron gain.

How these points work out in specific cases is illustrated in the following problems.

**PROBLEM 195**    When elemental Fe is oxidized to FeO, what is the weight for one gram-equivalent of Fe?

SOLUTION: Fe goes from 0 in Fe to +2 in FeO.
Each Fe atom gives up 2 electrons.
Each mole of Fe gives up 2 moles of electrons.
This, by definition, is 2 gram-equivalents reducing agent.
Therefore, one mole Fe = 2 gram-equivalents.
One mole Fe weighs 55.847 g.
Two gram-equivalents = 55.847 g.
One gram-equivalent = $\frac{1}{2}(55.847)$ = **27.923 g.**

**PROBLEM 196**    When elemental Fe is oxidized to $Fe_2O_3$, what is the weight for one gram-equivalent of Fe?

SOLUTION: Fe goes from 0 in Fe to +3 in $Fe_2O_3$.
Each Fe atom gives up 3 electrons.
Each mole of Fe gives up 3 moles of electrons.
This, by definition, is 3 gram-equivalents reducing agent.
Therefore, 1 mole Fe = 3 gram-equivalents.
One mole Fe weighs 55.847 g.
3 gram-equivalents = 55.847 g.
1 gram-equivalent = $\frac{1}{3}(55.847)$ = **18.616 g.**

**PROBLEM 197**    When elemental Fe is oxidized to $Fe_3O_4$, what is the weight for one gram-equivalent of Fe?

SOLUTION: Fe goes from 0 in Fe to $+\frac{8}{3}$ in $Fe_3O_4$.
Each Fe atom can be considered to give up $\frac{8}{3}$ of an electron.
Each mole of Fe gives up $\frac{8}{3}$ of a mole of electrons.
By definition, this is $\frac{8}{3}$ of a gram-equivalent.
One mole Fe = $\frac{8}{3}$ gram-equivalent.
One mole Fe weighs 55.847 g.
$\frac{8}{3}$ gram-equivalent = 1 mole = 55.847 g.
1 gram-equivalent = $\frac{3}{8}(55.847)$ = **20.943 g.**

[*Note:* In these three preceding problems elemental iron has been oxidized to three different products: FeO, $Fe_2O_3$, and $Fe_3O_4$. The gram-equivalent weight of iron is, respectively, 27.9 g, 18.6 g, and 20.9 g. These represent the weights that would yield $6.02 \times 10^{23}$ electrons. If you now ask "How much oxygen would be required to produce the above three products from these weights of Fe?" the answer would be "the same"—since it is just the amount of oxygen required to pick up $6.02 \times 10^{23}$ electrons.]

**PROBLEM 198** When elemental oxygen picks up electrons to form oxides, how many grams $O_2$ are required to pick up $6.02 \times 10^{23}$ electrons?

SOLUTION: Each O atom picks up 2 electrons in going from the zero state of the element to the $-2$ state in oxides.
Each $O_2$ molecule picks up 4 electrons.
Each mole $O_2$ picks up 4 moles of electrons.
$6.02 \times 10^{23}$ electrons = 1 mole of electrons.
To pick up 1 mole of electrons, we need $\frac{1}{4}$ mole $O_2$.
One mole $O_2$ = 31.9988 g.
$\frac{1}{4}$ mole $O_2 = \frac{1}{4}(31.9988) =$ **8.00 g.**

**PROBLEM 199** The element vanadium can react with $O_2$ to form $V_2O_5$. What weight of V would be needed to react with 1 gram-equivalent of oxygen to form this product?

SOLUTION: It takes 1 gram-equivalent reducing agent to react with 1 gram-equivalent oxidizing agent.
Since we are given 1 gram-equivalent oxygen, we need to take 1 gram-equivalent vanadium.
In this reaction, V goes from 0 to +5.
Each V atom gives up 5 electrons.
One mole V = 5 gram-equivalents.
One gram-equivalent = $\frac{1}{5}$ mole V = $\frac{1}{5}(50.942) =$ **10.188 g.**

**PROBLEM 200** You have an element X which reacts with $O_2$ to form an oxide, $X_2O_3$. If it takes 4.445 g X to react with 0.150 gram-equivalent oxygen, what is the atomic weight of X?

SOLUTION: To match 0.150 gram-equivalent oxygen, we need 0.150 gram-equivalent reducing agent X.

This means 4.445 g X contains 0.150 gram-equivalent.

One gram-equivalent X is $\dfrac{4.445 \text{ g}}{0.150 \text{ gram-equivalent}} = 29.6$ g.

In going from X to $X_2O_3$, each atom X changes oxidation number from 0 to +3. So, each atom of X must give up 3 electrons. Consequently, one mole X (or one gram-atom) is 3 gram-equivalents.

3 gram-equivalents is $(3)\left(29.6 \; \dfrac{\text{g}}{\text{gram-equivalent}}\right) = 88.8$ g.

One mole X = 88.8 g.

Therefore, the atomic weight of X is **88.8 a.m.u.**

PROBLEM 201    When $MnO_4^-$ gets reduced in neutral solution, the product is likely to be $MnO_2$. How many gram-equivalents are there per mole $MnO_4^-$ in such a reaction?

SOLUTION: Mn goes from +7 in $MnO_4^-$ to +4 in $MnO_2$.

This means each Mn atom picks up 3 electrons.

Each mole of $MnO_4^-$ picks up 3 moles of electrons.

By definition, this is 3 gram-equivalents oxidizing agent, so one mole $MnO_4^-$ is **3 gram-equivalents.**

PROBLEM 202    When $Cr_2O_7^=$ is reduced in acidic solution, the chromium is converted to $Cr^{+3}$. How many gram-equivalents of reducing agent would you need to reduce 1 mole $Cr_2O_7^=$ in such a reaction?

SOLUTION: Cr goes from +6 in $Cr_2O_7^=$ to +3 in $Cr^{+3}$.

Each Cr atom picks up 3 electrons.

But note, there are 2 Cr atoms per $Cr_2O_7^=$.

So, each $Cr_2O_7^=$ needs to pick up 6 electrons.

One mole $Cr_2O_7^=$ picks up 6 moles of electrons.

By definition, this is 6 gram-equivalents oxidizing agent.

Each gram-equivalent oxidizing agent requires 1 gram-equivalent reducing agent.

So, 6 gram-equivalents $Cr_2O_7^=$ require **6 gram-equivalents** reducing agent.

PROBLEM 203    How many gram-equivalents $Cr_2O_7^=$ would it take to oxidize 0.136 gram-equivalent of $N_2H_5^+$ by the reaction $N_2H_5^+ + Cr_2O_7^= \rightarrow N_2 + Cr^{+3}$?

SOLUTION: One gram-equivalent of any reducing agent requires one gram-equivalent of any oxidizing agent.

If we have 0.136 gram-equivalent $N_2H_5{}^+$, we must take **0.136 gram-equivalent** $Cr_2O_7{}^=$.

**P R O B L E M   204**   How   many   moles $Cr_2O_7{}^=$ would it take to oxidize 0.136 gram-equivalent of $N_2H_5{}^+$ by the reaction $N_2H_5{}^+ + Cr_2O_7{}^= \rightarrow N_2 + Cr^{+3}$?

SOLUTION: It takes 0.136 gram-equivalent $Cr_2O_7{}^=$ to do the job, be-cause each gram-equivalent reducing agent needs a gram-equiva-lent oxidizing agent.

In the reaction, Cr of $Cr_2O_7{}^=$ goes from $+6$ to $+3$.

This means 3 electrons per Cr atom, or 6 electrons per $Cr_2O_7{}^=$ ion.

One mole $Cr_2O_7{}^=$ equals 6 gram-equivalents.

To get 0.136 gram-equivalents we need

$$(0.136 \text{ gram-equivalent}) \left( \frac{1 \text{ mole}}{6 \text{ gram-equivalents}} \right) = \textbf{0.0227 mole.}$$

**P R O B L E M   205**   Suppose it takes 1.40 $\times 10^{-3}$ mole of an unknown reducing agent to reduce $8.40 \times 10^{-4}$ mole $MnO_4{}^-$ to $Mn^{++}$.  How many electrons would each formula-unit of the reducing agent need to furnish?

SOLUTION: Mn goes from $+7$ in $MnO_4{}^-$ to $+2$ in $Mn^{++}$.

Each Mn picks up 5 electrons.

Therefore, one mole $MnO_4{}^-$ is 5 gram-equivalents.

$8.40 \times 10^{-4}$ mole $MnO_4{}^-$ is $(5)(8.40 \times 10^{-4}) = 4.20 \times 10^{-3}$ gram-equivalent.

Oxidizing and reducing agents must match in gram-equivalents.

There must be $4.20 \times 10^{-3}$ gram-equivalent reducing agent in the $1.40 \times 10^{-3}$ mole of unknown.

This means $\dfrac{4.20 \times 10^{-3} \text{ gram-equivalent}}{1.40 \times 10^{-3} \text{ mole}} = 3$ gram-equivalents per mole of unknown.

Each mole of unknown supplies 3 moles of electrons.

Each formula-unit of unknown supplies **3 electrons**.

■ **P R O B L E M   206**   What is the gram-equiv-alent weight of titanium in the reaction where elemental titanium is converted to the dioxide, $TiO_2$?

ANSWER: **11.98 g**

■ PROBLEM 207    When tungsten is burned in air, it forms the trioxide, $WO_3$. What is the gram-equivalent weight of elemental tungsten in this reaction?

ANSWER: **30.64 g**

■ PROBLEM 208    When sodium is exposed to air, it gets converted to the peroxide, $Na_2O_2$. What is the weight of 1 gram-equivalent of elemental oxygen for this reaction? [*Note:* Peroxide contains oxygen in the $-1$ oxidation state.]

ANSWER: **16.00 g**

■ PROBLEM 209    When potassium is converted to superoxide, the change is from K to $KO_2$. What is the gram-equivalent weight of elemental oxygen in this reaction? [*Note:* Superoxide contains oxygen in the $-\frac{1}{2}$ oxidation state — very rare, but possible.]

ANSWER: **32.00 g**

■ PROBLEM 210    What is the weight of one gram-equivalent of elemental carbon when it reduces $Fe_2O_3$ to form FeO and CO?

ANSWER: **6.006 g**

■ PROBLEM 211    What is the weight of one gram-equivalent of elemental carbon when it is used to reduce $Fe_2O_3$ to Fe and $CO_2$?

ANSWER: **3.003 g**

■ PROBLEM 212    How many gram-equivalents of oxidizing agent would it take to convert $1.50 \times 10^{-4}$ mole $Fe^{++}$ to $Fe^{+3}$?

ANSWER: **$1.50 \times 10^{-4}$ gram-equivalent**

■ PROBLEM 213    How many gram-equivalents of oxidizing agent would it take to convert $1.89 \times 10^{-3}$ mole of $H_2SO_3$ to $HSO_4^-$?

ANSWER: **$3.78 \times 10^{-3}$ gram-equivalent**

■ P R O B L E M   214   How many moles $Ce^{+4}$ need to be reduced to $Ce^{+3}$ to convert 0.250 mole $H_2SO_3$ to $HSO_4^-$?
ANSWER: **0.500 mole**

■ P R O B L E M   215   How    many    moles $Cr_2O_7^=$ are needed to oxidize $1.65 \times 10^{-2}$ gram-equivalent of $Sn^{++}$ by the reaction $Sn^{++} + Cr_2O_7^= \rightarrow Sn^{+4} + Cr^{+3}$?
ANSWER: **$2.75 \times 10^{-3}$ mole**

■ P R O B L E M   216   How many moles $CrO_4^=$ are needed to oxidize $1.65 \times 10^{-2}$ gram-equivalent of Sn by the reaction $Sn + CrO_4^= \rightarrow Sn(OH)_6^= + Cr(OH)_2$?
ANSWER: **$4.12 \times 10^{-3}$ mole**

■ P R O B L E M   217   How    many    grams $Na_2S_2O_3$ would you need to take to furnish 0.0683 gram-equivalent of reducing action by the change $2S_2O_3^= \rightarrow S_4O_6^= + 2e^-$?
ANSWER: **10.8 g**

■ P R O B L E M   218   How    many    grams $H_2C_2O_4$ would you need to take to be able to reduce $7.83 \times 10^{-4}$ gram-equivalent of $KMnO_4$ in the reaction $H_2C_2O_4 + MnO_4^- \rightarrow CO_2 + Mn^{++}$?
ANSWER: **0.0352 g**

■ P R O B L E M   219   Suppose you are investigating the reaction $Zn + V(OH)_4^+ \rightarrow Zn^{++} + ???$. If you find it takes 2.14 g Zn to reduce 0.0218 mole $V(OH)_4^+$, what must be the oxidation state of the vanadium in the product?
ANSWER: **+2**

■ P R O B L E M   220   A   mixture   consisting only of Zn and Al shows 0.0530 gram-equivalent of reducing action per gram of mixture. Assuming the products are $Zn^{++}$ and $Al^{+3}$, calculate the per cent composition by weight of the initial mixture.
ANSWER: **72.2% Zn and 27.8% Al by weight**

# 6

# CALCULATIONS
# INVOLVING GASES

WHEN YOU HAVE to describe a sample of gas, the quantities that may be useful to you are the following:

$P$, the pressure, usually measured in atmospheres or millimeters of mercury (mm Hg). A relatively recent development, which is heartily to be encouraged, is to use the unit "Torr" instead of "mm of mercury." This does honor to Torricelli and also gets rid of an awkward phrase.

$V$, the volume, usually measured in cubic centimeters (cc or $cm^3$), milliliters (ml), or liters (l).

$n$, the number of moles, usually expressed as the number of moles but also calculable as the weight of sample divided by its molecular or molar weight. The number of moles can also be expressed as the number of molecules divided by the Avogadro number, $6.02 \times 10^{23}$.

$T$, the temperature, usually measured in degrees absolute (°A) or degrees Kelvin (°K). Referred to centigrade temperature (which is usually denoted by $t$ and is measured in °C), the absolute temperature is obtained by adding 273.15°.

$$T(°K) = t(°C) + 273.15°$$

People are trying to stamp out the Fahrenheit temperature (°F) but it refuses to disappear.  If you need to convert, the appropriate relation is

$$t(°C) = \tfrac{5}{9}[t(°F) - 32°]$$

For an ideal gas—i.e., one whose behavior is exactly describable by the gas laws discussed below—the product $PV$ divided by $nT$ comes out to be a constant, the universal gas constant, usually denoted by $R$. The value of $R$ depends on what units are used for $P$, $V$, $n$, and $T$. More about this general gas law later.

### Boyle's law

Boyle's law states that for an ideal gas sample of fixed weight at a fixed temperature, the volume varies inversely with the pressure exerted on it.

**PROBLEM 221**  If 3.0 g gas at 25°C occupies 3.60 l at a pressure of 1.00 atm, what will be its volume at a pressure of 2.50 atm?  Assume ideal behavior.

SOLUTION: The pressure increases from 1.00 atm to 2.50 atm.

The pressure, therefore, has increased to $\dfrac{2.50}{1.00}$ of its original value.

The volume changes inversely, so it must go to $\dfrac{1.00}{2.50}$ of its original value.

Final volume $= \left(\dfrac{1.00}{2.50}\right)(3.60\ l) = \mathbf{1.44\ l.}$

**PROBLEM 222**  A given sample of ideal gas occupies a volume of 11.2 l at 0.863 atm.  If you keep the temperature constant, to what pressure will you have to go to change the volume to 15.0 l?

SOLUTION: You want the volume to go from 11.2 l to 15.0 l.

Thus, you want the volume to increase to $\dfrac{15.0}{11.2}$ of its original value.

The pressure will have to change inversely.

So, you need the pressure to go to $\dfrac{11.2}{15.0}$ of its original value.

Final pressure $= \left(\dfrac{11.2}{15.0}\right)(0.863\ atm) = \mathbf{0.644\ atm.}$

PROBLEM 223  A sample of gas is trapped at a pressure of $1.55 \times 10^{-6}$ mm Hg in a volume of 250.0 cc. Assuming ideal behavior, what volume would this sample occupy if compressed to 1 atm pressure at the same temperature?

SOLUTION: One atm pressure is equivalent to 760 mm Hg.
Thus, you want the pressure to go from $1.55 \times 10^{-6}$ mm Hg to 760 mm Hg; in other words, to $\dfrac{760}{1.55 \times 10^{-6}}$ of its original value.

The volume would change inversely, or to $\dfrac{1.55 \times 10^{-6}}{760}$ of its original value.

Final volume $= \left( \dfrac{1.55 \times 10^{-6}}{760} \right)$ (250.0 cc) $= \mathbf{5.10 \times 10^{-7}\ cc.}$

PROBLEM 224  The gas in outer space is at a pressure of about $5 \times 10^{-14}$ Torr. Assuming constant temperature and ideal behavior, how much outer space could you compress into a 1-cc box at 1 atm?

SOLUTION: One atm is 760 mm Hg, or 760 Torr.
You are going to compress from $5 \times 10^{-14}$ Torr to 760 Torr— that is, to $\dfrac{760}{5 \times 10^{-14}}$ of the original.

Therefore, the final volume will have to be $\dfrac{5 \times 10^{-14}}{760}$ of the original.

Final volume $= 1$ cc $= \left( \dfrac{5 \times 10^{-14}}{760} \right)$ (original volume).

Original volume $= \left( \dfrac{760}{5 \times 10^{-14}} \right)$ (1 cc) $= \mathbf{2 \times 10^{16}\ cc.}$

[*Note:* Only one significant figure allowed here.]

In the above problems, the solutions have been worked out by what is called the logical approach. The reasoning requires visualization of the compression or expansion process. An alternate way of setting up these Boyle's law problems is to express the inverse proportionality as an algebraic equation:

$$\frac{V_{\text{initial}}}{V_{\text{final}}} = \frac{P_{\text{final}}}{P_{\text{initial}}}$$

If any three of these quantities are specified, the fourth can be calculated by simple arithmetic substitution.

PROBLEM 225   A lungful of air (350 cc) is exhaled into an evacuated chamber as big as an average room (75 cubic meters).  Assuming constant temperature and ideal behavior, what would be the final pressure in the chamber if we start with 750 mm Hg in the lung?

SOLUTION: $V_{\text{initial}} = 350$ cc
$V_{\text{final}} = 75 \text{ m}^3 = (75)(100 \text{ cm})^3 = 75 \times 10^6$ cc
$P_{\text{initial}} = 750$ mm Hg
$P_{\text{final}} = ???$
From the equation $(V_{\text{initial}}/V_{\text{final}}) = (P_{\text{final}}/P_{\text{initial}})$ we can deduce, by rearranging the terms, that

$$P_{\text{final}} = P_{\text{initial}} \left( \frac{V_{\text{initial}}}{V_{\text{final}}} \right) = (750 \text{ mm Hg}) \left( \frac{350 \text{ cc}}{75 \times 10^6 \text{ cc}} \right)$$
$$= 3.5 \times 10^{-3} \text{ mm Hg.}$$

## Charles' law

Charles' law states that given an ideal gas its volume is directly proportional to the absolute temperature, provided that the pressure stays constant and provided we are working with a gas sample of fixed weight.

PROBLEM 226   Two grams of gas occupy 1.56 l at 25°C and 1.00 atm pressure.  What will be the volume of this sample if the gas is heated to 35°C with the pressure staying constant?  Assume ideal behavior.

SOLUTION: Centigrade temperature goes from 25° to 35°.
Absolute temperature goes from $(273 + 25)$ to $(273 + 35)$, or from 298 to 308°K.

The absolute temperature has increased to $\dfrac{308}{298}$ of the original.

The volume must also change proportionally.

Volume goes to $\dfrac{308}{298}$ of the original.

Final volume $= \left( \dfrac{308}{298} \right) (1.56 \text{ l}) = \mathbf{1.61 \text{ l.}}$

PROBLEM 227    A 268-cc sample of ideal gas at 18°C and 748 Torr pressure is placed in an evacuated container of volume 648 cc. To what centigrade temperature must the assembly be heated so that the gas will fill the whole chamber at 748 Torr?

SOLUTION: The volume of the sample has to go from 268 to 648 cc, or to $\frac{648}{268}$ of the original.

Absolute temperature must change proportionally.

Absolute temperature is to go to $\frac{648}{268}$ of the original.

Original temperature is 18°C, or $18 + 273 = 291°K$.

Final temperature $= \left(\frac{648}{268}\right)(291°K) = 704°K$.

Final centigrade temperature $= 704° - 273° = 431°C$.

PROBLEM 228    Suppose you have a flask fitted with a capillary neck in which a glob of mercury rides so as to trap in the flask a certain sample of gas at atmospheric pressure. You put the flask in an ice bath (0°C) and you arbitrarily mark the mercury-blob position as 273 "volume units" of trapped gas. Now you put the flask in a water bath at 18°C. The mercury blob moves out. What number for volume should you put on the new position?

SOLUTION: The centigrade temperature has gone from 0 to 18°C. Absolute temperature has gone from 273 to 291°K.

If absolute temperature has gone to $\frac{291}{273}$ of the original, the volume must change proportionally.

Final volume $= \left(\frac{291}{273}\right)$ (initial volume) $= \left(\frac{291}{273}\right)$ (273 "volume units")

$= 291$ "volume units."

PROBLEM 229    A freely collapsible balloon contains a certain amount of hot gas at atmospheric pressure. The initial volume is $2.64 \times 10^6$ l. When the balloon falls into the ocean (15°C), the volume goes to $2.04 \times 10^6$ l. What must have been the temperature of the hot gas initially? Assume ideal behavior.

SOLUTION: Volume goes from $2.64 \times 10^6$ to $2.04 \times 10^6$ l.

Volume goes to $\dfrac{2.04 \times 10^6}{2.64 \times 10^6}$ of the original.

Absolute temperature must also go to $\dfrac{2.04}{2.64}$ of the original.

Final temperature is $15°C = 288°K$.

$288°K$ must be $\dfrac{2.04}{2.64}$ of original hot gas temperature.

Original temperature $= \left(\dfrac{2.64}{2.04}\right)(288°K) = 373°K$, or $100°C$.

## Dalton's law of partial pressures

This law simply states that when more than one gas is in the same container, the total pressure exerted by the mixture is the sum of the pressures that would have been exerted if each gas were there alone. In other words, so far as pressure is concerned, each gas acts completely independently of other gases present in the same volume. This can be stated mathematically in the following way: First, we invent something we call a "partial pressure." This is defined as the individual pressure one component exerts, treating it as if it were all by itself in the container. Let us designate the partial pressures of components 1, 2, 3, etc., as $p_1$, $p_2$, $p_3$, etc. Dalton's law states that the observed pressure $P$ will be the sum of the partial pressures, or

$$P = p_1 + p_2 + p_3 + \cdots$$

✔ PROBLEM 230 Given a completely evacuated 1.00-l box at $25°C$. Enough hydrogen is pumped in to make its partial pressure equal to 0.463 atm. At the same time enough oxygen is pumped in to make its partial pressure equal to 0.432 atm. What is the total pressure in the box, assuming ideal behavior?

SOLUTION: Total pressure equals sum of partial pressures.

Total pressure $= p_{\text{hydrogen}} + p_{\text{oxygen}} = 0.463$ atm $+ 0.432$ atm $=$ **0.895 atm**.

PROBLEM 231 A given gas mixture consists of helium, neon, and argon, all at the same partial pressure. If the total pressure of the sample is 746 mm Hg, what is the pressure exerted by the helium?

SOLUTION: Let $p_{He}$, $p_{Ne}$, $p_{Ar}$ be the partial pressures of the three components.

Then, total pressure $P = p_{He} + p_{Ne} + p_{Ar}$.

But, since the partial pressures are equal, $p_{He} = p_{Ne} = p_{Ar}$.

We can, therefore, substitute $p_{He}$ for $p_{Ne}$ and for $p_{Ar}$.

$P = 3p_{He} = 746$ mm Hg.

$p_{He} = \frac{1}{3}(746$ mm Hg$) = $ **249 mm Hg.**

PROBLEM 232    You are given three boxes, $A$, $B$, and $C$, all at the same temperature, with volumes, respectively, of 1.20 l, 2.63 l, and 3.05 l.   Box $A$ contains 0.695 g nitrogen gas at a pressure of 742 Torr; box $B$ contains 1.10 g argon gas at a pressure of 383 Torr; box $C$ is completely empty at the start of the experiment. What will the pressure become in box $C$ if the contents of $A$ and $B$ are completely transferred to $C$?   Assume ideal behavior.

SOLUTION: Treat the gases independently.

For pumping $A$ into $C$, the sample goes from 1.20 to 3.05 l.   This is an increase of volume to $\dfrac{3.05}{1.20}$ of the original.   By Boyle's law, the pressure should change inversely—that is, to $\dfrac{1.20}{3.05}$ of the original.

Therefore, sample $A$ in box $C$ gives a pressure of

$$\left(\frac{1.20}{3.05}\right)(742 \text{ Torr}) = 292 \text{ Torr.}$$

For pumping $B$ into $C$, the sample goes from 2.63 to 3.05 l.   This is an increase of volume to $\dfrac{3.05}{2.63}$ of the original.   By Boyle's law, the pressure should go to $\dfrac{2.63}{3.05}$ of the original, or

$$\left(\frac{2.63}{3.05}\right)(383 \text{ Torr}) = 330 \text{ Torr.}$$

The final total pressure in box $C$ will be the partial pressure exerted by gas $A$ plus the partial pressure exerted by gas $B$:

$$P = p_A + p_B = 292 \text{ Torr} + 330 \text{ Torr} = \textbf{622 Torr.}$$

## *Wet gases*

One of the most useful applications of Dalton's law of partial pressures is in the treatment of gases collected over water. The application is a common one because it is so simple to collect a gas X by allowing it to bubble into the mouth of an inverted bottle filled with water. However, gas X collected by such water displacement is invariably wet— that is, it is contaminated with water vapor. For most purposes, this contamination by water vapor is not serious, but it must be taken into account in calculating the pressure of the gas. Ordinarily, the pressure in the surrounding room can be read off a barometer (the so-called "barometric pressure"), and if the water levels inside the bottle and outside the bottle are identical then the total pressure inside the bottle is just equal to the barometric pressure. However, if the gas is "wet," the pressure inside the bottle is partly due to water vapor, and this has to be subtracted out from the barometric reading in order to find the actual partial pressure of gas X.

How much correction do we need to subtract? This depends on the temperature of the water through which gas X is bubbled. The hotter the water, the more volatile it is, and the "wetter" the gas gets. In general, we make the assumption that the gas sample is "saturated" with water vapor—i.e., it contains as much water vapor as it can hold under equilibrium conditions. If the gas sample is "saturated" with water vapor, then the partial pressure of the water vapor in the gas phase is fixed by the temperature of the water in contact with the gas. Appendix C shows the pressure of aqueous vapor over liquid water in mm Hg at various temperatures. When you meet a gas problem in which gas X is collected over water, look in this table to find out what correction for water vapor you will need to subtract from the observed total pressure. To do this, of course, you will need to have specified the temperature of the liquid water over which the gas is collected. In general, it is assumed that the liquid water and the gas above it are at the same temperature, but for precise work a thermometer needs to be stuck in the water to find out what its temperature really is.

✓PROBLEM 233 A sample of nitrogen gas is collected over water at 18°C. If the barometric reading is 742 mm Hg, what is the actual pressure of nitrogen in the sample?

SOLUTION: At 18°C, the vapor pressure of water is 15.48 mm Hg. The total pressure of the sample $= p_{nitrogen} + p_{water\ vapor}$.

So, $p_{nitrogen}$ = total pressure $- p_{water\ vapor}$

$$= 742 \text{ mm Hg } - 15.48 \text{ mm Hg}$$

$$= 727 \text{ mm Hg}$$

✔PROBLEM 234   You wish to collect a sample of oxygen gas in which the pressure of oxygen is 732 mm Hg. You want to do this by water displacement on a day when the barometric pressure in the lab is 742 mm Hg.   How cold should the water be?

SOLUTION: Total pressure = 742 mm Hg

$$= p_{oxygen} + p_{water\ vapor}$$

$$= 732 \text{ mm Hg} + p_{water\ vapor}$$

$p_{water\ vapor} = 742 - 732 = 10$ mm Hg.

Consult the table to see at what temperature the vapor pressure of water becomes equal to 10 mm Hg.   You will find it occurs when the water temperature is **11.2°C.**

PROBLEM 235   A given sample of dry methane occupies a volume of 368 cc at a temperature of 21.0°C and a pressure of 752 Torr.   Suppose this sample is now bubbled through water at 21.0°C until it gets saturated with water vapor.   If the total pressure remains 752 Torr, what volume will the "wet" gas have to occupy?   Assume ideal behavior.

SOLUTION: At 21.0°C the vapor pressure of water comes out to be 18.6 mm Hg, or 18.6 Torr.

If the total pressure of the "wet" gas is 752 Torr, and if 18.6 Torr is due to the water vapor, only the difference (752 − 18.6, or 733 Torr) is due to the methane.

In other words, the pressure of the methane has gone from 752 Torr (in the dry state) to 733 Torr (in the wet state).

According to Boyle's law, for the pressure to go to $\dfrac{733}{752}$ of the original,

the volume must change inversely—that is, go to $\dfrac{752}{733}$ of its original value.

Therefore, final volume $= \left(\dfrac{752}{733}\right)$ (368 cc) = **378 cc.**

[*Note:* This problem illustrates a very important point. The volume occupied by gas X depends on the pressure of X; it does not depend on what other gases are present. Once we know what the pressure of X is, we can ignore all the other gases present—provided, of course, ideal behavior is obeyed.]

### Combined Boyle's, Charles', and Dalton's law behavior

It is a fundamental principle that the state of a gas sample does not depend on how you got it there. Specifically, it makes no difference in what sequence you carry out operations such as changing pressure, changing temperature, adding other gases, etc. The end result will be the same, provided you end up doing all the same operations.

This principle has direct application to problems, because frequently a gas will be taken from one pressure and temperature ($P_1$ and $T_1$) to another pressure and temperature ($P_2$ and $T_2$). In calculating what happens to, say, the volume in this case, we can separate the change into two steps: one corresponding to changing pressure from $P_1$ to $P_2$ and the other, to changing temperature from $T_1$ to $T_2$. It makes no difference which we do first. The same principle holds for changing other variables—e.g., adding other gases.

What the above means is that, given a set of initial conditions for the gas and a set of final conditions, an unknown quantity can be calculated by applying each correction successively. This kind of combined calculation is frequently encountered when the problem calls for "reduction to standard conditions." Standard conditions, which are our reference conditions for comparison, are 0°C and 1 atm pressure. They are usually referred to as STP (standing for "standard temperature and pressure").

PROBLEM 236  Three grams of a gas occupies 0.963 l at 22°C and 0.969 atm. What will be the volume of this sample if taken to standard conditions, assuming ideal behavior?

SOLUTION: To go to standard conditions, the temperature must go from 22°C (or 295°K) to 0°C (or 273°K); the pressure must go from 0.969 to 1 atm.

In other words,

the temperature goes to $\dfrac{273}{295}$ of the original;

the pressure goes to $\dfrac{1.000}{0.969}$ of the original.

The temperature change produces a directly proportional effect on the volume, so from this standpoint alone the final volume must go to $\dfrac{273}{295}$ of the original.

The pressure change produces an inversely proportional effect on volume, so from this standpoint alone the final volume must go to $\dfrac{0.969}{1.000}$ of the original.

Applying both corrections, we find that

$$\text{final volume} = (\text{initial volume}) \left(\frac{273}{295}\right) \left(\frac{0.969}{1.000}\right)$$

$$= (0.963 \text{ l}) \left(\frac{273}{295}\right) \left(\frac{0.969}{1.000}\right) = \mathbf{0.864\ l.}$$

PROBLEM 237  Three grams of a dry gas at $-40°C$ and 742 mm Hg occupies a volume of 862 cc. Assuming ideal behavior, what volume would this sample occupy if it were saturated with water vapor at 19°C and held at a barometric pressure of 756 mm Hg?

SOLUTION: Temperature goes from $-40°C$ (233°K) to 19°C (292°K). Thus, temperature goes to $\dfrac{292}{233}$ of its original value.

Owing to temperature increase alone, the volume should go to $\dfrac{292}{233}$ of its original value.

In the final state, the total pressure is 756 mm Hg. This includes the vapor pressure of water at 19°C. From the tables, we find that the vapor pressure of water at 19°C equals 16.5 mm Hg. Subtracting this 16.5 mm Hg from 756 mm Hg leaves 740 mm Hg as the actual final pressure of the gas.

So, pressure of the gas has gone from 742 to 740 mm Hg.

Pressure has gone to $\dfrac{740}{742}$ of its original value.

According to Boyle's law, the volume should change inversely, and due to pressure change alone it should go to $\dfrac{742}{740}$ of its original value.

Final volume = (initial volume) $\left(\dfrac{292}{233}\right)\left(\dfrac{742}{740}\right)$, where the first fraction takes care of the temperature change and the second fraction takes care of the pressure change.

Final volume = (862 cc) $\left(\dfrac{292}{233}\right)\left(\dfrac{742}{740}\right)$ = **1080 cc.**

■ PROBLEM 238 Assuming ideal behavior, what would be the volume at STP of a sample of dry gas occupying 1.00 cc at 353°K and 765 Torr?

ANSWER: **0.778 cc**

■ PROBLEM 239 If 1.00 g of dry oxygen gas occupies 0.700 l at STP, what volume would it occupy if "wet" at 24°C and a barometric pressure of 726 mm Hg? Assume ideal behavior.

ANSWER: **0.822 l**

■ PROBLEM 240 You are given a 1.00-g sample of dry gas such that it exerts a pressure of 0.836 atm when confined in a 1.00-l box at 24°C. What would the pressure of the sample be if it were compressed to a volume of 0.963 l and heated to a temperature of 47°C? Assume ideal behavior.

ANSWER: **0.935 atm** $\quad \dfrac{320}{297} \times \dfrac{1.963}{1.00}$

■ PROBLEM 241 Suppose that 1.00 g of gas X occupies 0.747 l at STP; 1.00 g of gas Y occupies 0.718 l at 87°C and 710.0 Torr. These two samples are to be pumped simultaneously into a completely empty box of volume 2.00 l held at 25°C. What will be the final total pressure in the box, assuming ideality?

ANSWER: **521 Torr**

■■ PROBLEM 242   A sealed tube contains 10.0 cc of oxygen gas and 10.0 cc of liquid water at a temperature of 25°C and an internal pressure of 742 mm Hg. Suppose this tube is now plunged into a bath that takes it to 50°C. Neglecting any change in relative volumes of liquid and gas phases and assuming ideal behavior, calculate the final pressure.

ANSWER: 871 mm Hg

$$\frac{P_1}{P_2}\frac{V_1}{V_2} = \frac{T_1}{T_2} \qquad \frac{1.22.4}{.93 \times} = \frac{273}{294}$$

## Avogadro's principle and the molar volume

$$\frac{22.4}{.93 \times} = .93$$

The Avogadro principle states that at the same pressure and temperature, equal volumes of gases contain equal numbers of particles. This means, for example, that provided both are at the same temperature and pressure 1 liter of hydrogen gas contains as many molecules as 1 liter of oxygen gas or 1 liter of any other gas showing ideal behavior. Another way of stating the Avogadro principle is to say that the number of molecules per cubic centimeter of gas depends only on the temperature and pressure of the gas and not on what the identity of the gas is. The basic reason for the Avogadro principle is that gases are mostly empty space, so their behavior does not depend on what the molecules are that populate this empty space.

One mole of any gas contains the Avogadro number of molecules —i.e., $6.02 \times 10^{23}$ molecules. At STP, the volume occupied by these $6.02 \times 10^{23}$ molecules is equal to 22.4 liters (no matter what the molecules are, so long as they constitute a gas showing ideal behavior). The number 22.4 liters is called the molar volume of an ideal gas at STP.

PROBLEM 243 What would be the molar volume of an ideal gas at 25°C and 742 Torr?

SOLUTION: The molar volume is 22.4 l at 0°C (273°K) and 760 Torr. We change the temperature from 273 to 298°K—that is, to $\frac{298}{273}$ of its original value.

We also change the pressure from 760 to 742 Torr, thereby changing it to $\frac{742}{760}$ of its original value.

Owing to the increase in temperature, the volume will go up to $\frac{298}{273}$ of its original value.

Owing to the decrease in pressure, the volume will increase to $\frac{760}{742}$ of its original value.

Final volume = (initial volume at STP) $\left(\frac{298}{273}\right)\left(\frac{760}{742}\right)$

$$= (22.4 \text{ l}) \left(\frac{298}{273}\right)\left(\frac{760}{742}\right) = 25.0 \text{ l}$$

**PROBLEM 244** Assuming a gas behaves ideally, how many molecules per cubic centimeter will it contain at $-33°C$ and 726 Torr?

SOLUTION: One mole STP contains $6.02 \times 10^{23}$ molecules and occupies 22.4 l.

Therefore, at STP, we have $\dfrac{6.02 \times 10^{23} \text{ molecules}}{22,400 \text{ cc}} = 2.69 \times 10^{19}$ molecules per cc.

Now we decrease the temperature from STP (273°K) to $-33°C$ (240°K). This shrinks the gas to $\frac{240}{273}$ of the original, thereby increasing the particles per cubic centimeter to $\frac{273}{240}$ of the original.

We also release the pressure from STP (760 Torr) to 726 Torr. This reduction of pressure to $\frac{726}{760}$ of the original is the same as an expansion to $\frac{760}{726}$ of the original volume. If we expand the gas, there will be fewer molecules per cubic centimeter proportionately, so the pressure drop decreases the particles per cubic centimeter to $\frac{726}{760}$ of the original.

Final number of molecules per cubic centimeter = (initial number of molecules per cc at STP) $\left(\frac{273}{240}\right)\left(\frac{726}{760}\right)$ = ($2.69 \times 10^{19}$ molecules per cc) $\left(\frac{273}{240}\right)\left(\frac{726}{760}\right)$ = **$2.92 \times 10^{19}$ molecules per cc**

PROBLEM 245 An unknown gas X shows a density of 2.39 g per liter at 100.0°C and 715 Torr. What is the molecular weight of this gas, assuming ideal behavior?

SOLUTION: (We take our 2.39-g sample, reduce it to STP to find its volume at STP, then find out how many such volumes there would be in 22.4 l.)

We go from 100°C (or 373°K) to STP (273°K). Thus, the absolute temperature goes to $\frac{273}{373}$ of its original value.

The volume of 2.39 g goes to $\frac{273}{373}$ of its original value.

Then we go from 715 Torr to STP (760 Torr). Thus, the pressure goes to $\frac{760}{715}$ of the original.

The volume goes to $\frac{715}{760}$ of its starting value.

Final volume of 2.39 g gas at STP = $(1.00 \text{ l}) \left(\frac{273}{373}\right) \left(\frac{715}{760}\right) = 0.689 \text{ l}$.

Molar volume at STP is 22.4 l. If we divide this 22.4 l by 0.689 l we will find out how many 2.39-g portions we need to get a mole. Then if we multiply the number of such portions—actually 22.4/0.689—by 2.39 g, we shall have the weight of one mole:

$$\left(\frac{22.4 \text{ l/mole}}{0.689 \text{ l}}\right) (2.39 \text{ g}) = 77.7 \frac{\text{g}}{\text{mole}}.$$

■PROBLEM 246 If the vapor pressure of water at 25°C is 23.8 mm Hg, how many water molecules per cubic centimeter does this correspond to? Assume ideal behavior.

ANSWER: $7.71 \times 10^{17}$ molecules per cc

■PROBLEM 247 An open flask initially filled with bromine vapor at 25°C contains a certain number of $Br_2$ molecules. To what temperature must the flask be heated so that expansion pushes 10% of the $Br_2$ molecules out of the flask?

ANSWER: 58°C

■PROBLEM 248 1.00 g of benzene liquid is put in the bottom of an evacuated and sealed 250-cc flask. The flask and contents are now placed in boiling water (100°C) so that all the benzene is volatilized. What pressure will develop in the flask? Assume ideal behavior. (Benzene is $C_6H_6$.)

ANSWER: **1.57 atm**

■■ P R O B L E M 249 A 500-cc flask full of steam (water vapor) at 750 Torr and 100°C is sealed and plunged into a water bath at 25°C. What weight of liquid water will condense in the flask? Assume ideal behavior.

ANSWER: **0.279 g**

■■ P R O B L E M 250 A given gas mixture consisting of 10.0% by weight $CH_4$, 30.0% $C_2H_6$, and 60.0% $C_3H_8$ is bubbled through 19° water and collected over the 19° water at a barometric pressure of 737 Torr. To get 1.00 g $CH_4$, what total volume of gas mixture will you have to collect?

ANSWER: **7.53 l**

## Equation of state for an ideal gas

Boyle's law, Charles' law, and the Avogadro principle are special cases of gas behavior. The most general way of summarizing the behavior of a gas is in what is called the "equation of state." An equation of state tells mathematically how the pressure, temperature, volume, and number of moles in a sample must be related. For an ideal gas the equation is

$$PV = nRT$$

where $P$ is the pressure, $V$ is the volume, $n$ is the number of moles, $T$ is the absolute temperature, and $R$ is a constant, usually called the "universal gas constant." If $P$ is in atmospheres, $V$ in liters, $T$ in degrees absolute, then $R$ has the numerical value of 0.08206 liter-atmosphere per degree per mole. So long as a sample of gas approximates ideal behavior, $PV$ divided by $nT$ must come out to be equal to $R$ no matter what the gas is and no matter what condition it is in.

P R O B L E M 251 Show that Boyle's law can be derived from the equation of state for an ideal gas.

SOLUTION: Boyle's law holds for a fixed weight of sample at a fixed temperature. In other words, $n$ and $T$ are specific numbers as well as $R$. This means we can lump $n$, $R$, and $T$ into one constant—call it $c$. So, under Boyle's law conditions

$$PV = nRT = c$$

Suppose $P_1$ and $V_1$ describe the sample in the initial state and $P_2$ and $V_2$ describe the sample in the final state. The product $PV$ must stay constant, so we can write

$$P_1 V_1 = c = P_2 V_2$$

which can be rewritten as

$$\frac{V_1}{V_2} = \frac{P_2}{P_1}$$

showing the Boyle's law inverse proportionality.

The equation of state is extremely useful because it enables us to calculate one of the variables $P$, $V$, $n$, or $T$ as soon as three of the others are specified. In particular, we can calculate $n$ if $P$, $V$, and $T$ are given. This kind of calculation takes on added significance if you stop to think that number of moles is hard to measure but $P$, $V$, and $T$ can usually be determined with readily available instruments.

⚹  PROBLEM 252  A tube of volume 36.8 cc contains oxygen ($O_2$) at a pressure of 2000 pounds per square inch and a temperature of 343°C. How many grams of oxygen in this sample?

SOLUTION: We can calculate the number of moles of oxygen from the relation $n = (PV)/(RT)$, provided we use the proper units.

$$V = \text{volume in liters} = \frac{36.8 \text{ cc}}{1000 \text{ cc/l}} = 0.0368 \text{ l.}$$

$$P = \text{pressure in atmospheres} = \frac{2000 \text{ lb/in}^2}{14.7 \text{ lb/in}^2 \text{ per atm}} = 136 \text{ atm.}$$

$R = 0.08206$ liter-atm per deg per mole.
$T = 343°C = 343 + 273$, or $616°K$.
$$n = \frac{PV}{RT} = \frac{(136)(0.0368)}{(0.08206)(616)} = 0.0990 \text{ mole.}$$

One mole oxygen = 32.00 g.

$$0.0990 \text{ mole} = (0.0990 \text{ mole}) \left(32.00 \frac{g}{\text{mole}}\right) = 3.17 \text{ g}.$$

■ PROBLEM 253  If you want to have 1.50 mg hydrogen ($H_2$) at standard conditions, what volume must you take?

ANSWER: **16.7 cc**

■ PROBLEM 254  Suppose you want to collect 1.50 mg hydrogen ($H_2$) over water at 23°C at a barometric pressure of 746 Torr.  What volume of "wet" gas must you take?
[Hint: The volume $V$ is occupied by the $H_2$ and by the water vapor simultaneously.  This is the $V$ that goes into the equation.  The $P$ that goes into the equation is the pressure of the hydrogen—that is, barometer reading less water-vapor correction.]

ANSWER: **18.9 cc**

■ PROBLEM 255  You have a shock tube 20.0 m in length and 10.0 cm in radius.  You need to fill this with carbon dioxide at 25°C and 865 Torr.  How many grams $CO_2$ are required?

ANSWER: **$1.29 \times 10^3$ g**

## Kinetic theory

The ideal equation of state can be derived from the simple model that gases consist of independent molecules which exert pressure by making elastic collisions with the walls of the container.  The principal assumption that has to be introduced is that the average kinetic energy of the gas molecules ($\frac{1}{2}mv^2$, where $m$ is the mass of the molecule and $v$ is its average velocity) is proportional to the absolute temperature.

The implication of this assumption that average kinetic energy is proportional to temperature is that once the temperature is fixed, the product $mv^2$ is fixed.  This means that, given two gases at the same temperature, $m_1v_1{}^2 = m_2v_2{}^2$ or $v_1/v_2 = \sqrt{m_2/m_1}$, or "velocities are inversely proportional to the square roots of the molecular masses." A direct outgrowth of this is Graham's law of diffusion, which states that the "rate of diffusion of a gas is inversely proportional to the square root of its molecular mass." The other implication is that, for a given gas, the product $mv^2$ is proportional to the temperature. Since $m$ for a given gas is constant, this means that the average velocity of a gas molecule increases as the square root of the absolute temperature.

PROBLEM 256  If the average velocity of an oxygen molecule ($O_2$) is $4.25 \times 10^4$ cm per sec at 0°C, what is the average velocity of a $CO_2$ molecule at the same temperature?

SOLUTION: At the same temperature, average kinetic energies are equal.

$$\tfrac{1}{2}m_{O_2}v_{O_2}^2 = \tfrac{1}{2}m_{CO_2}v_{CO_2}^2$$

$$v_{CO_2}^2 = v_{O_2}^2(m_{O_2}/m_{CO_2})$$

$$v_{CO_2} = v_{O_2}\sqrt{m_{O_2}/m_{CO_2}}$$

The ratio of the masses of the $O_2$ and $CO_2$ molecules will be the same as the ratio of their molecular weights—that is, 32.00 to 44.01.

$$v_{CO_2} = v_{O_2}\sqrt{32.00/44.01}$$

$$= \left(4.25 \times 10^4 \frac{cm}{sec}\right)(0.853) = 3.62 \times 10^4 \frac{cm}{sec}$$

PROBLEM 257  If the average velocity of an $O_2$ molecule is $4.25 \times 10^4$ cm per sec at 0°C, what would it be at 25°C?

SOLUTION: The kinetic energy changes proportionally to the absolute temperature.

The absolute temperature changes from 273°K (for 0°C) to 298°K (for 25°C).

The kinetic energies will be in the same ratio as the absolute temperatures.

$$\frac{\tfrac{1}{2}mv_{0°C}^2}{\tfrac{1}{2}mv_{25°C}^2} = \frac{273}{298}$$

From this we deduce, cancelling $\tfrac{1}{2}m$ in the numerator against $\tfrac{1}{2}m$ in the denominator, that

$$\frac{v_{0°C}}{v_{25°C}} = \sqrt{\frac{273}{298}}$$

from which

$$v_{25°C} = \sqrt{298/273}\ v_{0°C}$$

$$= (1.04)(4.25 \times 10^4) = 4.42 \times 10^4\ \frac{cm}{sec}.$$

■ PROBLEM 258 What will be the relative velocities of the $C_3H_8$ molecules to the $CH_4$ molecules in the same mixture at the same temperature?

ANSWER: 1 to 1.66

■ PROBLEM 259 You have a batch of molecules at $-33°C$. You wish to increase their average velocity by 10.0%. To what temperature should the gas be heated?

ANSWER: 17°C

■ PROBLEM 260 What ratio would you expect between the rate of diffusion of CO at 25°C and that of argon at 57°C?

ANSWER: 1.13 to 1

## Reactions involving gases

Once you have a balanced chemical equation, you know directly from the coefficients the relative number of moles of each substance involved in the reaction. If a particular reactant or product is a gas, then we can (by introducing the equation of state) say something about volumes of reagents as well as weights and numbers of moles. For example, in the reaction

$$Zn_{(s)} + 2H^+_{(solution)} \rightarrow Zn^{++}_{(solution)} + H_{2(g)}$$

the product $H_2$ is gaseous, so we cannot only say we get one mole of $H_2$ in the reaction but alternatively we can say we get 22.4 liters at STP of $H_2$. In other words, it may sometimes be convenient to focus attention on a directly measurable aspect of a gaseous reagent, such as its volume.

PROBLEM 261 You are given 1.00 pound zinc. How many liters of hydrogen to be measured over water at

22°C and a barometric pressure of 743 mm Hg can you generate from it?

SOLUTION: (Figure out how many moles of Zn you have. From the balanced equation figure out how many moles $H_2$ this will give. Use the gas laws to find out what volume this occupies under the specified conditions.)

$$1.00 \text{ lb Zn} = (1.00 \text{ lb}) \left(454 \frac{g}{lb}\right) = 454 \text{ g Zn.}$$

One mole (or one gram-atom) of Zn weighs 65.37 g.

$$454 \text{ g Zn} = \frac{454 \text{ g}}{65.37 \text{ g/mole}} = 6.95 \text{ moles Zn.}$$

The equation $Zn + 2H^+ \rightarrow Zn^{++} + H_2$ says that one mole Zn reacts to produce one mole $H_2$. So, we conclude that 6.95 moles Zn will produce 6.95 moles $H_2$. This $H_2$ is to be measured under the following conditions:

temperature = 22°C = 295°K

pressure = (743 mm Hg) − (vapor pressure of $H_2O$ at 22°C)

= 743 − 19.8 = 723 mm Hg

$$= \frac{723 \text{ mm Hg}}{760 \text{ mm Hg/atm}} = 0.951 \text{ atm}$$

number of moles = 6.95 moles

From the equation of state $PV = nRT$ we calculate

$$V = \frac{nRT}{P} = \frac{(6.95)(0.08206)(295)}{(0.951)} = 177 \text{ l.}$$

PROBLEM 262    Given that a Bunsen burner consumes $CH_4$ at 5.0 l per min (pressure 773 Torr and temperature 28°C), how many liters per minute of oxygen need to be supplied (pressure 742 Torr and temperature 29°C) if the $CH_4$ is to be oxidized by $O_2$ to $CO_2$ and $H_2O$?

SOLUTION: (Figure out how many moles of $CH_4$ are consumed per minute. Then calculate from the equation the required number of moles $O_2$. Convert to volume of $O_2$ at specified conditions.)

5.0 l $CH_4$ at 773 Torr and 301°K can be reduced to standard conditions as $(5.0) \left(\dfrac{773}{760}\right) \left(\dfrac{273}{301}\right) = 4.6$ l.

At STP, one mole equals 22.4 l, so 4.6 l gas STP is $\dfrac{4.6\ l}{22.4\ l/mole} = 0.21$ mole.

The equation for the reaction is

$$CH_4 + 2O_2 \rightarrow CO_2 + 2H_2O$$

and shows that for every mole $CH_4$, we need two moles $O_2$. Therefore, for 0.21 mole $CH_4$ we need 0.42 mole $O_2$.

At 742 Torr and 302°K, 0.42 mole is

$$(0.42\ \text{mole}) \left(22.4\ \frac{\text{liter}}{\text{mole}}\right) \left(\frac{760}{742}\right) \left(\frac{302}{273}\right) = 11\ l.$$

Thus, we need **11 liters $O_2$ per min.**

■ **P R O B L E M  263**  How many grams NaCN do you need so that via the reaction NaCN + HCl → HCN + NaCl you can get enough hydrogen cyanide gas to fill a chamber 10.0 m by 5.0 m by 5.0 m to a partial pressure of 0.0076 Torr of HCN at a temperature of 25°C?

ANSWER: **5.0 g**

■ **P R O B L E M  264**  Phosphine, $PH_3$, is toxic when it reaches a concentration of 0.00007 mg per l. What pressure would this correspond to at 25°C?

ANSWER: $4 \times 10^{-5}$ **mm Hg**

■■ **P R O B L E M  265**  Given a 1.00-l box which contains dry hydrogen gas at a pressure of 326 Torr and a temperature of 168°C and oxygen gas at a pressure of 652 Torr and a temperature of 168°C. A spark is passed through the mixture so the reaction $2H_{2(g)} + O_{2(g)} \rightarrow 2H_2O_{(g)}$ occurs to its maximum extent. What will be the final pressure in the box if the final temperature becomes 197°C?

ANSWER: **869 Torr**

■■ **P R O B L E M  266**  Given a box which contains over water 1.00 l of wet hydrogen gas at a partial pressure of 326

Torr and a temperature of 19°C and wet oxygen gas at a partial pressure of 652 Torr and a temperature of 19°C. A spark is passed through the gas mixture so the reaction $2H_{2(g)} + O_{2(g)} \rightarrow 2H_2O_{(l)}$ occurs to its maximum extent. If the final temperature is 32°C, what is the total final pressure in the box?

ANSWER: **546 Torr**

■ PROBLEM 267 In a mercury barometer, the space above the mercury is normally considered to be "empty." Yet, mercury has a finite vapor pressure, which, for example, is 0.001691 Torr at 24°C. How many mercury atoms are there per cubic centimeter in this "empty" space at 24°C?

ANSWER: **$5.50 \times 10^{13}$ Hg atoms per cc**

■ PROBLEM 268 You are given a 1.50-mg sample of solid $WO_3$ with the instruction you are to remove all the oxygen via a reduction reaction with $H_2$ leading to the formation of W and $H_2O$. How many cubic centimeters of $H_2$ at 28°C and 751 Torr will you need?

ANSWER: **0.485 cc**

■ PROBLEM 269 You are given the assignment of supplying an astronaut with oxygen gas for 24 hours from a solid source. He will need a lungful of $O_2$ (350 cc at a pressure of 150 Torr and a temperature of 37°C) every 6 seconds. You decide to get the $O_2$ from lithium superoxide, $LiO_2$, by the reaction $4LiO_{2(s)} + 2CO_{2(g)} \rightarrow 2Li_2CO_{3(s)} + 3O_{2(g)}$. How many grams $LiO_2$ do you need to synthesize for the job?

ANSWER: **2030 g**

■■ PROBLEM 270 You have a stream of gas consisting of a mixture of $CH_4$ and $C_3H_8$. You wish to know the relative pressures of these two gases in the stream, so you burn the mixture in excess $O_2$ and collect the $CO_2$ and $H_2O$ formed. If you find 1.09 g $CO_2$ for every 0.606 g $H_2O$, what is the ratio of the pressures?

ANSWER: **$p_{CH_4}/p_{C_3H_8} = 0.12$**

# 7

# CALCULATIONS
# INVOLVING LIQUIDS

A GAS is mostly empty space. From this standpoint, we would expect most gases to behave alike. Furthermore, the energy of gas molecules is primarily kinetic ($\frac{1}{2}mv^2$, where molecules of high mass have lower velocities to compensate), so this term depends on the temperature and not on the nature of the gas. As a result, it is possible to write one general equation ($PV = nRT$) which describes a large variety of gases under a whole gamut of conditions of $P$, $V$, $n$, and $T$. Of course, if $P$ gets too high or $T$ gets too low, we get into trouble because the molecules start attracting each other, potential-energy terms appear, and deviations from ideal behavior set in.

## Kinetic model of liquids

In a liquid, the situation is much more complex than in a gas. For one thing, the molecules are so close together that there is little free space left. For another thing, the attractive forces between neighboring molecules are so great that the molecules cannot be treated independently. Finally, the attractive forces are so intimately connected with the specific identity of the individual molecules that we cannot just count molecules, as we do in a gas, but have to consider each liquid as an individual case. For such reasons, it has not been possible to write a simple equation of state for liquids that would tell us how its $P$, $V$, $n$, and $T$ are related, although at first sight it might seem that we could do this. The following calculations illustrate how computations are done in several specific cases.

PROBLEM 271 Ethyl alcohol ($C_2H_5OH$) has a density of 0.7895 g/cc at 20°C and 0.7793 g/cc at 32°C. What is its molar volume at 20°C and what per cent expansion occurs in going to 32°C?

SOLUTION: Molar volume = volume occupied by one mole.
One mole of $C_2H_5OH$ weighs 46.07 g.
At 20°C the density is 0.7895 g/cc.
Therefore, at 20°C, the volume of one mole is

$$\frac{46.07 \text{ g/mole}}{0.7895 \text{ g/cc}} = 58.35 \text{ cc/mole}$$

At 32°C the density is 0.7793 g/cc.
Therefore, at 32°C, the volume of one mole is

$$\frac{46.07 \text{ g/mole}}{0.7793 \text{ g/cc}} = 59.12 \text{ cc/mole.}$$

The expansion is $59.12 - 58.35 = 0.77$ cc/mole.

Per cent expansion is $\dfrac{0.77}{58.35} \times 100 = 1.3\%$.

■ PROBLEM 272 Liquid mercury has a density of 13.546 g/cc at 20°C and 13.517 g/cc at 32°C. What is its molar volume at 20°C and what per cent expansion occurs in going to 32°C?

ANSWER: 14.808 cc/mole; 0.22%

PROBLEM 273 Neopentane, $(CH_3)_4C$, has a density as a liquid at 0°C of 0.613 g/cc. What is the average volume occupied per molecule of neopentane in this liquid state?

SOLUTION: (Figure out the volume occupied by one mole and divide by the Avogadro number.)

One mole $(CH_3)_4C$ weighs 72.15 g.

At 0°C the density is 0.613 g/cc.

The volume of one mole $= \dfrac{72.15 \text{ g/mole}}{0.613 \text{ g/cc}} = 118$ cc/mole.

One mole of anything contains $6.02 \times 10^{23}$ molecules.

Therefore, the volume per molecule is

$$\frac{118 \text{ cc/mole}}{6.02 \times 10^{23} \text{ molecules/mole}} = 1.96 \times 10^{-22} \text{ cc/molecule}$$

PROBLEM 274 The neopentane molecule, $(CH_3)_4C$, is approximately spherical with an effective radius of 3.1 Å. Combining this information with Problem 463, what per cent of liquid neopentane seems to be empty space?

SOLUTION: (Calculate the volume of a neopentane molecule and compare it to the average volume per molecule as calculated above.)

Volume of a sphere $= \frac{4}{3}\pi r^3$.

$r =$ radius of sphere $= 3.1 \times 10^{-8}$ cm for neopentane.

Volume $= \frac{4}{3}\pi(3.1 \times 10^{-8})^3 = 1.2 \times 10^{-22}$ cc.

From Problem 463, we find that the molar volume 118 cc divided amongst $6.02 \times 10^{23}$ molecules seems to indicate $1.96 \times 10^{-22}$ cc available per molecule.

The difference, $1.96 \times 10^{-22} - 1.2 \times 10^{-22} = 0.8 \times 10^{-22}$ cc per molecule, is apparently empty space.

Per cent empty $= \dfrac{\text{volume empty}}{\text{volume available}} \times 100 = \dfrac{0.8 \times 10^{-22} \text{ cc}}{1.96 \times 10^{-22} \text{ cc}} \times 100$

$= 40\%$.

[*Note:* Only one significant figure permitted here.]

■ PROBLEM 275 The mercury atom has an effective radius of $1.51 \times 10^{-8}$ cm. If the density of liquid mercury is 13.55 g/cc at 20°C and if it is assumed liquid mercury consists of discrete spheres, what per cent of the liquid would have to be considered empty space?

ANSWER: 41%

PROBLEM 276 Liquid argon has a density of 1.40 g/cc at −186°C, which is its boiling point. Assuming that argon gas behaves as an ideal gas, calculate how much increase in volume occurs when one mole of argon passes from the liquid to the gaseous state at $-186°C$ and 760 Torr.

SOLUTION: (Calculate the volume occupied by one mole of argon in the liquid and compare it to the volume occupied by one mole of ideal gas under the conditions specified.)

Liquid argon has density 1.40 g/cc.

One mole argon weighs 39.948 g.

Volume of one mole liquid argon $= \dfrac{39.948 \text{ g/mole}}{1.40 \text{ g/cc}} = 28.5 \dfrac{\text{cc}}{\text{mole}}$.

An ideal gas at $-186°C$ (or $87°K$) and 760 Torr (or 1 atm) has a volume given by the equation of state $PV = nRT$. For one mole, the volume would be

$$V = \frac{nRT}{P} = \frac{(1)(0.08206)(87)}{1} = 7.1 \text{ l/mole}.$$

The increase in volume on going from liquid to gas is the difference between these two volumes, 7.1 l and 28.5 cc. The difference is $7.1 \text{ l} - 0.0285 = 7.1 \text{ l}$.

In other words, to the precision we can work with, the volume of the starting liquid is negligible.

■ PROBLEM 277   Suppose that 1.00 cc of liquid argon (density $= 1.40$ g/cc) is injected into a completely evacuated chamber of volume 368 cc. The temperature is kept at 25°C so all the argon evaporates. What will be the final pressure in the chamber?

ANSWER: **2.33 atm**

■ PROBLEM 278   Carbon monoxide, CO, and nitrogen, $N_2$, are supposed to have effective molecular radii of 1.56 Å and 1.58 Å, respectively. Assuming in the liquid they have the same per cent of free volume (empty space), what ratio would you expect between the density of liquid CO and that of liquid $N_2$ just below their boiling points?

ANSWER: **expect density of CO to be 1.04 times as great**

■ PROBLEM 279   You have a cylinder fitted with a piston. The chamber contains only water vapor and boiling water at the normal boiling point of $H_2O$. If you want 50.0% of the $H_2O$ molecules to be in each phase, what should be the relative volumes of the two phases? Assume ideal behavior for the gas; the density of liquid water at its normal boiling point is 0.958 g/cc.

ANSWER: gas:liquid = 1630:1

■■ PROBLEM 280   You have a capillary tube 10.0 cm long and 3.0 mm in internal diameter. It is sealed at one end. Working in the open lab at 760.0 Torr and 25°C you put 0.00050 cc of liquid mercury (density 13.55 g/cc) into the capillary and seal it up. The whole assembly is then put into a furnace at 425°C and heated until all the mercury evaporates. What would be the final pressure in the capillary, assuming ideal behavior?

ANSWER: 5.1 atm

## Vapor pressure of liquids

All liquids are volatile to some extent. This means that the space above a liquid will become saturated with the vapor corresponding to that liquid, so long as we have a closed system and wait long enough for equilibrium to be established. To a first approximation—that is, assuming ideal behavior—the evaporation of a liquid into a gas space does not depend on whether other gases are already there. Each liquid will evaporate as if into a vacuum. The actual partial pressure that can be built up in the vapor phase depends on the specific identity of the liquid and on its temperature. We have considered one example of this in the case of gases collected over water where the vapor pressure of the water depends only on the temperature of the water. It does not depend on what other gas is above the water nor on what volume of gas space there is above the water. The only requirement is that there be enough liquid water so that it can evaporate to fill the available space to the proper pressure and still have some liquid left over. There should be some liquid left over so that we can be sure the gas phase is saturated—that is, is in equilibrium with the excess liquid.

PROBLEM 281   A drop of water (0.050 cc) is injected into a 1.00-l box that was completely evacuated. If the temperature of the system is kept at 27°C, how much liquid water will be left when equilibrium is established? The density of liquid water at 27°C is 0.9965 g/cc. Assume ideal behavior of the gas.

SOLUTION: At 27°C the vapor pressure of water is 26.7 Torr.

This corresponds to (26.7/760), or 0.0351, atm.

At equilibrium, we need to have 1.00 l water vapor at $P$ = 0.0351 atm and $T$ = 273 + 27 = 300°K.

From the equation of state $PV = nRT$

$$n = \frac{PV}{RT} = \frac{(0.0351)(1.00)}{(0.08206)(300)} = 0.00143 \text{ mole } H_2O.$$

One mole $H_2O$ weighs 18.015 g.

0.00143 mole $H_2O$ weighs (0.00143 mole) $\left(18.015 \frac{g}{mole}\right)$ = 0.0258 g.

This 0.0258 g $H_2O$ came from evaporation of the liquid water, which has a density of 0.9965 g/cc.  So, in the evaporation we must have used up $\dfrac{0.0258 \text{ g}}{0.9965 \text{ g/cc}}$ , or 0.0259 cc.

We started with 0.050 cc liquid $H_2O$; we evaporated 0.0259 cc.

Therefore, we have left 0.050 − 0.0259 = 0.024 cc.

PROBLEM 282   A drop of water (0.050 cc) at 27°C is injected into a 1.00-l box that is filled with hydrogen at 745 Torr pressure.  If the temperature of the system is kept at 27°C, how much liquid water will be left when equilibrium is established?  The density of liquid water at 27°C is 0.9965 g/cc.  Assume ideal behavior of the gas.

SOLUTION: The solution to this problem is precisely the same as that shown for Problem 281.  The hydrogen gas initially present has no effect on the amount of water vapor it takes to fill the gas space.  In fact, the only effect of the hydrogen is to make longer the time required to reach equilibrium.

PROBLEM 283   A drop of water (0.050 cc) at 54°C is injected into a 1.00-l box that was completely evacuated.  If the temperature of the system is kept at 54°C, how much liquid water will be left when equilibrium is established?  The density of liquid water at 54°C is 0.9862 g/cc.  Assume ideal behavior of the gas.

SOLUTION: At 54°C the vapor pressure of water is 112.51 Torr.

This corresponds to a pressure of (112.51/760), or 0.148, atm.

$P$ = 0.148 atm; $V$ = 1.00 liter; $T$ = 273 + 54 = 327°K.

Substituting these values in the equation of state $PV = nRT$, we find

$$n = \frac{PV}{RT} = \frac{(0.148)(1.00)}{(0.08206)(327)} = 0.00552 \text{ mole } H_2O.$$

Since the weight of one mole $H_2O$ is 18.015 g, this corresponds to

$$(0.00552 \text{ mole}) \left( 18.015 \frac{g}{mole} \right) = 0.0994 \text{ g}.$$

As liquid water of density 0.9862 g/cc, this would amount to

$$\frac{0.0994 \text{ g}}{0.9862 \text{ g/cc}} = 0.101 \text{ cc}.$$

But we are given only 0.050 cc liquid water, whereas to fill the box to the required pressure needs 0.101 cc. The conclusion, then, is that all the liquid water will evaporate, and **none** is left over.

PROBLEM 284 What will be the pressure in the box at the end of the experiment described in Problem 283?

SOLUTION: We would need 0.101 cc liquid $H_2O$ to give the equilibrium vapor pressure of 112.5 Torr.
We are putting in 0.050 cc liquid $H_2O$.
Therefore, with complete evaporation we could only build up the pressure to $\dfrac{0.050}{0.101}$ of the saturation value.

Final pressure in the box $= \left( \dfrac{0.050}{0.101} \right) (112.5 \text{ Torr}) = \textbf{56 Torr.}$

■ PROBLEM 285 The equilibrium vapor pressure of ethyl alcohol is 40.0 mm Hg at 19.0°C. The density of liquid $C_2H_5OH$ is 0.789 g/cc at 19°C. What is the minimum number of cubic centimeters of liquid $C_2H_5OH$ you need to inject into a 1.00-l box to make sure the vapor phase becomes saturated with $C_2H_5OH$ at 19°C?

ANSWER: **0.128 cc**

PROBLEM 286 You have collected 38.9 cc of oxygen gas by ethyl alcohol displacement at 19°C. The temperature of the gas is 19°C; the barometric pressure is 757 Torr. At 19°C the vapor pressure of ethyl alcohol is 40.0 Torr. How many moles of $O_2$ have you collected?

SOLUTION: When a gas is collected over a liquid, the total pressure in the gas phase equals the sum of the partial pressure of the gas plus the vapor pressure of the liquid.

Total pressure = 757 Torr = $p_{O_2}$ + $p_{\text{ethyl alcohol}}$

At 19°C, the vapor pressure of ethyl alcohol = 40.0 Torr.

$p_{O_2}$ = 757 − 40.0 = 717 Torr, or 717/760 atm.

Volume of the $O_2$ = 38.9 cc, or 0.0389 l.

Temperature of the $O_2$ = 19°C, or 273 + 19 = 292°K.

From the equation of state $PV = nRT$

$$n = \frac{PV}{RT} = \frac{(717/760)(0.0389)}{(0.08206)(292)} = 0.00153 \text{ mole}$$

■ PROBLEM 287   You have 38.9 cc of oxygen gas collected over water at 19°C and a barometric pressure of 757 Torr. You now take this sample of oxygen, pass it through concentrated sulfuric acid to dry it, and then collect it over ethyl alcohol at 19°C and a barometric pressure of 757 Torr. The vapor pressure of ethyl alcohol at 19°C is 40.0 Torr. Assuming ideal behavior, what will be the final observed volume of your oxygen sample?

ANSWER: 40.2 cc

■ PROBLEM 288   You have collected 38.9 cc oxygen gas over ethyl alcohol at 19°C and a barometric pressure of 757 Torr. The sun beats down on your apparatus and the temperature of the whole assembly rises to 35°C. You trim up the leveling bulb again to match the liquid levels inside and outside your gas collector and, lo and behold, you now have 44.7 cc oxygen gas. What must be the vapor pressure of ethyl alcohol at 35°C, assuming ideal behavior? At 19°C, its vapor pressure is 40.0 Torr.

ANSWER: 99 Torr

■ PROBLEM 289   You are given a cylinder fitted with a movable piston, whereby 40.0 cc nitrogen gas has been trapped in contact with volatile liquid X at 23°C and total pressure 751 Torr. When you push the piston in so the pressure inside rises to 940 Torr, you find the volume of gas has been reduced to 29.9 cc still at 23°C. Assuming ideal behavior, what can you conclude about the vapor pressure of X?

ANSWER: 190 Torr at 23°C

## The Clausius-Clapeyron equation

The smaller the attractive forces between molecules of a liquid, the more likely the liquid is to be volatile. We should expect then that there will be a connection between the energy required to separate liquid molecules from each other and the degree of volatility. A quantitative measure of the energy required to separate liquid molecules from each other is the heat of evaporation—that is, the heat required to convert one mole of the liquid to one mole of the vapor. A quantitative measure of the degree of volatility is, of course, the vapor pressure of the liquid. So, we look for a relation between the heat of evaporation of a liquid and its vapor pressure. The relation will also need to involve the temperature because the temperature measures the average kinetic energy of the molecules, which after all is the source of the energy that overcomes the attractive forces in the evaporation process.

Such a relation, deducible from the first principles of thermodynamics, is the Clausius-Clapeyron equation. If ideal behavior is assumed in the gas phase, it has the form

$$\log p = \frac{-\Delta H}{4.576T} + C$$

where $p$ is the vapor pressure of the liquid at absolute temperature $T$, $\Delta H$ is the heat required to evaporate one mole, and $C$ is a constant which varies from liquid to liquid, depending also on the units used for pressure. For $p$ we shall use mm Hg (or Torr). $\Delta H$, which is read "delta aitch," is expressed in calories per mole. If we know the numerical values of $\Delta H$ and $C$, we should be able to calculate $p$ at any temperature $T$. Numerical values of $\Delta H$ and $C$ can be found in certain tables in the handbooks; they can also be determined by knowing the vapor pressure $p$ at two different temperatures.

PROBLEM 290 For liquid water, the vapor pressure is 17.535 Torr at 20.0°C and 55.324 Torr at 40.0°C. Calculate $\Delta H$ and $C$ from these data.

SOLUTION: (1) One set of conditions is $T = 20.0 + 273.15 = 293.2°K$, where $p = 17.535$ Torr. Substitute these numbers in the Clapeyron equation and get

$$\log p = -\frac{\Delta H}{4.576T} + C$$

$$\log (17.535) = -\frac{\Delta H}{(4.576)(293.2)} + C$$

$$1.2439 = -\frac{\Delta H}{1342} + C.$$

(2) The other set of conditions is $T = 40.0 + 273.15 = 313.2°K$, where $p = 55.324$ Torr. Substitute these in the equation and get

$$\log (55.324) = -\frac{\Delta H}{(4.576)(313.2)} + C$$

$$1.7429 = -\frac{\Delta H}{1433} + C$$

We have two simultaneous equations, (1) and (2), solve for $C$ in each case and set the results equal to each other:

$$1.2439 + \frac{\Delta H}{1342} = 1.7429 + \frac{\Delta H}{1433}$$

In this way we get $\Delta H = 10,500$ cal/mole and $C = 9.07$

PROBLEM 291 Using the constants calculated in Problem 290, what vapor pressure would you expect for liquid water at 30.0°C?

SOLUTION: For $H_2O$ the Clapeyron equation would have the form

$$\log p = \frac{-10,500}{4.576T} + 9.07$$

Substitute $T = 30°C = 30 + 273 = 303°K$.
Get $p = 31.4$ Torr.

■ PROBLEM 292 The measured vapor pressure of ethyl alcohol is 40.0 Torr at 19.0°C and 100.0 Torr at 34.9°C. Using the Clausius-Clapeyron equation, figure out how much heat would be required to evaporate one mole of ethyl alcohol in the temperature range 19.0 to 34.9°C.

ANSWER: **10,300 cal/mole**

■ **P R O B L E M  293**  The measured vapor pressure of ethyl alcohol is 100.0 Torr at 34.9°C and 400.0 Torr at 63.5°C. Using the Clausius-Clapeyron equation, calculate the molar heat of evaporation of ethyl alcohol in the temperature range 34.9 to 63.5°C.

ANSWER: **9990 cal/mole**

■ **P R O B L E M  294**  The measured vapor pressure of ethyl alcohol is 400.0 Torr at 63.5°C and 760.0 Torr at 78.4°C. Using the Clausius-Clapeyron equation, calculate the ideal molar heat of evaporation of ethyl alcohol in the temperature range 63.5 to 78.4°C.

ANSWER: **10,100 cal/mole**

■ **P R O B L E M  295**  A vapor pressure of 40.0 Torr is measured for carbon tetrachloride at 4.3°C and for carbon disulfide at −22.5°C. (The $CS_2$ is more volatile at a given temperature.) A vapor pressure of 100.0 Torr is measured for $CCl_4$ at 23.0°C and for $CS_2$ at −5.1°C. Compare the heats required to evaporate one mole of each of these liquids.

ANSWER: **8000 cal/mole** for $CCl_4$; **7000 cal/mole** for $CS_2$

> [*Note:* This answer is in the direction you predict. We generally assume that the more volatile liquid has the lower heat of evaporation.]

**P R O B L E M  296**  Acetone, $CH_3COCH_3$, shows a measured vapor pressure of 100 Torr at 7.7°C and 400 Torr at 39.5°C. At what temperature would you predict that its normal boiling point will occur? Assume $\Delta H$ to be a constant over the temperature range required and that behavior is ideal.

SOLUTION: Substituting the two sets of data into the Clapeyron equation, we solve for $\Delta H$ and $C$. We get 7600 cal/mole and 7.91, respectively. Then we feed these constants into the Clapeyron equation, getting

$$\log p = \frac{-7600}{4.576T} + 7.92$$

The normal boiling point is defined as the temperature at which the vapor pressure of the liquid reaches 1 atmosphere (760 Torr). So, we solve the above equation for $T$ after substituting $p = 760$ Torr. We find $T = 330°K$ (or $57°C$), which compares to the observed normal boiling point of $56.5°C$.

■ P R O B L E M  297  The vapor pressure of liquid sodium changes from 1.0 Torr at $439°C$ to 10.0 Torr at $549°C$. What is the heat of vaporization required per mole Na?

ANSWER: **24,300 cal/mole**

■ P R O B L E M  298  Using the data from Problem 297, calculate a predicted normal boiling point for liquid Na.

ANSWER: **886°C (observed value is 892°C)**

■■ P R O B L E M  299  Liquid nitrogen is a very useful refrigerant for low-temperature experiments. Its normal boiling point is $-195.8°C$; its vapor pressure is 400 Torr at $-200.9°C$. You can cool liquid nitrogen by pumping on it to reduce the pressure above the liquid. If you regulate your pump so as to keep this pressure at 30 Torr, to what temperature will the boiling nitrogen drop (and stay there)?

ANSWER: **57°K (or −216°C)**

■■ P R O B L E M  300  Liquid helium has a normal boiling point of $-268.6°C$. At this temperature, it takes 6.0 cal to evaporate a gram of helium from the liquid state to the gaseous state. Suppose you want to use a liquid helium bath to produce a temperature of $3.0°$ above absolute zero. To what pressure would you need to keep evacuated the space above the liquid helium?

ANSWER: **190 Torr**

# 8

## CALCULATIONS
## INVOLVING SOLIDS

THE MOST STRIKING FEATURE of the solid state is its regularity both in external appearance of crystals and in the internal ordering of the atoms. The types of calculations most frequently encountered are those which connect bulk properties such as density or chemical analysis with atomic models of the solid state.

### Unit cells

X-ray analysis of solids indicates that the atoms occupy regularly spaced positions in space. Strictly speaking, it is only the centers of the atoms that are located, because it is only an approximation to consider an atom as a rigid sphere touching other rigid spheres. However, this model of a solid as consisting of spheres in contact is useful in many respects, so we shall use it.

A *space lattice* represents the collection of points in space required to describe the atomic positions in the crystal. A *unit cell* is the smallest portion of this space lattice required to show the symmetry of the whole collection. Figure 57 shows the three kinds of unit cells encountered in the cubic system of crystals. The colored dots represent posi-

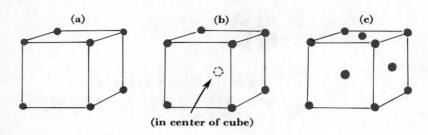

(in center of cube)

*Figure 57*

tions occupied by the centers of atoms or molecules relative to each other in space.  All three patterns are referred to as cubic but (a) is called simple cubic, (b) is body-centered cubic, and (c) is face-centered cubic.  The designation cubic comes from the fact that the edges of the unit cell are all equal in length and perpendicular to each other.

PROBLEM 301  How many atoms are there per unit cell in a simple cubic arrangement of atoms?

SOLUTION: The trick here is to recognize that a hard sphere with its center located at the corner of a cube has only $\frac{1}{8}$ of its volume inside the cube.  (The other $\frac{7}{8}$ of the sphere belongs to the other seven cubes which come together to share the same corner as the original cube.)  There are 8 corners to the cube, so with each of 8 spheres contributing $\frac{1}{8}$ of itself to the cube, there is $8 \times \frac{1}{8}$ or **one** sphere per cube.

PROBLEM 302  In a body-centered cubic arrangement of atoms, how many atoms are there per unit cell?

SOLUTION: As Figure 57b shows, there is 1 atom in the center of the cube as well as the 8 at the corners.  The 8 corner atoms each contribute $\frac{1}{8}$ of themselves to the unit cell, so there is a contribution of $8 \times \frac{1}{8}$ from this source.  The body-centered atom is, of course, entirely in the unit cell.  Thus, the total number of atoms per unit cell is **two.**

■ P R O B L E M  303 How many atoms are there per unit cell in a face-centered cubic arrangement?

ANSWER:  **four**

P R O B L E M  304 Suppose that atoms X, of radius $2.00 \times 10^{-8}$ cm, are packed in a simple cubic arrangement. If the atoms can be assumed to be rigid spheres in contact, what volume will be required to accommodate the Avogadro number of atoms X?

SOLUTION: In simple cubic arrangement, there is one atom per unit cell. If the spheres are in contact along the cube edge, the length of the edge will be $(2)(2.00 \times 10^{-8}$ cm), or $4.00 \times 10^{-8}$ cm.
The volume of this unit cell is $(4.00 \times 10^{-8})^3 = 6.4 \times 10^{-23}$ cc.
To accommodate $6.02 \times 10^{23}$ atoms we need

$$(6.02 \times 10^{23} \text{ atoms}) \left( 6.40 \times 10^{-23} \frac{\text{cc}}{\text{unit cell}} \right) \left( 1 \frac{\text{unit cell}}{\text{atom}} \right),$$

or  **38.6 cc.**

P R O B L E M  305 When hard spheres are shaken together in a box, they are very likely to pack with a face-centered cubic arrangement. Thus, it is not surprising that face-centered cubic is a commonly observed packing for atoms. Given in such a collection that the unit cell edge is $3.608 \times 10^{-8}$ cm in length, calculate what volume would be needed to take care of $6.02 \times 10^{23}$ atoms in face-centered cubic packing.

SOLUTION: The unit cell has volume of $(3.608 \times 10^{-8})^3$, or $4.697 \times 10^{-23}$ cc.
The unit cell in face-centered cubic contains 4 atoms.
Volume per atom is $\dfrac{4.697 \times 10^{-23} \text{ cc}}{4 \text{ atoms}}$, or $1.174 \times 10^{-23} \dfrac{\text{cc}}{\text{atom}}$.
For $6.02 \times 10^{23}$ atoms, we need

$$(6.02 \times 10^{23} \text{ atoms}) \left( 1.174 \times 10^{-23} \frac{\text{cc}}{\text{atom}} \right), \text{ or } 7.07 \text{ cc.}$$

P R O B L E M  306 In metallic silver, the silver atoms pack in a face-centered cubic arrangement. The unit cell edge is 4.078 Å. Calculate the density of metallic silver.

$D = \frac{M}{V}$

SOLUTION: Volume of one unit cell is $(4.078 \times 10^{-8} \text{ cm})^3$, or $6.782 \times 10^{-23}$ cc.

In face-centered cubic there are 4 atoms per unit cell, so we use $\dfrac{6.782 \times 10^{-23} \text{ cc}}{4 \text{ atoms}}$, or $1.696 \times 10^{-23}$ cc/atom.

For 1 mole of Ag atoms, we would have

$$(6.02 \times 10^{23} \text{ atoms}) \left(1.696 \times 10^{-23} \frac{\text{cc}}{\text{atom}}\right), \text{ or } 10.2 \text{ cc.}$$

One mole of Ag atoms weighs 107.87 grams.

$$\text{Density} = \frac{107.87 \text{ g}}{10.2 \text{ cc}} = 10.6 \text{ g/cc (observed value is } 10.5 \text{ g/cc).}$$

■ P R O B L E M  307    Sodium metal crystallizes in the body-centered cubic arrangement. If the unit cell edge is 4.24 Å, what would be the calculated density of sodium?

ANSWER: **1.00 g/cc** (observed value is 0.97 g/cc)

$7.62 \times 10^{\,.23} \dfrac{cc}{atom} = 3.81 \text{ cc/atom} = 2.29 \text{ cc}$

■ P R O B L E M  308    Aluminum crystallizes in the face-centered cubic arrangement. If the observed density of aluminum metal is 2.702 g/cc, what would you predict for the unit cell dimension?

ANSWER: **4.05 $\times$ 10$^{-8}$ cm** (observed value is 4.041 Å)

P R O B L E M  309    Gold crystallizes in the face-centered cubic arrangement; the observed unit cell length is 4.070 Å. If you can assume that gold consists of hard-sphere atoms in contact, what radius would you need to assign to a gold atom in the solid state?

SOLUTION: Figure 58 shows the five atoms that form one face of a face-centered cubic structure. The atom that lies at the center of the face touches each of the four atoms at the corners. The face of the cube (shown by dashed lines) is a square, for which the diagonal equals the diameter of the center atom plus twice the radius of the corner atoms. Since all the atoms are identical with the same $r$, we can say that the length of the diagonal is $2r + 2r$, or

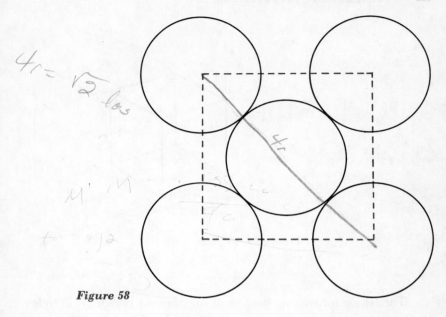

*Figure 58*

$4r$.  For any square, the length of its diagonal is $\sqrt{2}$ times the length of one side.  If the length of a side is 4.070 Å, and if $4r = \sqrt{2}$ (4.070), then $r = $ **1.439 Å**.

■ PROBLEM 310   Barium crystallizes with body-centered cubic structure.  Assuming a hard-sphere model, calculate the apparent radius of a barium atom based on the observation that the unit cell edge is 5.015 Å.

ANSWER: **2.172 Å**

When a unit cell has been properly defined, any operation which moves the unit cell along a direction parallel to one edge through a distance equal to the edge length should bring about coincidence with the same kinds of atoms.  As an example, in Figure 59, if we move the unit cell outlined in color to the right along the $x$-axis, then by moving the distance $a$, the edge 1–2 moves to coincide with edge 2–3.  Whatever was at 1 must also be at 2 and also at 3, if the unit cell is to be a proper unit cell.

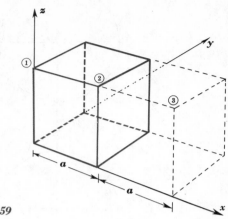

*Figure 59*

The reason for making the fuss of the previous paragraph is to lay the basis for choosing a proper unit cell for NaCl and for other ionic solids of this type. The unit cell of NaCl is *not* a simple cube containing $Na^+$ at four corners and $Cl^-$ at the other four corners, as shown in Figure 60a. Such a unit *cannot* be displaced through its own dimension to reproduce the structure (viz., a $Na^+$ would fall in a $Cl^-$ position and vice versa). A more proper unit cell for NaCl is shown in Figure 60b. The $Na^+$ ions by themselves form a face-centered cubic pattern,

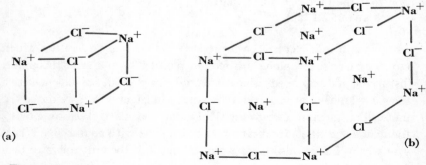

(a)

(b)

*Figure 60*

as do the $Cl^-$ ions by themselves. For this reason, NaCl is said to have a face-centered cubic structure. The edge length of the unit cell is twice the $Na^+$—to—$Cl^-$ distance, and there are four NaCl formula-units per unit cell.

PROBLEM 311 X-ray analysis shows that the unit cell length in NaCl is 5.628 Å. Calculate the density you expect on this basis. Avogadro number is $6.0225 \times 10^{23}$.

SOLUTION: The volume of the unit cell is $(5.628 \times 10^{-8}$ cm$)^3$, or $1.783 \times 10^{-22}$ cc.

There are four NaCl units per unit cell, so the volume per NaCl formula-unit is $\frac{1}{4}(1.783 \times 10^{-22})$, or $4.458 \times 10^{-23}$ cc.

For $6.0225 \times 10^{23}$ formula-units, the volume will be

$$(6.0225 \times 10^{23} \text{ formula-units}) \left(4.458 \times 10^{-23} \frac{cc}{\text{formula-unit}}\right),$$

or 26.85 cc.

One mole of NaCl weighs 58.44 g.

$$\text{Expected density} = \frac{58.44 \text{ g}}{26.85 \text{ cc}} = 2.177 \text{ g/cc}$$

(The observed density of NaCl is 2.165 g/cc.)

■ PROBLEM 312 In many solids the density observed experimentally is less than that calculated from the X-ray dimensions. The difference has been attributed to atoms missing from the structure. What per cent of the lattice points would need to be vacant of $Na^+$ and $Cl^-$ in order to account for the discrepancy between the expected and observed densities in Problem 311?

ANSWER: 0.55%

In the hexagonal system of crystals, an arrangement of atoms frequently encountered is that shown in Figure 61. The arrangement can be described as a hexagonal prism, where the top and bottom of the cell shown are regular hexagons and there are three atoms sandwiched in between. To make a space-filling model of this structure, which is called *hexagonal close-packed*, put a sphere on a flat surface and surround it in the same plane by six identical spheres as closely

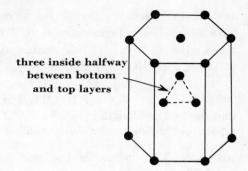

three inside halfway
between bottom
and top layers

*Figure 61*

as possible.  The pattern looks like the one shown in Figure 62.  Then put three other spheres over the first layer so that they fit snugly over the depressions marked X in Figure 62.  These represent a second layer.  Finally, cover with a third layer which is identical in relative position over the bottom layer.

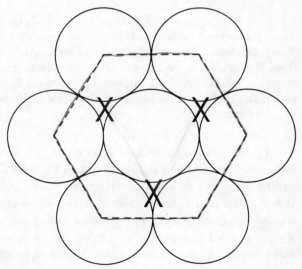

*Figure 62*

PROBLEM 313 How many atoms are there in the cell shown in Figure 61?

SOLUTION: The atoms in the center of the top and bottom faces are only half inside the cell, the other half belonging to neighboring cells. This gives us $2 \times \frac{1}{2} = 1$ atom.

The 3 atoms in the interior are completely in the cell, so this gives us 3 more atoms.

All the other atoms, of which there are 12 (6 on top and 6 on the bottom), are only one-sixth in our unit cell. You can visualize this by slicing an atom in two with a horizontal plane passing through its middle, then cutting the hemisphere into thirds by slicing downward with three cuts at 120° to each other. This gives us $12 \times \frac{1}{6} = 2$ atoms.

The total number of atoms in the cell is $1 + 3 + 2 = 6$.

PROBLEM 314 Suppose you have hard spheres of radius $r$ in contact with each other in hexagonal close-packing. For such hexagonal close-packing, what would be the volume of the unit cell shown in Figure 61, expressed in terms of $r$?

SOLUTION: You need to calculate the volume of a hexagonal prism.

The base of the prism is as shown in Figure 62, where each edge is equal to $2r$. By drawing the three diagonals of the hexagon, we can imagine the base to consist of six equilateral triangles of edge $2r$. The area of such a base is $6r^2\sqrt{3}$.

The height of the prism is just twice the height of a regular tetrahedron formed by spheres of radius $r$. The altitude of a tetrahedron of edge length $l$ is $(\sqrt{6}\,l)/3$. Here $l$ is $2r$, so the altitude would be $(2\sqrt{6}\,r)/3$. Thus, the height of the prism is $(4\sqrt{6}\,r)/3$.

The volume of the prism = area of base × height = $(6r^2\sqrt{3}) \times (4\sqrt{6}\,r)/3 = 24\sqrt{2}\,r^3$.

■ PROBLEM 315 Magnesium metal is very close to being a hexagonal close-packed array of atoms. X-ray studies show that the Mg-Mg distance is 3.203 Å. Using the results of Problems 313 and 314, calculate a predicted density for metallic magnesium.

ANSWER: 1.739 g/cc (observed density is 1.745 g/cc)

■ PROBLEM 316   Zinc   metal   approximates hexagonal close-packing of atoms.  The observed density of zinc is 7.14 g/cc.  What would you predict for the Zn-Zn distance?
ANSWER: 2.78 Å (observed spacing is 2.66 Å)

■ PROBLEM 317   The   two   atomic   arrangements that make the best utilization of space are the face-centered cubic and the hexagonal close-packed.  If you have identical hard-sphere atoms which pack one way or the other, in which case will the per cent empty space be greater?  [*Hint:* Calculate the volume of each unit cell.  Then calculate the volume actually filled by the atoms there are in each.]
ANSWER: both exactly the same at 25.94%

## Stoichiometry of solids

The chemical formula expresses the relative number of atoms of the different sorts present in a compound.  The crystal structure must be consistent with this chemical formula.

PROBLEM 318   You have a face-centered cubic arrangement of atoms in which the corner atoms are type A and those at the face-centers are type B.  What is the simplest formula of the compound in terms of A and B?

SOLUTION: In face-centered cubic there are 8 corner atoms, each contributing $\frac{1}{8}$ of itself to the unit cell.  So, our unit cell has $8 \times \frac{1}{8} = 1$ atom of A.
There are 6 face-center atoms, each contributing $\frac{1}{2}$ of itself to the unit cell.  So, our unit cell has $6 \times \frac{1}{2} = 3$ atoms of type B.
Thus, there are 3 atoms of B and 1 atom of A per unit cell, so the formula must be $AB_3$.

■ PROBLEM 319   You   have   a   mixed body-center cubic arrangement where all the corner atoms are type A and all the body-center atoms are type B.  What is the simplest formula?
ANSWER: AB

■ PROBLEM 320   Suppose you have a mixed hexagonal close-packed arrangement where the unit cell of

Figure 61 has all corner and face atoms of type A and all interior atoms of type B. What is the simplest formula?

ANSWER: **AB**

■ **PROBLEM** 321 Suppose you have a mixed hexagonal close-packed arrangement where, referring to the unit cell of Figure 61, the interior atoms are type A, the corner atoms are type B, and the atoms in the middle of the top and bottom faces are type C. What is the simplest formula?

ANSWER: $A_3B_2C$

■ **PROBLEM** 322 Suppose you had a face-centered cubic arrangement of A and B atoms where A atoms were at the corners of the unit cell and B atoms were at face-centers. Suppose in each unit cell, one of the A atoms was missing from one corner. What then would be the simplest formula of the compound?

ANSWER: $A_7B_{24}$

**PROBLEM** 323 Suppose you have an NaCl crystal characterized by the unit cell of Figure 60b except that two $Na^+$ ions at the ends of one diagonal of the cube have been pulled out and replaced by one $Ca^{++}$. What will be the chemical formula of the resulting material?

SOLUTION: Referring to Figure 60b, there are 8 corner $Na^+$ ions of which we lose 2. We have left only 6 corner $Na^+$, each contributing $\frac{1}{8}$ of itself to the unit cell. The net contribution from the corners is $6 \times \frac{1}{8}$, or $\frac{6}{8}Na^+$.

There are 6 face-centered $Na^+$, each belonging half to this unit cell. This gives us $6 \times \frac{1}{2}$, or $3Na^+$.

The total $Na^+$ per unit cell is 3 plus $\frac{6}{8}$.

Counting $Cl^-$ ions, there are 12 on the 12 edges, where each can contribute only $\frac{1}{4}$ to this unit cell. Thus, we have $12 \times \frac{1}{4} = 3Cl^-$ from the edges. In addition, there is one $Cl^-$ in full center of the unit cell, so we count it in its entirety.

The total $Cl^-$ per unit cell is $3 + 1 = 4$.

Finally, there is one $Ca^{++}$ at a corner position, so we count it as being $\frac{1}{8}$ in the cell.

The total picture is $\frac{1}{8}Ca^{++}$, $3\frac{6}{8}Na^+$, $4Cl^-$. We can write the formula as $Ca_{1/8}Na_{39/8}Cl_4$, or, multiplying through by 8, get **$CaNa_{30}Cl_{32}$**.

■ PROBLEM 324 Regarding the $Ca^{++}$ as an impurity in Problem 323, what per cent of the weight of the final material is due to calcium?

ANSWER: 2.15%

■ PROBLEM 325 Suppose that one of the $Cl^-$ ions on an edge of the NaCl unit cell shown in Figure 60b is replaced by a bromide ion. What per cent (by weight) of bromide impurity would this mean for the whole material?

ANSWER: 8.16%

## Defect solid state

The ideal crystal has a regular position for every atom and every atom is in its regular position. However, in practice there is no such thing as a perfect crystal with all atoms stacked up perfectly in identical matching planes. There are always some defects in the structure, and there is good theoretical reason to believe that some of these defects are inevitable in any real crystal. The most common kinds of defects are the following: (1) impurity atoms which are stuck in the structure in place of regular atoms; (2) misplaced atoms which do not fall at regular lattice sites but are squeezed in between normal sites—these are sometimes called *interstitial atoms;* and (3) missing atoms, or *lattice vacancies.* We have already seen some examples of these defects in preceding problems. For example, as shown in Problem 312, the density observed for a crystal is frequently *less* than that calculated on the basis of perfectly regular spacing—because some atoms may just be missing from their appropriate positions.

PROBLEM 326 Sodium bromide, NaBr, crystallizes in the NaCl structure with unit cell as shown in Figure 60b. If the observed unit cell length is 5.94 Å and if the observed density of NaBr is 3.203 g/cc, what fraction of the lattice sites might be empty?

SOLUTION: Unit cell length is $5.94 \times 10^{-8}$ cm.
Volume of unit cell is $(5.94 \times 10^{-8} \text{ cm})^3$, or $2.10 \times 10^{-22}$ cc.
There are four NaBr formula-units per unit cell.

Volume per formula-unit is $\dfrac{2.10 \times 10^{-22} \text{ cc}}{4} = 5.25 \times 10^{-23} \text{ cc.}$

Volume per $6.02 \times 10^{23}$ formula-units is $(6.02 \times 10^{23})(5.25 \times 10^{-23})$
$= 31.6$ cc.

One mole NaBr weighs 102.90 g.

Expected density is $\dfrac{102.90 \text{ g}}{31.6 \text{ cc}} = 3.26 \text{ g/cc.}$

Observed density is 3.203 g/cc.

% of sites that are unoccupied $= \dfrac{(3.26 - 3.20)}{3.26} \times 100 = 2\%.$

PROBLEM 327  When alkali halides such as NaBr are heated in Na vapor, they get colored and take on additional Na to produce compounds which are nonstoichiometric—that is, compounds in which atomic ratios are not given by simple whole numbers. It has been assumed that the take-up of additional Na comes about by having the added $Na \rightarrow Na^+ + e^-$, where the $Na^+$ then sits on a vacant $Na^+$ site and the $e^-$ sits on a vacant $Br^-$ site. If the crystal in Problem 326 takes on the maximum amount of Na in this way, what would be the formula of the material formed?

SOLUTION: Suppose we take the initial crystal to have 100 $Na^+$ and 100 $Br^-$ sites. Problem 326 tells us that 2% of these sites are empty. This means that 2 $Na^+$ sites are empty and 2 $Br^-$ sites are empty. So, although there are 100 $Na^+$ and 100 $Br^-$ positions, only 98 of each are occupied. We could write our initial crystal as $Na_{98}Br_{98}$.

Now we add enough Na to fill up the vacant $Na^+$ sites. This means we put 2 additional $Na^+$ ions and 2 $e^-$'s into the crystal.

The total number of $Na^+$ ions is now 100, because every $Na^+$ site is occupied by a $Na^+$ ion. However, the number of $Br^-$ ions in the crystal is 98, since we have added no $Br^-$, but only $e^-$.

Thus, the formula of the final crystal is $Na_{100}Br_{98}$, or $NaBr_{0.98}$, or $Na_{1.02}Br$.

PROBLEM 328  For the crystal of Na-added NaBr prepared in Problem 327, calculate the number of electrons per cubic centimeter sitting on $Br^-$ sites. Assume the unit cell length has not changed.

SOLUTION: One mole $NaBr_{0.98}$ weighs 101.30 g.
Its volume is 31.6 cc (from Problem 516).
It contains 0.02 mole of $e^-$ on $Br^-$ sites.
This amounts to $(0.02 \text{ mole})(6.02 \times 10^{23})\ e^-$, or $1 \times 10^{22}\ e^-$.

Therefore, the electron density is $\dfrac{1 \times 10^{22}\ e^-}{31.6 \text{ cc}} = 3 \times 10^{20}\ e^-/\text{cc}$.

■ PROBLEM 329    Titanium    monoxide, TiO, crystallizes with the same structure as NaCl. The same unit cell as shown in Figure 60b can be used except that each $Na^+$ is to be replaced by a $Ti^{++}$ and each $Cl^-$ by $O^=$. By X-ray analysis the unit cell length of TiO is found to be 4.235 Å. The measured density is 4.93 g/cc. What per cent of the sites are presumably vacant?

ANSWER: 12%

■ PROBLEM 330    When the TiO mentioned in Problem 329 is gently heated in low-pressure oxygen, the empty $O^=$ sites get filled up by taking up oxygen atoms. What would be the formula of the new material formed, if all the empty oxygen sites were so filled up?

ANSWER: $TiO_{1.14}$

■■ PROBLEM 331    Silver bromide is very unusual because not only are some of the $Ag^+$ and $Br^-$ sites vacant as discussed above but also some of the $Ag^+$ ions are found to have been moved from their normal sites to interstitial sites. Given that AgBr crystallizes with the NaCl structure and that its unit cell length is 5.755 Å, calculate the density of an AgBr crystal in which 1.24% of the $Ag^+$ sites and 1.14% of the $Br^-$ sites are vacant and 0.10% of the $Ag^+$ ions are in interstitial positions.

ANSWER: 6.47 g/cc

# 9

# THERMOCHEMISTRY

THE FIELD of thermochemistry includes two important types of problems: (1) what temperature change occurs when a certain amount of heat is added to a substance? and (2) what heat effects occur when substances undergo chemical change?

## Specific heat

"Specific heat" is commonly defined as the number of calories of heat which need to be added to 1 gram of a substance in order to raise its temperature by 1°C. (If you really want to be fussy, the above is a definition of "thermal capacity," and you should define specific heat as a unitless quantity which tells the ratio of the thermal capacity of a substance to the thermal capacity of water. However, very few chemists stick with the exact definition, and since the term "specific" is now generally taken to mean per gram or per some other given unit, to take specific heat to mean "per gram" is acceptable.) At any rate, we shall refer to specific heat in terms of "calories per gram per degree." The *calorie* is defined as the amount of heat needed to warm up 1 gram of $H_2O$ from 14.5 to 15.5°C. In practice, it turns out that the specific heat of water is 1.00 cal per g deg all the way from 0 to 100°C.

The specific heat of an element or a compound is a characteristic property of the element or compound. Its numerical value depends on how the added heat gets distributed among the various forms of kinetic energy, such as vibrational motion. This in turn depends on the masses of the atoms involved and their bonding. Many years ago, before much was known about the structure of materials, it was recognized as an experimental fact that, for many solid elements, especially at higher temperatures, the "specific heat" times the "atomic weight" is about equal to 6.3. This law is frequently referred to as the law of Dulong and Petit, and the value 6.3, as the Dulong and Petit constant.

**PROBLEM** 332   If it takes 9.98 cal to heat a chunk of gold weighing 18.69 g from 10.0 to 27.0°C, what is the specific heat of gold?

SOLUTION: It takes 9.98 cal for 18.69 g.

Per gram the required heat is $\dfrac{9.98 \text{ cal}}{18.69 \text{ g}} = 0.534 \dfrac{\text{cal}}{\text{g}}$ .

But this takes it from 10.0 to 27.0°C, a rise of 17.0°C.

Per degree, the rise would be $\dfrac{0.534 \text{ cal/g}}{17.0 \text{ deg}} = \textbf{0.0314 cal/g deg}$ .

[*Note:* Both the "gram" and the "degree" are in the denominator.]

**PROBLEM** 333   If the specific heat of nickel is 0.1146 cal/g deg, how much heat would you need to take a 168-g slug of nickel from $-18.6$ to $+57.2$°C?

SOLUTION: The increase in temperature is 75.8°.
The weight of the sample is 168 g.

Therefore, the heat required $= \left( 0.1146 \dfrac{\text{cal}}{\text{g deg}} \right) (75.8 \text{ deg}) (168 \text{ g})$

$= \textbf{1.46 kcal}$ .

**PROBLEM** 334   A stick of molybdenum weighing 237 g and starting at a temperature of 100.0°C is thrust into 244-g $H_2O$ starting at 10.0°C. If the final observed temperature of the whole system is 15.3°C, what would be the specific heat of molybdenum?

SOLUTION: The heat gained by the water on warming up equals the heat loss by the molybdenum on cooling.

Heat gained by $H_2O$ = (specific heat)(mass)(temperature change)

$$= \left(1.00 \frac{cal}{g \ deg}\right)(244 \ g)(15.3° - 10.0°) = 1300 \ cal.$$

Heat lost by Mo = (specific heat)(mass)(temperature change) = (sp. heat of Mo)(237 g)(100.0° − 15.3°) = 1300 cal, also.

$$\text{Specific heat of Mo} = \frac{1300 \ cal}{(237 \ g)(84.7 \ deg)} = 0.065 \frac{cal}{g \ deg}.$$

■ **PROBLEM 335** A chunk of metal X weighing 27.3 g is heated to 98.9°C and then dropped into 15.0 cc $H_2O$ at 25.00°C. If the final temperature of the whole system becomes 29.87°C, what is the specific heat of X?

ANSWER: **0.0388 cal/g deg**

■ **PROBLEM 336** A piece of zinc weighing 13.8 g and initially at 99.3°C is dropped into 15.0 cc $H_2O$ at 25.00°C. Given that the specific heat of zinc is 0.0925 cal/g deg, what will be the final temperature of the system?

ANSWER: **30.8°C**

■■ **PROBLEM 337** $BaSO_4$, an insoluble solid, has a specific heat of 0.111 cal/g deg. $Al_2O_3$, another insoluble solid, has a specific heat of 0.174 cal/g deg. A 1.00-g mixture, containing only $BaSO_4$ and $Al_2O_3$, is heated to 100.00°C and then poured into 15.00 g $H_2O$ initially at 24.78°C. If the final temperature of the system becomes 25.55°C, what is the per cent composition of the original solid mixture?

ANSWER: **30% $BaSO_4$ and 70% $Al_2O_3$**

**PROBLEM 338** An unknown metal X has a measured specific heat of 0.0408 cal/g deg. What would you estimate for its atomic weight?

SOLUTION: The Dulong and Petit law says (sp. heat)(at. wt.) = 6.3.

So, at. wt. $= \dfrac{6.3}{\text{sp. heat}} = \dfrac{6.3}{0.0408} = 150.$

■ **PROBLEM 339** What would you predict for the specific heat of uranium?

ANSWER: **0.026 cal/g deg** (observed value is 0.028 cal/g deg)

■ PROBLEM 340   For the Group I elements, Li, Na, K, Rb, and Cs, the specific heats are 0.79, 0.295, 0.18, 0.0802, and 0.0502 cal/g deg, respectively.   Calculate the Dulong and Petit constant for each of these elements.

ANSWER:   **5.5, 6.78, 7.0, 6.85, 6.67**

■ PROBLEM 341   For the element magnesium, the specific heat has been measured at several temperatures as follows: 0.177 at −150°C, 0.203 at −100°C, 0.223 at −50°C, 0.232 at 0°C, 0.257 at 100°C, and 0.279 at 300°C.   Calculate the Dulong and Petit constant as a function of temperature.

ANSWER: **4.30, 4.94, 5.42, 5.64, 6.25, 6.78**

### Heat of fusion

When a substance melts, it takes a certain amount of heat to convert it from the solid state to the liquid state.   This heat is generally specified at the normal melting point and is called the *heat of fusion* or the *heat of melting*.   It can be calculated and presented either per gram or, more meaningfully, per mole.   If per mole, it is called the *molar heat of fusion*.

PROBLEM 342   It takes 79.71 cal to melt 1 g $H_2O$.   What is the molar heat of fusion of $H_2O$?

SOLUTION: One mole $H_2O$ weighs 18.015 g.

If it takes 79.71 cal to melt 1 g, it will take $\left(79.71 \dfrac{cal}{g}\right)\left(18.015 \dfrac{g}{mole}\right)$ or 1436 cal to melt 18.015 g.

Thus, the molar heat of fusion of $H_2O$ is **1.436 kcal/mole.**

■ PROBLEM 343   The molar heat of fusion of NaCl is 6.8 kcal/mole.   How much heat does it take to melt 0.278 g NaCl?

ANSWER: **32 cal**

The amount of heat required to melt one mole of material is equal numerically to the amount of heat liberated when one mole of material is frozen or solidified.   Thus, we sometimes talk about *heat of freezing* or *heat of solidification*.   Because heat of fusion needs to be *added* to the system, whereas heat of freezing comes *out of* the system to the surroundings, we say that these are of opposite sign. However, they are of equal magnitude.

P R O B L E M  344  If the heat of fusion of $H_2O$ is $+1.436$ kcal/mole, what is the molar heat of freezing of $H_2O$?

SOLUTION: To go from 1 mole solid $H_2O$ to 1 mole liquid $H_2O$ requires 1.436 kcal from the surroundings.

If we reverse the process and go from 1 mole liquid $H_2O$ to 1 mole solid $H_2O$, we give up to the surroundings 1.436 kcal. Thus, if we assign a $(+)$ sign to the take-up of heat, we give a $(-)$ sign for the evolution of heat.

Therefore, the molar heat of freezing of $H_2O$ is **$-1.436$ kcal/mole**.

The question of sign $(+$ or $-)$ for a heat effect is apt to be very confusing because there are two major ways of indicating heat changes, one writing it as a chemical change and the other writing it as a change in a property. For example, the fact that one mole of solid $H_2O$ absorbs 1.436 kcal of heat in being converted to one mole of liquid $H_2O$ can be represented as

$$H_2O_{(s)} + 1.436 \text{ kcal} \rightarrow H_2O_{(l)}$$

where the 1.436 kcal is treated like a chemical reagent that is used up in the change from left to right. (We don't need to say 1.436 kcal "per mole" because we are reading the whole equation in terms of moles.) But anything appearing on the left side of a chemical equation can be moved over to the right side provided the algebraic sign is reversed. In other words, the above fusion reaction can also be written

$$H_2O_{(s)} \rightarrow H_2O_{(l)} - 1.436 \text{ kcal}$$

where the 1.436 kcal appears as a negative reagent on the right.

■P R O B L E M  345  Given that the molar heat of fusion of NaCl is 6.8 kcal/mole, write the fusion process as a chemical equation.

ANSWER: $NaCl_{(s)} + 6.8 \text{ kcal} \rightarrow NaCl_{(l)}$

or

$$NaCl_{(s)} \rightarrow NaCl_{(l)} - 6.8 \text{ kcal}$$

So, we have one obvious source of trouble: The heat shows up as a (+) or (−), depending on which side of the equation we put it on. Difficulties from this source can be minimized if we agree to try to keep the heat on the side where it has the (+) sign. In other words, for Problem 535, the first way of writing the answer

$$NaCl_{(s)} + 6.8 \text{ kcal} \rightarrow NaCl_{(l)}$$

is preferred, and this is always the case if the heat is to be treated as a reagent used up or formed in the course of the chemical change considered.

■ PROBLEM 346 Including the heat effect, write the chemical equation for the process one mole liquid NaCl going to one mole solid NaCl.

ANSWER: $NaCl_{(l)} \rightarrow NaCl_{(s)} + 6.8 \text{ kcal}$

Note there is no ambiguity here. When we go from left to right, 6.8 kcal is produced as a product and gets liberated by the system to the surroundings. The ambiguity comes in if we do not write the equation and if we do not consider the heat as a reagent. Then we have to decide how we are going to distinguish liberation of heat from consumption of heat. The problem becomes crucial when, as frequently done, the chemical change is written as a chemical equation but the heat effect is indicated separately to the side. In such cases, you need a strict rule to follow and it is this: "A heat effect is considered positive if heat is absorbed *by the system*." The rationale for this is that there is a property called the "heat content" (or enthalpy), symbolized by $H$, which can be used to describe a system. If the system absorbs heat, its heat content increases. The change in heat content is usually designated as $\Delta H$, which you read "delta aitch," and frequently it is given alongside the chemical equation. For example,

$$NaCl_{(s)} \rightarrow NaCl_{(l)}; \Delta H = +6.8 \text{ kcal}$$

or

$$NaCl_{(l)} \rightarrow NaCl_{(s)}; \Delta H = -6.8 \text{ kcal}$$

Obviously, there may be troubles. To minimize them, remember a positive $\Delta H$ means heat absorbed by the system and a negative $\Delta H$

means heat evolved to the surroundings. $\Delta H$ is a molar quantity and applies if the chemical equation is read in moles.

■PROBLEM 347   What is the $\Delta H$ for the conversion of one mole solid $H_2O$ to liquid $H_2O$?

ANSWER: $\Delta H = +1.436$ kcal

■PROBLEM 348   It takes 11.6 cal to melt 1 g silver bromide, AgBr. What is the $\Delta H$ for the process

$$AgBr_{(s)} \rightarrow AgBr_{(l)}$$

and is heat evolved or absorbed in the process?

ANSWER: $\Delta H = +2.18$ kcal; heat is **absorbed** by the system

■PROBLEM 349   It takes 30.3 cal to melt 1 g benzene, $C_6H_6$. Calculate the $\Delta H$ for the process

$$C_6H_{6(l)} \rightarrow C_6H_{6(s)}$$

and tell whether heat is evolved or absorbed in the process.

ANSWER: $\Delta H = -2.37$ kcal; heat is **evolved** to the surroundings

## Heat of evaporation

It takes heat to convert one mole of a substance from a condensed phase, such as liquid or solid, to the gas phase. For liquids, the quantity is called the molar *heat of evaporation* (or heat of vaporization) and is generally quoted at the normal boiling point of the liquid. For solids, the heat required to convert one mole to the vapor is frequently called *heat of sublimation*, although heat of evaporation is also acceptable. For solids, the heat of evaporation can be quoted at almost any temperature, so it is usual to specify at what pressure the gas formed will be. The amount of heat required is, of course, characteristic of the material, but also it depends on the pressure of the gas phase produced.

Heat effects associated with vaporization can be indicated by writing a chemical equation in which heat is a reactant or product, or by specifying the $\Delta H$ associated with the given change. For example, for $H_2O$, where it takes 9.717 kcal to convert one mole of liquid $H_2O$ into one mole of gaseous $H_2O$ at 1 atm pressure, we can write either

$$9.717 \text{ kcal} + H_2O_{(l)} \rightarrow H_2O_{(g,\, p=1 \text{ atm})}$$

or

$$H_2O_{(l)} \rightarrow H_2O_{(g,\, p=1 \text{ atm})};\ \Delta H = +9.717 \text{ kcal}$$

PROBLEM 350  If it takes 9.717 kcal to evaporate one mole liquid $H_2O$ at the normal boiling point to gas at 1 atm, how much heat would be required to do this for 1.00 g $H_2O$?

SOLUTION: One mole of $H_2O$ weighs 18.015 g.
To evaporate one mole $H_2O$ requires 9.717 kcal.
Therefore, for 1.00 g it takes $\dfrac{9.717 \text{ kcal/mole}}{18.015 \text{ g/mole}} = \mathbf{0.5394\ kcal.}$

■ PROBLEM 351  It takes 10.77 kcal to evaporate one mole liquid $H_2O$ to gas at 4.58 mm Hg pressure.  How much heat is needed to do this for 1.00 g $H_2O$?
ANSWER: **0.5978 kcal**

PROBLEM 352  How many calories of heat would you have available if you took 1.00 l steam ($T = 373°K$, $p = 1.00$ atm) and condensed it to liquid $H_2O$ at 100°C?  Assume ideal behavior.

SOLUTION: (From Problem 350 we know that under these conditions the heat of evaporation is 9.717 kcal/mole.  All we have to do is to figure out how many moles are condensed under these conditions.)
The general gas law says $PV = nRT$.
$$n = \frac{PV}{RT} = \frac{(1.00)(1.00)}{(0.08206)(373)} = 0.0327 \text{ mole.}$$
If it takes 9.717 kcal to evaporate one mole $H_2O$, the same heat must be liberated when one mole condenses.
If we get 9.717 kcal liberated on condensation of one mole, then with 0.0327 mole we liberate

$$(0.0327 \text{ mole}) \left( 9.717 \frac{\text{kcal}}{\text{mole}} \right) = 0.318 \text{ kcal} = \mathbf{318\ cal.}$$

■ PROBLEM 353  In a given experiment in which solid iodine, $I_2$, is converted at 25°C to gas at 0.31 Torr, we find that it takes 4.09 cal to evaporate 69.7 mg iodine.   Calculate the molar heat of sublimation of $I_2$ under these conditions.

ANSWER: **14.9 kcal/mole**

■ PROBLEM 354   Very pure sulfur can be made by condensing $S_8$ at 0.0047 Torr to the solid state at 95.4°C. Given that $\Delta H = +3.01$ kcal for

$$S_{8(s)} \rightarrow S_{8(g, p=0.0047\ \text{Torr})}$$

calculate the amount of heat given up to the surface on which condensation occurs if 0.437 g pure sulfur is prepared this way.

ANSWER: **5.13 cal**

■ PROBLEM 355   A red-hot iron poker (868 g at 600°C) is thrust into liquid water at 100°C.   Given that the specific heat of iron is 0.13 cal/g deg in this range, calculate how many grams of steam should be formed at 1 atm pressure.   At 1 atm the molar heat of evaporation of water is 9.717 kcal.

ANSWER: **$1.0 \times 10^2$ g**

## Heat of reaction

The amount of heat produced or consumed in a chemical reaction is called the "heat of reaction," and it can be shown either as a heat term in the chemical equation or by giving the $\Delta H$ for the chemical change as written.   Because the heat change associated with a reaction is affected by the state of the materials—whether solid, liquid, or gas—you should be careful in writing the chemical equations to indicate by $(s)$, $(l)$, or $(g)$ what the state is for each material.   The heat of reaction generally quoted is for molar quantities and is applicable when the accompanying chemical equation is read off in moles.   For example,

$$2H_{2(g)} + O_{2(g)} \rightarrow 2H_2O_{(g)};\ \Delta H = -115.60\ \text{kcal}$$

means the following; two moles of gaseous hydrogen react with one mole of gaseous oxygen to produce two moles of gaseous water and liberate 115.60 kcal in the process.

PROBLEM 356 Using the data just given, calculate how much heat will be liberated when 1.00 g hydrogen reacts as in the above equation.

SOLUTION: The equation tells us that when two moles $H_2$ are used up, 115.60 kcal heat is liberated.

Per mole, the heat liberated is $\dfrac{115.60 \text{ kcal}}{2 \text{ moles } H_2} = 57.80$ kcal.

One mole $H_2$ weighs 2.016 g.

1.00 g $H_2$ is $\dfrac{1.00 \text{ g}}{2.016 \text{ g/mole}} = 0.496$ mole $H_2$.

If we are to use up 0.496 mole of $H_2$ and the heat liberated is 57.80 kcal/mole $H_2$, the total heat liberated will be the product of these two:

$$(0.496 \text{ mole}) \left( 57.80 \frac{\text{kcal}}{\text{mole}} \right) = 28.7 \text{ kcal}.$$

■ PROBLEM 357 When 1.00 g Pb reacts by the reaction

$$2Pb_{(s)} + O_{2(g)} \rightarrow 2PbO_{(s)}$$

253 cal of heat are evolved to the surroundings. What is the $\Delta H$ for the reaction as it is written?

ANSWER: $\Delta H = -105$ kcal

■ PROBLEM 358 How many calories of heat are absorbed from the surroundings when 1.00 g Pb reacts by the following reaction:

$$Pb_{(s)} + O_{2(g)} \rightarrow PbO_{2(s)}; \Delta H = -66.12 \text{ kcal}$$

ANSWER: (This is a trick question. Heat is not absorbed from the surroundings but is evolved to them by the reaction. Therefore, to answer the question we need a minus sign to indicate that the direction of heat transfer is opposite to that asked.)   $-319.1$ cal

Although the term heat of reaction is generally applicable to any change for which the chemical equation is specified, there are some special types of reaction for which heats take on special names. For example, the heat liberated by the reaction A + B → AB, where AB is a compound formed from the elements A and B, is called the *heat of formation*. In fact, if we are told that the heat of formation of compound X is so much, then we understand it to mean that we form X from the component elements in their standard (or commonly referred to) states and we liberate the heat specified. Thus, if we are told that the heat of formation of $CaCO_{3(s)}$ is 288.45 kcal/mole, we can refer this to the elemental states $Ca_{(s)}$, $C_{(s)}$, $O_{2(g)}$ from which $CaCO_3$ can be considered to be derived and can write an appropriate equation which would be

$$Ca_{(s)} + C_{(s)} + \tfrac{3}{2}O_{2(g)} \rightarrow CaCO_{3(s)}; \Delta H = -288.45 \text{ kcal}$$

If you want to get rid of the fraction, you can double the whole equation, but then you must double $\Delta H$ also.

■ **PROBLEM 359** The heat of formation of solid $KClO_3$ is 93.50 kcal/mole. The standard states for the component elements are $K_{(s)}$, $Cl_{2(g)}$, and $O_{2(g)}$. Write an appropriate equation and $\Delta H$ for forming $KClO_3$.

ANSWER: $K_{(s)} + \tfrac{1}{2}Cl_{2(g)} + \tfrac{3}{2}O_{2(g)} \rightarrow KClO_{3(s)}$;
$\Delta H = -93.50 \text{ kcal}$

Another special kind of reaction is the combustion reaction in which a compound, generally a hydrocarbon or derivative thereof, is oxidized by $O_2$ to form $CO_{2(g)}$, $H_2O_{(g)}$, and perhaps other products (e.g., $N_{2(g)}$ if N is one of the elements in the compound). Again, there is a special name for the associated heat of reaction and it is called *heat of combustion*. There are extended tables in the handbooks which list heats of combustion in tabular form giving the formula of the compound, its state, and the number of kilocalories in the combustion reaction. For example, you might be told that the heat of combustion of acetaldehyde, $CH_3CHO$, in its liquid state is 279.0 kcal. Immediately, you can write the chemical equation for the combustion reaction, since it is assumed the products are $CO_{2(g)}$ and $H_2O_{(g)}$ [and $N_{2(g)}$ if necessary]. You supply the $O_{2(g)}$ and the coefficients for the equation

$$CH_3CHO_{(l)} + \tfrac{5}{2}O_{2(g)} \rightarrow 2CO_{2(g)} + 2H_2O_{(g)}; \Delta H = -279.0 \text{ kcal}$$

PROBLEM 360  How much heat would be liberated by burning 1.00 g liquid $CH_3CHO$ as in the equation just given?

SOLUTION: The equation tells us 279.0 kcal is liberated when one mole $CH_3CHO$ is burned.

One mole $CH_3CHO$ weighs 44.05 g.

1.00 g $CH_3CHO$ is $\dfrac{1.00 \text{ g}}{44.05 \text{ g/mole}}$ = 0.0227 mole.

If burning of one mole liberates 279.0 kcal, then burning 0.0227 mole will liberate

$$(0.0227 \text{ mole}) \left(279.0 \ \frac{\text{kcal}}{\text{mole}}\right) = \textbf{6.33 kcal.}$$

■ PROBLEM 361  The heat of combustion of solid sucrose, $C_{12}H_{22}O_{11}$, is 1349.6 kcal/mole. How much heat would be liberated by burning a 12.0-g lump of sucrose?
ANSWER: **47.3 kcal**

■ PROBLEM 362  Given that the heat of combustion of solid urea, $(NH_2)_2CO$, is 151.6 kcal/mole. What is the $\Delta H$ for the combustion reaction per mole $O_2$ consumed?
ANSWER: **−101.1 kcal**

## Hess's law

This law summarizes the observation that the amount of heat liberated or absorbed in a chemical change is the same whether the change occurs in one step or in several consecutive steps. In other words, once the initial state and final state are specified, the heat change is fixed and does not depend on how we go from the initial state to the final state. In practice, Hess's law is important, because it means that we can evaluate indirectly heats of reaction which perhaps are difficult to measure in a direct experiment. We can do this because, just as chemical equations can be added together (or subtracted), their heat changes can also be added (or subtracted).

The following shows how the Hess law works. We have been told that the heat of formation of $CaCO_{3(s)}$ is 288.45 kcal. This means we can write the chemical equation, including the heat effect, as follows:

$$Ca_{(s)} + C_{(s)} + \tfrac{3}{2}O_{2(g)} \rightarrow CaCO_{3(s)} + 288.45 \text{ kcal}$$

However, the reaction as written is very hard to study directly, and it is much more practical to examine the following set of reactions:

$$Ca_{(s)} + \tfrac{1}{2}O_{2(g)} \rightarrow CaO_{(s)} + 151.85 \text{ kcal}$$

$$C_{(s)} + O_{2(g)} \rightarrow CO_{2(g)} + 94.05 \text{ kcal}$$

$$CaO_{(s)} + CO_{2(g)} \rightarrow CaCO_{3(s)} + 42.55 \text{ kcal}$$

If we just add up these equations, keeping to the left and to the right of the arrow each of the molar quantities as it appears, then we get

$$\begin{pmatrix} Ca_{(s)} + \tfrac{3}{2}O_{2(g)} + C_{(s)} \\ + CaO_{(s)} + CO_{2(g)} \end{pmatrix} \rightarrow \begin{pmatrix} CaO_{(s)} + CO_{2(g)} + CaCO_{3(s)} \\ + 151.85 \text{ kcal} + 94.05 \text{ kcal} \\ + 42.55 \text{ kcal} \end{pmatrix}$$

Cancelling those items which are duplicated on left and right, we get

$$Ca_{(s)} + \tfrac{3}{2}O_{2(g)} + C_{(s)} \rightarrow CaCO_{3(s)} + 288.45 \text{ kcal}$$

which is the over-all reaction we wish to study.

The above sequence is not unique in leading to the final equation. For example, another possible set, which adds up to the same over-all equation, is the following:

$$Ca_{(s)} + 2C_{(s)} \rightarrow CaC_{2(s)} + 15.0 \text{ kcal}$$
$$CaC_{2(s)} + \tfrac{5}{2}O_{2(g)} \rightarrow CaCO_{3(s)} + CO_{2(g)} + 367.5 \text{ kcal}$$
$$\underline{94.05 \text{ kcal} + CO_{2(g)} \rightarrow C_{(s)} + O_{2(g)}}$$
$$Ca_{(s)} + C_{(s)} + \tfrac{3}{2}O_{2(g)} \rightarrow CaCO_{3(s)} + 288.4 \text{ kcal}$$

Note that in this sequence the reaction for the formation of $CO_2$ occurs in the reverse sense as the third step.

**PROBLEM 363** Calculate the heat evolved in the formation of one mole $PbSO_{4(s)}$ from its elements, given the following:

$$Pb_{(s)} + S_{(s)} \rightarrow PbS_{(s)} + 22.54 \text{ kcal}$$

$$PbS_{(s)} + 2O_{2(g)} \rightarrow PbSO_{4(s)} + 196.96 \text{ kcal}$$

SOLUTION: Add the two equations, cancel the $PbS_{(s)}$ which will appear on both sides, and the result is

$$Pb_{(s)} + S_{(s)} + 2O_{2(g)} \rightarrow PbSO_{4(s)} + 219.50 \text{ kcal}$$

So, the heat evolved in the formation of one mole $PbSO_{4(s)}$ is **219.50 kcal.**

**PROBLEM 364** Given that $\Delta H$ of formation of $CO_{2(g)}$ is $-94.05$ kcal/mole and the $\Delta H$ of formation of $CO_{(g)}$ is $-26.41$ kcal/mole, calculate the $\Delta H$ for $CO_{(g)} + \frac{1}{2}O_{2(g)} \rightarrow CO_{2(g)}$.

SOLUTION: Write the chemical equations for formation of $CO_2$ and of $CO$ from the elements and subtract the $CO$ equation from the $CO_2$ equation.

$$C_{(s)} + O_{2(g)} \rightarrow CO_{2(g)}; \quad \Delta H = -94.05 \text{ kcal}$$
$$-(C_{(s)} + \tfrac{1}{2}O_{2(g)} \rightarrow CO_{(g)}; \quad \Delta H = -26.41 \text{ kcal})$$
$$\overline{\tfrac{1}{2}O_{2(g)} \rightarrow CO_{2(g)} - CO_{(g)}; \Delta H = -94.05 - (-26.41)}$$
$$= -67.64 \text{ kcal}$$

Note that we subtract $\Delta H$'s just like everything else.
Note also that $CO_{(g)}$ occurs with a minus sign to the right of the arrow, so it can be transferred to the left of the arrow if we change sign. We get finally

$$CO_{(g)} + \tfrac{1}{2}O_{2(g)} \rightarrow CO_{2(g)}; \quad \Delta H = -67.64 \text{ kcal}$$

■ **PROBLEM 365** Given that the $\Delta H$ of formation of $BaSO_{3(s)}$ is $-282.6$ kcal/mole and the $\Delta H$ of formation of $BaSO_{4(s)}$ is $-350.2$ kcal/mole, calculate the $\Delta H$ for

$$BaSO_{3(s)} + \tfrac{1}{2}O_{2(g)} \rightarrow BaSO_{4(s)}$$

ANSWER: $\Delta H = -67.6 \text{ kcal}$

■ **PROBLEM 366** Given that the $\Delta H$ of formation of $FeO_{(s)}$ is $-64.04$ kcal/mole and the $\Delta H$ of formation of $Fe_2O_{3(s)}$ is $-196.5$ kcal/mole, calculate the $\Delta H$ for the reaction

$$2FeO_{(s)} + \tfrac{1}{2}O_{2(g)} \rightarrow Fe_2O_{3(s)}$$

ANSWER: $-68.4 \text{ kcal}$

[*Note:* In this case you need to double the chemical equation for the formation of FeO$_{(s)}$ and also double its $\Delta H$ before subtracting it from the equation for the formation of Fe$_2$O$_{3(s)}$.]

■**PROBLEM** 367   The $\Delta H$ of formation of H$_2$O$_{(g)}$ is $-57.798$ kcal/mole and the $\Delta H$ of formation of WO$_{3(s)}$ is $-200.84$ kcal/mole.   Calculate the $\Delta H$ for the reaction

$$3H_{2(g)} + WO_{3(s)} \rightarrow W_{(s)} + 3H_2O_{(g)}$$

ANSWER:$\Delta H = +27.45$ **kcal** (the reaction is endothermic)

■**PROBLEM** 368   The $\Delta H$ of formation of H$_2$O$_{(l)}$ is $-68.317$ kcal/mole; of CaO$_{(s)}$, $-151.9$ kcal/mole; of Ca(OH)$_{2(s)}$, $-235.8$ kcal/mole.   Calculate the $\Delta H$ for the reaction

$$CaO_{(s)} + H_2O_{(l)} \rightarrow Ca(OH)_{2(s)}$$

ANSWER: $\Delta H = -15.6$ **kcal**

■■ **PROBLEM** 369   Given that the heat of combustion of sugar C$_6$H$_{12}$O$_{6(s)}$ is 3.74 kcal/g, the heat of combustion of alcohol C$_2$H$_5$OH$_{(l)}$ is 7.11 kcal/g, and the $\Delta H$ of formation of CO$_{2(g)}$ is $-94.0$ kcal/mole, calculate the amount of heat liberated in the fermentation reaction

$$C_6H_{12}O_{6(s)} \rightarrow 2C_2H_5OH_{(l)} + 2CO_{2(g)}$$

ANSWER: **18.7 kcal**

■■ **PROBLEM** 370   Calculate how much heat is liberated when one mole gaseous Na$^+$ combines with one mole gaseous Cl$^-$ to form solid NaCl, given the following data:

$$Na_{(s)} + \tfrac{1}{2}Cl_{2(g)} \rightarrow NaCl_{(s)}; \quad \Delta H = -98.23 \text{ kcal}$$
$$Na_{(s)} \rightarrow Na_{(g)}; \quad \Delta H = +25.98 \text{ kcal}$$
$$Na_{(g)} \rightarrow Na^+_{(g)} + e^-; \quad \Delta H = +120.0 \text{ kcal}$$
$$Cl_{2(g)} \rightarrow 2Cl_{(g)}; \quad \Delta H = +58.02 \text{ kcal}$$
$$Cl^-_{(g)} \rightarrow Cl_{(g)} + e^-; \quad \Delta H = +87.3 \text{ kcal}$$

ANSWER: **185.9 kcal**

## *Calorimetry*

Calorimetry refers to the experimental determination of the heat of chemical reaction. The requirements are a well-insulated container in which to carry out the reaction, knowledge of the weight of each reactant and product, and some way to determine the heat change that accompanies the conversion from reactants to products. For the latter purpose, one of the simplest ways is to have the reaction vessel immersed in a known weight of water, for which the temperature change is carefully measured as the reaction occurs. Knowing the specific heat of water and its temperature change, we can calculate the number of calories gained (or lost) by the water. Assuming no heat leaks to the surroundings, the heat change must be matched by the heat produced (or used up) in the reaction.

PROBLEM 371   A solid sample of benzoic acid, $C_6H_5COOH$, weighing 1.89 g is placed with excess oxygen in a sealed bomb in a calorimeter containing 18.94 kg $H_2O$ at 25.00°C. The reaction of complete oxidation is set off and there is observed a temperature rise in the $H_2O$ of 0.632°C. What is the molar heat of combustion of benzoic acid? At 25.00°C, the specific heat of water is 0.99828 cal/g deg.

SOLUTION: Amount of heat absorbed by the water
= (mass of water)(specific heat)(temperature rise)

$$= (18{,}940 \text{ g}) \left( 0.99828 \frac{\text{cal}}{\text{g deg}} \right) (0.632 \text{ deg}) = 11{,}900 \text{ cal}$$

= amount of heat liberated by the combustion.

If the combustion of 1.89 g benzoic acid liberates 11,900 cal, then for one mole benzoic acid (which weighs 122.13 g) the amount of heat liberated would be

$$\left( 122.13 \frac{\text{g}}{\text{mole}} \right) \left( \frac{11{,}900 \text{ cal}}{1.89 \text{ g}} \right) = 769 \frac{\text{kcal}}{\text{mole}}.$$

Thus, the molar heat of combustion of $C_6H_5COOH$ is **769 kcal**.

■ PROBLEM 372   The molar heat of combustion of liquid methyl alcohol, $CH_3OH$, is 170.9 kcal/mole. What temperature rise would you expect to see on burning 3.20 g $CH_3OH$ in a calorimeter starting with 18.94 kg $H_2O$ at 25.00°C? Specific heat of water at 25.00°C is 0.9983 cal/g deg.

ANSWER: **0.902°**

Another kind of calorimeter, called the "ice calorimeter," measures heat changes by the amount of ice that is melted or frozen by the heat of the reaction. Since the heat of fusion of ice is well-known at 1.436 kcal/mole, the product of moles-of-ice-melted times 1.436 kcal/mole tells us how much heat has been given up by the chemical change under study.

PROBLEM 373   A bomb containing 5.40 g Al and 15.97 g $Fe_2O_3$ is placed in an ice calorimeter containing initially 8.000 kg ice and 8.000 kg liquid water. The reaction $2Al_{(s)} + Fe_2O_{3(s)} \rightarrow Al_2O_{3(s)} + 2Fe_{(s)}$ is set off by remote control, and it is then observed the calorimeter contains 7.746 kg ice and 8.254 kg water. What is the $\Delta H$ for the above reaction as written?

SOLUTION: The decrease in the amount of ice is from 8.000 to 7.746 kg, amounting to 254 g. So, 254 g $H_2O$ has been melted. This is

$$\frac{254 \text{ g}}{18.015 \text{ g/mole}} = 14.1 \text{ mole } H_2O.$$

One mole $H_2O$ requires 1.436 kcal for melting.

14.1 mole $H_2O$ requires $(14.1 \text{ mole}) \left( 1.436 \frac{\text{kcal}}{\text{mole}} \right) = 20.2 \text{ kcal.}$

This amount of heat, 20.2 kcal, has been liberated by the reaction of 5.40 g Al and 15.97 g $Fe_2O_3$.

$$5.40 \text{ g Al} = \frac{5.40 \text{ g}}{26.98 \text{ g/mole}} = 0.200 \text{ mole Al.}$$

$$15.97 \text{ g } Fe_2O_3 = \frac{15.97 \text{ g}}{159.7 \text{ g/mole}} = 0.100 \text{ mole } Fe_2O_3.$$

Since the balanced equation shows one mole $Fe_2O_3$, we work with that reagent.

20.2 kcal heat per 0.100 mole $Fe_2O_3$ means 202 kcal heat per 1 mole $Fe_2O_3$.

So, when the reaction $2Al_{(s)} + Fe_2O_{3(s)} \rightarrow 2Fe_{(s)} + Al_2O_{3(s)}$ occurs as written, 202 kcal is liberated to the surroundings. The heat content of the chemical system goes down by 202 kcal, so we write $\Delta H = -202$ **kcal** for the process.

■ PROBLEM 374 How many grams of ice could you melt in an ice calorimeter by allowing 1.86 g sodium to react by the following reaction:

$$Na_{(s)} + H_2O_{(l)} \rightarrow Na^+_{(aq)} + OH^-_{(aq)} + \tfrac{1}{2}H_{2(g)};$$
$$\Delta H = -43.9 \text{ kcal}$$

ANSWER: **44.6 g**

■■ PROBLEM 375 For studying solutions in liquid ammonia, an ingenious calorimeter has been developed in which heat effects are measured by analyzing for the amount of $NH_3$ evaporated from or condensed into liquid $NH_3$ at its normal boiling point, $-33°C$, by the reaction in question. The heat of vaporization of liquid ammonia is 5.581 kcal/mole. When a piece of sodium metal weighing 0.638 g is dropped into liquid ammonia, 140 cc $NH_3$ gas at 752 Torr and $-33°C$ is condensed into the liquid phase. What is $\Delta H$ for the following reaction:

$$Na_{(s)} \rightarrow Na_{(in \text{ liquid } NH_3)}$$

ANSWER: $\Delta H = +1.4$ **kcal**

# 10

# ELECTROCHEMISTRY

SO FAR as we are concerned, at the introductory level, the important quantitative aspects of electrochemistry are units, the relation between chemical change and electrical current, and the relation between tendency for chemical reaction to occur and voltage.

## Units

The practical unit of electrical charge is the *coulomb*, the exact definition of which is so complicated that very few people know exactly what it means. For us, it is enough to say that 1 coulomb equals $2.998 \times 10^9$ electrostatic units. The electrostatic unit (e.s.u.) is the amount of charge which repels an identical charge 1 centimeter away in a vacuum with unit force (1 dyne, or 1 gram-centimeter per second squared).

PROBLEM 376    The charge on an electron is $-1.602 \times 10^{-19}$ coulomb. How many e.s.u. is this?

SOLUTION: One coulomb = $2.998 \times 10^9$ e.s.u.

$1.602 \times 10^{-19}$ coulomb = $(1.602 \times 10^{-19}$ coulomb$) \times$

$$\left( 2.998 \times 10^9 \, \frac{\text{e.s.u.}}{\text{coulomb}} \right) = 4.803 \times 10^{-10} \text{ e.s.u.}$$

Electronic charge = $-4.803 \times 10^{-10}$ e.s.u.

167

PROBLEM 377   The electric charge on the aluminum ion is usually referred to as $+3$. How much is this in coulombs?

SOLUTION: $+3$ means three units of positive charge on the scale where the charge of the electron is $-1$. We saw in Problem 566 that the electronic charge is $-1.602 \times 10^{-19}$ coulomb. For the $Al^{+3}$ ion we need three such charges but of opposite sign—viz., $3(+1.602 \times 10^{-19}) = 4.806 \times 10^{-19}$ coulomb.

■ PROBLEM 378   What would be the electric charge in coulombs of the Avogadro number $(6.0225 \times 10^{23})$ of $Na^+$ ions?

ANSWER: $9.648 \times 10^4$ coulombs

The practical unit of electrical current is the *ampere*, which is the amount of current flowing when 1 coulomb passes a given point in 1 second. Frequently, an ampere is referred to as a "coulomb per second." It should be obvious from the dimensions that "current" times "time" gives charge, if current is in amperes (or coulombs/second) and if time is in seconds.

PROBLEM 379   The current in a given wire is 1.80 amp. How many coulombs will pass a given point on the wire in 1.36 min?

SOLUTION: 1.36 min is $(1.36 \text{ min}) \left( 60 \dfrac{\text{sec}}{\text{min}} \right) = 81.6$ sec.

1.80 amp is 1.80 coulombs/sec.

For 1.80 amp flowing for 81.6 sec, the charge transferred is

$$\left( 1.80 \dfrac{\text{coulomb}}{\text{sec}} \right) (81.6 \text{ sec}) = 147 \text{ coulombs.}$$

PROBLEM 380   Given that the electronic charge is $1.60 \times 10^{-19}$ coulomb, how much current would be flowing in a wire in which $1.27 \times 10^{18}$ electrons are being transferred per minute?

SOLUTION: Number of electrons transferred per second

$$= \left( 1.27 \times 10^{18} \dfrac{\text{electrons}}{\text{min}} \right) \left( \dfrac{1 \text{ min}}{60 \text{ sec}} \right) = 2.12 \times 10^{16} \dfrac{\text{electrons}}{\text{sec}} .$$

Charge transferred per second $= \left( 2.12 \times 10^{16} \dfrac{\text{electrons}}{\text{sec}} \right) \times$

$\left( 1.60 \times 10^{-19} \dfrac{\text{coulomb}}{\text{electron}} \right) = 3.39 \times 10^{-3} \dfrac{\text{coulomb}}{\text{sec}} ,$

or $3.39 \times 10^{-3}$ **amp.**

■ **PROBLEM** 381  If 0.068 mole $Al^{+3}$ ions moves past a given point in 1 hour, what electric current is flowing?
ANSWER: **5.46 amp**

■ **PROBLEM** 382  Passing a current of 4.67 milliamp, how much time is required to get 96,500 coulombs?
ANSWER: $2.07 \times 10^7$ **sec**

Although the coulomb is the usual unit for measuring charge, the chemist finds (for reasons soon to be discussed) that a more convenient unit is the *faraday*.  It corresponds to the charge carried by a mole of electrons and amounts to 96,487 coulombs.  A common step in electrochemical computations is to convert information given in coulombs, or amperes and seconds, into faradays, or vice versa.

**PROBLEM** 383  If a current of 80.0 microamp is drawn from a solar cell for 100 days, how many faradays are involved?

SOLUTION: Time in seconds

$= (100 \text{ days}) \left( 24 \dfrac{\text{hours}}{\text{day}} \right) \left( 60 \dfrac{\text{min}}{\text{hr}} \right) \left( 60 \dfrac{\text{sec}}{\text{min}} \right) = 8.64 \times 10^6 \text{ sec.}$

Current $= 80.0 \ \mu\text{amp} = 80.0 \times 10^{-6}$ amp.

(See page 11 for meaning of prefixes on units.)

Charge $=$ current $\times$ time $= \left( 80.0 \times 10^{-6} \dfrac{\text{coulomb}}{\text{sec}} \right) (8.64 \times 10^6 \text{ sec})$

$= 691$ coulombs.

Since 1 faraday equals 96,500 coulombs, 691 coulombs must equal

$\dfrac{691 \text{ coulombs}}{96,500 \text{ coulombs/faraday}} = 7.16 \times 10^{-3} \text{ faraday.}$

■ **PROBLEM** 384  A wire carries $1.80 \times 10^{18}$ electrons per second past a given point.  How many faradays could you accumulate from such a current in 1 hour? The charge on an electron is $1.60 \times 10^{-19}$ coulomb.

ANSWER: **0.0108**

■ **PROBLEM 385**  A stream of $Cl^-$ ions is flowing through a tube so that the equivalent of $6.09 \times 10^{-4}$ faraday of negative charge is transferred in 10 min. What is the flow rate of the $Cl^-$ ions in number of ions per second?

ANSWER: **$6.11 \times 10^{17}$ ions/sec**

## Electrolysis

The term electrolysis is applied to the process in which chemical change is brought about by electric current. To make computations for electrolysis, the main requirement is to know the half-reaction that occurs at each electrode. For example, when an aqueous solution of sodium chloride is electrolyzed, the changes that occur are the following:

*at the anode* (where oxidation occurs):

$$2Cl^- \rightarrow Cl_{2(g)} + 2e^-$$

*at the cathode* (where reduction occurs):

$$2H_2O + 2e^- \rightarrow H_{2(g)} + 2OH^-$$

[Note the plug put in here for defining anode as the "electrode where oxidation occurs" and the cathode as the "electrode where reduction occurs." Some people prefer to define the cathode as the negative electrode and the anode as the positive electrode, as done with vacuum radio tubes, but then there is risk of confusion as to whether internal or external circuits are being used as the basis of the sign definition. It is better to link "cathode" with "reduction" and "anode" with "oxidation."]

Once the half-reaction is written, it can be read off either in terms of individual ions, molecules, and electrons or in terms of *moles* of ions, *moles* of molecules, and *moles* of electrons. As indicated on page 169, one mole of electrons is 1 faraday (96,500 coulombs), so when half-reactions are read off in moles, the coefficient of $e^-$ can be taken to give directly the number of faradays involved in the reaction.

**PROBLEM 386** When aqueous NaCl solution is electrolyzed, how many faradays need to be transferred at the anode to release 0.015 mole of $Cl_2$ gas?

SOLUTION: The half-reaction $2Cl^- \rightarrow Cl_2 + 2e^-$ tells us that at the anode, for every two moles $Cl^-$ ion used up, one mole $Cl_2$ is formed along with two faradays of electrical charge that get transferred from the solution to the electrode and out the external circuit. Thus, we can say we get 1 mole $Cl_2$ per 2 faradays transferred. In order to get 0.015 mole $Cl_2$, we need

$$(0.015 \text{ mole } Cl_2)\left(\frac{2 \text{ faradays}}{1 \text{ mole } Cl_2}\right) = 0.030 \text{ faraday.}$$

**PROBLEM 387** When aqueous NaCl solution is electrolyzed, how long must a current of 0.010 amp run in order to liberate 0.015 mole of $H_2$ at the cathode?

SOLUTION: The cathode half-reaction is $\underline{2H_2O + 2e^- \rightarrow H_{2(g)} + 2OH^-}$. It states that for every two faradays consumed, one mole $H_2$ is liberated.

This means to get 0.015 mole $H_2$ we need to use

$$(0.015 \text{ mole } H_2)\left(\frac{2 \text{ faradays}}{1 \text{ mole } H_2}\right) = 0.030 \text{ faraday.}$$

But 1 faraday = 96,500 coulombs.

$$0.030 \text{ faraday} = (0.030 \text{ faraday})\left(96{,}500 \frac{\text{coulombs}}{\text{faraday}}\right) = 2900 \text{ coulombs.}$$

If the current is 0.010 amp (or 0.010 coulomb/sec), to get 2900 coulombs we need to wait

$$\frac{2900 \text{ coulombs}}{0.010 \text{ coulomb/sec}} = 2.9 \times 10^5 \text{ sec.}$$

**PROBLEM 388** In the electrolysis of molten zinc chloride, $ZnCl_2$, how many grams of Zn metal can be deposited at the cathode by passage of 0.010 amp for 1 hour?

SOLUTION: 0.010 amp for 1 hour is

$$\left(0.010 \frac{\text{coulomb}}{\text{sec}}\right)\left(60 \frac{\text{min}}{\text{hour}}\right)\left(60 \frac{\text{sec}}{\text{min}}\right) = 36 \text{ coulombs.}$$

One faraday is 96,500 coulombs, so 36 coulombs is

$$\frac{36 \text{ coulombs}}{96,500 \text{ coulombs/faraday}} = 3.7 \times 10^{-4} \text{ faraday.}$$

In molten zinc chloride, the cathode reaction is

$$Zn^{++} + 2e^- \rightarrow Zn$$

which states that for every 2 faradays of electricity used up, one mole Zn forms. Since we use $3.7 \times 10^{-4}$ faraday, we must be getting

$$(3.7 \times 10^{-4} \text{ faraday}) \left( \frac{1 \text{ mole Zn}}{2 \text{ faradays}} \right) = 1.8 \times 10^{-4} \text{ mole Zn.}$$

One mole Zn is 65.37 g.

$1.8 \times 10^{-4}$ mole Zn is $(1.8 \times 10^{-4} \text{ mole}) \left( 65.37 \frac{g}{\text{mole}} \right) = 0.012 \text{ g.}$

PROBLEM 389   A simple way to measure the amount of charge going through an electrolytic cell is to set up in series with the studied cell one in which an aqueous solution of $AgNO_3$ is electrolyzed. ("In series" means hook up two cells so that the cathode of one is wired directly to the anode of the other. The result will be that any electricity that goes through one cell has to come out of the other.) Suppose you have an aqueous $AgNO_3$ cell in series with one in which aqueous NaCl is being electrolyzed. If 0.0198 g Ag is plated out on the cathode of the first cell, how many moles of $H_2$ will be liberated at the cathode of the second cell?

SOLUTION:
*in the first cell:*
The cathode half-reaction is $Ag^+ + e^- \rightarrow Ag_{(s)}$. This shows that one mole Ag is plated out for every faraday passed.

$$0.0198 \text{ g Ag} = \frac{0.0198 \text{ g}}{107.870 \text{ g/mole}} = 1.84 \times 10^{-4} \text{ mole Ag.}$$

Number of faradays passed $= (1.84 \times 10^{-4} \text{ mole Ag}) \times$

$$\left( 1 \frac{\text{faraday}}{\text{mole Ag}} \right) = 1.84 \times 10^{-4} \text{ faraday.}$$

*in the second cell:*

The number of faradays passed equals the same number ($1.84 \times 10^{-4}$) as in the first cell, because all the electricity fed through the first cell must go into the second cell.

The cathode half-reaction is $2H_2O + 2e^- \rightarrow H_2 + 2OH^-$, which states that one mole $H_2$ is formed for every 2 faradays passed through. Therefore, if we pass $1.84 \times 10^{-4}$ faradays through the second cell, we must get

$$(1.84 \times 10^{-4} \text{ faraday}) \left(\frac{1 \text{ mole } H_2}{2 \text{ faradays}}\right) = 9.20 \times 10^{-5} \text{ mole } H_2.$$

■ PROBLEM 390   Given the half-reaction $Al^{+3} + 3e^- \rightarrow Al_{(s)}$ at an electrode. How many grams of $Al_{(s)}$ can you produce from 0.69 faraday?

ANSWER: **6.2 g**

■ PROBLEM 391   Given the half-reaction $Fe^{++} + 2e^- \rightarrow Fe_{(s)}$ at an electrode. How long would you need to pass a current of 0.0205 amp through the cell in order to form 6.93 g of iron?

ANSWER: $1.17 \times 10^6$ sec

PROBLEM 392   Suppose the half-reaction $2H_2O \rightarrow O_2 + 4H^+ + 4e^-$ is occurring at an anode. You observe the formation of 36.5 cc wet oxygen at barometric pressure 743 Torr and 25°C. How many moles $H^+$ have been set free at the anode?

SOLUTION: (Figure out how many moles $O_2$ you have. Then use the half-reaction to calculate $H^+$ formed.)

At 25°C, the vapor pressure of water is 23.8 Torr.

Therefore, the pressure of the oxygen is $743 - 23.8$, or 719 Torr. This corresponds to 719/760 atm.

Using $PV = nRT$:

$$n = \frac{PV}{RT} = \frac{(719/760)(0.0365)}{(0.08206)(273 + 25)} = 1.41 \times 10^{-3} \text{ mole } O_2.$$

From the half-reaction $2H_2O \rightarrow O_2 + 4H^+ + 4e^-$ we see there are 4 moles $H^+$ formed per mole $O_2$. So, if we get $1.41 \times 10^{-3}$ mole

$O_2$, we must form

$$(1.41 \times 10^{-3} \text{ mole } O_2) \left( \frac{4 \text{ moles } H^+}{1 \text{ mole } O_2} \right) = 5.64 \times 10^{-3} \text{ mole } H^+ .$$

■PROBLEM 393    Suppose the reaction $2e^- + 2H_2O \rightarrow 2OH^- + H_2$ is occurring at a cathode. If 0.010 amp passes through the cell for 18.6 sec, how many moles $OH^-$ will be set free at the cathode?

ANSWER: $1.93 \times 10^{-6}$ mole

■PROBLEM 394    When you electrolyze aqueous $AgNO_3$ solution under appropriate conditions, the anode reaction will be $2H_2O \rightarrow O_2 + 4H^+ + 4e^-$, while the cathode reaction is $Ag^+ + e^- \rightarrow Ag_{(s)}$. If, in such an electrolysis, you observe 23.8 mg $Ag_{(s)}$ plating out at the cathode, how many cc $O_2$(STP) should you see formed at the anode?

ANSWER: 1.24 cc

■PROBLEM 395    If you electrolyze dilute aqueous $H_2SO_4$ solution, using copper electrodes, the electrode reactions are likely to be $2H^+ + 2e^- \rightarrow H_2$ at the cathode and $2Cu_{(s)} + H_2O \rightarrow Cu_2O_{(s)} + 2H^+ + 2e^-$ at the anode. If you observe that 27.4 cc of wet hydrogen (barometer 751 Torr, temperature 22.3°C) has formed at the cathode, what weight change should there be simultaneously at the anode?

ANSWER: increase of weight by 17.4 mg

■PROBLEM 396    Given an electrode at which the reaction

$$PbSO_{4(s)} + 2H_2O \rightarrow PbO_{2(s)} + 3H^+ + HSO_4^- + 2e^-$$

is made to occur by appropriate means. If 1.00 amp is passed through for 100 hours, what will be the weight change of the solid phase?

ANSWER: decrease in weight of 119 g

■■ PROBLEM 397    When you electrolyze aqueous $H_2SO_4$ with inert electrodes you get hydrogen at the cathode and oxygen at the anode, supposedly in the volume ratio of 2 to 1. If you try the experiment, you will find the ratio is *not* 2 to 1, mainly because part of the anode current goes to convert $H_2O$ to $H_2O_2$. If in a given experiment you observe formed 43.76 cc $H_2$ at the cathode (wet, total pressure 765 Torr, temperature 29°C) and 21.32 cc $O_2$ at the anode (wet, total pressure 755 Torr, temperature 29°C), what per cent of the anode current can be attributed to $H_2O_2$ formation?

ANSWER: **3.9%**

## Galvanic cells

In *electrolysis*, current is forced by some external means to pass through a cell so as to produce chemical changes at the electrodes—specifically, an oxidation half-reaction at the anode and a reduction half-reaction at the cathode. A *galvanic cell* (sometimes also called a *voltaic* cell) is the direct opposite of this—i.e., it has reactions occurring spontaneously at electrodes, the result of which is to produce an electric current in an external circuit. In making computations for galvanic cells, the most important thing again is to be able to specify the half-reactions. Once the half-reaction is written, it is an easy matter to figure out how many faradays are pushed out from the anode or sucked into the cell at the cathode.

In principle, any oxidation-reduction reaction can be used as a basis for a galvanic cell. The first step is to split the whole reaction into half-reactions (as we have done for balancing equations). Then set up a cell, divided into two by a porous partition, so that the components taking part in the oxidation half-reaction are in one compartment and the components taking part in the reduction half-reaction are in the other compartment. Appropriate electrodes, either inert (e.g., platinum) or one of the conducting components (e.g., zinc), serve to carry electrons out of the anode compartment or into the cathode compartment. The number of faradays coming out of the anode must just equal the number going into the cathode; this number is fixed by the amount of chemical change occurring at the electrodes.

PROBLEM 398 Given a galvanic cell in which the anode reaction is $Zn_{(s)} \rightarrow Zn^{++} + 2e^-$. How many faradays will you get out of the cell if you consume 1.00 g Zn by this reaction?

SOLUTION: The half-reaction indicates that, for every 1 mole of Zn consumed, 2 moles of electrons (or 2 faradays of electrical charge) is set free.

One mole Zn weighs 65.37 g.

$$1.00 \text{ g Zn} = \frac{1.00 \text{ g}}{65.37 \text{ g/mole}} = 0.0153 \text{ mole.}$$

If one mole Zn can liberate 2 faradays, then from 0.0153 mole Zn we can get

$$(0.0153 \text{ mole Zn}) \left( \frac{2 \text{ faradays}}{1 \text{ mole Zn}} \right) = \textbf{0.0306 faraday .}$$

PROBLEM 399   Given a galvanic cell in which the cathode reaction is $Cl_{2(g)} + 2e^- \rightarrow 2Cl^-$. If 1.00 g chlorine is consumed in this reaction, how many faradays will be pulled into the cell from outside?

SOLUTION: One mole $Cl_2$ weighs 70.906 g.

$$1.00 \text{ g } Cl_2 = \frac{1.00 \text{ g}}{70.906 \text{ g/mole}} = 0.0141 \text{ mole.}$$

The half-reaction says each time 1 mole $Cl_2$ disappears, two faradays have to go with it. Therefore, if 0.0141 mole $Cl_2$ is used up, the required electric charge is

$$(0.0141 \text{ mole } Cl_2) \left( \frac{2 \text{ faradays}}{1 \text{ mole } Cl_2} \right) = \textbf{0.0282 faraday .}$$

PROBLEM 400   Given a galvanic cell in which the over-all reaction is $Zn_{(s)} + Cl_{2(g)} \rightarrow Zn^{++} + 2Cl^-$. Using up 1.50 g Zn by the reaction, how long could such a cell deliver 0.10 amp to the outside?

SOLUTION: We need consider only one half-reaction, since the other must occur in equivalent amount.

The zinc half-reaction is $Zn_{(s)} \rightarrow Zn^{++} + 2e^-$.

It states that two faradays are released when 1 mole Zn is used.

$$1.50 \text{ g Zn} = \frac{1.50 \text{ g}}{65.37 \text{ g/mole}} = 0.0229 \text{ mole Zn.}$$

This will give $(0.0229 \text{ mole Zn}) \left( \frac{2 \text{ faradays}}{1 \text{ mole Zn}} \right) = 0.0458 \text{ faraday.}$

One faraday = 96,500 coulombs.

$$0.0458 \text{ faraday} = (0.0458 \text{ faraday}) \left( 96,500 \, \frac{\text{coulombs}}{\text{faraday}} \right)$$
$$= 4420 \text{ coulombs.}$$

The desired current is 0.10 amp, or 0.10 coulomb/sec.

To pass 4420 coulombs will require $\dfrac{4420 \text{ coulombs}}{0.10 \text{ coulomb/sec}}$

$$= 4.4 \times 10^4 \text{ sec.}$$

**P R O B L E M  401**  In the lead storage battery, the anode reaction is $Pb_{(s)} + HSO_4^- \rightarrow PbSO_{4(s)} + H^+ + 2e^-$. A typical battery would be rated "100 ampere-hours," which means it has the chemical capacity to deliver 100 amperes for 1 hour or 1 ampere for 100 hours.  How many grams of Pb would be used up at the above anode to accomplish this?

SOLUTION: (Figure out how many faradays are involved.  Then use the half-reaction to relate the faradays to the chemical change.)

One ampere for 100 hours is $\left( 1 \, \dfrac{\text{coulomb}}{\text{sec}} \right)$ (100 hours) $\times$

$\left( 60 \, \dfrac{\text{min}}{\text{hour}} \right) \left( 60 \, \dfrac{\text{sec}}{\text{min}} \right) = 3.6 \times 10^5$ coulombs.

This can be converted to faradays by dividing by the number of coulombs per faraday:

$$\frac{360,000 \text{ coulombs}}{96,500 \text{ coulombs/faraday}} = 3.73 \text{ faradays.}$$

The half-reaction says one mole Pb disappears for each two faradays liberated.  If we liberate 3.73 faradays, we use (3.73 faradays) $\times$

$\left( \dfrac{1 \text{ mole Pb}}{2 \text{ faradays}} \right) = 1.86$ mole Pb.

One mole Pb is 207.19 g.

1.86 moles Pb is (1.86 moles) $\left( 207.19 \, \dfrac{\text{g}}{\text{mole}} \right) = \mathbf{385\ g.}$

**P R O B L E M  402**  In a flashlight cell the cathode reaction can be written $2MnO_{2(s)} + Zn^{++} + 2e^- \rightarrow ZnMn_2O_{4(s)}$.  If your flashlight cell is to give out a current of 4.6 milliamp, how long could it do this if we start with 3.50 g $MnO_2$?

SOLUTION: One mole $MnO_2$ weighs 86.94 g.

3.50 g $MnO_2$ is $\dfrac{3.50 \text{ g}}{86.94 \text{ g/mole}} = 0.0403$ mole.

The above half-reaction indicates 2 faradays will be transferred each time two moles $MnO_2$ get used up. Therefore, if we use up 0.0403 mole $MnO_2$, we must transfer

$$(0.0403 \text{ mole } MnO_2) \left( \frac{2 \text{ faradays}}{2 \text{ moles } MnO_2} \right) = 0.0403 \text{ faraday.}$$

If one faraday is 96,500 coulombs, 0.0403 faraday is (0.0403 faraday) $\times$ $\left( 96,500 \dfrac{\text{coulomb}}{\text{faraday}} \right) = 3890$ coulombs.

At the rate of 4.6 milliamp, or 0.0046 $\dfrac{\text{coulomb}}{\text{sec}}$, 3890 coulombs last

$\dfrac{3890 \text{ coulombs}}{0.0046 \text{ coulomb/sec}} = 8.5 \times 10^5$ sec (which is about 10 days).

■ PROBLEM 403    In the Daniell cell the over-all reaction is $Zn_{(s)} + Cu^{++} \rightarrow Cu + Zn^{++}$. If a given Daniell cell is used to deliver 865 coulombs, what weight of zinc will need to be dissolved in the process?

ANSWER: **0.293 g**

■ PROBLEM 404    A lead storage battery is used to deliver a current of 174.6 amp for 1.2 sec (typical conditions involved in starting a car). Given that the anode reaction is $Pb_{(s)} + HSO_4^- \rightarrow PbSO_{4(s)} + H^+ + 2e^-$, calculate the weight of lead required for this operation. Allow for the fact that six identical cells are operating in series.

ANSWER: **1.4 g**

■ PROBLEM 405    A flashlight cell in which the over-all reaction is $Zn_{(s)} + 2MnO_{2(s)} \rightarrow ZnMn_2O_{4(s)}$ has been running for 9.63 hours delivering a steady 1.86 μamp. How many grams of $MnO_2$ would be used up?

ANSWER: **$5.81 \times 10^{-5}$ g**

■ PROBLEM 406    For the cathode reaction of a lead storage cell we can write $PbO_{2(s)} + HSO_4^- + 3H^+ +$

$2e^- \rightarrow PbSO_{4(s)} + 2H_2O$.  In practice, the solid $PbSO_4$ formed sticks to the $PbO_2$ that constitutes the electrode.  If the cell is used to deliver 50.0 milliamp for 87.6 hours, what weight change would you observe for the cathode electrode?

ANSWER: **increase in weight of 5.23 g**

■ PROBLEM 407  In the Edison cell, the over-all reaction can usually be written $Fe_{(s)} + Ni_2O_{3(s)} + 3H_2O \rightarrow$ $2Ni(OH)_{2(s)} + Fe(OH)_{2(s)}$.  If you want such a cell to be good for 100 amp-hours, how many grams Fe and $Ni_2O_3$ must you provide?

ANSWER: **104 g Fe and 309 g $Ni_2O_3$**

■ PROBLEM 408  In the lead storage cell, the over-all reaction is $Pb_{(s)} + PbO_{2(s)} + 2H^+ + 2HSO_4^- \rightarrow$ $2PbSO_{4(s)} + 2H_2O$.  If you want such a cell to be good for 100 amp-hours, how many grams of each starting material must you provide?

ANSWER: **386 g Pb, 446 g $PbO_2$, 366 g $H_2SO_4$**

## *Oxidation potentials*

In setting up a galvanic cell, we take an oxidation-reduction reaction, separate it into the two half-reactions, and set these half-reactions up to occur individually in the two compartments of the cell (the so-called *half-cells*).  In the preceding section we considered how much current can be fed to the outside by such a cell.  But now, suppose we raise the question "What is the situation if there is no external connection between the anode and the cathode?"  There is still a drive tending to push electrons out of the anode relative to the cathode but the electrons have no place to go.  The only thing that can happen is that a difference in voltage, also called a difference in potential, establishes itself between the anode and the cathode.  We can measure this difference in voltage by hooking up a gadget, called a potentiometer, between the anode and cathode.  Such a potentiometer can measure the voltage difference without itself drawing any electric current from the cell.

The observed voltage difference between two electrodes of a galvanic cell depends on the materials present in each compartment— what they are and at what concentration.  For reference purposes, it has been agreed to consider the hydrogen half-cell based on the reaction $H_2 \rightarrow 2H^+ + 2e^-$ as a standard. We arbitrarily assign it a value of zero—that is, say that it makes zero contribution to the observed voltage of a cell in which the hydrogen half-cell is part of the assembly. This assignment of zero contribution holds only if the $H_2$ and the $H^+$ are in what are called their standard states. Strictly speaking, "standard state" means $25^0C$ and "unit activity," but for our purposes it will be sufficient to interpret unit activity for a gas component as 1 atmosphere pressure and unit activity for a dissolved species as 1 molal concentration. (Concentrations are discussed in detail in Chapter 11.)

Figure 63 shows a galvanic cell set up to measure the voltage difference between the anode and cathode of a cell designed to use the reaction

$$Zn_{(s)} + 2H^+ \rightarrow H_{2(g)} + Zn^{++}$$

The half-reaction $Zn_{(s)} \rightarrow Zn^{++} + 2e^-$ is set up in the left-hand compartment by putting a zinc bar into a solution containing $Zn^{++}$ and some anion $A^-$. The half-reaction $2H^+ + 2e^- \rightarrow H_{2(g)}$ is set up in the right-hand compartment by dipping an inert conductor such as

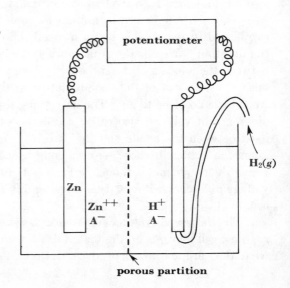

*Figure 63*

potentiometer

$H_2(g)$

Zn

$Zn^{++}$
$A^-$

$H^+$
$A^-$

porous partition

carbon or platinum into a solution containing $H^+$ and $A^-$ and then allowing $H_2$ gas to bubble over the electrode surface. If the pressure of the hydrogen gas is 1 atmosphere and everything else is at unit concentration, then the potentiometer will show a reading of 0.76 volt. *We assume that all of this 0.76 volt can be attributed to the Zn electrode*, since we decided to regard the hydrogen contribution as zero. Such voltages, referred to hydrogen, are called *oxidation potentials*, and they are used to give a quantitative measure of the tendency of a half-reaction to give off electrons.

In Appendix D some common half-reactions are listed along with their oxidation potentials. The numerical values hold strictly only when each species appearing in the half-reaction is in its standard state. Departures from unit pressure for gases and from unit molality for dissolved species are considered in Section 13.5.

When every species is in its standard state, the oxidation potential is usually designated $E^0$ (read "eeh zero"). The following problems illustrate how $E^0$'s are used. An $E^0$ for a single half-reaction gives a quantitative measure of the tendency of that half-reaction to occur, but also $E^0$'s for two half-reactions can be combined to tell us something about the voltage to be expected for a corresponding galvanic cell and also whether its over-all chemical reaction tends to go spontaneously as written. If the over-all $E^0$ is positive, the reaction tends to go spontaneously; if negative, it does not. "Spontaneously" means without having to put on an external voltage to force the reaction to go opposite its natural tendency.

PROBLEM 409 If the $E^0$ for $H_{2(g)} \rightarrow 2H^+ + 2e^-$ is zero, what is the $E^0$ for $2H^+ + 2e^- \rightarrow H_{2(g)}$?

SOLUTION: $E^0$ is **zero** in both directions.
If we say that a half-reaction is arbitrarily labeled as having zero tendency to go from left to right, then it must have zero tendency to go from right to left.

PROBLEM 410 If the $E^0$ for $Zn_{(s)} \rightarrow Zn^{++} + 2e^-$ is $+0.76$ volt, what is the $E^0$ for $2e^- + Zn^{++} \rightarrow Zn_{(s)}$?

SOLUTION: We are really asking this: "If a half-reaction has a big tendency to go to the right, compared to some standard reaction, what can you say about its tendency to go to the left, compared to that same standard?" The answer seems obvious: big tendency to go to the right means small tendency to go to the left. Specifically, Zn has a bigger tendency than $H_2$ to give off electrons by 0.76 volt. Therefore, the species formed from the Zn (namely, $Zn^{++}$) must have a smaller tendency to pick up electrons than the species formed from $H_2$ (namely, $H^+$). If we use zero for the hydrogen half-reaction in either direction, then reversing the direction of $Zn \rightarrow Zn^{++} + 2e^-$ means reversing the sign of its $E^0$. In display form, this looks as follows:

$$Zn_{(s)} \rightarrow Zn^{++} + 2e^-    \qquad E^0 = +0.76 \text{ volt}$$

$$H_{2(g)} \rightarrow 2H^+ + 2e^-    \qquad E^0 = 0.00000 \text{ volt}$$

$$2e^- + 2H^+ \rightarrow H_{2(g)}    \qquad E^0 = 0.00000 \text{ volt}$$

$$2e^- + Zn^{++} \rightarrow Zn_{(s)}    \qquad E^0 = -0.76 \text{ volt}$$

■ PROBLEM 411    If the $E^0$ for $Sn^{++} \rightarrow Sn^{+4} + 2e^-$ is $-0.15$ volt, what is the $E^0$ for $Sn^{+4} + 2e^- \rightarrow Sn^{++}$?
ANSWER: $E^0 = +0.15$ volt

■ PROBLEM 412    If the $E^0$ for $Mn^{++} + 4H_2O \rightarrow MnO_4^- + 8H^+ + 5e^-$ is $-1.51$ volts, what is the $E^0$ for $MnO_4^-$ acting as an oxidizing agent?
ANSWER: $E^0 = +1.51$ volts

■ PROBLEM 413    The $E^0$ for $Cr_2O_7^=$ going to $Cr^{+3}$ in acidic solution is $+1.33$ volts. What would be the $E^0$ for $Cr^{+3}$ acting as a reducing agent and going to $Cr_2O_7^=$ in acidic solution? Write the appropriate half-reaction.
ANSWER: $2Cr^{+3} + 7H_2O \rightarrow Cr_2O_7^= + 14H^+ + 6e^-$;
$E^0 = -1.33$ volts

In most tabulations of $E^0$'s, the half-reactions are written so that the electrons appear on the right. This means that the value given applies when the species shown on the left of the half-reaction acts as a *reducing* agent. If we are interested in the reverse half-reaction, in which the species shown on the right of the half-reaction acts as an *oxidizing* agent, then we need to reverse the arrow and change the sign on $E^0$.

For deducing an $E^0$ for an over-all reaction, we can add the $E^0$'s for the two half-reactions involved so long as the half-reactions have been written to oppose each other. In other words, one half-reaction must show electrons on its right and the other half-reaction must show electrons on its left. When adding $E^0$'s in this way, we ignore any disparity in number of electrons on right and left, since $E^0$ is a per-electron property.

**PROBLEM** 414  What is the $E^0$ for the reaction $Zn_{(s)} + 2H^+ \rightarrow Zn^{++} + H_{2(g)}$?

SOLUTION: (Write the two half-reactions with corresponding $E^0$'s and add them.)

$$Zn_{(s)} \rightarrow Zn^{++} + 2e^- \qquad\qquad E^0 = +0.76 \text{ volt}$$
$$\underline{2e^- + 2H^+ \rightarrow H_{2(g)} \qquad\qquad E^0 = 0.00 \text{ volt}}$$
$$Zn_{(s)} + 2H^+ \rightarrow Zn^{++} + H_{2(g)} \qquad E^0 = +0.76 \text{ volt}$$

**PROBLEM** 415  What is the $E^0$ for the reaction $H_{2(g)} + Zn^{++} \rightarrow Zn_{(s)} + 2H^+$?

SOLUTION:

$$H_{2(g)} \rightarrow 2H^+ + 2e^- \qquad\qquad E^0 = 0.00 \text{ volt}$$
$$\underline{2e^- + Zn^{++} \rightarrow Zn_{(s)} \qquad\qquad E^0 = -0.76 \text{ volt}}$$
$$H_{2(g)} + Zn^{++} \rightarrow 2H^+ + Zn_{(s)} \qquad E^0 = -0.76 \text{ volt}$$

**PROBLEM** 416  What is the $E^0$ for the reaction

$$Zn_{(s)} + Cl_{2(g)} \rightarrow Zn^{++} + 2Cl^-$$?

SOLUTION:

$$Zn_{(s)} \rightarrow Zn^{++} + 2e^- \qquad\qquad E^0 = +0.76 \text{ volt}$$
$$\underline{Cl_{2(g)} + 2e^- \rightarrow 2\,Cl^- \qquad\qquad E^0 = +1.36 \text{ volts}}$$
$$Zn_{(s)} + Cl_{2(g)} \rightarrow Zn^{++} + 2Cl^- \qquad E^0 = +2.12 \text{ volts}$$

[Note that the $E^0$ for the Zn half-reaction is as given in Appendix D. But for the chlorine half-reaction, we find in the table $2Cl^- \rightarrow Cl_2 + 2e^-$ with $E^0 = -1.36$ volts. This is the reverse half-reaction of what we need, so we flip the half-reaction over and change sign on $E^0$.]

PROBLEM 417    Under standard conditions, what will be the $E^0$ for the oxidation of $I^-$ by $H_3AsO_4$ to $I_2$ and $HAsO_2$ in acidic solution? Should the reaction occur spontaneously?

SOLUTION: Write the two half-reactions

$$2I^- \rightarrow I_2 + 2e^-$$

$$2e^- + 2H^+ + H_3AsO_4 \rightarrow HAsO_2 + 2H_2O$$

Get the $E^0$'s from Appendix D.    Add.

| | |
|---|---|
| $2I^- \rightarrow I_2 + 2e^-$ | $E^0 = -0.54$ volt |
| $2e^- + 2H^+ + H_3AsO_4 \rightarrow HAsO_2 + 2H_2O$ | $E^0 = +0.56$ volt |
| $H_3AsO_4 + 2H^+ + 2I^- \rightarrow HAsO_2 + I_2 + 2H_2O$ | $E^0 = +0.02$ volt |

Since the $E^0$ for the over-all reaction is greater than zero, the reaction **ought to occur** spontaneously from left to right.

PROBLEM 418    Write the equation for the oxidation of $Cr^{+3}$ by $Br_2$ in acidic solution to form $Cr_2O_7^=$ and $Br^-$. From the over-all $E^0$ decide whether this oxidation should occur spontaneously.

SOLUTION:

| | |
|---|---|
| $2Cr^{+3} + 7H_2O \rightarrow Cr_2O_7^= + 14H^+ + 6e^-$ | $E^0 = -1.33$ volt |
| $Br_2 + 2e^- \rightarrow 2Br^-$ | $E^0 = +1.07$ volts |
| $3Br_2 + 2Cr^{+3} + 7H_2O \rightarrow Cr_2O_7^= + 14H^+ + 6Br^-$ | $E^0 = -0.26$ volt |

[Note that in getting the balanced equation we need to multiply the second half-reaction by three before adding. However, when we combine the $E^0$'s, we add them directly, since they do not depend on how much reaction occurs. The fact that $E^0$ for the final reaction is less than zero means that the change written will **not occur** spontaneously from left to right. Its natural tendency is to go in the opposite direction.]

■PROBLEM 419    What is the $E^0$ for the reaction $Fe_{(s)} + Sn^{+4} \rightarrow Fe^{++} + Sn^{++}$?
ANSWER: $E^0 = +0.59$ volt

■PROBLEM 420    What is the $E^0$ for the reaction $3Fe^{++} + NO_3^- + 4H^+ \rightarrow 3Fe^{+3} + NO + 2H_2O$?
ANSWER: $+0.19$ volt

■ P R O B L E M   421   What would be the $E^0$ for the oxidation of $I^-$ to $I_2$ by $NO_3^-$ forming NO in acidic solution?

ANSWER: $E^0 = +0.42$ volt

■ P R O B L E M   422   Write a balanced equation for the oxidation of $Br^-$ to $Br_2$ by $IO_3^-$ going to $I_2$ in acidic solution.   Compute the $E^0$ and decide whether the reaction should go spontaneously.

ANSWER: $10Br^- + 2IO_3^- + 12H^+ \rightarrow 5Br_2 + I_2 + 6H_2O$;

$E^0 = +0.13$ volt;

the reaction **should occur** spontaneously

■ P R O B L E M   423   What is the $E^0$ for the oxidation of $Cr^{+3}$ by $O_2$ to form $H_2O$ and $Cr_2O_7^=$ in acidic solution? Should the reaction go?

ANSWER: $E^0 = -0.10$ volt . No ; the reaction actually ought to go spontaneously in the reverse direction.   However, it is normally too slow to be observed.

■ P R O B L E M   424   If you could make a galvanic cell in which the over-all reaction were the oxidation of $Al_{(s)}$ to $Al^{+3}$ by $O_2$ going to $H_2O$, what voltage would you expect under standard conditions?

ANSWER: **2.89 volts**

■ P R O B L E M   425   Write   the   balanced equation for the oxidation of $I_2$ by $AuCl_4^-$ in acidic solution to produce $IO_3^-$ and $Au_{(s)}$ and decide from the $E^0$ whether the reaction should go.

ANSWER: $5AuCl_4^- + 9H_2O + \frac{3}{2}I_2 \rightarrow 5Au_{(s)} + 20Cl^-$
$$+ 3IO_3^- + 18H^+$$

$E^0 = -0.20$ volt; the reaction **should not go**

### Nernst equation

Special note was taken of the fact that the oxidation potentials listed in the tabulations hold only for standard conditions, which generally mean 1 atmosphere pressure and 1 molal concentration.   What happens if we change these conditions?   Properly speaking, we should delay this discussion until after Chapter 11 treats the topic of concentration in solution.  However, the Nernst equation gives us a very simple way of expressing how the voltage of a half-reaction or of an over-all reaction varies with concentration, so it really needs to be considered as part of electrochemistry.  For anyone unfamiliar with methods of expressing concentration in solution, reference to Chapter 11 is advisable.

As expected, increasing the concentration of a reagent on the left of a reaction (or half-reaction) or increasing a concentration on the right gives an increased tendency of the reaction to go from left to right.  Since the voltage expresses the tendency to go to the right, any influence that increases this tendency should make the voltage more positive.  For example, the half-reaction

$$H_{2(g)} \rightarrow 2H^+ + 2e^-$$

has a certain tendency to go to the right, which we are labeling zero. If we raise the pressure of $H_{2(g)}$ or decrease the concentration of $H^+$, we increase the tendency to go to the right—that is, we make the voltage become higher than zero.  Alternatively, if we decrease the pressure of $H_{2(g)}$ to less than 1 atmosphere or if we raise the concentration of $H^+$ to more than 1 molal, we make the voltage of the reaction less than zero, or negative.  If we let $E^0$ represent the voltage of the reaction when everything is in its standard state and $E$ for the voltage when any state is considered, we can relate one to the other by the Nernst equation:

$$E = E^0 - \frac{0.0592}{n} \log \left[ \frac{\text{concentrations of species on right}}{\text{concentrations of species on left}} \right]$$

Here $n$ stands for the number of electrons appearing in the half-reaction or the number of electrons transferred in an over-all reaction.  The expression in square brackets is made up by multiplying together the concentration of each species appearing in the equation raised to a power given by the coefficient of the species.  Specifically, for

$$H_{2(g)} \rightarrow 2H^+ + 2e^-$$

we can write

$$E = E^0 - \frac{0.0592}{2} \log \frac{[H^+]^2}{[H_{2(g)}]}$$

Note that the $H^+$ is taken to the square power because of the coefficient 2 before $H^+$ in the half-reaction; $H_2$ is taken to the first power because of the coefficient 1 before $H_2$ in the half-reaction. $[H^+]^2$ appears in the numerator because it comes from the right-hand side of the half-reaction; $[H_2]$ appears in the denominator because it appears on the left side of the reaction. (The $2e^-$ which appears in the half-reaction does not come into the logarithm expression; it is effectively taken care of by $n = 2$, dividing the 0.0592.)

How to express $[H^+]$ and $[H_{2(g)}]$? For gases, we use pressure, so in place of $[H_{2(g)}]$ we can put $p_{H_2}$. For dissolved species, we use molality (normally indicated by small $m$). In dilute solutions, the numerical values of molality are almost the same as those for molarity, but we shall be precise and stick with molality. For $[H^+]$ we thus use $m_{H^+}$. So, the Nernst equation says for the hydrogen electrode

$$E = E^0 - \frac{0.0592}{2} \log \frac{m_{H^+}^2}{p_{H_2}}$$

PROBLEM 426 What does the Nernst equation give for the hydrogen electrode when $H^+$ is at 1 molal concentration and $H_2$ is at 1 atm pressure?

SOLUTION: For $H_{2(g)} \rightarrow 2H^+ + 2e^-$; $E^0 = 0$.

$$E = E^0 - \frac{0.0592}{2} \log \frac{m_{H^+}^2}{p_{H_2}} = 0 - 0.0296 \log \frac{(1)^2}{1} = 0.$$

Having substituted $m_{H^+} = 1$ and $p_{H_2} = 1$, we get the logarithm of one, which turns out to be zero. So, not surprisingly, we find that $E = E^0 = 0$ in the standard state for this hydrogen half-reaction.

PROBLEM 427 What happens to the voltage of the hydrogen electrode when the pressure of hydrogen is increased to 100 atm, assuming the concentration of $H^+$ stays at 1 molal?

SOLUTION: $H_{2(g)} \rightarrow 2H^+ + 2e^-$; $E^0 = 0$

$$E = E^0 - \frac{0.0592}{2} \log \frac{m_{H^+}^2}{p_{H_2}}, \text{ where } m_{H^+} = 1 \text{ and } p_{H_2} = 100.$$

$$E = 0 - 0.0296 \log \frac{1}{100} = (-0.0296)(\log 10^{-2}) = (-0.0296)(-2)$$

$$= +0.0592 \text{ volt}.$$

Thus, not surprisingly, the $E$ for $H_{2(100 \text{ atm})} \rightarrow 2H^+(1\ m) + 2e^-$ is more positive than for $H_{2(1 \text{ atm})} \rightarrow 2H^+_{(1\ m)} + 2e^-$. Increasing the pressure of $H_2$ makes for a greater tendency to go to the right.

**PROBLEM 428** What happens to the voltage of the hydrogen electrode when the molality of $H^+$ is cut to $10^{-2}\ m$, assuming the hydrogen pressure stays at 1 atm?

SOLUTION: $H_{2(g)} \rightarrow 2H^+ + 2e^-$; $E^0 = 0$.

$$E = E^0 - \frac{0.0592}{2} \log \frac{m^2_{H^+}}{p_{H_2}}, \text{ where } m_{H^+} = 10^{-2} \text{ and } p_{H_2} = 1.$$

$$E = 0 - 0.0296 \log \frac{(10^{-2})^2}{1} = -0.0296 \log (10^{-4}) = +\textbf{0.118 volt.}$$

■ **PROBLEM 429** What will be the $E$ for the half-reaction $H_{2(g)} \rightarrow 2H^+ + 2e^-$ if $p_{H_2} = 100$ atm and $m_{H^+} = 10^{-2}$?

ANSWER: $E = +\textbf{0.178 volt}$

■ **PROBLEM 430** Given that $E^0 = -1.36$ volt for $2Cl^- \rightarrow Cl_{2(g)} + 2e^-$, what will be the $E$ value if $Cl^-$ is at $10^{-2}\ m$ and $Cl_{2(g)}$ is at 100-atm pressure?

ANSWER: $E = -\textbf{1.54 volt}$

**PROBLEM 431** What $E$ do you expect for $Pb_{(s)} \rightarrow Pb^{++} + 2e^-$ in 0.015 $m$ $Pb^{++}$ solution? The $E^0$ is $+0.13$ volt.

SOLUTION: $Pb_{(s)} \rightarrow Pb^{++} + 2e^-$; $E^0 = +0.13$ volt.

$$E = E^0 - \frac{0.0592}{2} \log m_{Pb^{++}}, \text{ where } m_{Pb^{++}} = 0.015.$$

$$E = +0.13 - 0.0296 \log (0.015), \text{ where } \log (0.015) = -1.824.$$

$$E = +\textbf{0.18.}$$

[*Note:* This problem illustrates the general point that for solids, such as $Pb_{(s)}$, there is no effective way to change their concentration from their standard-state values. They are assigned unit activity, which means we can ignore them in working with the Nernst equation.]

**PROBLEM 432** What will be the $E$ for the half-reaction $2H_2O + HAsO_2 \rightarrow H_3AsO_4 + 2H^+ + 2e^-$ under conditions where $HAsO_2$ is 0.10 $m$; $H_3AsO_4$ is 0.050 $m$; $H^+$ is $10^{-6}$ $m$? The $E^0$ for this half-reaction is $-0.56$ volt.

SOLUTION: $2H_2O + HAsO_2 \rightarrow H_3AsO_4 + 2H^+ + 2e^-$; $E^0 = -0.56$ volt.

$$E = E^0 - \frac{0.0592}{2} \log \frac{(m_{H_3AsO_4})(m_{H^+})^2}{m_{HAsO_2}}.$$

$$E = -0.56 - 0.0296 \log \frac{(0.050)(10^{-6})^2}{0.10} = -0.20 \text{ volt}.$$

[*Note:* This problem illustrates several points. One is that $H_2O$ is ignored, again on the basis that its activity does not change perceptibly from the standard state. The other point to note is that when there are several species showing up on one side of a half-reaction, their concentrations (taken to the appropriate powers) are multiplied together in setting up the logarithm term.]

■**PROBLEM 433** Given that $E^0 = -1.00$ volt for $4Cl^- + Au_{(s)} \rightarrow AuCl_4^- + 3e^-$. What will be the $E$ for this half-reaction if the $Cl^-$ concentration is 0.10 $m$ and the concentration of $AuCl_4^-$ is 0.20 $m$?

ANSWER: $E = -1.06$ volt

■**PROBLEM 434** Given that $E^0 = -0.96$ volt for $2H_2O + NO_{(g)} \rightarrow NO_3^- + 4H^+ + 3e^-$, what will be the $E$ for this half-reaction if the pressure of $NO_{(g)}$ is 0.01 atm, the concentration of $NO_3^-$ is 0.50 $m$, and the concentration of $H^+$ is $2 \times 10^{-2}$ $m$?

ANSWER: $E = -0.86$ volt

**PROBLEM 435** What will be the $E$ for the reaction $Pb_{(s)} + 2H^+ \rightarrow Pb^{++} + H_{2(g)}$ under conditions where $H^+$ is 0.010 $m$, $Pb^{++}$ is 0.10 $m$, and $p_{H_2}$ is $10^{-6}$ atm?

SOLUTION: (Use the Nernst equation with the same procedure as above, putting all the species on the right of the chemical equation in the numerator and all the species on the left in the denominator. For $n$, note that two electrons are being transferred from Pb to $2H^+$. This could be figured out either from noting that one Pb goes to one $Pb^{++}$ plus two electrons or that two $H^+$ pick up two electrons to form one $H_2$.)

But first we need to figure out the $E^0$ from the values in Appendix D.

$$Pb_{(s)} \rightarrow Pb^{++} + 2e^- \qquad\qquad E^0 = +0.13 \text{ volt}$$
$$\underline{2H^+ + 2e^- \rightarrow H_{2(g)} \qquad\qquad E^0 = 0}$$
$$Pb_{(s)} + 2H^+ \rightarrow Pb^{++} + H_{2(g)} \qquad E^0 = +0.13 \text{ volt}$$

$$E = E^0 - \frac{0.0592}{2} \log \frac{(m_{Pb^{++}})(p_{H_2})}{(m_{H^+})^2}$$

$$= +0.13 - 0.0296 \log \frac{(0.10)(10^{-6})}{(0.010)^2} = 0.22 \text{ volt}$$

**PROBLEM 436**   What will be the $E$ for the reaction $2Al_{(s)} + 3I_{2(s)} \rightarrow 2Al^{+3} + 6I^-$ under conditions where $Al^{+3}$ is 0.10 $m$ and $I^-$ is 0.010 $m$?

SOLUTION: 
$$Al_{(s)} \rightarrow Al^{+3} + 3e^- \qquad\qquad E^0 = +1.66 \text{ volts}$$
$$\underline{I_{2(s)} + 2e^- \rightarrow 2I^- \qquad\qquad E^0 = +0.54 \text{ volt}}$$
$$2Al_{(s)} + 3I_{2(s)} \rightarrow 2Al^{+3} + 6I^- \qquad E^0 = +2.20 \text{ volts}$$

Recall that the $E^0$ for a total reaction is just the sum of the $E^0$'s for the individual half-reactions, provided the sign is consistent with the direction of reaction as it actually occurs. However, to get the net balanced equation we need to double the first half-reaction and triple the second half-reaction before adding the half-reactions up. To get $n$ for the total reaction $2Al_{(s)} + 3I_{2(s)} \rightarrow 2Al^{+3} + 6I^-$ we can note that $2Al_{(s)}$ must give up six electrons and $3I_{2(s)}$ must pick up six electrons to accomplish the process. Therefore, $n = 6$.

$$E = E^0 - \frac{0.0592}{6} \log (m_{Al^{+3}})^2 (m_{I^-})^6.$$

Note that, since there is only solid phase on the left of the net chemical equation, no species appear in the denominator of the logarithm term:

$$m_{Al^{+3}} = 0.10 \ m; \ m_{I^-} = 0.010 \ m.$$

$$E = 2.20 - 0.00987 \log (0.10)^2 (0.010)^6 = +2.34 \text{ volts}.$$

**PROBLEM 437**   Calculate the $E$ for the reaction $2H_{2(g)} + O_{2(g)} \rightarrow 2H_2O$, when $p_{H_2} = 5.0$ atm, $p_{O_2} = 2.5$ atm, and $m_{H^+} = 0.60 \ m$.

SOLUTION: $H_{2(g)} \rightarrow 2H^+ + 2e^-$ $\qquad E^0 = 0$
$\qquad \dfrac{O_{2(g)} + 4H^+ + 4e^- \rightarrow 2H_2O}{2H_{2(g)} + O_{2(g)} \rightarrow 2H_2O}$ $\qquad \dfrac{E^0 = +1.23 \text{ volts}}{E^0 = +1.23 \text{ volts}}$

$$E = E^0 - \frac{0.0592}{n} \log \frac{1}{(p_{H_2})^2 (p_{O_2})}, \text{ where } n = 4$$

$$E = +1.23 - \frac{0.0592}{4} \log \frac{1}{(5.0)^2 (2.5)} = +1.26 \text{ volts}$$

■ PROBLEM 438  Calculate the $E^0$ for the reaction $2H^+ + 2I^- + H_3AsO_4 \rightarrow I_2 + HAsO_2 + 2H_2O$. Should this reaction go under standard conditions? What happens when $H^+$ is decreased from 1 $m$ to $10^{-3}$ $m$?

ANSWER: $E^0 = 0.02$ volt, so the reaction should go spontaneously from left to right under standard conditions. If $H^+$ is decreased from 1 $m$ to $10^{-3}$ $m$, $E$ becomes $-0.16$ volt, so the spontaneous tendency reverses toward the left.

■ PROBLEM 439  The $E^0$ for the reaction $2H_2O + 2I_2 + 5O_{2(g)} \rightarrow 4IO_3^- + 4H^+$ has a value of $+0.03$ volt. To what concentration must the $H^+$ be adjusted, leaving everything else constant, so as to make $E = 0$?

ANSWER: The $H^+$ would have to be made equal to 340 $m$. [*Note:* This would be such a concentrated solution that the Nernst equation given above would no longer be valid.]

■ PROBLEM 440  Given that $E^0 = 0$ for $H_{2(g)} \rightarrow 2H^+ + 2e^-$, what would be the $E$ for this half-reaction in pure water? Pure water is neutral with $H^+$ concentration at $1.0 \times 10^{-7}$ $m$. Assume the $H_2$ pressure stays at 1 atm.

ANSWER: $E = +0.414$ volt

■ PROBLEM 441  Given that $E^0 = -1.23$ volts for $2H_2O \rightarrow O_2 + 4H^+ + 4e^-$, what would $E$ become in pure water, assuming everything else stays at standard conditions?

ANSWER: $E = -0.82$ volt

■ **PROBLEM** 442 The $E^0$ for oxidation of $Cl^-$ by $Cr_2O_7^=$ to give $Cl_2$ and $Cr^{+3}$ in acidic solution is $-0.03$ volt, so we do not expect this reaction to go very far. To what value should the $H^+$ concentration be adjusted to make $E$ at least equal to zero?

ANSWER: **1.65** $m$

■ **PROBLEM** 443 Assuming all dissolved species are at $1$ $m$ concentration, what pressure of hydrogen would be required theoretically to reverse the reaction $Pb_{(s)} + 2H^+ \rightarrow Pb^{++} + H_{2(g)}$?

ANSWER: **25,000 atm**

# 11

# SOLUTIONS

(a) How do we express concentrations in solution? (b) What are some of the quantitative relations between the concentration of a solution and its properties (e.g., freezing point, boiling point, vapor pressure)?

For describing the concentration of a solution, the following are in common use, more or less in order of decreasing importance: molarity, normality, molality, mole fraction, formality, weight per cent, and volume per cent.

## *Molarity*

The molarity of a solution is defined as the number of moles of solute per liter of solution. It is usually designated by $M$. Unless otherwise specified, the solvent is assumed to be water, although in cases where ambiguity may arise, we often talk of *aqueous solutions*. Since we assume the solvent to be water, we need for the molarity only a number (which tells us how many moles of solute are used to make a liter of solution) and a formula to tell what the solute is. Thus, 0.15 molar HCl (also written 0.15 $M$ HCl) means a concentration corresponding to 0.15 mole of HCl per liter of aqueous solution.

Since the molarity only gives us the strength of the solution (and not how much we have of it) we generally need to specify how much solution we are working with, so we can know how much reagent in total is available. The number of moles of solute available is equal to (molarity) $\times$ (volume in liters). This is consistent dimensionally, moles = (moles/liter)(liters) = moles.

*The most common source of difficulty in working molarity problems is failure to distinguish between moles and moles per liter.*

**PROBLEM 444**   A solution is made by dissolving 127 g ethyl alcohol ($C_2H_5OH$) in enough water to make 1.35 l of solution. What is the molarity of the solution?

SOLUTION: One mole $C_2H_5OH$ weighs 46.07 g.

$$127 \text{ g } C_2H_5OH = \frac{127 \text{ g}}{46.07 \text{ g/mole}} = 2.76 \text{ moles.}$$

We have 2.76 moles $C_2H_5OH$ in 1.35 l solution.

Therefore, the molarity $= \dfrac{\text{moles}}{\text{liter}} = \dfrac{2.76 \text{ moles}}{1.35 \text{ l}} = 2.04 \ M.$

[*Note:* At this point we might re-emphasize that the dividing line between a numerator and a denominator means "per." So, $\dfrac{\text{moles}}{\text{liter}}$ is "moles *per* liter."]

**PROBLEM 445**   You have a solution which is 0.693 $M$ HCl. You need for a certain reaction to have 0.0525 mole HCl. How much solution do you take?

SOLUTION: 0.693 $M$ HCl means 0.693 mole HCl per liter of solution. You need 0.0525 mole HCl. Therefore, if you divide moles needed by moles per liter, you will have liters needed.

$$\frac{0.0525 \text{ mole HCl}}{0.693 \text{ mole/liter}} = 0.0758 \text{ l.}$$

■ **PROBLEM 446**   If you dissolve 8.96 g $H_2SO_4$ in enough water to make 396 ml solution, what will be its molarity?

ANSWER: 0.231 $M$ $H_2SO_4$

■ PROBLEM 447 What volume of 0.231 $M$ $H_2SO_4$ would you need to take to supply $1.50 \times 10^{-3}$ mole $H_2SO_4$ for a given reaction?

ANSWER: **6.49 ml**

PROBLEM 448 Suppose you mix 3.65 l of 0.105 $M$ NaCl with 5.11 l of 0.162 $M$ NaCl. Assuming the volumes are additive—that is, that the total volume after mixing is 8.76 l—what would be the concentration of the final solution?

SOLUTION: 3.65 l of 0.105 $M$ NaCl contributes (3.65 liters) $\left( 0.105 \dfrac{\text{mole}}{\text{liter}} \right)$
= 0.383 mole NaCl.

5.11 l 0.162 $M$ NaCl contributes (5.11 liters) $\left( 0.162 \dfrac{\text{mole}}{\text{liter}} \right)$
= 0.828 mole NaCl.

The total moles of NaCl is $0.383 + 0.828 = 1.211$ moles.
The total volume of the solution is 8.76 l.

Therefore, the final concentration is $\dfrac{1.211 \text{ moles}}{8.76 \text{ liters}} = 0.138 \; M$.

PROBLEM 449 You have a supply of 0.100 $M$ $KMnO_4$. You wish to make 40.0 ml of $1.95 \times 10^{-3}$ $M$ $KMnO_4$ by diluting with water. How do you proceed? Assume volumes are additive.

SOLUTION: You want 40.0 ml of $1.95 \times 10^{-3}$ $M$ $KMnO_4$.
$1.95 \times 10^{-3}$ $M$ means $1.95 \times 10^{-3}$ mole $KMnO_4$ per liter.
Therefore, in 40.0 ml, or 0.0400 liter, you will have

$$(0.0400 \text{ liter}) \left( 1.95 \times 10^{-3} \frac{\text{mole } KMnO_4}{\text{liter}} \right) = 7.80 \times 10^{-5} \text{ mole.}$$

To get this $7.80 \times 10^{-5}$ mole $KMnO_4$ you need to use 0.100 $M$ $KMnO_4$, which contains 0.100 mole $KMnO_4$ per liter. If you divide moles required by moles per liter, you will get liters of 0.100 $M$ solution needed.

$$\frac{7.80 \times 10^{-5} \text{ mole}}{0.100 \text{ mole/liter}} = 7.80 \times 10^{-4} \text{ liter, or 0.780 ml.}$$

So, you take **0.780 ml of 0.100 $M$ $KMnO_4$ solution and add enough water to bring the total volume to 40.0 ml.**

■ PROBLEM 450 You wish to make 0.150 l of 0.240 $M$ $CuSO_4$ solution. How many grams of $CuSO_4 \cdot 5H_2O$ crystals will you need?

ANSWER: **8.99 g**

■ PROBLEM 451 You mix 10.0 ml of 0.10 $M$ HCl, 23.5 ml of 0.25 $M$ HCl, and 8.6 ml of 0.32 $M$ HCl. Assuming volumes are additive, what will be the molarity of the final solution?

ANSWER: **0.23 $M$**

PROBLEM 452 If you have a supply of 0.150 $M$ NaOH solution and a supply of 0.250 $M$ NaOH, in what ratio should you mix these solutions to prepare some 0.169 $M$ NaOH? Assume additive volumes.

SOLUTION: Let $x$ = liters of 0.150 $M$ NaOH to be used and let $y$ = liters of 0.250 $M$ NaOH to be used.

Total moles of NaOH = $0.150x + 0.250y$.

Total volume of solution = $x + y$.

Final concentration = $\dfrac{(0.150x + 0.250y)\text{ mole}}{(x + y)\text{ liters}}$ = 0.169 $M$.

Solve this equation for the ratio $x/y$.

Cross-multiply to get $0.150x + 0.250y = 0.169x + 0.169y$.

Simplify to $0.081y = 0.019x$.

Solve to $\dfrac{x}{y} = \dfrac{0.081}{0.019} = 4.3$.

Therefore, we need to take **4.3 times as much 0.150 $M$ NaOH** solution as we take of the 0.250 $M$ NaOH solution.

■ PROBLEM 453 You have 1 l of 0.183 $M$ HCl and 1 l of 0.381 $M$ HCl. What is the maximum volume you can make of 0.243 $M$ HCl from these two solutions alone? Assume additive volumes.

ANSWER: **1.43 l**

■■ PROBLEM 454 You are given 1 l of 0.10 $M$ $H_2SO_4$, 1 l of 0.20 $M$ $H_2SO_4$, and 1 l of 0.30 $M$ $H_2SO_4$. Using only these sources—i.e., no additional water—what is the maximum volume of 0.22 $M$ $H_2SO_4$ you can make? Assume additive volumes.

ANSWER: **2.5 l**

## *Normality*

The normality of a solution is defined as the number of gram-equivalents of solute per liter of solution; it usually is designated by a capital $N$ preceded by a number.   $6\,N$ HCl is read "six normal HCl" and means a solution which contains 6 gram-equivalents of HCl per liter of solution.   Normality is a convenient concentration term for work with solutions of acids and bases and also for work with solutions of oxidizing and reducing agents.   As discussed in detail in Chapter 8, the concept of gram-equivalent simplifies acid-base calculations and oxidation-reduction calculations.   Since the bulk of the work with such reactions is done by mixing solutions, the importance of normality as a concentration unit cannot be slighted.   You should review Chapter 8, albeit rapidly, at this point.

For acids and bases, the points to remember are these: one gram-equivalent of acid furnishes one mole of $H^+$.   One gram-equivalent of base uses up one mole of $H^+$.   In a neutralization reaction, one gram-equivalent of any acid is required for stoichiometric reaction with one gram-equivalent of any base.   Since "normality" specifies the number of gram-equivalents *per liter*, the product of normality times volume (*in liters*) gives the number of gram-equivalents of the reagent.   The requirement that the number of gram-equivalents of acid be equal to the number of gram-equivalents of base leads to the simple relation that the (normality of the acid solution)(volume of the acid solution) = (normality of the base solution)(volume of base solution).

**PROBLEM 455**   You are directed to make a solution of phosphoric acid, $H_3PO_4$, for use in a neutralization reaction where all three hydrogens are to be neutralized.   How many grams $H_3PO_4$ do you need to make 18.68 ml of 0.1079 $N$ $H_3PO_4$?

SOLUTION: 0.1079 $N$ means 0.1079 gram-equivalent per liter. 18.68 ml of such solution contains

$$(0.01868 \text{ liter})\left(0.1079\,\frac{\text{gram-equivalent}}{\text{liter}}\right)$$
$$= 0.002016 \text{ gram-equivalent.}$$

One mole $H_3PO_4$ furnishes 3 moles $H^+$, so one mole $H_3PO_4$ is the same as 3 gram-equivalents.  One mole $H_3PO_4$ weighs 97.995 g, so one gram-equivalent is $\frac{1}{3}$ of this, or 32.665 g.

To get 0.002016 gram-equivalent $H_3PO_4$ we need to take

$$(0.002016 \text{ gram-equivalent}) \left( 32.665 \ \frac{g}{\text{gram-equivalent}} \right)$$
$$= 0.06585 \text{ g.}$$

**PROBLEM 456**  What is the normality of an $H_2SO_4$ solution, 23.67 ml of which is required to neutralize 26.73 ml of 0.0936 $N$ NaOH solution?

SOLUTION: (Figure out how many gram-equivalents of base you have. You will then know how many gram-equivalents of acid you will need.  Then calculate the concentration needed.)

0.0936 $N$ NaOH means 0.0936 gram-equivalent NaOH per liter of solution.  You have 0.02673 liter, or

$$(0.02673 \text{ liter}) \left( 0.0936 \ \frac{\text{gram-equivalent}}{\text{liter}} \right)$$
$$= 0.00250 \text{ gram-equivalent NaOH.}$$

You need an equal number of gram-equivalents acid, so you need 0.00250 gram-equivalent $H_2SO_4$, which you will find in the 23.67 ml acid solution.

Therefore, the normality of the acid solution must be

$$\frac{0.00250 \text{ gram-equivalent}}{0.02367 \text{ liter}} = 0.106 \ N$$

■ **PROBLEM 457**  What is the normality of an $H_2SO_4$ solution, 13.68 ml of which is required to neutralize 0.0539 gram-equivalent of base?

ANSWER: 3.94 $N$

**PROBLEM 458**  You are given a solution which is $7.69 \times 10^{-3}$ $M$ $Ca(OH)_2$.  What would be its normality for complete neutralization?

SOLUTION: One mole $Ca(OH)_2$ furnishes 2 moles $OH^-$ if completely neutralized.  One mole $Ca(OH)_2$ therefore equals 2 gram-equivalents.

$7.69 \times 10^{-3}$ $M$ means $7.69 \times 10^{-3}$ mole/l.

$7.69 \times 10^{-3}$ mole is $(7.69 \times 10^{-3} \text{ mole}) \left( 2 \dfrac{\text{gram-equivalents}}{\text{mole}} \right)$

$= 1.54 \times 10^{-2}$ gram-equivalent $Ca(OH)_2$.

$7.69 \times 10^{-3}$ mole/l means $1.54 \times 10^{-2}$ gram-equivalent/l.

So, $7.69 \times 10^{-3}$ $M$ $Ca(OH)_2$ is $1.54 \times 10^{-2}$ $N$ $Ca(OH)_2$.

PROBLEM 459  You are given a solution which is $6.68 \times 10^{-3}$ $M$ $H_3PO_4$. If you add 36.2 ml water to 18.6 ml of this solution, what will be the normality of the final solution? Assume additive volumes.

SOLUTION: You start with 18.6 ml of $6.68 \times 10^{-3}$ $M$ $H_3PO_4$.

This contains $(0.0186 \text{ liter}) \left( 6.68 \times 10^{-3} \dfrac{\text{mole}}{\text{liter}} \right)$

$= 1.24 \times 10^{-4}$ mole $H_3PO_4$.

When you add water, you do not change the number of moles $H_3PO_4$ present.

One mole $H_3PO_4$ equals three gram-equivalents.

$1.24 \times 10^{-4}$ mole $H_3PO_4 = 3.72 \times 10^{-4}$ gram-equivalent $H_3PO_4$.

The final volume of solution is $36.2 + 18.6 = 54.8$ ml.

Therefore, the final normality is

$$\frac{3.72 \times 10^{-4} \text{ gram-equivalent}}{0.0548 \text{ l}} = 6.79 \times 10^{-3} \ N \ H_3PO_4.$$

■ PROBLEM 460  If you mix 36.82 ml of $6.68 \times 10^{-3}$ $N$ $H_3PO_4$ with 21.87 ml of $5.40 \times 10^{-3}$ $N$ $H_3PO_4$, what will be the normality of the final solution? Assume additive volumes.

ANSWER: $6.20 \times 10^{-3}$ $N$

■ PROBLEM 461  You dump into a beaker the following ingredients: 0.438 g $Ba(OH)_2$, $1.55 \times 10^{-3}$ mole $Ba(OH)_2$, $1.05 \times 10^{-3}$ gram-equivalent $Ba(OH)_2$, 27.00 ml of 0.0103 $M$ $Ba(OH)_2$, and 38.69 ml of 0.075 $N$ $Ba(OH)_2$. If the total final volume of the solution is 65.82 ml, what is its normality (for complete neutralization)?

ANSWER: $0.193$ $N$

For oxidizing and reducing agents, the points to remember are these: One gram-equivalent of a reducing agent furnishes one mole of electrons.   One gram-equivalent of an oxidizing agent uses up one mole of electrons.   In an oxidation-reduction reaction, one gram-equivalent of any reducing agent is required for stoichiometric reaction with one gram-equivalent of any oxidizing agent.   Again, since normality gives gram-equivalents per liter, the product (normality of oxidizing solution)(volume of oxidizing solution) gives the number of gram-equivalents of oxidizing agent.   This must equal the number of gram-equivalents of reducing agent, which is given by (normality of reducing solution)(volume of reducing solution).

Because oxidizing and reducing agents can frequently form a variety of products for which the electron change differs, it is necessary to make clear what electron change is being considered when the normality of an oxidizing or reducing solution is defined.   In other words, you are supposed to tell what the solution will be used for before you can really interpret a normality label on the bottle.

PROBLEM 461A   You wish to make up 17.31 ml of 0.692 $N$ $KMnO_4$ solution to be used in a reaction where $MnO_4^-$ goes to $Mn^{++}$.   How many grams $KMnO_4$ do you need?

SOLUTION: 0.692 $N$ $KMnO_4$ means 0.692 gram-equivalent $KMnO_4$ per liter.   In 17.31 ml of such a solution, you will have (0.01731 liter)

$$\times \left( 0.692 \, \frac{\text{gram-equivalent}}{\text{liter}} \right), \text{ or } 0.0120 \text{ gram-equivalent } KMnO_4.$$

To be used where $MnO_4^-$ goes to $Mn^{++}$ means a five-electron change.   So, we want one mole $KMnO_4$ to pick up five moles of electrons— i.e., one mole $KMnO_4$ to be five gram-equivalents.
One mole $KMnO_4$ weighs 158.04 g.
One gram-equivalent = $\frac{1}{5}$ mole = $\frac{1}{5}(158.04)$ = 31.608 g.
Since we need 0.0120 gram-equivalent $KMnO_4$, we will need to take

$$(0.0120 \text{ gram-equivalent}) \left( 31.608 \, \frac{g}{\text{gram-equivalent}} \right), \text{ or } \mathbf{0.379 \ g.}$$

■ PROBLEM 462.   You wish to make up 17.31 ml of 0.692 $N$ $KMnO_4$ solution to be used in a reaction where $MnO_4^-$ will go to $MnO_2$.   How many grams $KMnO_4$ do you need?
ANSWER: **0.632 g**

PROBLEM 463   In acidic solution $Cr_2O_7^=$ oxidizes $Sn^{++}$ to form $Cr^{+3}$ and $Sn^{+4}$. How many milliliters of 0.1097 $N$ $K_2Cr_2O_7$ will you need to react with 25.36 ml of 0.2153 $N$ $SnCl_2$ in this way?

SOLUTION: (Figure out how many gram-equivalents you have in the reducing solution. You will then know you need an equal number of gram-equivalents of oxidizing agent.)

0.2153 $N$ means 0.2153 gram-equivalent reducing agent per liter. In 25.36 ml you will have

$$(0.02536 \text{ liter}) \left( 0.2153 \frac{\text{gram-equivalent}}{\text{liter}} \right) = 0.005460 \text{ gram-equiva-}$$

lent reducing agent.

You need 0.005460 gram-equivalent oxidizing agent.

It comes from 0.1097 $N$ $K_2Cr_2O_7$, which means 0.1097 gram-equivalent oxidizing agent per liter.

To get 0.005460 gram-equivalent oxidizing agent, you need to take

$$\frac{0.005460 \text{ gram-equivalent}}{0.1097 \text{ gram-equivalent/l}} = 0.04977 \text{ l or } \mathbf{49.77 \text{ ml}}.$$

PROBLEM 464   Working under conditions where $ClO_3^-$ will go to $Cl^-$, how many ml of $1.79 \times 10^{-3}$ $M$ $NaClO_3$ solution need to be taken to oxidize 36.92 ml of $1.50 \times 10^{-4}$ $N$ $NaHSO_3$ and $2.345 \times 10^{-5}$ gram-equivalent solid $NaHSO_3$ to give $HSO_4^-$?

SOLUTION: (Figure out the total number of gram-equivalents of reducing agent that need to be oxidized. Take enough oxidizing solution to provide the gram-equivalents needed to do this.)

$1.50 \times 10^{-4}$ $N$ $NaHSO_3$ means $1.50 \times 10^{-4}$ gram-equivalent/l. In 36.92 ml, there will be

$$(0.03692 \text{ l}) \left( 1.50 \times 10^{-4} \frac{\text{gram-equivalent}}{l} \right)$$
$$= 0.554 \times 10^{-5} \text{ gram-equivalent.}$$

This has to be added to the $2.34 \times 10^{-5}$ gram-equivalent to give a total of $2.89 \times 10^{-5}$ gram-equivalent $NaHSO_3$ that needs to be oxidized.

Since one gram-equivalent reducing agent needs one gram-equivalent oxidizing agent, we conclude that $2.89 \times 10^{-5}$ gram-equivalent $NaClO_3$ will be needed. Since the $ClO_3^-$ will go to $Cl^-$, a six-electron change, one mole $NaClO_3$ will act as 6 gram-equivalents. To get $2.89 \times 10^{-5}$ gram-equivalent $NaClO_3$, we need to take

$$(2.89 \times 10^{-5} \text{ gram-equivalent}) \left( \frac{1 \text{ mole}}{6 \text{ gram-equivalents}} \right)$$
$$= 4.82 \times 10^{-6} \text{ mole}.$$

The $NaClO_3$ solution is specified to be $1.79 \times 10^{-3}$ $M$, so we need

$$\frac{4.82 \times 10^{-6} \text{ mole}}{1.79 \times 10^{-3} \text{ mole/l}} = 2.69 \times 10^{-3} \text{ l, or } 2.69 \text{ ml}.$$

■ PROBLEM 465    You are trying to determine the concentration of an unknown $KMnO_4$ solution by allowing it to react with solid $Na_2C_2O_4$ under conditions where $Mn^{++}$ and $CO_2$ will be products. If it takes 18.69 ml of the unknown solution to oxidize 0.1348 g $Na_2C_2O_4$, what is the normality of the solution?
ANSWER: $0.1076$ $N$

■ PROBLEM 466    You are given an unknown oxidizing agent which contains the element X in the $+5$ state. If it takes 26.98 ml of $0.1326$ $N$ $Na_2SO_3$ to reduce $7.16 \times 10^{-4}$ mole $XO(OH)_2^+$ to a lower state, what will be the final oxidation state of X? Assume $SO_3^=$ goes to $SO_4^=$ in the process.
ANSWER: zero

## Molality

A 1 molal solution (designated 1 $m$ and pronounced with a decided accent on the "a" of molal) is a solution in which there is one mole of solute dissolved per kilogram of solvent. For aqueous solutions, this means 1000 g of $H_2O$ plus one mole of solute. As an example, 1 $m$ NaCl is read "one molal NaCl" and designates a solution composed of one mole of NaCl per 1000 g of $H_2O$. The big advantage of molality, one that appeals mightily to the physical chemists, is that the molality of a given solution does not change if the temperature of the solution is changed. The same cannot be said for molarity where, for example, the expansion usually brought about by raising the temperature changes the volume of the solution and therefore changes the moles per liter of solution.  For this reason, the high-precision chemist affixes to his molarity designation the temperature at which the label applies— e.g., 0.6843 $M$ HCl (18°C).  Fortunately, at least near room temperature, solutions do not expand much, so the change of molarity with temperature is likely to be small (less than 1% change for a 10°C rise). The other fortunate fact is that the density of water and of most dilute aqueous solutions is very close to 1 g per ml, which means that molarity will be almost equal to molality *for dilute solutions*.  (Dilute here means less concentrated than 0.01 $M$ or 0.01 $m$.)

To convert from molality to molarity, we need to know the density of the solution.  Otherwise, we cannot figure out the volume of solution.

PROBLEM 467   A solution is made by dissolving 1.69 g NaCl in 869 g $H_2O$.  What is its molality (or molal concentration)?

SOLUTION: One mole NaCl weighs 58.44 g.

$$1.68 \text{ g NaCl} = \frac{1.68 \text{ g}}{58.44 \text{ g/mole}} = 0.0287 \text{ mole NaCl.}$$

869 g $H_2O$ = 0.869 kg $H_2O$.

$$\text{Molality} = \frac{0.0287 \text{ mole NaCl}}{0.869 \text{ kg } H_2O} = 0.0330 \text{ } m \text{ NaCl.}$$

PROBLEM 468   How many grams of $Al_2(SO_4)_3$ do you need to make 87.62 g of 0.0162 $m$ $Al_2(SO_4)_3$ solution?

SOLUTION: 0.0162 $m$ $Al_2(SO_4)_3$ means 0.0162 mole $Al_2(SO_4)_3$ per kg $H_2O$.

One mole $Al_2(SO_4)_3$ weighs 342.15 g.

0.0162 mole $Al_2(SO_4)_3$ weighs (0.0162 mole) $\left( 342.15 \dfrac{g}{\text{mole}} \right) = 5.54$ g.

So, in this solution there are 5.54 g $Al_2(SO_4)_3$ per 1000 g $H_2O$.  Stated another way, there are 5.54 g $Al_2(SO_4)_3$ per 1005.54 g solution, where we have simply added the weights of the two components. If there are 5.54 g $Al_2(SO_4)_3$ per 1005.54 g solution, then given 87.62 g of the solution there will be

$$(87.62 \text{ g solution}) \left( \frac{5.54 \text{ g } Al_2(SO_4)_3}{1005.54 \text{ g solution}} \right) = 0.483 \text{ g } Al_2(SO_4)_3.$$

**PROBLEM 469** You have a solution which contains 410.3 g $H_2SO_4$ per liter of solution at 20°C. If the density of the solution is 1.243 g per ml, what is the molality and molarity of the solution?

SOLUTION: The density of the solution is 1.243 g/ml.

Therefore, 1 l solution weighs $\left(1.243 \dfrac{g}{ml}\right)\left(1000 \dfrac{ml}{liter}\right)$ = 1243 g.

We are told that 410.3 g of this is $H_2SO_4$, so the rest of the weight (1243 − 410 = 833 g) must be water.

$$410.3 \text{ g } H_2SO_4 = \frac{410.3 \text{ g}}{98.078 \text{ g/mole}} = 4.183 \text{ moles.}$$

833 g $H_2O$ = 0.833 kg $H_2O$.

$$\text{Molality} = \frac{4.183 \text{ moles } H_2SO_4}{0.833 \text{ kg } H_2O} = 5.02 \ m \ H_2SO_4.$$

$$\text{Molarity} = \frac{4.183 \text{ moles } H_2SO_4}{1 \text{ l solution}} = 4.183 \ M \ H_2SO_4.$$

■ **PROBLEM 470** How many grams of 0.207 $m$ $CuSO_4$ solution would you need to take to get 1.45 g $CuSO_4$?

ANSWER: **45.3 g solution**

■ **PROBLEM 471** Suppose you mix 1.86 g HCl, 0.0302 mole HCl, and 26.9 g 0.105 $m$ HCl solution. What will be the molality of the resulting solution?

ANSWER: **3.13 $m$ HCl**

■■ **PROBLEM 472** Suppose you mix equal volumes of 4.55 $m$ $HNO_3$ (density equals 1.1294 g/ml) and 4.55 $M$ $HNO_3$ (density equals 1.1469 g/ml). What will be the molal concentration of the final solution?

ANSWER: **4.92 $m$ $HNO_3$**

## Mole fraction

For some solutions, particularly gases and nonaqueous solutions, the most useful concentration expression is the one that tells what fraction of the molecules present are of a particular species.  Thus, mole fraction is the number of moles of one substance in the solution divided by the total number of moles of all kinds of substances in the solution. Because mole fraction is computed as moles divided by moles, it has no units.  Furthermore, if you know the mole fraction of all but one component in a solution, then you can calculate the mole fraction of that last component from the fact that in a given mixture the sum of the mole fractions equals unity.

**PROBLEM**  473  A box contains $3.89 \times 10^{-3}$ mole $N_2$ gas and $1.54 \times 10^{-3}$ mole $H_2$ gas.  What is the mole fraction of each component present?

SOLUTION: You have $3.89 \times 10^{-3}$ mole $N_2$ plus $1.54 \times 10^{-3}$ mole $H_2$, which makes a total of $5.43 \times 10^{-3}$ mole present.
Of the total $5.43 \times 10^{-3}$ mole, $N_2$ accounts for $3.89 \times 10^{-3}$ mole. Therefore, the mole fraction of $N_2$ is

$$\frac{3.89 \times 10^{-3} \text{ mole } N_2}{5.43 \times 10^{-3} \text{ mole total}} = 0.716.$$

The mole fraction of $H_2$ must be $1 - 0.716 = 0.284$.  Or, calculating it directly, the mole fraction of $H_2$ is

$$\frac{1.54 \times 10^{-3} \text{ mole } H_2}{5.43 \times 10^{-3} \text{ mole total}} = 0.284.$$

**PROBLEM**  474  What is the mole fraction of $C_2H_5OH$ in an aqueous solution that is simultaneously 3.86 $m$ $C_2H_5OH$ and 2.14 $m$ $CH_3OH$?

SOLUTION: 3.86 $m$ $C_2H_5OH$ means 3.86 moles $C_2H_5OH$ per kg $H_2O$.
2.14 $m$ $CH_3OH$ means 2.14 moles $CH_3OH$/kg $H_2O$.
In 1 kg $H_2O$, we have $\dfrac{1000 \text{ g}}{18.015 \text{ g/mole}} = 55.51$ moles $H_2O$.
Total moles in the solution = 3.86 moles $C_2H_5OH$ + 2.14 moles $CH_3OH$ + 55.51 moles $H_2O$ = 61.51 moles.
Mole fraction of $C_2H_5OH = \dfrac{3.86 \text{ moles } C_2H_5OH}{61.51 \text{ moles total}} = 0.0628.$

■ P R O B L E M  475  A solution is made by dissolving 2.869 g Na in 48.96 g liquid $NH_3$.  What is the mole fraction of Na in the final solution?

ANSWER: 0.0416

■■ P R O B L E M  476  You are given 6.08 g of a solution which contains 0.0862 mole fraction of Na in liquid $NH_3$. How many grams $NH_3$ must you distill off so the Na concentrates to a mole fraction of 0.1530?

ANSWER: 2.58 g

### Formality

Formality was introduced as a concentration unit because some people felt that there was too much ambiguity in the term molarity, particularly when it was used to describe solutions in which the species placed in solution broke up or otherwise changed to create other species.  In such cases, the only thing you could be sure of was what you put into the solution; only formally did you know what was there after the interaction with the solvent had occurred.  There was also another cogent consideration.  In many cases we know only the simplest formula of the solute, not its true molecular formula.  In such cases, one mole of solute means nothing unless the precise formula is also written down for which the formula-weight can be unambiguously calculated.  This puts the burden of describing the solution concentration in terms of a specified formula, and in this sense the term "formal" and "formality" are closely tied to the formula given.

A "one formal solution," designated as 1 $F$, means a solution in which one gram-formula-weight of the specific formula-designated solute has been dissolved in enough water to make 1 liter of solution. As an example, 0.69 $F$ HCl is read "oh point six nine formal HCl" and designates a solution wherein 0.69 gram-formula-weights of HCl have been dissolved per liter of solution.  Since most people would call such a solution 0.69 $M$ HCl, there are arguments for not bothering with formal concentration units at all.  However, they have considerable use, particularly on the West Coast, and you should know what all the shouting is about.  The case in favor of "formal" and "formality" is easier to defend once we are aware of the fact that 0.69 $M$ HCl has *no* HCl molecules in solution, all of them having busted up into $H^+$ and $Cl^-$.

**PROBLEM** 477 If you dissolve 1.89 g $Na_2SO_4$ in enough water to make 0.086 l solution, what will be its formal concentration?

SOLUTION: The formula-weight of $Na_2SO_4$ is 142.04.

$$1.89 \text{ g } Na_2SO_4 = \frac{1.89 \text{ g}}{142.04 \text{ g/g-formula-wt}}$$
$$= 0.0133 \text{ gram-formula-weight}.$$

Formality is defined as the number of gram-formula-weights per liter, so we divide 0.0133 by 0.086:

$$\frac{0.0133 \text{ g-formula-wt}}{0.086 \text{ l}} = 0.15 \ F$$

**PROBLEM** 478 You are given 0.692 l of 0.106 $F$ HCl. Knowing that HCl in water is 100% dissociated into $H^+$ and $Cl^-$, how many moles of $Cl^-$ are there in this sample?

SOLUTION: 0.106 $F$ HCl means 0.106 gram-formula-weight of HCl per liter.

Since we have 0.692 l solution, we must have used (0.692 l) $\times$

$$\left( 0.106 \frac{\text{g-formula-wt}}{\text{l}} \right) = 0.0734 \text{ gram-formula-weight}.$$

One gram-formula-weight of HCl furnishes one mole $H^+$ and one mole $Cl^-$ when it dissociates.

Therefore, 0.0734 gram-formula-weight of HCl dissociates to furnish **0.0734 mole $Cl^-$**.

■ **PROBLEM** 479 You wish to make up 1.638 l of $4.52 \times 10^{-3}$ $F$ $CuSO_4$ solution. How many grams $CuSO_4$ do you need?

ANSWER: **1.18 g**

■■ **PROBLEM** 480 Assuming $Al_2(SO_4)_3$ in water is completely dissociated into $2Al^{+3}$ and $3SO_4^=$, calculate the molar concentration of sulfate ion in a solution made by dissolving 3.86 g $Al_2(SO_4)_3 \cdot 18H_2O$ in 126.9 ml of 0.0732 $F$ $Al_2(SO_4)_3$. The final volume of the solution is 128.2 ml.

ANSWER: **0.353 $M$ $SO_4^=$**

## *Per cent by weight and per cent by volume*

Since many solutions are made up simply by weighing out the various constituents and mixing them up, it is a simple matter to calculate what per cent of the total weight of the solution is contributed by each component. Obviously, the sum of all the per cents by weight should add up to 100%.

PROBLEM 481 The concentrated sulfuric acid that is peddled commercially is normally 95% $H_2SO_4$ by weight. If its density is 1.834 g/ml, what is its molarity?

SOLUTION: Take 1 l of the solution. Since its density is given as 1.834 g/ml, you know that 1 l must weigh (1000 ml) $\left(1.834 \frac{g}{ml}\right)$ = 1834 g.

Of this total weight, 95% is $H_2SO_4$.

(0.95)(1834 g) = 1700 g $H_2SO_4$.

One mole $H_2SO_4$ weighs 98.08 g.

In 1700 g $H_2SO_4$, we have $\dfrac{1700 \text{ g}}{98.08 \text{ g/mole}}$ = 17 moles.

Since we have 17 moles $H_2SO_4$ per liter of solution, the molarity of the solution must be 17 $M$ $H_2SO_4$.

■ PROBLEM 482 Commercial concentrated nitric acid is usually about 15.5 $M$ $HNO_3$. If its density is 1.409 g/ml, what is its composition expressed as weight per cent $H_2O$?

ANSWER: 30.7%

Per cent by weight as a concentration unit is perfectly straightforward, since every time we add $x$ grams of substance A to $y$ grams of substance B we always get $x + y$ grams of mixture. Per cent by volume has the added fillip that volumes do not behave this way. In fact, if we dissolve $x$ ml of A in $y$ ml of B we will generally not end up with $x + y$ ml of solution. Still, per cent by volume is defined as the per cent of the final volume that is represented by the initial volume of the component in question. As a specific example, if we mix 50.00 ml $C_2H_5OH$ with 50.00 ml $H_2O$ we get only 96.54 ml total solution. If we compute the per cent by volume of $C_2H_5OH$, we get

$$\frac{50.00 \text{ ml } C_2H_5OH}{96.54 \text{ ml total solution}} \times 100 = 51.79\%.$$

If we compute the per cent by volume of $H_2O$, we get

$$\frac{50.00 \text{ ml } H_2O}{96.54 \text{ ml total solution}} \times 100 = 51.79\%.$$

So, we have the interesting point that per cent by volume will not necessarily add up to a hundred.

PROBLEM 483   A solution is made by adding enough water to 32.86 g $C_2H_5OH$ to make a total volume of 100.00 ml.   If the density of pure $C_2H_5OH$ is 0.7851 g/ml, what will be the concentration of the solution expressed as per cent $C_2H_5OH$ by volume?

SOLUTION: Initial weight of $C_2H_5OH$ is 32.86 g.
We are given its density as 0.7851 g/ml.
Therefore, we know the initial volume of the $C_2H_5OH$ to be

$$\frac{32.86 \text{ g}}{0.7851 \text{ g/ml}} = 41.85 \text{ ml.}$$

We are told that the final volume of the solution is 100.00 ml.
Therefore, % by volume $= \dfrac{41.85 \text{ ml}}{100.00 \text{ ml}} \times 100 = \mathbf{41.85\%.}$

■PROBLEM 484   If 30.00 ml $H_2O$ (density 1.000 g/ml) is mixed with 70.00 ml methyl alcohol ($CH_3OH$; density 0.7958 g/ml), the resulting solution has a density of 0.8866 g/ml. Figure out the concentration of the solution in terms of molarity, molality, per cent by weight, and per cent by volume of $CH_3OH$.
   ANSWER: **17.99** $M$; **57.96** $m$; **65.00%** **by weight; 72.41% by volume**

## Raoult's law

One of the most important observations made for solutions is that the vapor pressure of the solvent is lowered proportionally to the concentration of dissolved particles in the solution.   This is the gist of Raoult's law, which states that the partial pressure, $p_1$, of the solvent above the solution divided by the vapor pressure of the pure solvent, $p_1°$, is equal to the mole fraction of solvent present. If we designate by $x_1$ the mole fraction of solvent in the system, then Raoult's law can be written

$$\frac{p_1}{p_1°} = x_1$$

For a two-component system—that is, one consisting of solvent 1 and solute 2—the mole fractions $x_1$ and $x_2$ must add up to unity. So, we can write $x_1 + x_2 = 1$ or $x_1 = 1 - x_2$. Substituting above, we get

$$\frac{p_1}{p_1°} = 1 - x_2.$$

Solving this for $x_2$, we get

$$x_2 = 1 - \frac{p_1}{p_1°} = \frac{p_1° - p_1}{p_1°}$$

which is another way of stating Raoult's law. This latter part is important because it states that the vapor-pressure lowering, $p_1° - p_1$, is directly proportional to the mole fraction of solute. (Recall that $p_1°$ is a constant number characteristic of the pure solvent.) Experimentally, this is significant because it means that a measurement of the vapor-pressure lowering brought about by the addition of a solute can tell us what fraction of all the particles in the final solution are actually derived from the solute. This may be particularly useful to know when the solute molecules break up into smaller fragments on coming in contact with solvent.

PROBLEM 485    Assuming Raoult's law is followed, what happens to the vapor pressure of water if 43.68 g sugar, $C_{12}H_{22}O_{11}$, is dissolved in 245.0 ml water at 25°C? At 25°C the density of water is 0.9971 g/ml and its vapor pressure is 23.756 mm Hg. Sugar does not dissociate in water.

SOLUTION: (Figure out the mole fraction that is water. Then use Raoult's law to calculate the vapor pressure.)

$$(245.0 \text{ ml H}_2\text{O}) \left( 0.9971 \frac{g}{ml} \right) = 244.3 \text{ g H}_2\text{O}.$$

One mole $H_2O$ is 18.015 g.

244.3 g $H_2O$ is $\dfrac{244.3 \text{ g}}{18.015 \text{ g/mole}}$ = 13.56 moles $H_2O$.

One mole $C_{12}H_{22}O_{11}$ weighs 342.30 g.

43.68 g $C_{12}H_{22}O_{11}$ is $\dfrac{43.68 \text{ g}}{342.30 \text{ g/mole}}$ = 0.128 mole.

Total moles = 13.56 moles $H_2O$ + 0.128 mole sugar = 13.69 moles.

Mole fraction $H_2O$ = $\dfrac{13.56 \text{ moles } H_2O}{13.69 \text{ moles total}}$ = 0.9905.

According to Raoult's law, $p_1 = x_1 p_1°$:

$x_1$ = mole fraction of water = 0.9905

$p_1°$ = vapor pressure of the pure water = 23.756 mm Hg

$p_1$ = vapor pressure of $H_2O$ over the solution

$p_1$ = (0.9905)(23.756 mm Hg) = 23.53 mm Hg.

PROBLEM 486  If 106.3 g compound Z dissolves in 863.5 g benzene ($C_6H_6$) to lower the vapor pressure of benzene from 98.6 to 86.7 Torr, what must be the molecular weight of Z? Assume no dissociation.

SOLUTION: (Use the vapor-pressure lowering to fix the mole fraction of Z in the solution. Then calculate the weight of one mole Z.)

The vapor pressure of the benzene goes from 98.6 to 86.7 Torr. This represents a decrease of 11.9 Torr. According to Raoult's law, the drop in vapor pressure (11.9 Torr) divided by the original vapor pressure (98.6 Torr) gives the mole fraction of solute. So, in this solution the mole fraction of compound Z is 11.9/98.6, or 0.121.

Mole fraction of Z = $\dfrac{\text{moles Z}}{\text{moles Z + moles benzene}}$ = 0.121.

We have 863.5 g benzene. One mole $C_6H_6$ weighs 78.11 g, so 863.5 g is $\dfrac{863.5 \text{ g}}{78.11 \text{ g/mole}}$ = 11.05 moles benzene. Substituting this above we get

mole fraction of Z = $\dfrac{\text{moles Z}}{\text{moles Z + 11.05}}$ = 0.121.

Solving for moles Z, we get 1.52 moles.

The problem tells us what weight of Z we have, 106.3 g.

So, molecular weight of $Z = \dfrac{106.3 \text{ g}}{1.52 \text{ moles}} = 69.9 \dfrac{\textbf{g}}{\textbf{mole}}$.

■ **PROBLEM** 487   At 23°C, the vapor pressure of pure $CCl_4$ is 0.132 atm.  Suppose you dissolve 2.97 g $I_2$ in 29.7 g $CCl_4$.  What will the vapor pressure due to $CCl_4$ become?

ANSWER: **0.124 atm**

■ **PROBLEM** 488   When $CaCl_2$ dissolves in water, each mole of $CaCl_2$ forms one mole $Ca^{++}$ and 2 moles $Cl^-$. Assuming Raoult's law to hold, calculate what should be the vapor pressure of water at 25°C over an aqueous solution that is 0.550 $m$ $CaCl_2$. Vapor pressure of pure water at 25°C is 23.756 Torr.

ANSWER: **23.07 Torr**

■ **PROBLEM** 489   A new compound between selenium and sulfur has just been discovered.  Its formula is $Se_xS_y$.  From the following data, calculate $x$ and $y$: The compound consists of 45% selenium by weight.  It dissolves in benzene at 20°C to the extent of 12 g $Se_xS_y$ per 880.0 g $C_6H_6$, where it lowers the vapor pressure of $C_6H_6$ from 75.50 to 75.27 Torr.

ANSWER: $x = 2; y = 6$; compound is $Se_2S_6$

## Henry's law

The more you squeeze on a gas, the more likely you are to dissolve it in a solvent.  Stated more elegantly, the concentration of a dissolved gas is proportional to the pressure of the gas, at least for dilute solutions and for cases where there is no chemical reaction between gas and solvent.  This is called Henry's law.  It is usually written

$$K = \frac{p}{x}$$

where $p$ is the partial pressure of the gas in question in the gas phase over the solution (in mm Hg, or Torr) and $x$ is the mole fraction of the dissolved gas in the liquid solution phase.  $K$ is called the Henry's law constant and is characteristic of the solute, the solvent, and the temperature.

PROBLEM 490   At 20°C, oxygen gas, $O_2$, dissolves in water to an extent consistent with a Henry's law constant of $2.95 \times 10^7$. Under ordinary atmospheric conditions, where $p_{O_2}$ is about 0.21 atm, how many moles $O_2$ gas will be dissolved in 1000 g water?

SOLUTION: $p_{O_2} = 0.21$ atm $= (0.21$ atm$) \left( 760 \dfrac{\text{Torr}}{\text{atm}} \right) = 160$ Torr.

We are given the Henry's law constant, $K$, as $2.95 \times 10^7$.

$$K = 2.95 \times 10^7 = \frac{p_{O_2}}{x_{O_2}} = \frac{160}{x_{O_2}}.$$

From this, we calculate $x_{O_2}$, the mole fraction $O_2$ in the solution, as
$160/2.95 \times 10^7 = 5.4 \times 10^{-6}$.

$$\text{Mole fraction } O_2 = \frac{\text{moles } O_2}{\text{moles } O_2 + \text{moles } H_2O}.$$

This is such a very dilute solution that, in the denominator, moles $O_2$ is negligible when added to moles $H_2O$.

$$\text{Moles } H_2O = \frac{1000 \text{ g}}{18.015 \text{ g/mole}} = 55.51 \text{ moles.}$$

$$\text{Mole fraction } O_2 = 5.4 \times 10^{-6} = \frac{\text{moles } O_2}{55.51 \text{ moles total}}.$$

Moles $O_2 = (55.51)(5.4 \times 10^{-6}) = \mathbf{3.0 \times 10^{-4}}.$

PROBLEM 491   At 20°C, 9.3 cc helium gas (temperature 20°C and pressure 730 Torr) can be dissolved in 1000 g water if the helium pressure over the solution is kept at 730 Torr. Calculate the Henry's law constant for helium. Assume ideal behavior.

SOLUTION: (Figure out how many moles of helium you have. Then calculate the mole fraction of helium in the solution. Then get $K$.)
From the ideal gas law $PV = nRT$ we get

$$n = \frac{PV}{RT} = \frac{(730/760)(0.0093)}{(0.08206)(293)} = 3.7 \times 10^{-4} \text{ mole helium.}$$

1000 g $H_2O$ is $\dfrac{1000 \text{ g}}{18.015 \text{ g/mole}} = 55.5$ moles $H_2O$.

$$\text{Mole fraction helium} = \frac{3.7 \times 10^{-4}}{55.5 + 3.7 \times 10^{-4}} = 6.7 \times 10^{-6}.$$

Henry's law constant $= \dfrac{p}{x} = \dfrac{730}{6.7 \times 10^{-6}} = 1.1 \times 10^8.$

■ PROBLEM 492   At 24°C, 0.00178 g $N_2$ gas will dissolve in 100 g $H_2O$ if the nitrogen pressure is 737 mm Hg. Calculate the Henry's law constant.

ANSWER: $6.44 \times 10^7$

■ PROBLEM 493   At 20°C, the Henry's law constant for neon in water is $9.14 \times 10^7$. How many grams neon can you dissolve in 1000 g $H_2O$ if the pressure of the neon gas above the water is 724 Torr?

ANSWER: $8.88 \times 10^{-3}$ g

■■ PROBLEM 494   At 20°C, the Henry's law constant for dissolving $CO_2$ in water is $1.08 \times 10^6$. Suppose you have a large amount of "wet" $CO_2$ gas in contact with 1.00 cc liquid water at a total barometric pressure of 753.6 Torr and 20°C. How many cubic centimeters of this $CO_2$ gas can you dissolve in the 1.00 cc water? Density of water is 0.998 g/cc; vapor pressure of water is 17.54 Torr.

ANSWER: 0.938 cc

## Elevation of boiling point

Because addition of a nonvolatile solute lowers the vapor pressure of a solution, a higher temperature will be needed to produce boiling and, therefore, there is raising of the boiling point (b.p.).  The b.p. elevation is characteristic for each solvent; it is proportional to the molal concentration of solute particles dissolved therein.  For $H_2O$ as a solvent, one mole of dissolved particles in 1000 grams of $H_2O$ produces a b.p. elevation of 0.512°C.  This is called the *molal boiling-point elevation constant for water*.  Because it is the concentration of particles and not their identity that is important, observed boiling-point elevations can be used to deduce how many moles of particles there are in the solution per kilogram of solvent.  This can be particularly useful in experimentally fixing the molecular weight of a dissolved species.  However, in cases where the solute molecules dissociate into smaller particles, the number of moles of particles in the solution will exceed the apparent number put into the solution; this will have to be taken into account because each particle contributes equally to the boiling-point elevation.

PROBLEM 495 What will be the normal boiling point of a solution made by dissolving 4.26 g glucose ($C_6H_{12}O_6$) in 87.9 g $H_2O$? Glucose is a nondissociating molecular solute. The molal boiling-point elevation constant for $H_2O$ is 0.512°C.

SOLUTION: One mole $C_6H_{12}O_6$ is 180.16 g.

$$4.26 \text{ g } C_6H_{12}O_6 = \frac{4.26 \text{ g}}{180.16 \text{ g/mole}} = 0.0236 \text{ mole } C_6H_{12}O_6.$$

0.0236 mole $C_6H_{12}O_6$ per 0.0879 kg $H_2O$ is the same as

$$\frac{0.0236 \text{ mole } C_6H_{12}O_6}{0.0879 \text{ kg } H_2O} = 0.268 \ m.$$

For a 1 $m$ solution, the b.p. elevation is 0.512°C.

For a 0.268 $m$ solution, the b.p. is 0.268 as much, or $(0.268 \ m)\left(0.512 \dfrac{°C}{m}\right)$

= 0.137°C.

If the original boiling point was 100°C (corresponding to pure water), it will now be 100.137°C.

■ PROBLEM 496 The normal boiling point of pure $CCl_4$ is 76.8°C. Its molal boiling-point elevation constant is 5.03°C. Neglecting the volatility of the $I_2$, calculate the expected boiling point of a solution containing 1.00 g $I_2$ and 25.38 g $CCl_4$.

ANSWER: 77.6°C

PROBLEM 497 Compound X dissolves in water to the extent of 1.89 g X per 85.00 ml $H_2O$ (density 0.998 g/ml). The boiling point under atmospheric pressure of this solution is 100.106°C. What is the apparent molecular weight of X?

SOLUTION: The boiling-point elevation observed is 0.106°C.

For a 1 $m$ solution, the b.p. elevation would have been 0.512°C.

Therefore, we have a solution which is $\dfrac{0.106°C}{0.512°C/m}$, or 0.207 $m$.

The solution has 1.89 g X per 85.00 ml $H_2O$, which is the same as 1.89 g X per (85.00 ml) $\left(0.998 \dfrac{g}{ml}\right)$ or per 84.83 g $H_2O$.  But 1.89 g X per 84.83 g $H_2O$ corresponds to

$$\left(\frac{1.89 \text{ g X}}{84.83 \text{ g } H_2O}\right)\left(1000 \frac{g}{kg}\right) = 22.3 \text{ g X/kg } H_2O.$$

Equating the 0.207 $m$ and the 22.3 g X/kg $H_2O$, we get

$$\frac{22.3 \text{ g X}}{0.207 \text{ mole}} = 108 \text{ g X per mole.}$$

Therefore, the apparent molecular weight of X is 108 .

■PROBLEM 498  Compound Z dissolves in chloroform, for which the normal boiling point is 61.26°C and the molal boiling-point elevation constant is 3.63°C.  If a solution consisting of 3.89 g Z and 187 g chloroform boils at 62.27°C, what is the apparent molecular weight of Z?

ANSWER:74.8

■PROBLEM 499  When you put $CaCl_2$ in water, you get one mole $Ca^{++}$ and two moles $Cl^-$ per mole of dissolved $CaCl_2$.  If you make a solution consisting of 9.99 g $CaCl_2$ in 162 g $H_2O$, what boiling-point elevation over pure water would you expect to have produced?

ANSWER: 0.854°C

## Depression of the freezing point

In the same way that dissolved particles raise the boiling point proportional to their molal concentration, they depress the freezing point (f.p.) as well.  The f.p. lowering is characteristic of the solvent and is directly proportional to the molal concentration of dissolved particles in the solution.  For $H_2O$, one mole of any kind of dissolved particles in 1 kilogram of water depresses the freezing point by 1.86°C.  This number is called the *molal freezing-point depression constant*.  Because freezing points are generally easier to measure accurately than boiling points, freezing-point lowering is a common experimental technique for finding out molecular weights of dissolved species. Here again, however, you have to be on guard for the possibility of dissociation of the solute when it is put in the water. Any increase in the concentration of particles proportionally depresses the freezing point.

PROBLEM 500    Given that the molal freezing-point depression constant of $H_2O$ is 1.86°C, what freezing point do you expect for water in which there is dissolved 17.9 g $C_{12}H_{22}O_{11}$ (a nondissociating solute) per 47.6 g $H_2O$?

SOLUTION: One mole $C_{12}H_{22}O_{11}$ is 342.30 g.

$$17.9 \text{ g } C_{12}H_{22}O_{11} = \frac{17.9 \text{ g}}{342.30 \text{ g/mole}} = 0.0523 \text{ mole.}$$

0.0523 mole $C_{12}H_{22}O_{11}$ per 47.6 g $H_2O$ is the same as

$$\left(\frac{0.0523 \text{ mole}}{47.6 \text{ g}}\right)\left(1000 \frac{\text{g}}{\text{kg}}\right) = 1.10 \text{ moles/kg } H_2O.$$

If one mole/kg $H_2O$ produces a f.p. lowering of 1.86°C, then 1.10 moles/kg $H_2O$ should produce a lowering which is 1.10 as great, or

$$(1.10 \ m)\left(1.86 \frac{°C}{m}\right) = 2.05°C.$$

So, the freezing point of the solution ought to be $-2.05°C$.

■PROBLEM 501    What do you expect for the freezing point of a solution made up of 1.00 g methyl alcohol ($CH_3OH$) and 10.00 g water?

ANSWER: $-5.80°C$

PROBLEM 502    Substance X dissolves in water to give a solution which contains 4.68 g X per 287 g $H_2O$. If the measured freezing point of the solution is 0.153°C below zero, what is the apparent molecular weight of X?

SOLUTION: 4.68 g X per 287 g $H_2O$ is the same as

$$\left(\frac{4.68 \text{ g X}}{287 \text{ g } H_2O}\right)\left(1000 \frac{\text{g } H_2O}{\text{kg } H_2O}\right) = 16.3 \frac{\text{g X}}{\text{kg } H_2O}.$$

**SOLUTIONS**

The observed f.p. is $-0.153°C$. For a $1\ m$ solution, it would be $-1.86°C$. Therefore, the concentration of the solution is

$$\frac{0.153°C}{1.86°C/m} = 0.0823\ m.$$

So, the $16.3\ \dfrac{g\ X}{kg\ H_2O}$ must represent $0.0823\ m$.

$16.3\ g\ X$ must be $0.0823$ mole X.

One mole X is $\dfrac{16.3\ g}{0.0823\ mole} = $ **$198\ g/mole\ X$**

■ **P R O B L E M  503**  The molal freezing-point depression constant of benzene ($C_6H_6$) is $4.90°C$. You suspect that selenium is a polymer of the type $Se_x$, so you dissolve some solid selenium in benzene and measure the f.p. depression of the benzene. With $3.26$ g selenium dissolved in $226$ g benzene, the observed freezing point is $0.112°C$ lower than for pure benzene. Figure out the molecular formula of selenium.

ANSWER: $Se_8$

**P R O B L E M  504**  Zinc sulfate, $ZnSO_4$, is expected as a salt to be dissociated into $Zn^{++}$ and $SO_4^=$ in solution. For a solution which is made up by dissolving $0.5811$ g $ZnSO_4$ in $0.180$ kg $H_2O$, the observed freezing point is $-0.0530°C$. Calculate the apparent per cent of dissociation of $ZnSO_4$ into $Zn^{++}$ and $SO_4^=$.

SOLUTION: One mole $ZnSO_4$ weighs $161.43$ g.

$$0.5811\ g\ ZnSO_4 = \frac{0.5811\ g}{161.43\ g/mole} = 0.00360\ mole\ ZnSO_4.$$

$$\frac{0.00360\ mole\ ZnSO_4}{0.180\ kg\ H_2O} = 0.0200\ mole\ ZnSO_4/kg\ H_2O.$$

Let $x =$ number of moles $ZnSO_4$ apparently dissociated. This will produce $x$ moles $Zn^{++}$ and $x$ moles $SO_4^=$ and leave $0.0200 - x$ moles of undissociated $ZnSO_4/kg$ water. The total number of moles of all kinds of particles will be $x$ of $Zn^{++} + x$ of $SO_4^= + (0.0200 - x)$ of $ZnSO_4$, or $0.0200 + x$ moles total/kg $H_2O$. The observed freezing-point depression is $0.0530°C$, which corresponds to $\dfrac{0.0530°C}{1.86°C/m} = 0.0285\ m.$

We equate the $0.0200 + x$ moles of particles per kg $H_2O$ to the $0.0285$ $m$ and solve for $x$:

$$0.0200 + x = 0.0285$$

$$x = 0.0085$$

The question asks for per cent dissociation.

$$\% \text{ dissociation} = \frac{\text{moles dissociated}}{\text{moles originally available}} \times 100$$

$$= \frac{0.0085}{0.0200} \times 100 = 42\%$$

■ PROBLEM 505    Acetic acid, $HC_2H_3O_2$, dissociates in water to give $H^+$ and $C_2H_3O_2{}^-$.  A solution labeled 0.100 $m$ $HC_2H_3O_2$ shows an observed freezing point which is 0.190°C below that of pure water.  Calculate the apparent per cent dissociation.

ANSWER: 2%

# 12

## GASEOUS
## EQUILIBRIA

IN THIS CHAPTER we take up a general consideration of chemical equilibrium based on the behavior of gases. In succeeding chapters we consider the various special types of chemical equilibrium normally encountered in aqueous solutions.

### *Evaluation of K*

The whole idea of chemical equilibrium is essentially this: All chemical reactions, such as $A + B \rightarrow C + D$, are reversible in the sense that the products of the reaction, C and D, can react to regenerate the starting materials, A and B. If allowed enough time, the system will come to rest (i.e., to equilibrium) where not only C and D but also A and B are present at characteristic concentrations which do not change with time. The condition required for equilibrium is that the concentrations of species on the right of the equation raised to powers conforming to the coefficients in the chemical equation divided by the concentrations of species on the left of the equation raised to the proper powers must equal a constant characteristic of the system. For example, for the system

$$N_{2(g)} + 3H_{2(g)} \rightleftharpoons 2NH_{3(g)}$$

where the double arrow sign, $\rightleftharpoons$, emphasizes that the chemical equation is to be read in both directions, the condition for equilibrium is that

$$\frac{C_{NH_3}^2}{C_{N_2}C_{H_2}^3} = K$$

Here $C_{NH_3}$ stands for the concentration of ammonia; $C_{N_2}$ stands for the concentration of nitrogen; and $C_{H_2}$ stands for the concentration of hydrogen in the system containing $NH_3$, $N_2$, and $H_2$ all together at equilibrium. $K$ is a number which is fixed for the system consisting of $NH_3$, $N_2$, and $H_2$, although in general it will vary if the temperature is changed. It is called the equilibrium constant for the reaction.

PROBLEM 506   You are given a box containing $NH_3$, $N_2$, and $H_2$ at equilibrium at 1000°K. Analysis of the contents shows that the concentration of $NH_3$ is 0.102 mole/l, $N_2$ is 1.03 moles/l, and $H_2$ is 1.62 moles/l. Calculate $K$ for the reaction $N_{2(g)} + 3H_{2(g)} \rightleftharpoons 2NH_{3(g)}$ at 1000°K.

SOLUTION: Write the correct expression for $K$ so that it corresponds to the reaction as written. Be careful to put the stuff from the right of the equation in the numerator and the stuff from the left of the equation in the denominator. Make sure that the exponents match the coefficients in the equation:

$$K = \frac{C_{NH_3}^2}{C_{N_2}C_{H_2}^3}$$

Then substitute $C_{NH_3} = 0.102$ mole/l, $C_{N_2} = 1.03$ moles/l, and $C_{H_2} = 1.62$ moles/l.

$$K = \frac{(0.102)^2}{(1.03)(1.62)^3} = 2.37 \times 10^{-3}$$

Strictly speaking, we should put units on the $K$ to correspond to the concentration units employed. In Problem 506, for example, $K$ would be in units of one-over-(moles per liter) squared. However, there are several good reasons for not bothering with the dimensional units. One is that they are easily supplied if necessary by looking at the exponents in the numerator and denominator. The units will cancel out if the number of gas molecules is the same on the two sides of the chemical equation, but not if they differ. The second point is that we almost always work with molar concentrations (i.e., moles per liter) when calculating with $K$. If other concentration units are used, it is customary to call attention to them; if nothing is said about concentration units, we assume we are dealing with $K$ calculated in terms of moles per liter for each species. Third, in the real sophisticated treatment of chemical equilibrium a very clever dodge has been invented whereby each species concentration is expressed as a ratio to what the concentration would be in its standard reference state. As a result, concentration units *per se* disappear and are replaced by unitless parameters called *activities*. All of this is just for the record. So far as your present work with equilibrium constants is concerned, calculate with moles per liter unless otherwise directed.

A more immediate caution is to note that $K$ will take on a different numerical value depending on which way you choose to write the chemical equation, as is illustrated in the next problem. To be absolutely clear, it is strongly recommended that you specifically write the chemical equation for which your $K$ is being defined.

### PROBLEM 507

You are given a box containing $NH_3$, $N_2$, and $H_2$ at equilibrium at 1000°K. Analysis of the contents shows that the concentration of $NH_3$ is 0.102 mole/l, $N_2$ is 1.03 moles/l, and $H_2$ is 1.62 moles/l. Calculate $K$ for the reaction $2NH_{3(g)} \rightleftharpoons N_{2(g)} + 3H_{2(g)}$.

SOLUTION: Write the expression for $K$ so it matches the chemical equation

$$K = \frac{C_{N_2} C_{H_2}^3}{C_{NH_3}^2}$$

Species from the right of the chemical equation go in the numerator; species from the left of the equation go in the denominator. Then substitute the equilibrium concentrations: $C_{N_2} = 1.03 \; M$; $C_{H_2} = 1.62 \; M$; $C_{NH_3} = 0.102 \; M$.

$$K = \frac{(1.03)(1.62)^3}{(0.102)^2} = 4.21 \times 10^2$$

Note particularly that the numerical value of this $K$ is the reciprocal of that obtained in Problem 506. The general point is that when you reverse the direction of the chemical equation, you invert the equilibrium constant.

## PROBLEM 508

You are given a box containing $NH_3$, $N_2$, and $H_2$ at equilibrium at 1000°K. Analysis of the contents shows that the concentration of $NH_3$ is 0.102 mole/l, $N_2$ is 1.03 moles/l, and $H_2$ is 1.62 moles/l. Calculate $K$ for the reaction

$$NH_{3(g)} \rightleftharpoons \tfrac{1}{2}N_{2(g)} + \tfrac{3}{2}H_{2(g)}$$

SOLUTION: Set up the $K$ so it matches the chemical equation.

$$K = \frac{(C_{N_2})^{\frac{1}{2}}(C_{H_2})^{\frac{3}{2}}}{C_{NH_3}}$$

The powers to which the concentrations are to be raised must match the coefficients in the chemical equation. Then substitute the equilibrium concentrations: $C_{N_2} = 1.03\ M$; $C_{H_2} = 1.62\ M$; $C_{NH_3} = 0.102\ M$.

$$K = \frac{(1.03)^{\frac{1}{2}}(1.62)^{\frac{3}{2}}}{0.102} = 20.5$$

You should note that this $K$ is the square root of the $K$ we got in Problem 507. The general rule is that if you double a chemical equation throughout, the corresponding $K$ will be the square of the original; if you triple the equation, the $K$ will be the cube of the original value.

## PROBLEM 509

Hydrogen gas, sulfur vapor, and hydrogen sulfide gas are in equilibrium with each other under the following conditions: 1.68 moles $H_2S$, 1.37 moles $H_2$, and $2.88 \times 10^{-5}$ mole $S_2$ are in a volume of 18.0 l at 750°C. Calculate the $K$ for the reaction

$$2H_{2(g)} + S_{2(g)} \rightleftharpoons 2H_2S_{(g)}$$

SOLUTION: Set up the $K$ to correspond with the chemical equation.

$$K = \frac{(C_{H_2S})^2}{(C_{H_2})^2(C_{S_2})}$$

Then calculate the moles per liter of each constituent.

$$C_{H_2S} = \frac{1.68 \text{ moles}}{18.0 \text{ l}} = 0.0933 \ M$$

$$C_{H_2} = \frac{1.37 \text{ moles}}{18.0 \text{ l}} = 0.0761 \ M$$

$$C_{S_2} = \frac{2.88 \times 10^{-5} \text{ mole}}{18.0 \text{ l}} = 1.60 \times 10^{-6} \ M$$

Substitute these values in the expression for $K$.

$$K = \frac{(0.0933)^2}{(0.0761)^2(1.60 \times 10^{-6})} = 9.39 \times 10^5$$

■ **PROBLEM 510** Given 1.68 moles $H_2S$, 1.37 moles $H_2$, and $2.88 \times 10^{-5}$ mole $S_2$ at equilibrium in 18.0 l at 750°C. Calculate $K$ for

$$H_2S_{(g)} \rightleftharpoons H_{2(g)} + \tfrac{1}{2}S_{2(g)}$$

ANSWER: $1.03 \times 10^{-3}$

■ **PROBLEM 511** Calculate $K$ for $2NO_{(g)} + O_{2(g)} \rightleftharpoons 2NO_{2(g)}$ from the observation that equilibrium is established when there are present at 500°K 0.190 mole $NO_2$, $2.65 \times 10^{-4}$ mole NO, and 0.606 mole $O_2$ in a volume of 0.759 l.

ANSWER: $6.45 \times 10^5$

■ **PROBLEM 512** Given the equilibrium system consisting of 0.190 mole $NO_2$, $2.65 \times 10^{-4}$ mole NO, and 0.606 mole $O_2$ in a 0.759-l box at 500°K, calculate $K$ for the reaction $NO_{2(g)} \rightleftharpoons NO_{(g)} + \tfrac{1}{2}O_{2(g)}$.

ANSWER: $1.25 \times 10^{-3}$

**PROBLEM 513** At 500°K, $PCl_5$ decomposes rather extensively into $PCl_3$ and $Cl_2$. It is found, for example, that if you put 1.000 mole $PCl_5$ in a 1-l box at 500°K, 13.9% of it decomposes to $PCl_3$ and $Cl_2$. Calculate $K$ for the decomposition reaction $PCl_{5(g)} \rightleftharpoons PCl_{3(g)} + Cl_{2(g)}$.

SOLUTION: According to the equation $PCl_5 \rightarrow PCl_3 + Cl_2$, for every one mole $PCl_5$ that decomposes, one mole $PCl_3$ and one mole $Cl_2$ appears. You are told that 13.9% of 1.000 mole, or 0.139 mole, of $PCl_5$ decomposes. This will produce 0.139 mole $PCl_3$ and 0.139 mole $Cl_2$ and leave $1.000 - 0.139$, or 0.861 mole $PCl_5$, undecomposed. So, for concentrations at equilibrium, we have the following:

$$C_{PCl_3} = 0.139 \text{ mole/l}$$

$$C_{Cl_2} = 0.139 \text{ mole/l}$$

$$C_{PCl_5} = 0.861 \text{ mole/l}$$

where we have divided the moles present by the volume, 1 liter:

$$K = \frac{C_{PCl_3} C_{Cl_2}}{C_{PCl_5}} = \frac{(0.139)(0.139)}{0.861} = 0.0224$$

■ PROBLEM 514   When gaseous iodine is heated, some of the diatomic molecules decompose to give atomic iodine. In a typical experiment at 1000°K, 2.74% of the $I_2$ decomposes this way when 0.00305 mole $I_2$ is placed in a volume of 0.250 l. Calculate $K$ for $I_{2(g)} \rightleftharpoons 2I_{(g)}$.
ANSWER: $3.76 \times 10^{-5}$

■ PROBLEM 515   When $H_2$ and $CO_2$ are brought together at high-enough temperature, they react to form some $H_2O$ and $CO$. In a given experiment at 2000°K, a mixture consisting initially of 1.000 mole $H_2$ and 2.000 moles $CO_2$ in a 20.0-l volume shows, after equilibrium has been established, that 85.5% of the $H_2$ has been converted to $H_2O$. Figure out the $K$ for the reaction $H_{2(g)} + CO_{2(g)} \rightleftharpoons H_2O_{(g)} + CO_{(g)}$.
ANSWER: 4.40

## Calculations from K

The numerical value of $K$ for a given reaction can be obtained by experimental study of one equilibrium set of concentrations involving that reaction at a specified temperature. Once $K$ is obtained, it can be used to describe any equilibrium system involving those same species at the same temperature. There are in special handbooks tabulations of $K$ for various reactions at different temperatures or else numbers from which $K$ can be derived.  So far as we are concerned, the $K$ value will be given, and what we need to look at now is how to calculate required data from the given $K$.

Before we look at some specific problems, it might be noted that there is a common way of designating concentrations that you should be familiar with.  In Section 15.1 we were careful to write, for example, $C_{NH_3}$ for the concentration of $NH_3$ in moles per liter in the system.  We did this to emphasize that $K$ involves *concentrations*—i.e., moles *per liter* and not just moles.  However, now that you know what $K$ is, we can introduce the common convention, which is to indicate the concentration in moles per liter of a species by putting its formula in square brackets.  Thus, $[NH_3]$ stands for moles of $NH_3$ per liter and is the same thing we previously designated as $C_{NH_3}$.  Similarly, instead of writing $C_{H_2}$, we can use $[H_2]$, meaning concentration of $H_2$ in moles per liter.  To emphasize the equivalence of these symbols, we shall show the $K$'s both ways for the first several problems and then gradually work over completely to the square-bracket notation.

**PROBLEM 516**   You are given that $K$ for $N_{2(g)} + 3H_{2(g)} \rightleftharpoons 2NH_{3(g)}$ is equal to $2.37 \times 10^{-3}$ at $1000°K$.  If you have a system containing these species at equilibrium at $1000°K$, what must be the concentration of $NH_3$ if you fix $N_2$ at 2.00 moles/l and $H_2$ at 3.00 moles/l?

SOLUTION: You are dealing with an equilibrium system, so the equilibrium condition

$$K = \frac{C_{NH_3}^2}{C_{N_2}C_{H_2}^3} = 2.37 \times 10^{-3} = \frac{[NH_3]^2}{[N_2][H_2]^3}$$

must be satisfied.  You are told that the concentration of $N_2$ is 2.00 moles/l; so, $C_{N_2} = 2.00$.  You are also told that the concentration of $H_2$ is 3.00 moles/l; therefore, $C_{H_2} = 3.00$.  All we have to do is to substitute these values in the above equation and solve for the concentration of $NH_3$:

$$\frac{C_{NH_3}^2}{C_{N_2}C_{H_2}^3} = \frac{C_{NH_3}^2}{(2.00)(3.00)^3} = 2.37 \times 10^{-3}$$

$$C_{NH_3} = 0.358 \text{ mole/l}$$

$$\frac{7 \cdot 8}{4\,(x)\,3} = 3$$

**PROBLEM 517**   If $K = 2.37 \times 10^{-3}$ at 1000°K for $N_{2(g)} + 3H_{2(g)} \rightleftharpoons 2NH_{3(g)}$ what must be the equilibrium concentration of $H_2$ in a system known to contain 0.683 $M$ $N_2$ and 1.05 $M$ $NH_3$?

SOLUTION:

$$K = \frac{C^2_{NH_3}}{C_{N_2}C^3_{H_2}} = 2.37 \times 10^{-3}$$

$C_{N_2} = 0.683\ M; C_{NH_3} = 1.05\ M; C_{H_2} = ?$

Substitute these values and solve for the concentration of $H_2$:

$$\frac{C^2_{NH_3}}{C_{N_2}C^3_{H_2}} = \frac{(1.05)^2}{(0.683)(C_{H_2})^3} = 2.37 \times 10^{-3}$$

$$C_{H_2} = 8.80\ \text{moles/l}$$

■ **PROBLEM 518**   Given $K = 0.0224$ for $PCl_{5(g)} \rightleftharpoons PCl_{3(g)} + Cl_{2(g)}$ at 500°K.   What must be the equilibrium concentration of $Cl_2$ in this system when $C_{PCl_5} = 0.0428$ mole/l and $C_{PCl_3} = 1.32$ moles/l?

ANSWER: $C_{Cl_2} = 7.26 \times 10^{-4}$ mole/l

■ **PROBLEM 519**   Given $K = 6.45 \times 10^5$ for $2NO_{(g)} + O_{2(g)} \rightleftharpoons 2NO_{2(g)}$ at 500°K.   What concentration of oxygen would be needed to maintain equilibrium in a system where NO and $NO_2$ are known to be at equal concentrations?

ANSWER: $C_{O_2} = 1.55 \times 10^{-6}$ mole/l

**PROBLEM 520**   Given $K = 1.03 \times 10^{-3}$ for $H_2S_{(g)} \rightleftharpoons H_{2(g)} + \frac{1}{2}S_{2(g)}$ at 750°C.   How many moles $S_2$ would you have at equilibrium in a 3.68-l box in which there are 1.63 moles $H_2S$ and 0.864 mole $H_2$?

SOLUTION: Remember, what goes into the constant is moles *per liter*. So, first we convert our given data into moles per liter:

$$C_{H_2S} = \frac{1.63\ \text{moles}}{3.68\ \text{l}} = 0.443\ M$$

$$C_{H_2} = \frac{0.864\ \text{mole}}{3.68\ \text{l}} = 0.235\ M$$

6.811.2

1.896

PROBLEM    229

Then we substitute these in the expression for the equilibrium constant.

$$K = \frac{C_{H_2}C_{S_2}^{\frac{1}{2}}}{C_{H_2S}} = 1.03 \times 10^{-3} = \frac{(0.235)(C_{S_2})^{\frac{1}{2}}}{0.443}$$

6.5

Solving for $C_{S_2}$, we get $3.77 \times 10^{-6}$ mole/l.

But the question asks for how many moles there are in the box. We know the concentration of $S_2$ must be $3.77 \times 10^{-6}$ mole/l; we know the total volume of the box is 3.68 l.

$$\text{Moles } S_2 = \left(3.77 \times 10^{-6} \frac{\text{mole}}{\text{liter}}\right)(3.68 \text{ l}) = \mathbf{1.39 \times 10^{-5} \text{ mole}}$$

■ PROBLEM 521   Given $K = 4.40$ for $H_{2(g)} + CO_{2(g)} \rightleftharpoons H_2O_{(g)} + CO_{(g)}$ at 2000°K. If you have a 1.00-l box containing 2.00 moles $H_2$, 3.00 moles $CO_2$, and 4.00 moles $H_2O$, what must be the number of moles CO in the box if equilibrium is to be maintained?

ANSWER: **6.60 moles**

PROBLEM 522   You are told that $K = 3.76 \times 10^{-5}$ for $I_{2(g)} \rightleftharpoons 2I_{(g)}$ at 1000°K. You start an experiment by injecting 1.00 mole of $I_2$ into a 2.00-l box at 1000°K. Let it come to equilibrium. What will be the concentration of $I_2$ and I in the system at equilibrium?

SOLUTION: (Figure out how many moles per liter $I_2$ you start with. Let $x$ of these break up to form I to establish equilibrium. Express $[I_2]$ and $[I]$ in terms of $x$ and calculate $x$ by substituting in the equilibrium constant expression.)

Given 1.00 mole $I_2$ in 2.00 l.

Therefore, the initial concentration of $I_2 = \dfrac{1.00 \text{ mole}}{2.00 \text{ l}} = 0.500 \ M$.

Let $x$ moles per liter break up. This leaves $(0.500 - x)$ moles/l $I_2$ at equilibrium. The reaction of break-up, $I_2 \rightarrow 2I$, shows that for every 1 mole $I_2$ that breaks up, 2 moles I are formed. If we break up $x$ moles $I_2$, we must form $2x$ moles I.

When equilibrium is finally established, there will be $(0.500 - x)$ moles/l $I_2$ and $2x$ moles/l I. We can write $[I_2] = 0.500 - x$ and $[I] = 2x$.

For $I_{2(g)} \rightleftharpoons 2I_{(g)}$ the equilibrium condition is given by

$$K = \frac{[I]^2}{[I_2]} = \frac{(2x)^2}{0.500 - x} = 3.76 \times 10^{-5}$$

We have one unknown and one algebraic equation, so we should be able to solve it by the method for quadratic equations. It gives $x = 2.16 \times 10^{-3}$. [We can also get an approximate answer by noting that, since the right-hand side of the algebraic equation is small, the left-hand side must also be small. This can be true only if $x$ is small, particularly compared to 0.500. If we neglect $x$ in the denominator, we have $(2x)^2/(0.500) \cong 3.76 \times 10^{-5}$ which solves to $x = 2.17 \times 10^{-3}$, close enough to the exact answer to be acceptable.]

We can say, finally, that the concentrations are

$$[I_2] = 0.500 - x = 0.500 - 2.17 \times 10^{-3} = 0.498 \ M$$

$$[I] = 2x = (2)(2.17 \times 10^{-3}) = 4.34 \times 10^{-3} \ M$$

■ PROBLEM 523    Given that $K = 3.76 \times 10^{-5}$ for $I_{2(g)} \rightleftharpoons 2I_{(g)}$ at 1000°K. What will be the final equilibrium concentrations of $I_2$ and $I$ after 0.750 mole $I_2$ has been injected into a 2.00-l box and allowed to come to equilibrium?

ANSWER: $[I_2] = 0.373 \ M$; $[I] = 3.74 \times 10^{-3} \ M$

PROBLEM 524    For the decomposition of $PCl_5$ at 760°K, the equilibrium constant is $K = 33.3$ for $PCl_{5(g)} \rightleftharpoons PCl_{3(g)} + Cl_{2(g)}$. You have a sample tube of volume 36.3 cc into which you inject 1.50 g $PCl_5$. What will be the concentration of $PCl_5$ in the tube when equilibrium is finally established? What will $PCl_3$ and $Cl_2$ be?

SOLUTION: (Figure out the initial concentration of $PCl_5$. Let $x$ moles/l decompose to give $x$ moles/l $PCl_3$ and $x$ moles/l $Cl_2$. Substitute the equilibrium concentrations in terms of $x$ into the expression for $K$ and solve for $x$.)

One mole $PCl_5$ weighs 208.24 g.

$$1.50 \text{ g } PCl_5 = \frac{1.50 \text{ g}}{208.24 \text{ g/mole}} = 0.00720 \text{ mole.}$$

The volume of the system is 36.3 cc, or 0.0363 l.

Therefore, the initial concentration of $PCl_5$ is

$$\frac{0.00720 \text{ mole}}{0.0363 \text{ l}} = 0.198 \text{ mole/l}.$$

Let $x$ equal the moles/l of $PCl_5$ that decompose.
This will leave $(0.198 - x)$ mole/l undecomposed, and it will produce $x$ moles/l $PCl_3$ and $x$ moles/l $Cl_2$.
At equilibrium:

$$[PCl_5] = 0.198 - x \qquad\qquad K = \frac{[PCl_3][Cl_2]}{[PCl_5]} = 33.3$$

$$[PCl_3] = x$$

$$[Cl_2] = x \qquad\qquad \frac{(x)(x)}{0.198 - x} = 33.3$$

Approximation methods are no good for solving this equation because the right-hand side can be large only if $(0.198 - x)$ is small. In other words, $x$ must be of the order of 0.198, which makes for lots of trouble. You can solve the equation by the quadratic formula and get $x = 0.197$. However, this does not help much because substituting this $x = 0.197$ into the expression $[PCl_5] = 0.198 - x$ gives $[PCl_5] = 0.198 - 0.197 = 0.001$ mole/l. By the rules of significant figures, we have only one digit in our answer and that, unfortunately, is a doubtful digit.

Can we get a better answer? We can, if we use a trick chemists frequently resort to when faced by approximation-method difficulties and that is "to approach equilibrium from the other side." Since the final equilibrium state does not depend on how we get there, we can use an indirect approach, the gist of which is to assume first that *all* the $PCl_5$ decomposes and then some of the $PCl_3$ and $Cl_2$ recombines. Specifically, if we start with 0.198 mole per liter of $PCl_5$ injected into the box, we first assume that all 0.198 mole of $PCl_5$ decomposes to form 0.198 mole of $PCl_3$ plus 0.198 mole of $Cl_2$ consistent with the equation $PCl_5 \rightarrow PCl_3 + Cl_2$. Then we look at the "back-reaction" $PCl_5 \leftarrow PCl_3 + Cl_2$ and define a new unknown $y$ to represent the moles per liter of $PCl_5$ "regenerated." Such regeneration of $PCl_5$, of course, can only come at the expense of the hypothetical $PCl_3$ and $Cl_2$ produced, so we need to reduce their hypothetical 0.198 $M$ concentrations by $y$.

In terms of this new unknown $y$, we have at equilibrium:

$[PCl_5] = y$

$[PCl_3] = 0.198 - y$

$[Cl_2] = 0.198 - y$

$K = \dfrac{[PCl_3][Cl_2]}{[PCl_5]} = 33.3$

$\dfrac{(0.198 - y)(0.198 - y)}{y} = 33.3$

where we have substituted in the same equation for $K$, since the requirement for equilibrium has not changed. The final algebraic equation may look just as hopeless as before, except now $y$ is small compared to 0.198. We can solve approximately, by neglecting $y$ in the numerator.

$$\frac{(0.198 - y)(0.198 - y)}{y} \cong \frac{(0.198)(0.198)}{y} \cong 33.3$$

The sign $\cong$ means "is approximately equal to." Solving the approximate equality on the right, we get $y \cong 0.00117$. Substituting this $y$ in the expressions for $[PCl_5]$, $[PCl_3]$, and $[Cl_2]$, we get for the final equilibrium concentrations:

$[PCl_5] = y = 0.00117\ M$

$[PCl_3] = 0.198 - y = 0.198 - 0.00117 = 0.197\ M$

$[Cl_2] = 0.198 - y = 0.198 - 0.00117 = 0.197\ M$

That these are really acceptable values can be checked by substituting them in $K = \dfrac{[PCl_3][Cl_2]}{[PCl_5]}$ to see if the value $K = 33.3$ is reproduced.

■ PROBLEM 525 At 760°K, $PCl_5$ decomposes to give $PCl_3$ and $Cl_2$, the equilibrium being described by $K = 33.3$ for the reaction $PCl_{5(g)} \rightleftharpoons PCl_{3(g)} + Cl_{2(g)}$. Calculate the equilibrium concentrations of $PCl_5$, $PCl_3$, and $Cl_2$ given that 18.0 g $PCl_5$ is injected at time zero into a volume of 208 cc at 760°K.

ANSWER: $[PCl_5] = 0.00505\ M$; $[PCl_3] = 0.411\ M$; $[Cl_2] = 0.411\ M$

PROBLEM 526 For $NO_{2(g)} \rightleftharpoons NO_{(g)} + \frac{1}{2}O_{2(g)}$ at 500°K, the equilibrium constant $K$ is $1.25 \times 10^{-3}$. Calculate the concentration of each species at equilibrium following the injection of 0.0683 mole $NO_2$ into a volume of 0.769 l at 500°K.

SOLUTION: Initial concentration of $NO_2 = \dfrac{0.0683 \text{ mole}}{0.769 \text{ l}} = 0.0888 \ M$.

Let $x$ = moles/l $NO_2$ that decompose. This leaves $(0.0888 - x)$ moles/l $NO_2$ at equilibrium. It will produce some NO and $O_2$ by the reaction $NO_2 \rightarrow NO + \frac{1}{2}O_2$. Since the disappearance of 1 mole $NO_2$ results in formation of 1 mole NO and $\frac{1}{2}$ mole $O_2$, we conclude that the decomposition of $x$ moles $NO_2$ must result in formation of $x$ moles NO and $\frac{1}{2}x$ moles $O_2$. At equilibrium, we will have

$[NO_2] = 0.0888 - x$ $\qquad\qquad K = \dfrac{[NO][O_2]^{\frac{1}{2}}}{[NO_2]} = 1.25 \times 10^{-3}$

$[NO] = x$

$[O_2] = \frac{1}{2}x$ $\qquad\qquad\qquad \dfrac{(x)(\frac{1}{2}x)^{\frac{1}{2}}}{0.0888 - x} = 1.25 \times 10^{-3}$

We can solve this equation exactly by squaring both sides and using the method for cubic equations. An easier method is by successive approximation. We note that $x$ may be small compared to 0.0888, so, as a first approximation, we ignore the $x$ in the denominator, assume $(0.0888 - x) \cong 0.0888$ and solve:

$\dfrac{(x)(\frac{1}{2}x)^{\frac{1}{2}}}{0.0888} \cong 1.25 \times 10^{-3}$

Multiplying both sides by 0.0888 gives

$(x)(\frac{1}{2}x)^{\frac{1}{2}} \cong (1.25 \times 10^{-3})(0.0888) = 1.11 \times 10^{-4}$

Squaring both sides gives

$(x)^2(\frac{1}{2}x) \cong (1.11 \times 10^{-4})^2 = 1.23 \times 10^{-8}$

Multiplying both sides by 2 gives

$x^3 \cong 2.46 \times 10^{-8}$

Taking the cube root of both sides gives

$x \cong 2.91 \times 10^{-3}$

This is almost but not quite negligible compared to 0.0888, so we try a second approximation where we estimate $x$ in $(0.0888 - x)$ to be equal to the value just computed. Assume $(0.0888 - x) \cong (0.0888 - 2.91 \times 10^{-3}) = 0.0859$ and put this in the denominator of the original equation to get

$\dfrac{(x)(\frac{1}{2}x)^{\frac{1}{2}}}{0.0859} \cong 1.25 \times 10^{-3}$

Solving this equation for $x$ gives $x = 2.85 \times 10^{-3}$. If $x = 2.85 \times 10^{-3}$ the denominator $(0.0888 - x)$ would be $0.0860$, which is close enough to the value $0.0859$ we estimated that we have some confidence in $x$. Using $x = 2.85 \times 10^{-3}$ $M$ we get for the equilibrium concentrations:

$$[NO_2] = 0.0888 - x = 0.0888 - 2.85 \times 10^{-3} = 0.0860 \, M$$

$$[NO] = x = 2.85 \times 10^{-3} \, M$$

$$[O_2] = \tfrac{1}{2}x = \tfrac{1}{2}(2.85 \times 10^{-3}) = 1.42 \times 10^{-3} \, M$$

If we put these values back in $K = \dfrac{[NO][O_2]^{1/2}}{[NO_2]}$ we get

$$K = \frac{(2.85 \times 10^{-3})(1.42 \times 10^{-3})^{1/2}}{0.0860} = 1.25 \times 10^{-3}, \text{ which checks}$$

out with the given $K = 1.25 \times 10^{-3}$ as well as can be expected.

■ P R O B L E M  527  For $H_2S_{(g)} \rightleftharpoons H_{2(g)} + \tfrac{1}{2}S_{2(g)}$ at 750°C, the equilibrium constant $K$ is equal to $1.03 \times 10^{-3}$. Calculate the concentrations of $H_2S$, $H_2$, and $S_2$ in an equilibrium system coming from injection of 0.0683 mole $H_2S$ into a volume of 0.769 l at 750°C.

ANSWER:  $[H_2S] = 0.0863 \, M$;  $[H_2] = 2.51 \times 10^{-3} \, M$;  $[S_2] = 1.26 \times 10^{-3} \, M$

P R O B L E M  528  Suppose that ammonia decomposes at 600°K to establish the equilibrium $NH_{3(g)} \rightleftharpoons \tfrac{1}{2}N_{2(g)} + \tfrac{3}{2}H_{2(g)}$ for which $K = 0.395$. You have a box of volume 1.00 l into which you inject 2.65 g $NH_3$ at 600°K. What will be the final concentrations of $NH_3$, $N_2$, and $H_2$ after equilibrium is established?

SOLUTION: (This is an example of a problem which is likely to be quite difficult, because $K$ is of the order of 1 and that means neither side of the chemical equation can be considered negligible with respect to the other in the final state. However, the troubles are usually of the pencil-pushing type, requiring lots of scratch paper; there is actually little difficulty in setting up the calculation.)

Initial concentration of $NH_3 = \dfrac{2.65 \text{ g}}{17.03 \text{ g/mole}} = 0.156 \, M$.

Let $x$ moles/l $NH_3$ decompose via $NH_3 \rightarrow \tfrac{1}{2}N_2 + \tfrac{3}{2}H_2$.

This will diminish the $NH_3$ concentration by $x$ and produce $\frac{1}{2}x$ moles $N_2$ and $\frac{3}{2}x$ moles $H_2$. So, in terms of $x$, at equilibrium we would have

$$[NH_3] = 0.156 - x; \ [N_2] = \tfrac{1}{2}x; \ [H_2] = \tfrac{3}{2}x$$

$$K = \frac{[N_2]^{1/2}[H_2]^{3/2}}{[NH_3]} = \frac{(\tfrac{1}{2}x)^{1/2}(\tfrac{3}{2}x)^{3/2}}{0.156 - x} = 0.395$$

This equation cannot be solved by the usual approximation methods because $x$ is not negligible compared to 0.156. (Try to neglect $x$ in the denominator and see what happens.) The alternative is to solve the equation exactly. In this case, we are fortunate, because the equation comes out to be a simple quadratic, although at first sight the exponents look more complicated. We simplify as follows:

$$\frac{(\tfrac{1}{2}x)^{1/2}(\tfrac{3}{2}x)^{3/2}}{0.156 - x} = \frac{(\tfrac{1}{2})^{1/2}(\tfrac{3}{2})^{3/2}(x^{1/2})(x^{3/2})}{0.156 - x} = \frac{(3)^{3/2}x^2}{(2)^2(0.156 - x)}$$

Here we have simply added up the exponents of the multiplied terms and split the fraction between numerator and denominator. $(3)^{3/2}$ is the square root of three "cubed," or $\sqrt{27}$, or 5.20. $(2)^2$ is, of course, two squared, or 4. Progressively simplifying, we get

$$\frac{5.20}{4} \frac{x^2}{0.156 - x} = 1.30 \frac{x^2}{0.156 - x} = 0.395$$

where the final number is the value of $K$. The final two terms $1.30 \dfrac{x^2}{0.156 - x} = 0.395$ reduce to the quadratic equation as conventionally written $1.30x^2 + 0.395x - 0.0616 = 0$. The solution to this equation from the quadratic formula gives $x = 0.114$. So, at equilibrium, we have

$$[NH_3] = 0.156 - x = 0.156 - 0.114 = \ \textbf{0.042 } \boldsymbol{M}$$

$$[N_2] = \tfrac{1}{2}x = \tfrac{1}{2}(0.114) = \ \textbf{0.0570 } \boldsymbol{M}$$

$$[H_2] = \tfrac{3}{2}x = \tfrac{3}{2}(0.114) = \ \textbf{0.171 } \boldsymbol{M}$$

■ PROBLEM 529 Given $K = 0.395$ for $NH_{3(g)} \rightleftharpoons \frac{1}{2}N_{2(g)} + \frac{3}{2}H_{2(g)}$ at 600°K. Calculate the concentration of each species at equilibrium following injection of 1.59 g $NH_3$ into a 15.0-cc bomb at 600°K.

ANSWER: $[NH_3]$ = 4.99 $M$; $[N_2]$ = 0.615 $M$; $[H_2]$ = 1.84 $M$

■■ P R O B L E M   530    Given $K$ = 5.31 × $10^{-10}$ for $2H_2O_{(g)} \rightleftharpoons 2H_{2(g)} + O_{2(g)}$ at 2000°K. If you fill a 10-l box with steam at 1 atm pressure and 2000°K, what per cent of the steam will be decomposed into $H_2$ and $O_2$ when equilibrium has been established?

ANSWER: 0.556%

In the preceding problems, decomposition has occurred to produce a material which was not there at the start of the experiment. In the more general case, some of the material may already be there initially, in which case it will have to be taken into account in setting up the expression for the concentrations.

P R O B L E M   531    Given that $K$ = 3.76 × $10^{-5}$ for $I_{2(g)} \rightleftharpoons 2I_{(g)}$ at 1000°K. Suppose you inject 1.00 mole $I_2$ into a 2.00-l box which already contains 5.00 × $10^{-3}$ mole I. What will be the concentrations of $I_2$ and I at equilibrium?

SOLUTION:

Injection concentration of $I_2$ is $\dfrac{1.00 \text{ mole}}{2.00 \text{ l}}$ = 0.500 $M$.

Let $x$ mole/l decompose. This will form $2x$ mole/l I in addition to the I already there, which is at a concentration of $\dfrac{5.00 \times 10^{-3} \text{ mole}}{2.00 \text{ liters}}$ = 2.50 × $10^{-3}$ mole/l. Therefore, at equilibrium,

$[I_2]$ = 0.500 − $x$;   $[I]$ = 2.50 × $10^{-3}$ + $2x$

where $[I_2]$ takes into account that $x$ mole/l of the injected 0.500 $M$ has disappeared, and the $[I]$ takes into account that $2x$ mole/l I has formed to add to the 2.50 × $10^{-3}$ $M$ originally present.

$$K = \frac{[I]^2}{[I_2]} = 3.76 \times 10^{-5} = \frac{(2.50 \times 10^{-3} + 2x)^2}{0.500 - x}$$

$x$ is probably small compared to 0.500 in the denominator, so we can approximate $(0.500 - x) \cong 0.500$. However, we cannot neglect the $2x$ compared to $2.50 \times 10^{-3}$ in the numerator, since the two terms may be about the same size.

So, solve the equation

$$3.76 \times 10^{-5} \cong \frac{(2.50 \times 10^{-3} + 2x)^2}{0.500}$$

The quadratic formula gives us $x = 9.15 \times 10^{-4}$. Substitute this value of $x$ in the expressions for $[I_2] = 0.500 - x$ and $[I] = 2.50 \times 10^{-3} + 2x$ to get the final equilibrium concentrations:

$$[I_2] = 0.500 - x = 0.500 - 9.15 \times 10^{-4} = \textbf{0.499 } \boldsymbol{M}$$

$$[I] = 2.50 \times 10^{-3} + 2x = 2.50 \times 10^{-3} + (2)(9.15 \times 10^{-4})$$

$$= \textbf{4.33} \times \textbf{10}^{-3} \boldsymbol{M}$$

**PROBLEM 532** Given that $K = 33.3$ for $PCl_{5(g)} \rightleftharpoons PCl_{3(g)} + Cl_{2(g)}$ at 760°K. What will be the final equilibrium state of the system if 1.50 g $PCl_5$ and 15.0 g $PCl_3$ are simultaneously injected into a volume of 36.3 cc at 760°K?

SOLUTION:

$$1.50 \text{ g } PCl_5 = \frac{1.50 \text{ g}}{208.24 \text{ g/mole}} = 0.00720 \text{ mole.}$$

$$\text{Injection concentration } PCl_5 = \frac{0.00720 \text{ mole}}{0.0363 \text{ l}} = 0.198 \text{ } M.$$

$$15.0 \text{ g } PCl_3 = \frac{15.0 \text{ g}}{137.33 \text{ g/mole}} = 0.109 \text{ mole.}$$

$$\text{Injection concentration of } PCl_3 = \frac{0.109 \text{ mole}}{0.0363 \text{ l}} = 3.00 \text{ } M.$$

At the start of the experiment, we thus have: $[PCl_5] = 0.198 \text{ } M$; $[PCl_3] = 3.00 \text{ } M$; and $[Cl_2] = 0 \text{ } M$.

Now let $x$ moles/l $PCl_5$ decompose via the reaction $PCl_5 \rightarrow PCl_3 + Cl_2$. This will decrease the $PCl_5$ concentration by $x$, and raise that of $PCl_3$ and of $Cl_2$ by $x$.

At equilibrium,

$$[PCl_5] = 0.198 - x; \; [PCl_3] = 3.00 + x; \; [Cl_2] = x$$

$$K = \frac{[PCl_3][Cl_2]}{[PCl_5]} = \frac{(3.00 + x)(x)}{0.198 - x} = 33.3$$

Solve this equation for $x$, using the quadratic formula, since the usual approximation of negligible $x$ will not hold in this case. It turns out that $x = 0.181\ M$:

$$[PCl_5] = 0.198 - x = 0.198 - 0.181 = 0.017\ M$$

$$[PCl_3] = 3.00 + x = 3.00 + 0.181 = 3.18\ M$$

$$[Cl_2] = x = 0.181\ M$$

■ PROBLEM 533   Given that $K = 33.3$ for $PCl_{5(g)} \rightleftharpoons PCl_{3(g)} + Cl_{2(g)}$ at 760°K. What will be the final equilibrium state of the system if 1.50 g $PCl_5$ and 15.0 g $Cl_2$ are simultaneously injected into a volume of 36.3 cc at 760°K?
ANSWER: $[PCl_5] = 0.030\ M$; $[PCl_3] = 0.168\ M$; $[Cl_2] = 5.99\ M$

PROBLEM 534   For the equilibrium $H_{2(g)} + CO_{2(g)} \rightleftharpoons H_2O_{(g)} + CO_{(g)}$ the $K$ is 4.40 at 2000°K. Calculate the concentration of each species at equilibrium after 1.00 mole $H_2$ and 1.00 mole $CO_2$ are simultaneously put into a 4.68-l box at 2000°K.

SOLUTION: Initial concentration of $H_2 = \dfrac{1.00\ \text{mole}}{4.68\ l} = 0.214\ M$.

Initial concentration of $CO_2 = \dfrac{1.00\ \text{mole}}{4.68\ l} = 0.214\ M$.

Initial concentrations of $H_2O$ and of CO = zero.
Let $x$ = moles/l $H_2O$ (or CO) formed in order to get equilibrium established. From the stoichiometry of the change $H_2 + CO_2 \rightarrow H_2O + CO$ we get $x$ moles of $H_2O$ and $x$ moles of CO each time $x$ moles of $H_2$ and $x$ moles of $CO_2$ disappear. Therefore, at equilibrium,

$$[H_2] = 0.214 - x;\ \ [CO_2] = 0.214 - x;\ \ [H_2O] = x;\ \ [CO] = x$$

$$K = \frac{[H_2O][CO]}{[H_2][CO_2]} = \frac{(x)(x)}{(0.214 - x)(0.214 - x)} = 4.40$$

This equation can be solved either by use of the quadratic formula or by noting that the left side is a perfect square:

$$\frac{(x)(x)}{(0.214 - x)(0.214 - x)} = 4.40$$

If we take the square root of both sides of this equation, we get

$$\frac{x}{0.214 - x} = \sqrt{4.40} = 2.10$$

The result is a simple linear equation which solves to give $x = 0.145$. Substituting for $x$ in the concentration expressions, we get the equilibrium values:

$[H_2] = 0.214 - x = 0.214 - 0.145 = \mathbf{0.069 \; M}$

$[CO_2] = 0.214 - x = 0.214 - 0.145 = \mathbf{0.069 \; M}$

$[H_2O] = x = \mathbf{0.145 \; M}$

$[CO] = x = \mathbf{0.145 \; M}$

■ PROBLEM 535    For    the    equilibrium $H_{2(g)} + CO_{2(g)} \rightleftharpoons H_2O_{(g)} + CO_{(g)}$ the $K$ is 4.40 at 2000°K. Calculate the concentration of each species at equilibrium after 1.00 mole $H_2O$ and 1.00 mole CO are simultaneously put into a 4.68-l box at 2000°K.

ANSWER: $[H_2] = \mathbf{0.069 \; M}$; $[CO_2] = \mathbf{0.069 \; M}$; $[H_2O] = \mathbf{0.145 \; M}$; $[CO] = \mathbf{0.145 \; M}$

[Note: The answer to Problem 535 must be the same as the answer to Problem 534, since we are assured of getting the same equilibrium system no matter from which direction we approach it, provided of course we mix equivalent quantities of chemicals.]

PROBLEM 536    For    the    equilibrium $H_{2(g)} + CO_{2(g)} \rightleftharpoons H_2O_{(g)} + CO_{(g)}$ the $K$ is 4.40 at 2000°K. What will be the composition of the final equilibrium system if 1.00 mole $H_2$, 1.00 mole $CO_2$, and 1.00 mole $H_2O$ are simultaneously put into a 4.68-l box at 2000°K?

SOLUTION: Initial concentration of $H_2 = \dfrac{1.00 \text{ mole}}{4.68 \text{ l}} = 0.214 \; M$.

Initial concentration of $CO_2 = \dfrac{1.00 \text{ mole}}{4.68 \text{ l}} = 0.214 \; M$.

Initial concentration of $H_2O = \dfrac{1.00 \text{ mole}}{4.68 \text{ l}} = 0.214 \; M$,

Initially, there is none of the fourth ingredient CO.

Let $x$ = moles/l CO that will form by the net change $H_2 + CO_2 \rightarrow$ $H_2O + CO$. This will increase the concentration of $H_2O$ by $x$ moles/l and decrease the concentrations of $H_2$ and of $CO_2$ by $x$ moles/l.

At equilibrium, then, we have

$$[H_2] = 0.214 - x;\ [CO_2] = 0.214 - x;\ [H_2O] = 0.214 + x;\ [CO] = x$$

$$K = \frac{[H_2O][CO]}{[H_2][CO_2]} = \frac{(0.214 + x)(x)}{(0.214 - x)(0.214 - x)} = 4.40$$

Solve this by the quadratic formula and get $x = 0.119$. This gives

$$[H_2] = 0.214 - x = 0.214 - 0.119 = \mathbf{0.095\ M}$$

$$[CO_2] = 0.214 - x = 0.214 - 0.119 = \mathbf{0.095\ M}$$

$$[H_2O] = 0.214 + x = 0.214 + 0.119 = \mathbf{0.333\ M}$$

$$[CO] = x = \mathbf{0.119\ M}$$

■ **PROBLEM** 537 For the equilibrium $H_{2(g)} + CO_{2(g)} \rightleftharpoons H_2O_{(g)} + CO_{(g)}$ the $K$ is 4.40 at 2000°K. What will be the composition of the final equilibrium system if 1.00 mole $H_2$, 1.00 mole $H_2O$, and 1.00 mole CO are simultaneously put into a 4.68-l box at 2000°K?

ANSWER: $[H_2] = \mathbf{0.245\ M};\ [CO_2] = \mathbf{0.0311\ M};\ [H_2O] = \mathbf{0.183\ M};$ $[CO] = \mathbf{0.183\ M}$

■■ **PROBLEM** 538 The $K$ for the equilibrium $2NO_{(g)} + O_{2(g)} \rightleftharpoons 2NO_{2(g)}$ is equal to $6.45 \times 10^5$ at 500°K. Suppose you mix two moles NO, one mole $O_2$, and two moles $NO_2$ in a 1.00-l container at 500°K. What will be the equilibrium concentration of each species?

ANSWER: $[NO] = \mathbf{0.0365\ M};\ [O_2] = \mathbf{0.0182\ M};\ [NO_2] = \mathbf{3.96\ M}$

**PROBLEM** 539 At high temperatures phosgene, $COCl_2$, decomposes to give carbon monoxide, CO, and chlorine, $Cl_2$. In a typical experiment 0.631 g $COCl_2$ is injected into a flask of volume 472.0 cc at 1000°K. When equilibrium has been established, it is found that the total pressure in the flask is 2.175 atm. Calculate $K$ for the reaction $COCl_{2(g)} \rightleftharpoons CO_{(g)} + Cl_{2(g)}$ at 1000°K.

SOLUTION: (Use $PV = nRT$ to find out how many moles there are in the system at equilibrium. Then compare this with the number of moles injected into the system to find out how far the decomposition has proceeded.)

In the final state $P = 2.175$ atm, $V = 0.4720$ l, and $T = 1000°K$:

$$n = \frac{PV}{RT} = \frac{(2.175)(0.4720)}{(0.08206)(1000)} = 0.01251 \text{ mole}$$

This represents the total number of moles in the final system and comprises $COCl_2$, $CO$, and $Cl_2$.

Initially, we put 0.631 g $COCl_2$ into the system. One mole $COCl_2$ weighs 98.917 g, so this amounts to

$$\frac{0.631 \text{ g}}{98.917 \text{ g/mole}} = 0.00638 \text{ mole } COCl_2.$$

If we let $x$ = moles $COCl_2$ that will decompose to establish equilibrium via $COCl_2 \rightarrow CO + Cl_2$, then we will have left $(0.00638 - x)$ moles $COCl_2$ and will have formed $x$ moles $CO$ and $x$ moles $Cl_2$. The total number of moles in the final system will be the sum of these: $(0.00638 - x)$ moles $COCl_2$ plus $x$ moles $CO$ plus $x$ moles $Cl_2$ = $0.00638 + x$.

But, above, we calculated the total number of moles to be equal to 0.01251. We set the two equal to each other $0.00638 + x = 0.01251$ and solve for $x = 0.00613$.

At equilibrium, we have then

$x$ moles $CO$ = 0.00613 mole $CO$

$x$ moles $Cl_2$ = 0.00613 mole $Cl_2$

$0.00638 - x$ mole $COCl_2$ = 0.00638 − 0.00613 = 0.00025 mole $COCl_2$

Dividing each of these by the volume of the system, 0.472 l, will give the concentrations at equilibrium:

$$[CO] = \frac{0.00613 \text{ mole}}{0.472 \text{ l}} = 0.0130 \text{ } M$$

$$[Cl_2] = \frac{0.00613 \text{ mole}}{0.472 \text{ l}} = 0.0130 \text{ } M$$

$$[COCl_2] = \frac{0.00025 \text{ mole}}{0.472 \text{ l}} = 5.3 \times 10^{-4} \; M$$

Substitute these in the constant for the equilibrium for

$$COCl_{2(g)} \rightleftharpoons CO_{(g)} + Cl_{2(g)}$$

$$K = \frac{[CO][Cl_2]}{[COCl_2]} = \frac{(0.0130)(0.0130)}{5.3 \times 10^{-4}} = 0.32$$

■ **PROBLEM 540** Suppose that 0.631 g $COCl_2$ is injected into a vessel of volume 472.0 cc at 900°K. When equilibrium has been established, it is found that the total pressure in the flask is 1.872 atm. Calculate $K$ for the reaction $COCl_{2(g)} \rightleftharpoons CO_{(g)} + Cl_{2(g)}$ at 900°K.

ANSWER: $K = 0.082$

## Different types of K: $K_c$, $K_p$, $K_x$

In all our preceding calculations we have gone along with the common convention in freshman chemistry that the equilibrium constant $K$ is evaluated by using moles per liter as the units for expressing concentration. In subsequent chapters we shall continue to follow this convention; however, you should be aware of the fact that there is nothing magic in using $C$ in moles per liter to describe the concentrations and that, in fact, two other conventions are in considerable use. One of these describes concentrations in terms of the partial pressures, $p$, in which case $K$ is designated as $K_p$. The other describes concentrations in terms of mole fractions, $x$, in which case $K$ is designated as $K_x$. Just plain $K$ implies moles per liter but if you want to be dead-sure, you can mark it $K_c$. What you get as the numerical value of the equilibrium constant for a particular reaction at a given temperature depends on whether you use $K_c$, $K_p$, or $K_x$.

## PROBLEM 541

You are given a box containing at equilibrium at 1000°K 0.102 mole/l $NH_3$, 1.03 moles/l $N_2$, and 1.62 moles/l $H_2$. For the reaction $N_{2(g)} + 3H_{2(g)} \rightleftharpoons 2NH_{3(g)}$ calculate $K_c$, $K_p$, and $K_x$ at 1000°K.

SOLUTION: To get $K_c$, we need moles per liter for each species:

$$[NH_3] = 0.102 \ M \qquad\qquad K_c = \frac{[NH_3]^2}{[N_2][H_2]^3} = \frac{(0.102)^2}{(1.03)(1.62)^3}$$

$$[N_2] = 1.03 \ M \qquad\qquad\qquad = 2.37 \times 10^{-3}$$

$$[H_2] = 1.62 \ M$$

To get $K_p$, we need the partial pressure of each species.

We can calculate $p$ by using $pV = nRT$, where $p = \left(\dfrac{n}{V}\right) RT$ and $\left(\dfrac{n}{V}\right)$ is just the given concentration in mole/l of each species:

$$p_{NH_3} = (0.102)(RT) = (0.102)(0.08206)(1000) = 8.37 \text{ atm}$$

$$p_{N_2} = (1.03)(RT) = (1.03)(0.08206)(1000) = 84.5 \text{ atm}$$

$$p_{H_2} = (1.62)(RT) = (1.62)(0.08206)(1000) = 133 \text{ atm}$$

For the reaction $N_{2(g)} + 3H_{2(g)} \rightleftharpoons 2NH_{3(g)}$,

$$K_p = \frac{p_{NH_3}^2}{p_{N_2}p_{H_2}^3} = \frac{(8.37)^2}{(84.5)(133)^3} = 3.52 \times 10^{-7}$$

To get $K_x$, we need the mole fraction of each species. If we take 1 l for reference, it contains 0.102 mole $NH_3$, 1.03 moles $N_2$, and 1.62 moles $H_2$, which comes to a total of 2.75 moles:

$$x_{NH_3} = \frac{0.102 \text{ mole } NH_3}{2.75 \text{ moles total}} = 0.0371$$

$$x_{N_2} = \frac{1.03 \text{ moles } N_2}{2.75 \text{ moles total}} = 0.375$$

$$x_{H_2} = \frac{1.62 \text{ moles } H_2}{2.75 \text{ moles total}} = 0.589$$

For the reaction $N_{2(g)} + 3H_{2(g)} \rightleftharpoons 2NH_{3(g)}$,

$$K_x = \frac{x_{NH_3}^2}{x_{N_2}x_{H_2}^3} = \frac{(0.0371)^2}{(0.375)(0.589)^3} = 1.80 \times 10^{-2}$$

So, in summary, $K_c = 2.37 \times 10^{-3}$; $K_p = 3.52 \times 10^{-7}$; $K_x = 1.80 \times 10^{-2}$. They are all equally valid for describing the same equilibrium state and can be used for calculations where different kinds of concentration units are employed.

244    GASEOUS EQUILIBRIA

■ PROBLEM 542
Given an equilibrium system containing at 750°C 1.68 moles $H_2S$, 1.37 moles $H_2$, and $2.88 \times 10^{-5}$ mole $S_2$ in a volume of 18.0 l. Calculate $K_c$, $K_p$, and $K_x$ for the reaction $2H_{2(g)} + S_{2(g)} \rightleftharpoons 2H_2S_{(g)}$.

ANSWER: $K_c = 9.39 \times 10^5$; $K_p = 1.12 \times 10^4$; $K_x = 1.59 \times 10^5$

■ PROBLEM 543   Given an equilibrium system at 2000°K consisting of 0.145 mole $H_2$, 1.145 moles $CO_2$, 0.855 mole $H_2O$, and 0.855 mole CO in a volume of 20.0 l. Calculate $K_c$, $K_p$, and $K_x$ for the reaction $H_{2(g)} + CO_{2(g)} \rightleftharpoons H_2O_{(g)} + CO_{(g)}$.

ANSWER: $K_c = 4.40$; $K_p = 4.40$; $K_x = 4.40$
[Note: When the number of gas molecules is the same on the left and right sides of the chemical equation, the value of $K$ calculated using the different concentration units comes out to be the same.]

PROBLEM 544   Given that $K_p$ for the equilibrium $2SO_{2(g)} + O_{2(g)} \rightleftharpoons 2SO_{3(g)}$ equals 3.18 at 1000°K, figure out what must be the value of $K_c$ for this same equilibrium at 1000°K. Assume ideal behavior.

SOLUTION: $2SO_{2(g)} + O_{2(g)} \rightleftharpoons 2SO_{3(g)}$.

$$K_p = \frac{p_{SO_3}^2}{p_{SO_2}^2 p_{O_2}} = 3.18$$

For each gas $pV = nRT$, or $p = \left(\dfrac{n}{V}\right) RT$. But $\dfrac{n}{V}$, the number of moles per liter, is just the concentration $C$. So we can write

$$p_{SO_3} = \left(\frac{n_{SO_3}}{V}\right) RT = C_{SO_3}RT$$

$$p_{SO_2} = \left(\frac{n_{SO_2}}{V}\right) RT = C_{SO_2}RT$$

$$p_{O_2} = \left(\frac{n_{O_2}}{V}\right) RT = C_{O_2}RT$$

Substitute these in the above expression for $K_p$:

$$K_p = \frac{(C_{SO_3}RT)^2}{(C_{SO_2}RT)^2(C_{O_2}RT)} = 3.18$$

Solve for $K_c$:

$$K_c = \frac{C_{SO_3}^2}{C_{SO_2}^2 C_{O_2}} = 3.18(RT)$$

But $R = 0.08206$ l atm/deg and $T = 1000$ deg:

$$K_c = (3.18)(0.08206)(1000) = \mathbf{261}$$

■ **PROBLEM 545** Calculate $K_c$ for the equilibrium $2CO_{(g)} + O_{2(g)} \rightleftharpoons 2CO_{2(g)}$ at 1000°K, given that $K_p = 2.73 \times 10^{20}$ at 1000°K.

ANSWER: $\mathbf{2.24 \times 10^{22}}$

■ **PROBLEM 546** The equilibrium between ozone, $O_3$, and oxygen, $O_2$, at 2000°K is characterized by a $K_p = 4.17 \times 10^{14}$ for the reaction $2O_{3(g)} \rightleftharpoons 3O_{2(g)}$. Calculate $K_c$ for this same reaction at 2000° K.

ANSWER: $K_c = \mathbf{2.54 \times 10^{12}}$

**PROBLEM 547** Suppose you have a 10-l box containing only $O_3$ and $O_2$ at equilibrium at 2000°K with $K_p = 4.17 \times 10^{14}$ for $2O_{3(g)} \rightleftharpoons 3O_{2(g)}$. If the total pressure in the box is 7.33 atm, what is the partial pressure of the ozone?

SOLUTION: $2O_{3(g)} \rightleftharpoons 3O_{2(g)}$.

$$K_p = \frac{p_{O_2}^3}{p_{O_3}^2} = 4.17 \times 10^{14}$$

Total pressure = 7.33 atm = $p_{O_3} + p_{O_2}$.
$K_p$ is such a large number that $p_{O_2}$ must be much, much greater than $p_{O_3}$. So, practically all the pressure in the box must be due to $O_2$—i.e., of the 7.33-atm pressure in the box, it is mostly $p_{O_2}$. Substitute $p_{O_2} \cong 7.33$ atm in $K_p$ and solve for $p_{O_3}$:

$$K_p = \frac{p_{O_2}^3}{p_{O_3}^2} = \frac{(7.33)^3}{p_{O_3}^2} = 4.17 \times 10^{14}$$

$$p_{O_3} = \mathbf{9.71 \times 10^{-7} \ atm}$$

■ PROBLEM 548    Given that $K_p = 3.18$ at 1000°K for $2SO_{2(g)} + O_{2(g)} \rightleftharpoons 2SO_{3(g)}$. You have a 10-l box containing only $SO_2$, $O_2$, and $SO_3$ at equilibrium at 1000°K. If the total pressure in the box is 5.50 atm and there is at equilibrium 3.90 g $O_2$ in the box, what must be the partial pressures of $SO_2$ and $SO_3$ therein?

ANSWER: $p_{SO_2} = 1.62$ atm; $p_{SO_3} = 2.88$ atm

■■ PROBLEM 549    You have a 10-l box at 1000°K containing only $SO_2$, $O_2$, and $SO_3$ at equilibrium corresponding to $K_p = 3.18$ for the reaction $2SO_{2(g)} + O_{2(g)} \rightleftharpoons 2SO_{3(g)}$. Initially the system contains $p_{O_2} = 1.00$ atm, $p_{SO_2} = 1.62$ atm, and $p_{SO_3} = 2.88$ atm. Being careful to keep the temperature constant at 1000°K, you squeeze the box until its volume gets reduced to 7.60 l. Assuming nothing escapes, what will be the final partial pressures of all species in the box when equilibrium is re-established?

ANSWER: $p_{O_2} = 1.24$ atm; $p_{SO_2} = 1.98$ atm; $p_{SO_3} = 3.94$ atm

# 13

## STRONG AND
## WEAK ELECTROLYTES

AN ELECTROLYTE is a substance which dissociates in water (or in some other suitable solvent) to produce an electrically conducting solution. Most electrolytes can be classified as *strong* or *weak*—the former being those which are extensively dissociated into ions and the latter, only to a slight extent. This distinction breaks down in very dilute solutions, because as the concentration of a solute decreases, its per cent dissociation increases. In very dilute solutions, even weak electrolytes behave like strong electrolytes.

The interaction between an electrolyte AB and the solvent, generally water, is a chemical reaction which can be written

$$AB + water \rightarrow A^+_{hydrated} + B^-_{hydrated}$$

Being reversible, this reaction comes to equilibrium, and in the equilibrium state there will be present undissociated AB as well as hydrated $A^+$ and hydrated $B^-$. For computation purposes, it is common to leave out the water and write the equilibrium as

$$AB \rightleftharpoons A^+ + B^-$$

with the understanding that all the species are hydrated. The equilibrium condition, as discussed in Chapter 12, is

$$K = \frac{C_{A^+}C_{B^-}}{C_{AB}} = \frac{[A^+][B^-]}{[AB]}$$

where we have used $C$ as well as the square brackets to represent concentration in moles per liter.

## *Strong electrolytes*

Most salts, a few acids, and a relatively few bases are strong electrolytes. For salts, representative compounds would be the sodium or potassium salts with almost any anion—e.g., $NaCl$, $KNO_3$, $Na_2SO_4$, $Na_2CO_3$, $KAl(SO_4)_2$. For acids, the best example of a strong electrolyte would be perchloric acid, $HClO_4$; other possible examples are $HNO_3$, $HCl$, and the first proton to come off $H_2SO_4$ (via $H_2SO_4 \rightarrow H^+ + HSO_4^-$). For bases, $NaOH$ and $KOH$ are good examples, as are $Ca(OH)_2$, $Sr(OH)_2$, and $Ba(OH)_2$. For these dihydroxides, both $OH^-$ groups are normally assumed to be fully dissociated. In all these cases listed, per cent dissociation is usually assumed to be 100%.

**PROBLEM 550**    If you have a solution which is 0.010 $M$ NaCl, what is the concentration of $Na^+$ and of $Cl^-$ in this solution?

SOLUTION: Assume 100% dissociation since this is a typical salt:

$$NaCl \rightarrow Na^+ + Cl^-$$

0.010 $M$ NaCl means 0.010 mole NaCl per liter, all of which is taken to be 100% dissociated into $Na^+$ and $Cl^-$. The dissociation equation shows that if one mole NaCl disappears on the left, we get one mole $Na^+$ and one mole $Cl^-$ on the right. So, if we break up 0.010 mole NaCl, we get 0.010 mole $Na^+$ and 0.010 mole $Cl^-$. Since the reference volume of solution is 1 l, we can say the concentration of $Na^+$ is 0.010 mole/l, or **0.010 $M$**, and the concentration of $Cl^-$ likewise equals **0.010 $M$**.

**PROBLEM 551**    In a solution which is 0.015 $M$ $K_2SO_4$, what is the concentration of $K^+$ and of $SO_4^=$?

SOLUTION: Assume 100% dissociation since this is a typical salt:

$$K_2SO_4 \rightarrow 2K^+ + SO_4^=$$

Each mole $K_2SO_4$ produces 2 moles $K^+$ and 1 mole $SO_4^=$. The 0.015 $M$ $K_2SO_4$ means 0.015 mole $K_2SO_4$ per liter of solution, which would give 0.030 mole $K^+$ and 0.015 mole $SO_4^=$. So, $[K^+] = 0.030\ M$; $[SO_4^=] = 0.015\ M$.

P R O B L E M  552  Suppose you add 3.63 g $KAl(SO_4)_2$ to enough water to make 0.250 l solution. What is the concentration of each ion?

SOLUTION: 3.63 g $KAl(SO_4)_2 = \dfrac{3.63\ g}{258.21\ g/mole} = 0.0141$ mole.

Assume 100% dissociation:

$$KAl(SO_4)_2 \rightarrow K^+ + Al^{+3} + 2SO_4^=$$

If we dissociate 0.0141 mole $KAl(SO_4)_2$ this way, the result will be 0.0141 mole $K^+$, 0.0141 mole $Al^{+3}$, and 0.0282 mole $SO_4^=$. To get concentrations, we divide the number of moles by the volume:

$$[K^+] = \frac{0.0141\ \text{mole}}{0.250\ \text{l}} = 0.0564\ M$$

$$[Al^{+3}] = \frac{0.0141\ \text{mole}}{0.250\ \text{l}} = 0.0564\ M$$

$$[SO_4^=] = \frac{0.0282\ \text{mole}}{0.250\ \text{l}} = 0.113\ M$$

■ P R O B L E M  553  What is the concentration of $Ca^{++}$ and of $NO_3^-$ in 0.0280 $M$ $Ca(NO_3)_2$ solution?
ANSWER: 0.0280 $M$ $Ca^{++}$ and 0.0560 $M$ $NO_3^-$

■ P R O B L E M  554  What is the concentration of each ion in a solution made by dissolving 3.63 g $KCr(SO_4)_2$ in enough water to make 0.250 l solution? Assume complete dissociation.
ANSWER: 0.0512 $M$ $K^+$; 0.0512 $M$ $Cr^{+3}$; 0.102 $M$ $SO_4^=$

P R O B L E M  555  Suppose you add 5.15 g $HClO_4$ to 0.250 l of 0.150 $M$ $HClO_4$. Assuming the solution volume stays at 0.250 l, calculate $[H^+]$ and $[ClO_4^-]$.

SOLUTION: (Whenever you have such a problem as this, where more than one source contributes reagent, your best bet is to figure out how many moles of each species are contributed from each source. Then use the total to figure out the concentration.)

One mole $HClO_4$ weighs 100.46 g.

$$5.15 \text{ g } HClO_4 = \frac{5.15 \text{ g}}{100.46 \text{ g/mole}} = 0.0513 \text{ mole } HClO_4$$

Since $HClO_4$ is a strong electrolyte, we assume 100% dissociation:

$$HClO_4 \rightarrow H^+ + ClO_4^-$$

to give 0.0513 mole $H^+$ and 0.0513 mole $ClO_4^-$. But the solution already is 0.150 $M$ $HClO_4$, which, corresponding to 100% dissociation via $HClO_4 \rightarrow H^+ + ClO_4^-$, would mean 0.150 $M$ $H^+$ and 0.150 $M$ $ClO_4^-$. Since we start with 0.250 l of 0.150 $M$ $HClO_4$, we have at the start:

$$(0.250 \text{ l}) \left( 0.150 \frac{\text{mole } H^+}{\text{l}} \right) = 0.0375 \text{ mole } H^+$$

$$(0.250 \text{ l}) \left( 0.150 \frac{\text{mole } ClO_4^-}{\text{l}} \right) = 0.0375 \text{ mole } ClO_4^-$$

Total moles $H^+ = 0.0513 + 0.0375 = 0.0888$ mole $H^+$.
Total moles $ClO_4^- = 0.0513 + 0.0375 = 0.0888$ mole $ClO_4^-$.
Total volume of final solution equals 0.250 l.

$$\text{Final } [H^+] = \frac{0.0888 \text{ mole}}{0.250 \text{ l}} = 0.355 \; M$$

$$[ClO_4^-] = \frac{0.0888 \text{ mole}}{0.250 \text{ l}} = 0.355 \; M$$

■ PROBLEM 556 If you add 0.269 g $HNO_3$ to 36.3 ml of 1.18 $M$ $HNO_3$, what will be the final concentration of $[H^+]$ and of $[NO_3^-]$ assuming no change in solution volume?

ANSWER: 1.30 $M$ $H^+$ and 1.30 $M$ $NO_3^-$

PROBLEM 557 Suppose you add 1.65 g $Ba(OH)_2$ to a mixture of 47.6 ml of 0.0562 $M$ $Ba(OH)_2$ and 23.2 ml of 0.100 $M$ $Ba(OH)_2$. Calculate the final concentrations of $Ba^{++}$ and $OH^-$, assuming complete dissociation and that the final volume of solution is just the sum of the two solutions mixed.

SOLUTION: Calculate the number of moles $Ba(OH)_2$ from each source.

$$1.65 \text{ g } Ba(OH)_2 = \frac{1.65 \text{ g}}{171.35 \text{ g/mole}} = 0.00963 \text{ mole } Ba(OH)_2.$$

47.6 ml of 0.0562 $M$ Ba(OH)$_2$ furnishes

$$(0.0476 \text{ l}) \left( 0.0562 \frac{\text{mole}}{\text{l}} \right) = 0.00268 \text{ mole Ba(OH)}_2.$$

23.2 ml of 0.100 $M$ Ba(OH)$_2$ furnishes

$$(0.0232 \text{ l}) \left( 0.100 \frac{\text{mole}}{\text{l}} \right) = 0.00232 \text{ mole Ba(OH)}_2.$$

Total moles Ba(OH)$_2$ = 0.00963 + 0.00268 + 0.00232 = 0.0146 mole Ba(OH)$_2$.

Assume 100% dissociation via Ba(OH)$_2$ → Ba$^{++}$ + 2OH$^-$.

This will give 0.0146 mole Ba$^{++}$ plus 0.0292 mole OH$^-$ in the final solution.

Total final volume = 47.6 ml + 23.2 ml = 70.8 ml.

$$\text{Final } [\text{Ba}^{++}] = \frac{0.0146 \text{ mole}}{0.0708 \text{ l}} = 0.206 \ M$$

$$[\text{OH}^-] = \frac{0.0292 \text{ mole}}{0.0708 \text{ l}} = 0.412 \ M$$

■ PROBLEM 558  Suppose you add 1.65 g Ba(OH)$_2$ to 47.6 ml of 0.0562 $M$ Ba(OH)$_2$ and add enough water to bring the total volume to 70.8 ml.  What will be the concentrations of Ba$^{++}$ and OH$^-$ in the final solution, assuming complete dissociation?

ANSWER: 0.174 $M$ Ba$^{++}$ and 0.348 $M$ OH$^-$

■ PROBLEM 559  You dissolve 198 g Al$_2$(SO$_4$)$_3$, 208 g K$_2$SO$_4$, and 318 g KAl(SO$_4$)$_2$ in enough water to make 12.6 l of solution.  Assuming complete dissociation and no other reactions, what will be the final concentrations of K$^+$, Al$^{+3}$, and SO$_4^=$?

ANSWER: 0.287 $M$ K$^+$; 0.190 $M$ Al$^{+3}$; 0.428 $M$ SO$_4^=$

## Weak acids (monoprotic)

A "monoprotic" acid is one which can furnish but one H$^+$ per molecule of acid.  "Weak" means that at ordinary concentrations only a small fraction of the molecules are dissociated into H$^+$ and another fragment.  The per cent dissociation and the concentration of the various species can be figured out by applying the techniques for equilibrium calculations as outlined in Chapter 12.  For the general example of a weak acid, HA, which can dissociate into H$^+$ and A$^-$, the dissociation reaction is reversible and can be written

$$HA \rightleftharpoons H^+ + A^-$$

for which the condition at equilibrium is

$$K = \frac{C_{H^+}C_{A^-}}{C_{HA}} = \frac{[H^+][A^-]}{[HA]}$$

$K$ is called the dissociation constant, or ionization constant, of the acid and is frequently designated $K_{diss}$. As before, we can use either $C$ or square brackets to designate the concentration of each species in moles per liter. To streamline the computations, it is customary, as we have done here, to leave water of hydration off each species; however, each species is believed to be hydrated and $H^+$, for example, could be written $H_3O^+$ or, perhaps more accurately, $H_9O_4^+$.

Some typical weak acids are the following:

$$HNO_2 \rightleftharpoons H^+ + NO_2^- \qquad K_{diss} = 4.5 \times 10^{-4}$$
*nitrous acid*

$$HOCl \rightleftharpoons H^+ + OCl^- \qquad K_{diss} = 3.2 \times 10^{-8}$$
*hypochlorous acid*

$$HCN \rightleftharpoons H^+ + CN^- \qquad K_{diss} = 4 \times 10^{-10}$$
*hydrocyanic acid*

$$HOAc \rightleftharpoons H^+ + OAc^- \qquad K_{diss} = 1.8 \times 10^{-5}$$
*acetic acid*

In the last case we follow standard practice as done in the field of organic chemistry and use the designation Ac to represent the acetyl grouping, $CH_3CO$. The acetate ion, which contains an additional oxygen atom attached to the acetyl group, is $CH_3COO^-$, also written $C_2H_3O_2^-$, and is represented here as $OAc^-$.

PROBLEM 560   Given a solution which is labeled 0.0200 $M$ $HNO_2$. What is the concentration of $H^+$, $NO_2^-$, and $HNO_2$ in this solution? The dissociation constant of $HNO_2$ is $4.5 \times 10^{-4}$.

SOLUTION: The label 0.0200 $M$ $HNO_2$ means that the solution was made up by adding 0.0200 mole $HNO_2$ to enough water to make a liter of solution. Let $x$ = moles/l $HNO_2$ that will need to dissociate to establish equilibrium via the reaction $HNO_2 \rightarrow H^+ + NO_2^-$. The stoichiometry of this equation shows that every time 1 mole $HNO_2$ breaks up, 1 mole $H^+$ and 1 mole $NO_2^-$ are produced. So, if $x$ moles $HNO_2$ break up, $x$ moles $H^+$ and $x$ moles $NO_2^-$ are produced. This means that, at equilibrium, there will be $(0.0200 - x)$ moles/l $HNO_2$ left undissociated along with $x$ moles/l $H^+$ and $x$ moles/l $NO_2^-$. The equilibrium condition for

$$HNO_2 \rightleftharpoons H^+ + NO_2^-$$

is that

$$K = \frac{[H^+][NO_2^-]}{[HNO_2]} = 4.5 \times 10^{-4}$$

We substitute $[H^+] = x$; $[NO_2^-] = x$; $[HNO_2] = 0.0200 - x$:

$$K = \frac{(x)(x)}{0.0200 - x} = 4.5 \times 10^{-4}$$

This is a single equation with one unknown, so it can be solved for $x$. For exact solution, we rewrite the algebraic equation in the form $x^2 + 4.5 \times 10^{-4}x - 9.0 \times 10^{-6} = 0$ and apply the quadratic formula. It gives us

$$x = \frac{-4.5 \times 10^{-4} \pm \sqrt{(4.5 \times 10^{-4})^2 - (4)(1)(-9.0 \times 10^{-6})}}{2}$$

from which, discarding the negative root because it is impossible to have a negative concentration, we find that $x = 2.8 \times 10^{-3}$. Thus, at equilibrium, we have

$$[H^+] = x = 2.8 \times 10^{-3} \ M$$
$$[NO_2^-] = x = 2.8 \times 10^{-3} \ M$$
$$[HNO_2] = 0.0200 - x = 0.0172 \ M$$

*Note:* We could also have gotten an approximate answer by noting that in the equation $K = \frac{(x)(x)}{0.0200 - x} = 4.5 \times 10^{-4}$ the $x$ is probably small compared to 0.0200 in the denominator. If we neglect $x$ with respect to 0.0200, we have the approximate relation $\frac{x^2}{0.0200}$

$\cong 4.5 \times 10^{-4}$, which quickly solves to $x = 3.0 \times 10^{-3}$. Checking our approximation $0.0200 - x \cong 0.0200$, we find that it did not stand up very well. With $x = 3.0 \times 10^{-3}$, the quantity $(0.0200 - x)$ is closer to 0.017 than it is to 0.0200. As a second approximation we could try that 0.017 value as a better guess for the denominator. $K = \dfrac{(x)(x)}{0.0200 - x} \cong \dfrac{(x)(x)}{0.017} \cong 4.5 \times 10^{-4}$. It gives $x = 2.8 \times 10^{-3}$, which is not in bad agreement with the exact solution as found above.

$K = \dfrac{H}{D}$

■ PROBLEM 561    Given a solution which is labeled 0.0136 $M$ HCNO (cyanic acid). What is the concentration of $H^+$, $CNO^-$, and HCNO in this solution? The dissociation constant of HCNO is $1.2 \times 10^{-4}$.

ANSWER: $1.2 \times 10^{-3}$ $M$ $H^+$; $1.2 \times 10^{-3}$ $M$ $CNO^-$; 0.0124 $M$ HCNO

PROBLEM 562    If you dissolve 1.08 g HBrO in enough water to make 42.7 ml solution, what will be the concentration of $H^+$, $BrO^-$, and HBrO in the final solution? $K_{diss} = 2.06 \times 10^{-9}$.

SOLUTION: 1.08 g HBrO = $\dfrac{1.08 \text{ g}}{96.916 \text{ g/mole}}$ = 0.0111 mole HBrO.

If none of the HBrO dissociated, then the 0.0111 mole HBrO in 42.7 ml solution would give a concentration of $\dfrac{0.0111 \text{ mole}}{0.0427 \text{ l}}$ = 0.260 $M$.

Let $x$ mole/l HBrO dissociate. This produces $x$ mole/l $H^+$ and $x$ mole/l $BrO^-$, leaving $0.260 - x$ mole/l HBrO undissociated. At equilibrium, we would have

$[H^+] = x$; $[BrO^-] = x$; $[HBrO] = 0.260 - x$

For

$HBrO \rightleftharpoons H^+ + BrO^-$

the equilibrium condition is

$K = \dfrac{[H^+][BrO^-]}{[HBrO]} = \dfrac{(x)(x)}{0.260 - x} = 2.06 \times 10^{-9}$

Since the value of $K$ is so small, $x$ is certainly negligible compared to 0.260 in the denominator. So, we solve

$$\frac{(x)(x)}{0.260} \cong 2.06 \times 10^{-9}$$

to get $x = 2.31 \times 10^{-5}$. At equilibrium, we will have

$[H^+] = 2.31 \times 10^{-5}\ M$; $[BrO^-] = 2.31 \times 10^{-5}\ M$; $[HBrO] = 0.260\ M$

The big question in these calculations is "When can I neglect the $x$ in the denominator?" Unfortunately, there is no simple answer, since it depends on $K$ and on the total concentration of solute. The bigger $K_{diss}$ is, the less able you are to neglect $x$ in the denominator; also, the more dilute the solution is, the less you can neglect $x$ compared to total solute concentration. Generally, if $K_{diss}$ is bigger than about $10^{-4}$ you cannot "neglect the $x$" over the whole range of concentration; if $K_{diss}$ is less than about $10^{-5}$ you can usually "neglect the $x$" except in very dilute solutions (i.e., less concentrated than 0.01 $M$).

Instead of trying to remember when you can neglect $x$ in the denominator, it is more reasonable to rely on the method of successive approximations in almost all cases: In the first step you neglect $x$ in the denominator, then you calculate a value of $x$ from the rest of the equation, put that value of $x$ into the denominator, and recalculate. Keep doing that until the value of $x$ settles down to a constant value. Only if $K_{diss}$ is $10^{-2}$ or larger does it pay to go directly to the quadratic formula.

Another major point to keep in mind is that dissociation constants are not generally known very precisely—rarely to three significant figures, occasionally to two figures, usually only to one. There is no point to your beating your brains out for an exact answer beyond the number of significant figures allowed by the value of $K_{diss}$.

■ PROBLEM 563  If you dissolve 1.08 g HClO (hypochlorous acid) in enough water to make 427 ml solution, what will be the concentrations of $H^+$, $ClO^-$, and HClO in the final solution? $K_{diss} = 3.2 \times 10^{-8}$.

ANSWER: $3.9 \times 10^{-5}\ M\ H^+$; $3.9 \times 10^{-5}\ M\ ClO^-$; 0.0482 $M$ HClO

■ P R O B L E M  564   If you dissolve 1.08 g $HClO_2$ (chlorous acid) in enough water to make 427 ml solution, what will be the concentrations of $H^+$, $ClO_2^-$, and $HClO_2$ in the final solution? $K_{diss} = 1.1 \times 10^{-2}$.

ANSWER: $0.015 \ M \ H^+$; $0.015 \ M \ ClO_2^-$; $0.022 \ M \ HClO_2$

In the above calculations we have dealt only with the situation where all the $H^+$ and all the $A^-$ comes from the solute added to the solution. In practice, however, it is quite frequently the case that the solution already contains either $H^+$ or $A^-$ from some other source. This is sometimes referred to as the "common-ion effect" because any species already there needs to be taken into account in describing the equilibrium state.

P R O B L E M  565   Suppose you add 1.08 g $HClO_2$ to 427 ml of 0.0150 $M$ $NaClO_2$ solution. Assuming no volume change, calculate the final concentrations of $H^+$, $ClO_2^-$, and $HClO_2$. $K_{diss} = 1.1 \times 10^{-2}$.

SOLUTION: $NaClO_2$ is a strong electrolyte; it is 100% dissociated into $Na^+$ and $ClO_2^-$. This means, before you do any adding of $HClO_2$, there is already 0.0150 $M$ $Na^+$ and 0.0150 $M$ $ClO_2^-$ in the solution.

$$1.08 \text{ g } HClO_2 = \frac{1.08 \text{ g}}{68.46 \text{ g/mole}} = 0.0158 \text{ mole } HClO_2$$

In a volume of 0.427 l, this comes to $\dfrac{0.0158 \text{ mole}}{0.427 \text{ l}}$

$= 0.0370$ molar added $HClO_2$.

If we let $x$ moles/l of this $HClO_2$ dissociate, we will get $x$ moles $H^+$ and $x$ moles $ClO_2^-$ from it, leaving $(0.0370 - x)$ moles/l $HClO_2$ undissociated. The $x$ moles/l $ClO_2^-$ will add to the 0.0150 $M$ already there. At equilibrium, then, we will have:

$$[H^+] = x; [ClO_2^-] = x + 0.0150; [HClO_2] = 0.0370 - x$$

These values must satisfy the equilibrium condition, so we substitute in the expression for $K_{diss}$:

$$K = \frac{[H^+][ClO_2^-]}{[HClO_2]} = \frac{(x)(x + 0.0150)}{0.0370 - x} = 1.1 \times 10^{-2}$$

The best way to solve this equation is through the quadratic formula, since $x$ does not appear to be negligible compared to 0.0150 or 0.0370. The proper equation is $x^2 + 0.026x - 4.07 \times 10^{-4} = 0$ for which the quadratic formula gives $x = 0.011$. Putting this $x$ into the above expressions for concentration, we get

$$[H^+] = 0.011 \ M; \ [ClO_2^-] = 0.026 \ M; \ [HClO_2] = 0.026 \ M$$

It is just a coincidence that $[ClO_2^-]$ and $[HClO_2]$ come out to be equal; the thing to note is that $[H^+]$ is *not* equal to $[ClO_2^-]$.

■ P R O B L E M  566  Suppose you add 1.00 g $HNO_2$ to 28.9 ml of 0.0100 $M$ $NaNO_2$. Assuming no volume change of the solution, calculate the final concentrations of $H^+$, $NO_2^-$, and $HNO_2$. $K_{diss} = 4.5 \times 10^{-4}$ for $HNO_2$.

ANSWER: 0.014 $M$ $H^+$; 0.024 $M$ $NO_2^-$; 0.723 $M$ $HNO_2$

Commonly, the dissociation of a weak acid $HA \rightarrow H^+ + A^-$ is emphasized as a way of getting $H^+$ and $A^-$ in the solution at the expense of break-up of HA molecules. However, this reaction is a typical reversible reaction, where the same equilibrium involving $H^+$, $A^-$, and HA can be "approached from the other side"—i.e., by mixing $H^+$ and $A^-$ and allowing them to form as much HA as is consistent with the dissociation constant $K_{diss}$ for HA. In other words, the equilibrium state is not dependent on how it is arrived at so long as equivalent amounts of reagent are involved. This business of approaching equilibrium from either side is particularly important to know when making computations for the final state expected on mixing some $H^+$ and $A^-$.

P R O B L E M  567  Hydrogen cyanide, HCN, is a weak acid with $K_{diss} = 4 \times 10^{-10}$ for $HCN \rightleftharpoons H^+ + CN^-$. If you mix 5.01 g HCl and 6.74 g NaCN in enough water to make 0.275 l solution, what will be the final concentrations of $H^+$, $CN^-$, and HCN?

SOLUTION: HCl and NaCN are strong electrolytes which are 100% dissociated into $H^+ + Cl^-$ and $Na^+ + CN^-$, respectively. $K_{diss}$ for HCN is so small that HCN is but very little dissociated. This means if $H^+$ and $CN^-$ are mixed together, they combine almost 100% to form HCN. The best way to solve the present problem is to take the available $H^+$ and $CN^-$, convert them (hypothetically) 100% to HCN, then allow this HCN to "back-dissociate" as much as it needs to establish equilibrium. The advantage of working this way is we will be able to introduce an unknown $x$ which is small compared to the number from which it will be subtracted.

$$5.01 \text{ g HCl} = \frac{5.01 \text{ g}}{36.46 \text{ g/mole}} = 0.137 \text{ mole HCl}$$

$$6.74 \text{ g NaCN} = \frac{6.74 \text{ g}}{49.01 \text{ g/mole}} = 0.137 \text{ mole NaCN}$$

Assuming 100% dissociation:

$$0.137 \text{ mole HCl} \rightarrow 0.137 \text{ mole } H^+ + 0.137 \text{ mole } Cl^-$$

$$0.137 \text{ mole NaCN} \rightarrow 0.137 \text{ mole } Na^+ + 0.137 \text{ mole } CN^-$$

Let us now let the 0.137 mole $H^+$ and the 0.137 mole $CN^-$ combine completely to give us 0.137 mole HCN. Since the volume of the solution is 0.275 liter, our hypothetical HCN would have a concentration of $\dfrac{0.137 \text{ mole}}{0.275 \text{ l}} = 0.498 \ M$. Let $x$ moles per liter of this HCN dissociate via HCN $\rightarrow H^+ + CN^-$. This will give at equilibrium:

$$[H^+] = x; \ [CN^-] = x; \ [HCN] = 0.498 - x$$

The equilibrium to be satisfied is

$$HCN \rightleftharpoons H^+ + CN^-$$

for which

$$K_{\text{diss}} = \frac{[H^+][CN^-]}{[HCN]} = \frac{(x)(x)}{0.498 - x} = 4 \times 10^{-10}$$

Because $K_{\text{diss}}$ is so small, $x$ is small and can be neglected in the denominator where it is subtracted from 0.498. Solving $\dfrac{(x)(x)}{0.498} \cong 4 \times 10^{-10}$ we get $x = 1.41 \times 10^{-5}$. However, since we are given $K$ to only one significant figure, we should quote $x = 1 \times 10^{-5}$. Final concentrations, then, are

$$[H^+] = 1 \times 10^{-5} \ M; \ [CN^-] = 1 \times 10^{-5} \ M; \ [HCN] = 0.498 \ M$$

■ **PROBLEM** 568    Hydrogen fluoride, HF, is a weak acid with $K_{\text{diss}} = 6.71 \times 10^{-4}$ for the equation HF $\rightleftharpoons$ H$^+$ + F$^-$. If you mix 5.01 g HCl and 5.77 g NaF in enough water to make 0.275 l solution, what will be the final concentrations of H$^+$, F$^-$, and HF?

ANSWER: **0.0180 $M$ H$^+$; 0.0180 $M$ F$^-$; 0.480 $M$ HF**

■■ **PROBLEM** 569    You dissolve 1.00 g HClO$_4$ and 1.00 g NaClO$_2$ in enough water to make 0.150 l solution. Recalling that HClO$_4$, NaClO$_2$, and NaClO$_4$ are all strong electrolytes but HClO$_2$ is a weak acid (HClO$_2$ $\rightleftharpoons$ H$^+$ + ClO$_2^-$) with $K_{\text{diss}} = 1.1 \times 10^{-2}$, calculate the concentration of H$^+$ in the final solution.

ANSWER: **0.019 $M$ H$^+$**

## Weak bases

A common way to define a "base" is to say it is a compound of the type MOH which can dissociate to give M$^+$ and OH$^-$. A "weak" base would be one for which the per cent dissociation of MOH into M$^+$ and OH$^-$ is small. There are relatively few bases of the type MOH, but for computation purposes it is frequently advantageous to postulate their existence to explain observed concentrations.

**PROBLEM** 570    When ammonia is dissolved in water, the solution has basic properties and contains a small but appreciable concentration of NH$_4^+$ and OH$^-$. To account for this, it is frequently assumed that NH$_3$ reacts with H$_2$O to form NH$_4$OH, which acts as a weak base in being slightly dissociated into NH$_4^+$ and OH$^-$. If 0.106 mole NH$_3$ in enough water to produce a liter of solution shows NH$_4^+$ and OH$^-$ concentrations each equal to $1.38 \times 10^{-3}$ $M$, what would be the dissociation constant for "NH$_4$OH," assuming all the dissolved NH$_3$ gets converted to NH$_4$OH?

SOLUTION: Assuming 100% conversion, 0.106 mole NH$_3$ would react with water via NH$_3$ + H$_2$O $\rightarrow$ NH$_4$OH to produce 0.106 mole NH$_4$OH. Enough of this has to dissociate to produce $1.38 \times 10^{-3}$ mole/l NH$_4^+$ and OH$^-$. From the equation NH$_4$OH $\rightarrow$ NH$_4^+$ + OH$^-$ we see one mole NH$_4$OH disappears for every mole of NH$_4^+$ and OH$^-$ produced. At equilibrium, then, the concentration of undissociated $NH_4OH$ would be $(0.106 - 1.38 \times 10^{-3}) = 0.105$ $M$; the concentration of $NH_4^+$ is $1.38 \times 10^{-3}$ $M$; the concentration of $OH^-$ is $1.38 \times 10^{-3}$ $M$.

$$NH_4OH \rightleftharpoons NH_4^+ + OH^-$$

$$K = \frac{[NH_4^+][OH^-]}{[NH_4OH]} = \frac{(1.38 \times 10^{-3})(1.38 \times 10^{-3})}{0.105}$$
$$= 1.81 \times 10^{-5}$$

■ PROBLEM 571    When hydrazine, $N_2H_4$, is added to water we get some $N_2H_5^+$ and $OH^-$, which is attributed to the dissociation of a hypothetical weak base $N_2H_5OH$. If 0.105 mole $N_2H_4$ in enough water to give a liter of solution shows $N_2H_5^+$ and $OH^-$ concentrations each equal to $3.2 \times 10^{-4}$ $M$, what would be the $K_{diss}$ of $N_2H_5OH$?

ANSWER: $9.8 \times 10^{-7}$

Actually, there is considerable evidence against the existence of $NH_4OH$ (or $N_2H_5OH$) in solution and there is a growing trend to discard it as a description of a species in solution. Probably the best way to describe aqueous ammonia solutions at the present time is to write the chemical reaction as

$$NH_3 + H_2O \rightleftharpoons NH_4^+ + OH^-$$

and the condition for equilibrium as

$$K = \frac{[NH_4^+][OH^-]}{[NH_3]} = 1.81 \times 10^{-5}$$

This expression for $K$, which is still referred to as the dissociation constant of ammonia, is the same as that given in Problem 760, except that the denominator shows the molar concentration of $NH_3$ instead of the molar concentration of a hypothetical $NH_4OH$. We do *not* show the concentration of $H_2O$ in the denominator because it is essentially constant (as is true in all dilute aqueous solutions) and its activity stays at unity. In dealing with aqueous solutions, we shall always omit the $H_2O$ from the equilibrium constant expression whether it shows up on the right or left side of the chemical equation.

PROBLEM 572    Given that $K = 1.81$ $\times 10^{-5}$ for the reaction $NH_3 + H_2O \rightleftharpoons NH_4^+ + OH^-$ calculate the concentrations of $NH_3$, $NH_4^+$, and $OH^-$ in a solution made by dissolving 2.63 g $NH_3$ in enough water to give 768 ml solution.

SOLUTION: $2.63$ g $NH_3 = \dfrac{2.63 \text{ g}}{17.03 \text{ g/mole}} = 0.154$ mole $NH_3$

$\dfrac{0.154 \text{ mole } NH_3}{0.768 \text{ l solution}} = 0.201$ mole/l $NH_3$

Let $x$ = moles/l $NH_3$ that react via $NH_3 + H_2O \rightarrow NH_4^+ + OH^-$. This will give at equilibrium:

$[NH_4^+] = x$; $[OH^-] = x$; $[NH_3] = 0.201 - x$

Substitute in the expression for $K$:

$$K = \frac{[NH_4^+][OH^-]}{[NH_3]} = \frac{(x)(x)}{0.201 - x} = 1.81 \times 10^{-5}$$

Solve to get $x = 1.90 \times 10^{-3}$. It is not a bad approximation to neglect $x$ in the denominator. We get finally

$[NH_4^+] = 1.90 \times 10^{-3}$ $M$; $[OH^-] = 1.90 \times 10^{-3}$ $M$; $[NH_3] = 0.199$ $M$

■ PROBLEM 573    Given a solution that is labeled $0.150$ $M$ $NH_3$.  Given that $K = 1.81 \times 10^{-5}$ for $NH_3 + H_2O \rightleftharpoons NH_4^+ + OH^-$, calculate the per cent of ammonia that is actually present as $NH_4^+$.

ANSWER: 1.09%

In the preceding section, it was stressed that the weak-acid dissociation equilibrium $HA \rightleftharpoons H^+ + A^-$ can be approached from either side—that is, by putting HA into water or by mixing $H^+$ and $A^-$.  In either case, the missing species will be produced in sufficient concentration to assure equilibrium.  The same reasoning applies to bases. For the general base BOH, which sets up the equilibrium $BOH \rightleftharpoons B^+ + OH^-$, the same dissociation equilibrium can be set up by dissolving BOH in water or by mixing $B^+$ and $OH^-$.

PROBLEM 574    Given that the weak base BOH has a dissociation constant of $1.50 \times 10^{-8}$, what will be the concentrations of $B^+$, $OH^-$, and BOH in a solution made by dissolving $1.25 \times 10^{-3}$ mole BCl (assumed to be a strong electrolyte) and $1.25 \times 10^{-3}$ mole NaOH in enough water to make 0.100 l solution?

SOLUTION: Since BCl and NaOH are strong electrolytes, they can be assumed to be 100% dissociated.

$1.25 \times 10^{-3}$ mole BCl gives $1.25 \times 10^{-3}$ mole $B^+$ and $1.25 \times 10^{-3}$ mole $Cl^-$.

$1.25 \times 10^{-3}$ mole NaOH gives $1.25 \times 10^{-3}$ mole $Na^+$ and $1.25 \times 10^{-3}$ mole $OH^-$.

The $B^+$ and $OH^-$, being the pieces of a weak electrolyte, are likely to combine together to form BOH. For the moment, let us assume this reaction goes 100% via $B^+ + OH^- \rightarrow$ BOH to produce $1.25 \times 10^{-3}$ mole BOH. In 0.100 l solution, this would give $\dfrac{1.25 \times 10^{-3} \text{ mole BOH}}{0.100\,l} = 1.25 \times 10^{-2}$ $M$ BOH. Let $x =$ moles/l of this BOH that "back-dissociates" to set up the equilibrium. This will give $x$ moles $B^+$, $x$ moles $OH^-$, and leave $(1.25 \times 10^{-2} - x)$ mole BOH/l. For the equilibrium

$$BOH \rightleftharpoons B^+ + OH^-$$

the equilibrium condition is

$$K = \frac{[B^+][OH^-]}{[BOH]} = 1.50 \times 10^{-8}$$

Substitute the concentration of each species in terms of $x$ and get

$$\frac{(x)(x)}{0.0125 - x} = 1.50 \times 10^{-8}$$

from which we get $x = 1.37 \times 10^{-5}$. At equilibrium, we have

$$[B^+] = x = 1.37 \times 10^{-5}\ M$$

$$[OH^-] = x = 1.37 \times 10^{-5}\ M$$

$$[BOH] = 1.25 \times 10^{-2} - x = 0.0125\ M$$

■ PROBLEM 575  Suppose you mix 0.525 mole $NH_4Cl$ and 0.525 mole NaOH in enough water to make 2.85 l solution. Given that $K = 1.81 \times 10^{-5}$ for $NH_3 + H_2O \rightleftharpoons NH_4^+ + OH^-$, calculate the final concentration of $NH_3$, $NH_4^+$, and $OH^-$. Note that $NH_4Cl$ is a strong electrolyte which dissociates to give $NH_4^+$ and $Cl^-$.

ANSWER: $1.81 \times 10^{-3}$ $M$ $NH_4^+$; $1.81 \times 10^{-3}$ $M$ $OH^-$; $0.182$ $M$ $NH_3$

## Weak salts

In general, in the absence of information to the contrary, one assumes that salts are strong electrolytes and are 100% dissociated in all but the most concentrated solutions. This assumption is a good one and it holds no matter how soluble the salt is. A common error is to confuse low solubility with low per cent dissociation, but they are different things. Barium sulfate, for example, is very low in solubility but, still, the small amount that goes into solution is 100% dissociated into $Ba^{++}$ and $SO_4^=$. Consequently, barium sulfate is a *strong* electrolyte.

However, not all salts are 100% dissociated into their component ions. Prime examples are the salts of zinc, cadmium, and mercury, particularly with the halides, and some of the salts of lead, particularly lead acetate. Most of these cases lend themselves to computation only with great difficulty because they usually involve more than one equilibrium at a time. Thus, for example, in a solution of mercuric chloride, $HgCl_2$, there is not only the equilibrium represented by

$$HgCl_2 \rightleftharpoons HgCl^+ + Cl^-$$

corresponding to the split-off of one chloride ion, but also

$$HgCl^+ \rightleftharpoons Hg^{++} + Cl^-$$

corresponding to the split-off of the second chloride ion. Not only that —$HgCl_2$ can also pick up a $Cl^-$ to form $HgCl_3^-$, which gives a third possible equilibrium:

$$HgCl_3^- \rightleftharpoons HgCl_2 + Cl^-$$

Similarly, $HgCl_3^-$ can pick up a chloride ion to form $HgCl_4^=$. To work with all these equilibria simultaneously is obviously quite a job, since all have to be satisfied at the same time by the same set of concentrations. Such complex problems can be treated by the methods to be discussed in Chapter 18. At this point we can only scratch the surface of the problem so as to get a little know-how about weak salts. We shall have to make some large simplifications.

PROBLEM 576    A saturated solution of the weak salt mercuric chloride, $HgCl_2$, is found to have a concentration of 0.26 mole/l of undissociated $HgCl_2$, $2.7 \times 10^{-4}$ $M$ $HgCl^+$, and $3.2 \times 10^{-4}$ $M$ chloride ion.   Calculate the dissociation $K$ for the reaction $HgCl_2 \rightleftharpoons HgCl^+ + Cl^-$.

SOLUTION: The equilibrium constant for this reaction is

$$K = \frac{[HgCl^+][Cl^-]}{[HgCl_2]}$$

All we have to do is to substitute in the equilibrium concentrations that are given to us: $[HgCl_2] = 0.26$ $M$; $[HgCl^+] = 2.7 \times 10^{-4}$ $M$; $[Cl^-] = 3.2 \times 10^{-4}$ $M$.

$$K = \frac{(2.7 \times 10^{-4})(3.2 \times 10^{-4})}{0.26} = 3.3 \times 10^{-7}$$

■ PROBLEM 577    In the same saturated solution mentioned for Problem 576 there is mercuric ion, $Hg^{++}$, at a concentration of $1.5 \times 10^{-7}$ $M$.   Calculate $K$ for $HgCl^+ \rightleftharpoons Hg^{++} + Cl^-$.

ANSWER: $1.8 \times 10^{-7}$

PROBLEM 578    Suppose you are given a solution that is labeled 0.10 $M$ $HgCl_2$.   Assuming that only the first step of the dissociation is important, calculate the concentration of chloride ion in this solution.   $K = 3.3 \times 10^{-7}$ for $HgCl_2 \rightleftharpoons HgCl^+ + Cl^-$.

SOLUTION: Let $x$ = moles/l $HgCl_2$ that dissociate to give $HgCl^+$ and $Cl^-$. This will give $x$ moles/l $HgCl^+$, $x$ moles/l $Cl^-$, and $(0.10 - x)$ mole/l undissociated $HgCl_2$:

$$[HgCl^+] = x; \; [Cl^-] = x; \; [HgCl_2] = 0.10 - x$$

For the dissociation

$$HgCl_2 \rightleftharpoons HgCl^+ + Cl^-$$

the equilibrium condition is

$$K = \frac{[\text{HgCl}^+][\text{Cl}^-]}{[\text{HgCl}_2]} = 3.3 \times 10^{-7} = \frac{(x)(x)}{0.10 - x}$$

This solves to $x = 1.8 \times 10^{-4}$, which gives us at equilibrium:

$[\text{HgCl}^+] = 1.8 \times 10^{-4}\,M$; $[\text{Cl}^-] = 1.8 \times 10^{-4}\,M$;
$[\text{HgCl}_2] = 0.10\,M$

[*Note:* The second dissociation step will not change these numbers very much because (*a*) there is not very much $\text{HgCl}^+$ from which to start the second dissociation reaction and (*b*) the $K$ constant for the second dissociation is not very big.]

■ PROBLEM 579  You have two solutions—one labeled 0.15 $M$ $\text{CaCl}_2$ and the other labeled 0.15 $M$ $\text{HgCl}_2$. Considering that $\text{CaCl}_2$ is a strong electrolyte for both steps of the dissociation and that $\text{HgCl}_2$ is weak with $K = 3.3 \times 10^{-7}$, calculate the ratio of free $[\text{Cl}^-]$ in these two solutions.

ANSWER: **1400-to-1** in the $\text{CaCl}_2$-to-$\text{HgCl}_2$ sense

PROBLEM 580  Suppose you mix 0.100 mole $\text{Hg(ClO}_4)_2$ and 0.080 mole NaCl in enough water to make 1.25 l solution. Given that these are strong electrolytes, but that $K = 1.8 \times 10^{-7}$ for $\text{HgCl}^+ \rightleftharpoons \text{Hg}^{++} + \text{Cl}^-$, calculate the final chloride-ion concentration in the final solution.

SOLUTION: 0.100 mole $\text{Hg(ClO}_4)_2$ gives 0.100 mole $\text{Hg}^{++}$.
0.080 mole NaCl gives 0.080 mole $\text{Cl}^-$.
Since the $K_{\text{diss}}$ for $\text{HgCl}^+$ is so small, $\text{Hg}^{++}$ and $\text{Cl}^-$ will have to combine to an appreciable extent. As a first guess, let us call for 100% association between the $\text{Hg}^{++}$ and the $\text{Cl}^-$. The 0.100 mole $\text{Hg}^{++}$ + 0.080 mole $\text{Cl}^-$ yields 0.080 mole $\text{HgCl}^+$ and 0.020 mole $\text{Hg}^{++}$ left over. In 1.25 l this would correspond to these concentrations:

$$\frac{0.080 \text{ mole HgCl}^+}{1.25 \text{ l}} = 0.064\,M\ \text{HgCl}^+$$

$$\frac{0.020 \text{ mole Hg}^{++}}{1.25 \text{ l}} = 0.016\,M\ \text{Hg}^{++}$$

But some of this $\text{HgCl}^+$ needs to dissociate to furnish $\text{Cl}^-$. Let $x =$ moles/l of this $\text{HgCl}^+$ that dissociates. This gives $x$ moles/l $\text{Cl}^-$

and $x$ moles/l $Hg^{++}$ to add to the 0.016 $M$ $Hg^{++}$ we already have. The $HgCl^+$ concentration will be reduced from 0.064 to 0.064 − $x$.
$[HgCl^+] = 0.064 - x$; $[Hg^{++}] = 0.016 + x$; $[Cl^-] = x$
For the equilibrium $HgCl^+ \rightleftharpoons Hg^{++} + Cl^-$ we have

$$K = \frac{[Hg^{++}][Cl^-]}{[HgCl^+]} = 1.8 \times 10^{-7} = \frac{(0.016 + x)(x)}{0.064 - x}$$

Solving this for $x$ is simple, since the $x$ is small compared to 0.016 or 0.064. We get $x = 7.2 \times 10^{-7}$.
Therefore, the final chloride-ion concentration is $7.2 \times 10^{-7}\ M$.

### Diprotic acids

A diprotic acid is one which can furnish two protons in neutralization reactions. In general, release of the first proton is much easier than that of the second. If we write $H_2X$ as the general formula of a diprotic acid, then the dissociation of the first proton can be written

$$H_2X \rightleftharpoons H^+ + HX^-$$

and the subsequent dissociation of the second proton can be written

$$HX^- \rightleftharpoons H^+ + X^=$$

where the double arrows again emphasize the reversibility of both reactions. The equilibrium constant for the first reaction is frequently designated $K_I$ and has the form

$$K_I = \frac{[H^+][HX^-]}{[H_2X]}$$

The equilibrium constant for the second reaction is frequently designated $K_{II}$; it has the form

$$K_{II} = \frac{[H^+][X^=]}{[HX^-]}$$

As a very rough rule, the value of $K_I$ is usually about $10^4$ or $10^5$ times as great as the value of $K_{II}$. This circumstance is what makes computations with diprotic acid systems so easy, since it makes one of the above reactions dominant over the other.

PROBLEM 581    Hydrogen sulfide, $H_2S$, is a diprotic acid with $K_I = 1.1 \times 10^{-7}$ and $K_{II} = 1 \times 10^{-14}$. Calculate the concentrations of $H_2S$, $HS^-$, $S^=$, and $H^+$ in a solution labeled 0.10 M $H_2S$.

SOLUTION: When $H_2S$ is placed in solution the first thing that happens is $H_2S$ dissociates to give $H^+$ and $HS^-$ in accord with the reaction

$$H_2S \rightleftharpoons H^+ + HS^-$$

Because $K_I$ for this reaction is much less than 1, only a small per cent of $H_2S$ will so dissociate.   Then, some of the $HS^-$ produced can also dissociate to give more $H^+$ and some $S^=$ via the reaction

$$HS^- \rightleftharpoons H^+ + S^=$$

However, the amount of this second dissociation cannot be very great, because (a) there is only a small amount of $HS^-$ available for the dissociation and (b) the $K_{II}$ for this second reaction is even smaller than $K_I$.   So, in the final solution, there should be mostly undissociated $H_2S$, considerably less $HS^-$, and only a trace of $S^=$.

The easiest way to solve the problem numerically is to neglect first the effect of the second dissociation as being trivial compared to the first.

Given 0.10 M $H_2S$.   Let $x =$ moles/l $H_2S$ that dissociate via $H_2S \rightarrow H^+ + HS^-$.   This will give us $x$ moles/l $H^+$, $x$ moles/l $HS^-$, and leave $(0.10 - x)$ moles/l undissociated $H_2S$.

$$[H^+] = x; [HS^-] = x; [H_2S] = 0.10 - x$$

The condition for equilibrium for the reaction

$$H_2S \rightleftharpoons H^+ + HS^-$$

is given by

$$K_I = \frac{[H^+][HS^-]}{[H_2S]} = 1.1 \times 10^{-7}$$

Substituting the above concentrations, we get

$$\frac{(x)(x)}{0.10 - x} = 1.1 \times 10^{-7}$$

which easily solves to $x = 1.05 \times 10^{-4}$.   Because $K_I$ is given only to two significant figures, we trim the answer to $x = 1.0 \times 10^{-4}$.

Put into the above concentration expressions, we get

$[H^+] = 1.0 \times 10^{-4}\ M$; $[HS^-] = 1.0 \times 10^{-4}\ M$; $[H_2S] = 0.10\ M$

Now we consider the second dissociation,

$$HS^- \rightleftharpoons H^+ + S^=$$

for which the equilibrium condition is

$$K_{II} = \frac{[H^+][S^=]}{[HS^-]} = 1 \times 10^{-14}$$

Suppose we let $y$ = moles/l of the $HS^-$ that will dissociate to set up this second equilibrium. This will reduce $[HS^-]$ from the $1.0 \times 10^{-4}\ M$ value we just calculated to $(1.0 \times 10^{-4} - y)$ and will increase the $[H^+]$ from the $1.0 \times 10^{-4}\ M$ we just calculated to $(1.0 \times 10^{-4} + y)$. At the same time, it will produce $y$ moles $S^=$. So, at equilibrium, we will have

$[H^+] = 1.0 \times 10^{-4} + y$; $[HS^-] = 1.0 \times 10^{-4} - y$; $[S^=] = y$

Substitute these values in the expression for $K_{II}$:

$$K_{II} = \frac{[H^+][S^=]}{[HS^-]} = \frac{(1.0 \times 10^{-4} + y)(y)}{1.0 \times 10^{-4} - y} = 1 \times 10^{-14}$$

This looks quite ominous as an equation to solve, but note the very small value of $K_{II} = 1 \times 10^{-14}$. It tells you that $y$ is indeed a very small number, so small that it can easily be neglected when added to or subtracted from $1.0 \times 10^{-4}$. If we scratch the $y$ where it can be neglected, we get the equation

$$\frac{(1.0 \times 10^{-4})(y)}{1.0 \times 10^{-4}} \cong 1 \times 10^{-14}$$

which quickly solves to $y = 1 \times 10^{-14}$, truly a small number.
In summary, then, we find in 0.10 $M$ $H_2S$ solution:

$[H_2S] = 0.10\ M$; $[HS^-] = 1.0 \times 10^{-4}\ M$; $[S^=] = 1 \times 10^{-14}\ M$; $[H^+] = 1.0 \times 10^{-4}\ M$

Some points to note especially are these: The second dissociation is important only as a source of $S^=$. It contributes negligibly to raising the $H^+$ or reducing the $HS^-$ concentrations. Second, if you substitute the calculated concentrations in the expression for $K_I$

$$\frac{[H^+][HS^-]}{[H_2S]} = \frac{(1.0 \times 10^{-4})(1.0 \times 10^{-4})}{0.10} = 1.0 \times 10^{-7}$$

you do not get $K_I = 1.1 \times 10^{-7}$ as given in the original problem. Don't fret about it. It is a straightforward consequence of our limitation here to two significant figures, the second of which is a doubtful digit. If you can reproduce the $K$ to $\pm 1$ in the last digit, you have done as much as you are entitled to. In the above problem, we would need to use $1.05 \times 10^{-4}$ for $[H^+]$ and $[HS^-]$ to reproduce $K_I = 1.1 \times 10^{-7}$. This would go beyond the precision allowed by the given data. If you insist on doing that, you should at least write $1.0_5 \times 10^{-4}$, following the convention that the digit dropped below the line is dubious.

■ PROBLEM 582 Hydrogen telluride, $H_2Te$, is a diprotic acid with $K_I = 2.3 \times 10^{-3}$ and $K_{II} = 1 \times 10^{-11}$. Calculate the concentrations of $H_2Te$, $HTe^-$, $Te^=$, and $H^+$ in a solution labeled $0.100\ M$ $H_2Te$.

ANSWER: $[H_2Te] = 0.086\ M$; $[HTe^-] = 0.014\ M$;
$[Te^=] = 1 \times 10^{-11}\ M$; $[H^+] = 0.014\ M$

■ PROBLEM 583 Hydrogen selenide, $H_2Se$, is a diprotic acid with $K_I = 1.88 \times 10^{-4}$ and $K_{II} = 1 \times 10^{-14}$. Calculate the concentrations of $H_2Se$, $HSe^-$, $Se^=$, and $H^+$ in a solution labeled $0.100\ M$ $H_2Se$.

ANSWER: $[H_2Se] = 0.096\ M$; $[HSe^-] = 4.25 \times 10^{-3}\ M$;
$[Se^=] = 1 \times 10^{-14}\ M$; $[H^+] = 4.25 \times 10^{-3}\ M$

One of the most important diprotic acids is sulfuric acid, $H_2SO_4$. It differs from the above examples in that the first dissociation is complete—that is, 100% of the $H_2SO_4$ is broken down into $H^+$ and $HSO_4^-$. The other point of difference is that the second dissociation—i.e., the breakdown of $HSO_4^-$ into more $H^+$ and some $SO_4^=$—is not at all negligible. We can write the chemical equations for the stepwise dissociation as follows:

$$H_2SO_4 \rightarrow H^+ + HSO_4^-$$

$$HSO_4^- \rightleftharpoons H^+ + SO_4^=$$

The single arrow to the right in the first equation emphasizes that $H_2SO_4$ is a strong acid for this dissociation. The first dissociation is assumed to go 100% to the right, although strictly speaking it also comes to equilibrium. However, $K_I$ is of the order of $10^3$, which for our purposes corresponds to 100% conversion to the right. $K_{II}$, for the second reaction, is equal to $1.26 \times 10^{-2}$, which is considerably larger than for most "weak" acids. For this reason, $HSO_4^-$ is frequently referred to as a "moderately strong" acid.

PROBLEM 584    Given a solution that is 0.150 $M$ $NaHSO_4$. What are the concentrations of $HSO_4^-$, $SO_4^=$, and $H^+$ in this solution?

SOLUTION: $NaHSO_4$ is a typical sodium salt and is a strong electrolyte in the sense that it is completely dissociated into $Na^+$ and $HSO_4^-$. So, our solution of 0.150 $M$ $NaHSO_4$ can be regarded initially as 0.150 $M$ $Na^+$ and 0.150 $M$ $HSO_4^-$. However, some of the $HSO_4^-$ will be dissociated into $H^+$ and $SO_4^=$. Let $x$ = moles/l $HSO_4^-$ that are dissociated. This will leave $(0.150 - x)$ moles/l undissociated $HSO_4^-$ and will produce $x$ moles/l $H^+$ and $x$ moles/l $SO_4^=$. At equilibrium, then, we will have the following:

$$[H^+] = x; [SO_4^=] = x; [HSO_4^-] = 0.150 - x$$

These concentrations must satisfy the equilibrium condition which, for the reaction

$$HSO_4^- \rightleftharpoons H^+ + SO_4^=$$

is given by

$$K_{II} = \frac{[H^+][SO_4^=]}{[HSO_4^-]} = 1.26 \times 10^{-2} = \frac{(x)(x)}{0.150 - x}$$

With a $K$ this big, it pays to go directly to the quadratic formula, since $x$ will certainly not be negligible compared to 0.150. The equation converts to $x^2 = 0.189 \times 10^{-2} - 1.26 \times 10^{-2}x$ which solves to $x = 3.76 \times 10^{-2}$. Putting this into the above concentration expressions, we get for the equilibrium concentrations:

$$[H^+] = 3.76 \times 10^{-2} M; [SO_4^=] = 3.76 \times 10^{-2} M;$$
$$[HSO_4^-] = 0.112 M$$

■ PROBLEM 585   If you dissolve 5.09 g
KHSO$_4$ in enough water to make 0.200 l solution, what will be the final
concentrations of H$^+$, SO$_4^=$, and HSO$_4^-$ in this solution? KHSO$_4$ is a
strong electrolyte; $K_{diss}$ for HSO$_4^-$ is 1.26 × 10$^{-2}$.

ANSWER: [H$^+$] = 4.26 × 10$^{-2}$ $M$; [SO$_4^=$] = 4.26 × 10$^{-2}$ $M$;
[HSO$_4^-$] = 0.144 $M$

PROBLEM 586   Given a solution that is
0.150 $M$ H$_2$SO$_4$. What are the concentrations of H$^+$, SO$_4^=$, and
HSO$_4^-$ in this solution?

SOLUTION: Compared to Problem 584, this one differs in that H$_2$SO$_4$ is
    completely dissociated into H$^+$ and HSO$_4^-$, and the H$^+$ from this
    dissociation tends to repress the further dissociation of HSO$_4^-$.
Assume 100% dissociation of H$_2$SO$_4$ → H$^+$ + HSO$_4^-$. This means
    that the 0.150 $M$ H$_2$SO$_4$ can be regarded initially as 0.150 $M$ H$^+$
    and 0.150 $M$ HSO$_4^-$. However, the HSO$_4^-$ will dissociate some-
    what to drive the concentration of H$^+$ somewhat higher than 0.150
    $M$. Let $x$ = moles/l HSO$_4^-$ that dissociate. This leaves (0.150 −
    $x$) moles/l HSO$_4^-$ undissociated and produces $x$ moles/l SO$_4^=$
    while adding $x$ moles/l H$^+$ to the 0.150 $M$ already there from the
    first dissociation. The equilibrium concentrations will be

[H$^+$] = 0.150 + $x$; [SO$_4^=$] = $x$; [HSO$_4^-$] = 0.150 − $x$

Substituting in the equilibrium condition, we get

$$K = \frac{[\text{H}^+][\text{SO}_4^=]}{[\text{HSO}_4^-]} = 1.26 \times 10^{-2} = \frac{(0.150 + x)(x)}{0.150 - x}$$

The resulting algebraic equation $x^2 + 0.163x - 0.00189 = 0$
solves by the quadratic formula to $x = 0.0109$. Substituting
above, we get for the final equilibrium concentrations:

[H$^+$] = 0.150 + $x$ = 0.150 + 0.0109 = **0.161 $M$**

[SO$_4^=$] = $x$ = **0.0109 $M$**

[HSO$_4^-$] = 0.150 − $x$ = 0.150 − 0.0109 = **0.139 $M$**

■ PROBLEM 587   If you dissolve 5.09 g
H$_2$SO$_4$ in enough water to make 0.200 l solution, what will be the final
concentrations of H$^+$, SO$_4^=$, and HSO$_4^-$ in this solution?

ANSWER: [H$^+$] = **0.271 $M$**; [SO$_4^=$] = **0.0115 $M$**;
[HSO$_4^-$] = **0.248 $M$**

Some of the stiffest problems involving diprotic acids arise when we try to approach some of the above equilibria from the other direction—for example, by mixing 0.1 mole of $H^+$ and 0.1 mole of $S^=$. Such a problem *cannot* be solved by just computing the dissociation of an equivalent amount of $HS^-$. Why it cannot be done this easily, we shall have to leave until Chapter 18. It has to do with the fact that $HS^-$ can not only dissociate to give $H^+$ and $S^=$ but can also pick up $H^+$ to form $H_2S$. Both equilibria need to be considered simultaneously. At this stage, we shall simply consider a few cases of "back reaction" where we do not run into this complication.

PROBLEM 588    Suppose you mix 1.00 l of 0.100 $M$ HCl with 1.00 l of 0.100 $M$ $Na_2SO_4$. What will be the concentrations of $H^+$, $SO_4^=$, and $HSO_4^-$ in the final solution? Assume volumes are additive.

SOLUTION: 1.00 l of 0.100 $M$ HCl gives $(1.00 \text{ l})\left(0.100 \dfrac{\text{mole}}{\text{l}}\right)$
= 0.100 mole HCl.

1.00 l of 0.100 $M$ $Na_2SO_4$ gives $(1.00 \text{ l})\left(0.100 \dfrac{\text{mole}}{\text{l}}\right)$
= 0.100 mole $Na_2SO_4$.

Both HCl and $Na_2SO_4$ are strong electrolytes and are 100% dissociated. 0.100 mole HCl gives 0.100 mole $H^+$ and 0.100 mole $Cl^-$; 0.100 mole $Na_2SO_4$ gives 0.200 mole $Na^+$ and 0.100 mole $SO_4^=$.

Initially, we assume that all the $H^+$ and all the $SO_4^=$ convert to $HSO_4^-$ via the reaction $H^+ + SO_4^= \rightarrow HSO_4^-$. This would make the 0.100 mole $H^+$ plus 0.100 mole $SO_4^=$ equivalent to 0.100 mole $HSO_4^-$. The total volume of the solution is (1.00 l + 1.00 l) = 2.00 l, so we have the equivalent of

$$\frac{0.100 \text{ mole } HSO_4^-}{2.00 \text{ l}} = 0.0500 \ M \ HSO_4^-$$

But this would make no allowance for dissociation. [*Note:* We do not have to worry about pick-up of $H^+$ by $HSO_4^-$, since $H_2SO_4$ would be 100% dissociated.] Let $x$ = moles/l of this hypothetical 0.0500 $M$ $HSO_4^-$ that dissociate. This gives

$[H^+] = x;\ [SO_4^=] = x;\ [HSO_4^-] = 0.0500 - x$

$HSO_4^- \rightleftharpoons H^+ + SO_4^=$

$$K = \frac{[H^+][SO_4^=]}{[HSO_4^-]} = \frac{(x)(x)}{0.0500 - x} = 1.26 \times 10^{-2}$$

$$x = 1.96 \times 10^{-2}$$

Final equilibrium concentrations are

$$[H^+] = 1.96 \times 10^{-2} \; M; \; [SO_4^=] = 1.96 \times 10^{-2} \; M;$$
$$[HSO_4^-] = 3.04 \times 10^{-2} \; M$$

■ P R O B L E M 589 Selenic acid, $H_2SeO_4$, is a strong electrolyte for dissociation of the first proton and has $K_{diss} = 8.9 \times 10^{-3}$ for the second. If you mix 0.360 l of 0.200 $M$ HCl with 0.360 l of 0.200 $M$ $Na_2SeO_4$, what will be the concentrations of $H^+$, $SeO_4^=$, and $HSeO_4^-$ in the final solution?

ANSWER: $[H^+] = 0.026 \; M; \; [SeO_4^=] = 0.026 \; M;$
$[HSeO_4^-] = 0.074 \; M$

P R O B L E M 590 Oxalic acid, $H_2C_2O_4$, is a diprotic acid for which $K_I$ is equal to $6.5 \times 10^{-2}$ and $K_{II}$ is equal to $6.1 \times 10^{-5}$. What will be the concentrations of $H^+$, $C_2O_4^=$, and $HC_2O_4^-$ in a solution made by dissolving $1.0 \times 10^{-2}$ mole HCl and $3.0 \times 10^{-2}$ mole $Na_2C_2O_4$ in enough water to make 0.250 l solution?

SOLUTION: Both HCl and $Na_2C_2O_4$ are strong electrolytes.
$1.0 \times 10^{-2}$ mole HCl gives $1.0 \times 10^{-2}$ mole $H^+$ and $1.0 \times 10^{-2}$ mole $Cl^-$.
$3.0 \times 10^{-2}$ mole $Na_2C_2O_4$ gives $6.0 \times 10^{-2}$ mole $Na^+$ and $3.0 \times 10^{-2}$ mole $C_2O_4^=$.
$H^+$ and $C_2O_4^=$ will extensively combine.
Assume 100% reaction by $H^+ + C_2O_4^= \rightarrow HC_2O_4^-$.
From $1.0 \times 10^{-2}$ mole $H^+$ and $3.0 \times 10^{-2}$ mole $C_2O_4^=$ we would get formed $1.0 \times 10^{-2}$ mole $HC_2O_4^-$ and $2.0 \times 10^{-2}$ mole $C_2O_4^=$ left over. In 0.250 l this would give

$$\frac{1.0 \times 10^{-2} \text{ mole } HC_2O_4^-}{0.250 \text{ l}} = 0.040 \; M \; HC_2O_4^-$$

$$\frac{2.0 \times 10^{-2} \text{ mole } C_2O_4^=}{0.250 \text{ l}} = 0.080 \; M \; C_2O_4^=$$

But this allows for no free $H^+$, which must be there if we are to have equilibrium. So, we need to let some of the $HC_2O_4^-$ dissociate to produce some $H^+$ and, incidentally, some additional $C_2O_4^=$. Let $x$ = moles/l of the $HC_2O_4^-$ that dissociate. At equilibrium, we would have

$$[H^+] = x; \quad [C_2O_4^=] = 0.080 + x; \quad [HC_2O_4^-] = 0.040 - x$$

The reaction is

$$HC_2O_4^- \rightleftharpoons H^+ + C_2O_4^=$$

for which the equilibrium condition is

$$K = \frac{[H^+][C_2O_4^=]}{[HC_2O_4^-]} = 6.1 \times 10^{-5} = \frac{(x)(0.080 + x)}{0.040 - x}$$

No need to use the quadratic formula, since the rather small $K$ value suggests an $x$ small compared to 0.080 or 0.040. Approximating $0.080 + x \cong 0.080$ and $0.040 - x \cong 0.040$, we get $x = 3.0 \times 10^{-5}$. The final concentrations will be

$$[H^+] = 3.0 \times 10^{-5} \, M; \quad [C_2O_4^=] = 0.080 \, M; \quad [HC_2O_4^-] = 0.040 \, M$$

■ PROBLEM 591   Sulfurous acid, $H_2SO_3$, is a diprotic acid with $K_I = 1.25 \times 10^{-2}$ and $K_{II} = 5.6 \times 10^{-8}$. Calculate the concentrations of $H^+$, $SO_3^=$, and $HSO_3^-$ in a solution made by mixing 0.100 l of 0.500 $M$ HCl with 0.300 l of 0.500 $M$ $Na_2SO_3$. Assume volumes are additive.

ANSWER: $[H^+] = 2.8 \times 10^{-8} \, M$; $[SO_3^=] = 0.250 \, M$; $[HSO_3^-] = 0.125 \, M$

An important but very complicated example of diprotic acid behavior is given by solutions containing dissolved carbon dioxide. These solutions contain $H^+$, $HCO_3^-$, and $CO_3^=$, and for many years it was assumed that the principal equilibria in the solution were

$$H_2CO_3 \rightleftharpoons H^+ + HCO_3^- \qquad K_I = 4.16 \times 10^{-7}$$

$$HCO_3^- \rightleftharpoons H^+ + CO_3^= \qquad K_{II} = 4.84 \times 10^{-11}$$

The reasoning was that $CO_2$ reacts with $H_2O$ to form $H_2CO_3$, and $H_2CO_3$ then dissociates stepwise to give $HCO_3^-$ and then $CO_3^=$. At the present time it is known that less than 1% of the $CO_2$ actually gets converted to $H_2CO_3$, so that the above $K_I$ is not really for $H_2CO_3$ but for dissolved $CO_2$.  Consequently, we are more accurate if we write

$$CO_2 + H_2O \rightleftharpoons H^+ + HCO_3^- \qquad K_I = 4.16 \times 10^{-7}$$

$$HCO_3^- \rightleftharpoons H^+ + CO_3^= \qquad K_{II} = 4.84 \times 10^{-11}$$

We can still call the first reaction and its constant as applying to the first step in the "dissociation" of aqueous $CO_2$.  Leaving out the water, as we did in the case of aqueous ammonia equilibria (see page 260), we would have

$$K_I = \frac{[H^+][HCO_3^-]}{[CO_2]} = 4.16 \times 10^{-7}$$

$$K_{II} = \frac{[H^+][CO_3^=]}{[HCO_3^-]} = 4.84 \times 10^{-11}$$

PROBLEM 592A  Given the constants above, what would be the concentrations of $H^+$, $CO_3^=$, and $HCO_3^-$ in a solution labeled 0.034 $M$ $CO_2$?

SOLUTION: (The method of solution is very much like that used in Problem 581.)  Let $x$ = moles/l $CO_2$ converted to $HCO_3^-$.  Ignoring for the moment the second dissociation we would have

$$[H^+] = x; [HCO_3^-] = x; [CO_2] = 0.034 - x$$

For the reaction

$$CO_2 + H_2O \rightleftharpoons H^+ + HCO_3^-$$

the equilibrium condition is

$$K = \frac{[H^+][HCO_3^-]}{[CO_2]} = \frac{(x)(x)}{0.034 - x} = 4.16 \times 10^{-7}$$

which solves to $x = 1.2 \times 10^{-4}$.  Substituting gives us

$$[H^+] = 1.2 \times 10^{-4} \ M; [HCO_3^-] = 1.2 \times 10^{-4} \ M;$$
$$[CO_2] = 0.034 \ M$$

Now worry about the second dissociation.  Let $y$ = moles/l of the $HCO_3^-$ that will be dissociated to $CO_3^=$ and more $H^+$ to add to that from the first step.

$$[H^+] = 1.2 \times 10^{-4} + y; \ [CO_3^=] = y; \ [HCO_3^-] = 1.2 \times 10^{-4} - y$$

$$HCO_3^- \rightleftharpoons H^+ + CO_3^=$$

$$K_{II} = \frac{[H^+][CO_3^=]}{[HCO_3^-]} = 4.84 \times 10^{-11} = \frac{(1.2 \times 10^{-4} + y)(y)}{1.2 \times 10^{-4} - y}$$

With such a very small $K$, $y$ is bound to be very small. Neglecting $y$ where it adds or subtracts, we get $y = 4.84 \times 10^{-11}$:

$$[H^+] = 1.2 \times 10^{-4} \ M; \ [CO_3^=] = 4.84 \times 10^{-11} \ M;$$
$$[HCO_3^-] = 1.2 \times 10^{-4} \ M$$

■ PROBLEM 592B    If you dissolve 171 cc $CO_2$ gas (STP) in 0.100 l water, what will be the concentrations of $CO_2$, $CO_3^=$, $HCO_3^-$, and $H^+$ in the final solution, assuming its final volume is 0.100 l?

ANSWER: $[CO_2] = 0.0763 \ M; \ [CO_3^=] = 4.84 \times 10^{-11} \ M;$
$[HCO_3^-] = 1.78 \times 10^{-4} \ M; \ [H^+] = 1.78 \times 10^{-4} \ M$

## Triprotic acids

A triprotic acid is one which can furnish three protons in neutralization reactions.    Again the reactions occur stepwise and the release of the first proton is easier than that of the second, which is easier than release of the third.    The general situation can be summarized in terms of a hypothetical triprotic acid $H_3X$, which can dissociate stepwise as follows:

$$H_3X \rightleftharpoons H^+ + H_2X^-$$
$$H_2X^- \rightleftharpoons H^+ + HX^=$$
$$HX^= \rightleftharpoons H^+ + X^{-3}$$

A solution of $H_3X$ will contain, besides undissociated $H_3X$, some $H_2X^-$, some $HX^=$, some $X^{-3}$, and some $H^+$.    The $H^+$ looks as if it is produced by three separate reactions, but, of course, there is only one hydrogen-ion concentration in the solution and it must be in equilibrium with all the other species present.    The equilibrium conditions for the above reactions are

$$K_I = \frac{[H^+][H_2X^-]}{[H_3X]} \ ; \quad K_{II} = \frac{[H^+][HX^=]}{[H_2X^-]} \ ; \quad K_{III} = \frac{[H^+][X^{-3}]}{[HX^=}$$

In general, $K_I$ is about $10^5$ times as big as $K_{II}$, and $K_{II}$ is about $10^5$ times as big as $K_{III}$.

Typical triprotic acids are $H_3PO_4$ and $H_3AsO_4$, but you must not jump to the obvious conclusion that all acids showing three hydrogen atoms in the formula are triprotic. $H_3PO_3$, for example, is only diprotic, the third hydrogen being stuck directly on the phosphorus and not neutralizable by regular bases.

**PROBLEM** 593 A typical solution of $H_3PO_4$ contains the following species at equilibrium: 0.076 $M$ $H_3PO_4$; 0.0239 $M$ $H_2PO_4^-$; $6.2 \times 10^{-8}$ $M$ $HPO_4^=$; $3 \times 10^{-18}$ $M$ $PO_4^{-3}$; 0.0239 $M$ $H^+$. Calculate $K_I$, $K_{II}$, and $K_{III}$ for this acid.

SOLUTION: The main equilibrium involves

$$H_3PO_4 \rightleftharpoons H^+ + H_2PO_4^-$$

The equilibrium condition for it is given by $K_I$:

$$K_I = \frac{[H^+][H_2PO_4^-]}{[H_3PO_4]} = \frac{(0.0239)(0.0239)}{0.076} = 7.5 \times 10^{-3}$$

where we have simply substituted the given concentrations.

The second step of the dissociation is written

$$H_2PO_4^- \rightleftharpoons H^+ + HPO_4^=$$

and has

$$K_{II} = \frac{[H^+][HPO_4^=]}{[H_2PO_4^-]} = \frac{(0.0239)(6.2 \times 10^{-8})}{0.0239} = 6.2 \times 10^{-8}$$

The third step is

$$HPO_4^= \rightleftharpoons H^+ + PO_4^{-3}$$

and has

$$K_{III} = \frac{[H^+][PO_4^{-3}]}{[HPO_4^=]} = \frac{(0.0239)(3 \times 10^{-18})}{6.2 \times 10^{-8}} = 1 \times 10^{-12}$$

■ **PROBLEM** 594 A typical solution of arsenic acid, $H_3AsO_4$, contains the following equilibrium concentrations: 0.19 $M$ $H_3AsO_4$; $6.95 \times 10^{-3}$ $M$ $H_2AsO_4^-$; $5.6 \times 10^{-8}$ $M$

$HAsO_4^=$; $2 \times 10^{-18}$ $M$ $AsO_4^{-3}$; 0.00695 $M$ $H^+$.   Calculate $K_I$, $K_{II}$, and $K_{III}$.

ANSWER: $K_I = 2.5 \times 10^{-4}$; $K_{II} = 5.6 \times 10^{-8}$; $K_{III} = 2 \times 10^{-13}$

In dealing with the dissociation of triprotic acids, the procedure is much like that used for diprotic acids.   Since the first dissociation is usually dominant, the second and third can be ignored in the first stage of calculation and then those results can be fed into the calculation of the second and third stages.

PROBLEM 595   Given a solution that is labeled 0.100 $M$ $H_3PO_4$.   Calculate the concentration of $H^+$, $H_2PO_4^-$, $HPO_4^=$, and $PO_4^{-3}$ in this solution, given that $K_I = 7.5 \times 10^{-3}$; $K_{II} = 6.2 \times 10^{-8}$; $K_{III} = 1 \times 10^{-12}$.

SOLUTION: First consider the dissociation of the first proton:

$$H_3PO_4 \rightleftharpoons H^+ + H_2PO_4^-$$

Let $x$ = moles/l $H_3PO_4$ that dissociate to establish the equilibrium. This will give us $x$ moles/l $H^+$, $x$ moles/l $H_2PO_4^-$, and will leave $(0.100 - x)$ mole $H_3PO_4$ in the undissociated state.   If we assume that the subsequent steps of ionization will be negligible compared to the first step, then we can write for the equilibrium concentrations:

$[H_3PO_4] = 0.100 - x$; $[H^+] = x$; $[H_2PO_4^-] = x$

The equilibrium condition

$$K_I = \frac{[H^+][H_2PO_4^-]}{[H_3PO_4]} = 7.5 \times 10^{-3} = \frac{(x)(x)}{0.100 - x}$$

Solve this by the quadratic formula or by successive approximation. (First: Neglect the $x$ in the denominator.   Solve the rest of the equation to give $x \cong 0.027$.   Second: Put $x \cong 0.027$ for $x$ in the denominator.   Solve the rest to give $x \cong 0.023$.   Third: Put $x \cong 0.023$ for $x$ in the denominator.   Solve the rest to get $x \cong 0.024$. Fourth: Put $x \cong 0.024$ for $x$ in the denominator.   Solve the rest to give $x = 0.024$.   That must be it!)   Substitute the solution $x = 0.024$ in the concentration expressions as set up above:

$[H_3PO_4] = 0.100 - x = 0.100 - 0.024 = 0.076\ M$

$[H^+] = x = 0.024\ M$

$[H_2PO_4^-] = x = 0.024\ M$

Now tackle the second dissociation step:

$$H_2PO_4^- \rightleftharpoons H^+ + HPO_4^=$$

It can't go very far because (a) there isn't much $H_2PO_4^-$ to start with and (b) $K_{II}$ is considerably smaller than $K_I$. Let $y$ = moles/l $H_2PO_4^-$ that dissociate. This will give $y$ more moles/l $H^+$ to add to the 0.024 $M$ we just calculated. At the same time, we will get $y$ moles $HPO_4^=$ and reduce the $H_2PO_4^-$ concentration from 0.024 to $0.024 - y$. At equilibrium, then, we would have

$[H_2PO_4^-] = 0.024 - y$;   $[H^+] = 0.024 + y$;   $[HPO_4^=] = y$

$$K_{II} = \frac{[H^+][HPO_4^=]}{[H_2PO_4^-]} = 6.2 \times 10^{-8} = \frac{(0.024 + y)(y)}{0.024 - y}$$

Because of the smallness of $K_{II}$, $y$ must be small and probably negligible when added to or subtracted from 0.024. The equation simplifies to

$$6.2 \times 10^{-8} \cong \frac{(0.024)(y)}{0.024}$$

which solves to $y = 6.2 \times 10^{-8}$. Substituting as above, we get

$[H_2PO_4^-] = 0.024\ M$; $[H^+] = 0.024\ M$; $[HPO_4^=] = 6.2 \times 10^{-8}\ M$

Finally we consider the third step of the dissociation:

$$HPO_4^= \rightleftharpoons H^+ + PO_4^{-3}$$

which must be trivial, for the same reasons outlined above, except it is the only source of $PO_4^{-3}$ concentration for our solution. Let $z$ = moles/l $HPO_4^=$ that dissociate.

$[HPO_4^=] = 6.2 \times 10^{-8} - z$; $[H^+] = 0.024$; $[PO_4^{-3}] = z$

$$K_{III} = \frac{[H^+][PO_4^{-3}]}{[HPO_4^=]} = 1 \times 10^{-12} = \frac{(0.024)(z)}{6.2 \times 10^{-8} - z}$$

Neglecting $z$ in the denominator, we solve for $z = 3 \times 10^{-18}$. Summarizing, we have as the final equilibrium concentrations in the solution

$[H^+] = 0.024\ M; [H_2PO_4^-] = 0.024\ M; [HPO_4^=] = 6.2 \times 10^{-8}\ M;$
$[PO_4^{-3}] = 3 \times 10^{-18}\ M$

■ PROBLEM 596    Given a solution that is labeled 0.100 $M$ $H_3AsO_4$. Calculate the concentrations of $H^+$, $H_2AsO_4^-$, $HAsO_4^=$, and $AsO_4^{-3}$ in this solution given that $K_I = 2.5 \times 10^{-4}$, $K_{II} = 5.6 \times 10^{-8}$, and $K_{III} = 3 \times 10^{-13}$.

ANSWER: $[H^+] = 4.9 \times 10^{-3}\ M$; $[H_2AsO_4^-] = 4.9 \times 10^{-3}\ M$; $[HAsO_4^=] = 5.6 \times 10^{-8}\ M$; $[AsO_4^{-3}] = 3 \times 10^{-18}\ M$

The above solutions are fairly complicated in that there are three equilibria that need to be satisfied simultaneously. The only reason we could handle the problems at all is that the first step in the dissociation is the dominant equilibrium and can be treated alone. The arithmetic gets considerably more complicated when this is not the case.

The following problems illustrate some of the more complex calculations involving triprotic acid equilibria but still based on dominance of the first step in the dissociation.

PROBLEM 597    Suppose you make a solution by dissolving 0.100 mole $H_3PO_4$ and 0.200 mole $NaH_2PO_4$ in enough water to make 1.00 l solution. Given $K_I = 7.5 \times 10^{-3}$, $K_{II} = 6.2 \times 10^{-8}$, and $K_{III} = 1 \times 10^{-12}$, calculate the concentrations of $H_3PO_4$, $H_2PO_4^-$, $HPO_4^=$, $PO_4^{-3}$, $H^+$, and $Na^+$ in this solution.

SOLUTION: $NaH_2PO_4$ is a strong electrolyte and is 100% dissociated in solution to give 0.200 mole $Na^+$ and 0.200 mole $H_2PO_4^-$. Let us ignore for the moment the slight amount of this $H_2PO_4^-$ that might further dissociate to $H^+$ and $HPO_4^=$. Regarding our solution initially as containing 0.100 mole $H_3PO_4$ and 0.200 mole $H_2PO_4^-$ their concentrations would be

$$\frac{0.100 \text{ mole } H_3PO_4}{1.00 \text{ l}} = 0.100 \ M \ H_3PO_4$$

$$\frac{0.200 \text{ mole } H_2PO_4{}^-}{1.00 \text{ l}} = 0.200 \ M \ H_2PO_4{}^-$$

Some of the $H_3PO_4$ must be dissociated to give $H^+$ and $H_2PO_4{}^-$. Let $x$ = moles/l $H_3PO_4$ that must be dissociated to establish equilibrium. This will reduce the concentration of $H_3PO_4$ from 0.100 to $0.100 - x$, increase the concentration of $H_2PO_4{}^-$ from 0.200 to $0.200 + x$, and produce $x$ moles/l $H^+$. When equilibrium is established we shall have

$$[H_3PO_4] = 0.100 - x; \quad [H_2PO_4{}^-] = 0.200 + x; \quad [H^+] = x$$

The equilibrium is

$$H_3PO_4 \rightleftharpoons H^+ + H_2PO_4{}^-$$

and the condition for equilibrium is that

$$K_I = \frac{[H^+][H_2PO_4{}^-]}{[H_3PO_4]} = 7.5 \times 10^{-3} = \frac{(x)(0.200 + x)}{0.100 - x}$$

This can be solved by the quadratic formula or by successive approximations. The latter is quicker in this case because only two simple steps are needed. First, assume $x$ is negligible when added to 0.200 or subtracted from 0.100. This gives the approximate relation $7.5 \times 10^{-3} \cong \dfrac{(x)(0.200)}{0.100}$, which solves to $x = 3.8 \times 10^{-3}$. Then feed this $x$ into the terms $(0.200 + x)$ and $(0.100 - x)$ to get an improved approximate relation $7.5 \times 10^{-3} = \dfrac{(x)(0.204)}{0.096}$, which solves to $x = 3.5 \times 10^{-3}$. This is close enough to the fed-in value to warrant confidence. (If in doubt, try another step in the approximation, feeding $x = 3.5 \times 10^{-3}$ into the $0.200 + x$ and $0.100 - x$. You get no change.) Substituting $x = 3.5 \times 10^{-3}$ into the above concentration expressions we get

$$[H_3PO_4] = 0.100 - x = 0.100 - 0.0035 = 0.096 \ M$$

$$[H_2PO_4{}^-] = 0.200 + x = 0.200 + 0.0035 = 0.204 \ M$$

$$[H^+] = x = 3.5 \times 10^{-3} \ M$$

Once you have calculated the principal equilibrium, all the others need to be consistent. If we let $y$ = moles/l of the $H_2PO_4^-$ that will be dissociated, we have

$$[H_2PO_4^-] = 0.204 - y; \quad [H^+] = 3.5 \times 10^{-3} + y; \quad [HPO_4^=] = y$$

$$H_2PO_4^- \rightleftharpoons H^+ + HPO_4^=$$

$$K_{II} = \frac{[H^+][HPO_4^=]}{[H_2PO_4^-]} = \frac{(3.5 \times 10^{-3} + y)(y)}{0.204 - y} = 6.2 \times 10^{-8}$$

Assuming that $y$ is very small and can be neglected when added to $3.5 \times 10^{-3}$ or subtracted from 0.204, we get $y = 3.6 \times 10^{-6}$. Substituting above, we get

$$[H_2PO_4^-] = 0.204 \ M; \quad [H^+] = 3.5 \times 10^{-3} \ M;$$
$$[HPO_4^=] = 3.6 \times 10^{-6} \ M$$

Finally, for the third dissociation step, let $z$ = moles/l $HPO_4^=$ that break up. This will give

$$[HPO_4^-] = 3.6 \times 10^{-6} - z; \quad [H^+] = 3.5 \times 10^{-3} + z; \quad [PO_4^{-3}] = z$$

$$HPO_4^= \rightleftharpoons H^+ + PO_4^{-3}$$

$$K_{III} = \frac{[H^+][PO_4^{-3}]}{[HPO_4^=]} = \frac{(3.5 \times 10^{-3} + z)(z)}{3.6 \times 10^{-6} - z} = 1 \times 10^{-12}$$

$$z = 1 \times 10^{-15}$$

Summarizing our results, we would have in the final solution the following equilibrium concentrations:

$$[H_2PO_4] = 0.096 \ M; \quad [H_2PO_4^-] = 0.204 \ M;$$
$$[HPO_4^=] = 3.6 \times 10^{-6} \ M; \quad [PO_4^{-3}] = 1 \times 10^{-15} \ M;$$
$$[H^+] = 3.5 \times 10^{-3} \ M; \quad [Na^+] = 0.200 \ M$$

■ PROBLEM 598 Suppose you make a solution by dissolving 0.295 mole $H_3PO_4$ and 0.105 mole $NaH_2PO_4$ in enough water to make 0.500 l solution. What will be the concentrations of $H_3PO_4$, $H_2PO_4^-$, $HPO_4^=$, $PO_4^{-3}$, $H^+$, and $Na^+$ in the final solution? $K_I = 7.5 \times 10^{-3}$; $K_{II} = 6.2 \times 10^{-8}$; $K_{III} = 1 \times 10^{-12}$.

ANSWER: $[H_3PO_4] = 0.571 \ M; \quad [H_2PO_4^-] = 0.229 \ M;$
$[HPO_4^=] = 7.5 \times 10^{-7} \ M; \quad [PO_4^{-3}] = 4 \times 10^{-17} \ M;$
$[H^+] = 0.019 \ M; \quad [Na^+] = 0.210 \ M$

■ P R O B L E M  599  Suppose you make a solution by mixing 18.6 ml of 0.398 $M$ $H_3AsO_4$ and 23.4 ml of 0.250 $M$ $NaH_2AsO_4$.  Given $K_I = 2.5 \times 10^{-4}$, $K_{II} = 5.6 \times 10^{-8}$, and $K_{III} = 3 \times 10^{-13}$, calculate the concentrations of $H_3AsO_4$, $H_2AsO_4^-$, $HAsO_4^=$, $AsO_4^{-3}$, $H^+$, and $Na^+$ in the final solution.

ANSWER: $[H_3AsO_4] = 0.176\ M$; $[H_2AsO_4^-] = 0.139\ M$;
$[HAsO_4^=] = 2.4 \times 10^{-5}\ M$; $[AsO_4^{-3}] = 2 \times 10^{-14}\ M$;
$[H^+] = 3.2 \times 10^{-4}\ M$; $[Na^+] = 0.139\ M$

■■ P R O B L E M  600  As pointed out above, there is usually a $10^4$ or $10^5$ factor between the successive dissociation constants of an acid.  However, this rule breaks down when successive protons come off different places in a molecular chain.  This happens, for example, with pyrophosphoric acid, $H_4P_2O_7$, a tetraprotic acid with the structure $H_IO$—P—O—P—$OH_{II}$.  Proton I comes off one end with

$$\underset{OH_{III}\quad OH_{IV}}{\left| \qquad \right|}$$

$K_I$; proton II comes off the other end with $K_{II}$, which is not much different from $K_I$.  Similarly, protons III and IV come off with about equal $K$'s.  Given that $K_I = 1.4 \times 10^{-1}$, $K_{II} = 1.1 \times 10^{-2}$, $K_{III} = 2.9 \times 10^{-7}$, and $K_{IV} = 3.6 \times 10^{-9}$, calculate the concentrations of $H_4P_2O_7$, $H_3P_2O_7^-$, $H_2P_2O_7^=$, $HP_2O_7^{-3}$, $P_2O_7^{-4}$, and $H^+$ in 0.100 $M$ $H_4P_2O_7$ solution.

ANSWER: $[H_4P_2O_7] = 0.032\ M$; $[H_3P_2O_7^-] = 0.059\ M$;
$[H_2P_2O_7^=] = 0.0086\ M$; $[HP_2O_7^{-3}] = 3.3 \times 10^{-8}\ M$;
$[P_2O_7^{-4}] = 1.6 \times 10^{-15}\ M$; $[H^+] = 0.076\ M$

# pH

WHEN A BASE, such as 0.1 $M$ NaOH, is added gradually to an acid, such as 0.1 $M$ HCl, the hydrogen-ion concentration goes through a change involving twelve powers of 10, or twelve orders of magnitude. In order to describe such a change, especially graphically, we take refuge, as one normally does in such cases, in representation by logarithms. In fact, the pH function is nothing more than a logarithmic way of representing the hydrogen-ion concentration.

## Definition of pH

It is customary to define the pH as the "negative of the logarithm of the hydrogen-ion concentration." Another way of saying the same thing is the "logarithm of the reciprocal of the hydrogen-ion concentration." Symbolically, these can be represented as follows:

$$pH = - \log C_{H^+} = - \log [H^+]$$

or

$$pH = \log \frac{1}{C_{H^+}} = \log \frac{1}{[H^+]}$$

where we have shown both $C_{H^+}$ and [$H^+$] as ways of representing concentration of hydrogen ion. The usual units for $C_{H^+}$ are moles per liter, or _molarity_. (This is one place where some trouble creeps in. Logarithms of $C_{H^+}$ do not have units, and, in fact, pH does not have units. In the strict definition, pH is the negative logarithm of the hydrogen-ion *activity*. Activity is a unitless quantity which we can regard as the actual concentration divided by unit concentration of a reference state. If it strains your mind, don't worry too much about this elegance. If you simply define pH $= -$log [$H^+$] and don't worry about the units, you will be doing what most chemists do in practice.)

PROBLEM 601    Given that the hydrogen-ion concentration of a particular solution is $3.0 \times 10^{-2}$ $M$, what is its pH?

SOLUTION: pH $= -$ log [$H^+$] $= -$ log $(3.0 \times 10^{-2})$.
Recall that the log of a product is the sum of the logs.

log $(3.0 \times 10^{-2}) =$ log $(3.0) +$ log $(10^{-2})$.

Recall also that the log of (10 raised to a power) is just equal to that power. For the log of 3.0 we look either in the table (Appendix A) or get it off the slide rule. We find log 3.0 $= 0.48$.

log $(3.0) +$ log $(10^{-2}) = 0.48 + (-2) = 0.48 - 2 = -1.52$.

pH $= -(-1.52) = +1.52$.

■PROBLEM 602    Given a solution with a hydrogen-ion concentration of $4.8 \times 10^{-6}$, what is its pH?
ANSWER: $+5.32$

There is always some confusion as to what is the proper number of significant figures when working with logarithms. The simple rule to follow is that the logarithm gets looked up to as many significant digits as there are in the *coefficient* of the exponential number. For example, in Problem 602, there are two significant figures in the number $4.8 \times 10^{-6}$, and these are the two decided by the coefficient 4.8.

The power $10^{-6}$ has nothing to do with significant figures; it just indicates where the decimal point goes. So, we look up the log of 4.8 and we find 0.6812. We take only two digits 0.68 and add them to $-6$. The $-6$ is an exact number, so we end up with $-5.32$. We end up with three digits, but only the two to the right of the decimal count as significant figures. This kind of monkey-business is special for the case of logarithms and should not be confused with the ordinary counting of significant figures.

**PROBLEM 603** You have a solution for which the hydrogen-ion concentration is $4.8 \times 10^{-13}$. What is its pH?

SOLUTION:
$$\begin{aligned} pH &= -[\log H^+] = -\log (4.8 \times 10^{-13}) \\ &= -(\log 4.8 + \log 10^{-13}) \\ &= -(0.68 - 13) = \mathbf{12.32} \end{aligned}$$

■ **PROBLEM 604** What is the pH of a solution whose hydrogen-ion concentration is $1.3 \times 10^{-13}$?
ANSWER: **12.89**

Many students have trouble in making the reverse calculation of going from a given pH to the hydrogen-ion concentration.

**PROBLEM 605** You are told that a solution has a pH of 4.00. What is its hydrogen-ion concentration?

SOLUTION:
$pH = -\log [H^+] = 4.00$.
$\log [H^+] = -4.00$.
$[H^+] = 10^{-4.00} = (10^{-4})(10^{0.00})$.
The number whose log is 0.00 is 1.0:

$$[H^+] = \mathbf{1.0 \times 10^{-4}} \ M$$

■ **PROBLEM 606** Given a pH of 13.00, what is the corresponding hydrogen-ion concentration?
ANSWER: **$1.0 \times 10^{-13}$ M**

PROBLEM 607 A typical blood sample shows a pH of 7.4. What is its hydrogen-ion concentration?

SOLUTION:

pH = $-\log [H^+]$ = 7.4.

$\log [H^+]$ = $-7.4$ = $-8 + 0.6$.

Note how you take the pH number before the decimal (the $-7$ of $-7.4$) and carry it to the next higher digit ($-8$) so the fractional part after the decimal (the $-0.4$ of $-7.4$) can be converted to a positive number ($+0.6$):

$[H^+]$ = $10^{-8} \times 10^{0.6}$

The antilog of 0.6 is 4:

$[H^+]$ = $4 \times 10^{-8}\ M$

■ PROBLEM 608 A typical beer will have a pH of 4.7. This corresponds to what hydrogen-ion concentration?
ANSWER: $2 \times 10^{-5}\ M$

There is no theoretical limit as to what pH values are allowed, although some people have the notion that negative pH values are automatically wrong. As the following problem shows, there is no *a priori* reason for rejecting a negative pH value.

PROBLEM 609 A given solution has a hydrogen-ion concentration of 2.89 $M$. What is its pH?

SOLUTION: pH = $-\log [H^+]$ = $-\log (2.89)$ = $-0.461$.

■ PROBLEM 610 You are given a solution with a pH of $-0.111$. What is the hydrogen-ion concentration therein?
ANSWER: 1.29 $M$

## The water equilibrium

Water is a weak electrolyte which is dissociated into hydrogen ion, $H^+$, and hydroxide ion, $OH^-$. The equilibrium reaction can be written

$$H_2O \rightleftharpoons H^+ + OH^-$$

and the condition for equilibrium is given by

$$K_w = [H^+][OH^-] = 1.00 \times 10^{-14}$$

$K_w$ is called the dissociation constant, or ion product, of water. Since in all dilute aqueous solutions the $H_2O$ stays at unit activity, its concentration does not appear in the condition for equilibrium.

The importance of the ion product of water comes from the fact that once the $H^+$ concentration of a solution is specified, the $OH^-$ can be calculated. Conversely, once you know the $OH^-$ concentration, you can calculate the $H^+$.

PROBLEM 611  What is the pH of pure water?

SOLUTION: Let $x =$ moles per liter of $H_2O$ that dissociate. This will give $x$ moles/l $H^+$ and $x$ moles/l $OH^-$ via the reaction $H_2O \rightarrow H^+ + OH^-$. The condition for equilibrium is the following:

$$K_w = [H^+][OH^-] = 1.00 \times 10^{-14}$$

$$(x)(x) = 1.00 \times 10^{-14}$$

$$x = 1.00 \times 10^{-7}$$

$$pH = -\log[H^+] = -\log(1.00 \times 10^{-7})$$

$$= -(\log 1.00 + \log 10^{-7})$$

$$= -(0.000 - 7) = 7.000$$

PROBLEM 612  Given a solution in which the concentration of $OH^-$ is $2.50 \times 10^{-3}$ $M$. What is the pH of the solution?

SOLUTION: $K_w = [H^+][OH^-] = 1.00 \times 10^{-14}$.
Substitute $[OH^-] = 2.50 \times 10^{-3}$.
Get $[H^+] = \dfrac{1.00 \times 10^{-14}}{2.50 \times 10^{-3}} = 0.400 \times 10^{-11} = 4.00 \times 10^{-12}$.
$pH = -\log[H^+] = -\log(4.00 \times 10^{-12}) = -(0.602 - 12)$

$$= 11.398$$

■ **PROBLEM** 613 Given a solution in which the concentration of hydroxide ion is $4.50 \times 10^{-11}$ $M$. What is the pH of the solution?

ANSWER: **3.653**

    PROBLEM 614 A solution has a pH of 12.68. What is its hydroxide-ion concentration?

SOLUTION:

pH $= - \log [H^+] = 12.68.$

$\log [H^+] = -12.68 = -13 + 0.32.$

$[H^+] = (10^{-13})(10^{0.32}) = (10^{-13})(2.1).$

Recall that the number whose log is $-13$ is just $10^{-13}$ and that the number whose log is 0.32 can be written as $10^{0.32}$. From the tables, the antilog of 0.32 is found to be 2.1. The condition for equilibrium is

$$K_w = [H^+][OH^-] = 1.00 \times 10^{-14}$$

If $[H^+] = 2.1 \times 10^{-13}$ as found above, then

$$[OH^-] = \frac{K_w}{[H^+]} = \frac{1.00 \times 10^{-14}}{2.1 \times 10^{-13}} = 4.8 \times 10^{-2} \ M$$

■ **PROBLEM** 615 What is the hydroxide-ion concentration of a solution having a pH of 9.806?

ANSWER: $6.40 \times 10^{-5} \ M$

■ **PROBLEM** 616 In cabbage the pH is 5.3. What is the concentration of hydroxide ion?

ANSWER: $2 \times 10^{-9} \ M$

## *Solutions of acids*

One way of defining an acid is to say that it is a substance which raises the hydrogen-ion concentration beyond that of pure water. This means $[H^+]$ has to go greater than $10^{-7}$ $M$; this means the pH has to fall below 7. With strong acids, we have no problem. We simply count the concentration of $H^+$ added. With weak acids, there may be trouble because the $H_2O \rightleftharpoons H^+ + OH^-$ equilibrium needs to be solved simultaneously with the $HX \rightleftharpoons H^+ + X^-$ equilibrium. The exact solution to this problem we shall postpone until Chapter 18. For the present, we just point out that if $K_{\text{diss}}$ of the weak acid HX is appreciably greater than $K_w$ and if the concentration of HX is not too small, then we shall be able to get away with the approximation that the HX equilibrium dominates the situation and effectively controls the $H_2O \rightleftharpoons H^+ + OH^-$ equilibrium.

**PROBLEM** 617　Given a solution that is 0.235 $M$ HCl. What is its pH?

SOLUTION: HCl is a strong electrolyte.
0.235 $M$ HCl is completely dissociated to give 0.235 $M$ $H^+$.

$pH = - \log [H^+] = - \log (0.235) = - \log (2.35 \times 10^{-1})$

$\quad = -(0.371 - 1) = 0.629$

■ **PROBLEM** 618　You make a solution by dissolving 0.0628 mole $HNO_3$ in 0.100 l. Assuming complete dissociation, what is the pH?

ANSWER: 0.202

■ **PROBLEM** 619　If you dissolve 9.22 cc HCl gas, measured at 27°C and 740 Torr pressure, in enough water to make 75.0 cc solution, what will be the pH of the resulting solution?

ANSWER: 2.313

**PROBLEM** 620　You have a solution that is 0.150 $M$ $HNO_2$. Given that $K_{\text{diss}}$ is $4.5 \times 10^{-4}$, calculate the pH of the solution.

SOLUTION:

$$HNO_2 \rightleftharpoons H^+ + NO_2^-$$

Let $x$ = moles per liter of $HNO_2$ that dissociate.
At equilibrium: $[HNO_2] = 0.150 - x$; $[H^+] = x$; $[NO_2^-] = x$.
Note that we implicitly neglect any $H^+$ contribution from the water dissociation.

$K_{\text{diss}} = \dfrac{[H^+][NO_2^-]}{[HNO_2]} = 4.5 \times 10^{-4} = \dfrac{(x)(x)}{0.150 - x}$

$x = 8.0 \times 10^{-3} = [H^+]$.

$pH = - \log [H^+] = - \log (8.0 \times 10^{-3}) = -(0.90 - 3) = 2.10.$

■ P R O B L E M  621  You have a solution that is 0.186 $M$ HClO. Given that $K_{diss} = 3.2 \times 10^{-8}$, calculate the pH of the solution.

ANSWER: **4.11**

P R O B L E M  622  You are told that the $K_{diss}$ of $HNO_2$ is $4.5 \times 10^{-4}$. You want a solution of $HNO_2$ which has a pH of 2.50. What concentration of $HNO_2$ would you need to take?

SOLUTION:

pH $= 2.50 = - \log [H^+]$.

$\log (H^+) = -2.50 = -3 + 0.50$.

$[H^+] = 10^{-3} \times 10^{0.50} = 3.2 \times 10^{-3} M$.

You want this $[H^+]$ to come from the dissociation of $HNO_2$.

$$HNO_2 \rightleftharpoons H^+ + NO_2^-$$

But each $H^+$ formed must be accompanied by formation of $NO_2^-$. Hence, we know that the solution must also contain $[NO_2^-] = 3.2 \times 10^{-3} M$. We substitute these known values of the concentration in the expression for $K_{diss}$:

$$K_{diss} = \frac{[H^+][NO_2^-]}{[HNO_2]} = 4.5 \times 10^{-4} = \frac{(3.2 \times 10^{-3})(3.2 \times 10^{-3})}{[HNO_2]}$$

$$[HNO_2] = \frac{(3.2 \times 10^{-3})(3.2 \times 10^{-3})}{4.5 \times 10^{-4}} = 2.3 \times 10^{-2} M$$

We need to furnish $2.3 \times 10^{-2}$ mole/l $HNO_2$ to build up this concentration of $HNO_2$ plus $3.2 \times 10^{-3}$ mole/l $HNO_2$ which will dissociate to give $3.2 \times 10^{-3} M H^+$ and $3.2 \times 10^{-3} M NO_2^-$. Total concentration of $HNO_2$ needs to be $2.3 \times 10^{-2} + 3.2 \times 10^{-3} = 2.6 \times 10^{-2} M$.

So, the solution needs to be **0.026 $M$ $HNO_2$**.

■ P R O B L E M  623  The dissociation constant for $HCNO \rightleftharpoons H^+ + CNO^-$ is $1.2 \times 10^{-4}$. You want a solution of HCNO which will have a pH of 2.65. What molarity of solute do you need?

ANSWER: **0.044 $M$ HCNO**

P R O B L E M  624  What will be the pH of 0.216 $M$ $H_3PO_4$ solution? For this acid $K_I = 7.5 \times 10^{-3}$, $K_{II} = 6.2 \times 10^{-8}$, and $K_{III} = 1 \times 10^{-12}$.

SOLUTION: First calculate the hydrogen-ion concentration of the solution.

$$H_3PO_4 \rightleftharpoons H^+ + H_2PO_4^-$$

Let $x$ = moles/l $H_3PO_4$ that dissociate.
$[H_3PO_4] = 0.216 - x$; $[H^+] = x$; $[H_2PO_4^-] = x$.

$$K_I = \frac{[H^+][H_2PO_4^-]}{[H_3PO_4]} = \frac{(x)(x)}{0.216 - x} = 7.5 \times 10^{-3}$$

$x = 3.7 \times 10^{-2}$ by successive approximations.
As discussed previously, the hydrogen-ion contribution from the second and third steps of the dissociation is negligible.
So, we take $[H^+] = x = 3.7 \times 10^{-2}$ $M$.

$$pH = -\log [H^+] = -\log (3.7 \times 10^{-2}) = -(0.57 - 2) = 1.43.$$

■ PROBLEM 625   For $H_2Te$, the dissociation constants are $K_I = 2.3 \times 10^{-3}$ and $K_{II} = 1 \times 10^{-11}$. Compute the pH of 0.192 $M$ $H_2Te$.
ANSWER: pH = 1.70

■ PROBLEM 626   Phosphorous acid, $H_3PO_3$, is a diprotic acid with $K_I = 1.6 \times 10^{-2}$ and $K_{II} = 7 \times 10^{-7}$. You want a solution of $H_3PO_3$ with a pH of 2.16. What should be the molarity of the $H_3PO_3$ solution?
ANSWER: 0.0099 $M$

PROBLEM 627   What would be the pH of 0.360 $M$ $H_2SO_4$? The $K_{II}$ for sulfuric acid is 1.26 $\times 10^{-2}$.

SOLUTION (compare Problem 586): Recall that $H_2SO_4$ is a strong electrolyte for the first dissociation. So, 0.360 $M$ $H_2SO_4$ is 100% dissociated to 0.360 $M$ $H^+$ and 0.360 $M$ $HSO_4^-$. Now let $x$ moles/l $HSO_4^-$ dissociate to produce $x$ moles/l more of $H^+$. At equilibrium:

$[HSO_4^-] = 0.360 - x$; $[H^+] = 0.360 + x$; $[SO_4^=] = x$

$$HSO_4^- \rightleftharpoons H^+ + SO_4^=$$

$$K_{II} = \frac{[H^+][SO_4^=]}{[HSO_4^-]} = 1.26 \times 10^{-2} = \frac{(0.360 + x)(x)}{0.360 - x}$$

By the quadratic formula, $x = 0.0118$. Substitute this in the above expression to get $[H^+] = 0.360 + x = 0.372 \ M$.

$$pH = - \log [H^+] = - \log (0.372) = - \log (3.72 \times 10^{-1})$$

$$= -(0.571 - 1) = 0.429$$

■ P R O B L E M  628  Given that $K_{II} = 1.26 \times 10^{-2}$ for $H_2SO_4$, calculate the pH of a 0.100 $M$ $H_2SO_4$ solution.
ANSWER: pH = 0.958

P R O B L E M  629  Suppose you wanted a sulfuric acid solution that had a pH of 1.000. Given that $K_{II}$ of $H_2SO_4$ is $1.26 \times 10^{-2}$, what molarity $H_2SO_4$ solution would you take?

SOLUTION:
pH = $1.000 = - \log [H^+]$.
$\log [H^+] = -1.000 = -1 + 0.000$.
$[H^+] = (10^{-1})(1.00) = 1.00 \times 10^{-1}$.
The principal equilibrium in the solution is

$$HSO_4^- \rightleftharpoons H^+ + SO_4^=$$

for which

$$K_{II} = \frac{[H^+][SO_4^=]}{[HSO_4^-]} = 1.26 \times 10^{-2}$$

But we know that $[H^+]$ must be $1.00 \times 10^{-1} \ M$, so we substitute $[H^+] = 1.00 \times 10^{-1}$.

$$\frac{(1.00 \times 10^{-1})[SO_4^=]}{[HSO_4^-]} = 1.26 \times 10^{-2}$$

which tells us that in this solution

$$\frac{[SO_4^=]}{[HSO_4^-]} = \frac{1.26 \times 10^{-2}}{1.00 \times 10^{-1}} = 1.26 \times 10^{-1} = 0.126$$

But we end up with two unknowns, $[SO_4^=]$ and $[HSO_4^-]$, and only one equation. Can we find another equation? The solution must be electrically neutral. This means that the concentration of positive charge (i.e., $H^+$) must equal the total concentration of negative charge (i.e., from $SO_4^=$ and $HSO_4^-$). The only point to be careful about is to make sure we allow for the fact that $SO_4^=$ is doubly charged whereas $HSO_4^-$ is only singly charged.   We get finally as the electrical neutrality condition

$$[H^+] = 2[SO_4^=] + [HSO_4^-]$$

where the concentration of sulfate is counted twice as heavily as the concentration of $HSO_4^-$.   But we know that in this solution $[H^+] = 1.00 \times 10^{-1}$ $M$, or 0.100 $M$, so we can write

$$0.100 = 2[SO_4^=] + [HSO_4^-] \text{ and } [SO_4^=] = 0.126[HSO_4^-]$$

which gives us two simultaneous equations to solve.
By substituting the second equation into the first, we get

$$0.100 = (2)(0.126[HSO_4^-]) + [HSO_4^-] = 1.252[HSO_4^-]$$

This solves to $[HSO_4^-] = 0.0799$ $M$ and gives $[SO_4^=] = 0.0101$ $M$. The solute $H_2SO_4$ must show up either as $HSO_4^-$ or $SO_4^=$, so we can calculate the total moles of solute needed simply as the sum of the $HSO_4^-$ and $SO_4^=$.   This gives $0.0799 + 0.0101 = 0.0900$ mole/l.   Thus, to get pH = 1.000, we need **0.0900 $M$ $H_2SO_4$**.

■ P R O B L E M   630   Given that $K_{II}$ of $H_2SO_4$ is $1.26 \times 10^{-2}$, what molarity $H_2SO_4$ solution would you need to get a pH of 2.000?

ANSWER: **0.00642 $M$ $H_2SO_4$**

## Solutions of bases

The same remarks on solutions of acids can equally well be made for solutions of bases—that is, strong bases can be taken care of by counting up the concentration of $OH^-$ added to the solution; weak bases can be considered as dominating over the $H_2O \leftrightarrows H^+ + OH^-$ equilibrium, so long as $K_{diss}$ of the base is bigger than $K_w$ of the water and so long as the concentration of base is not too small.   The only extra step we shall need to get the pH of basic solutions is to go from $[OH^-]$ to $[H^+]$ via $K_w = [H^+][OH^-]$.

P R O B L E M   631   What is the pH of 0.150 $M$ NaOH solution?

SOLUTION: NaOH is a strong electrolyte and is assumed to be 100% dissociated.   This means that 0.150 $M$ NaOH is taken to be 100%

dissociated into the form 0.150 $M$ Na$^+$ and 0.150 $M$ OH$^-$. Once we know the concentration of OH$^-$, we can calculate the hydrogen-ion concentration from $K_w = [H^+][OH^-] = 1.00 \times 10^{-14}$:

$$[H^+] = \frac{1.00 \times 10^{-14}}{[OH^-]} = \frac{1.00 \times 10^{-14}}{0.150} = 6.67 \times 10^{-14} \ M$$

$$pH = -\log[H^+] = -\log(6.67 \times 10^{-14}) = -(0.824 - 14)$$
$$= 13.176$$

■ PROBLEM 632 What is the pH of a solution made by dissolving 0.150 g KOH in enough water to make 25.0 ml solution?

ANSWER: **13.029**

PROBLEM 633 What would be the pH of $3.86 \times 10^{-3} \ M$ Ba(OH)$_2$ solution? Assume complete dissociation.

SOLUTION: Ba(OH)$_2$ is a strong electrolyte and is 100% dissociated into Ba$^{++}$ and 2OH$^-$. From $3.86 \times 10^{-3} \ M$ Ba(OH)$_2$, complete dissociation would give $3.86 \times 10^{-3} \ M$ Ba$^{++}$ and $(2)(3.86 \times 10^{-3})$, or $7.72 \times 10^{-3}$, $M$ OH$^-$.

$$[H^+] = \frac{K_w}{[OH^-]} = \frac{1.00 \times 10^{-14}}{7.22 \times 10^{-3}} = 1.38 \times 10^{-12} \ M$$
$$pH = -\log[H^+] = -\log(1.38 \times 10^{-12})$$
$$= -(0.140 - 12) = \mathbf{11.860}$$

■ PROBLEM 634 What is the pH of 0.100 $M$ Ba(OH)$_2$, assuming complete dissociation?

ANSWER: **13.301**

PROBLEM 635 Aqueous solutions of NH$_3$ are slightly basic because of the equilibrium NH$_3$ + H$_2$O $\rightleftharpoons$ NH$_4^+$ + OH$^-$, for which $K = 1.81 \times 10^{-5}$. What will be the pH of 0.55 $M$ NH$_3$ solution?

SOLUTION: (First calculate the [OH$^-$] as a problem in weak base dissociation. Then use the result to compute the [H$^+$].)

Let $x$ = moles/l NH$_3$ that convert to NH$_4^+$. At equilibrium, this will leave $(0.55 - x)$ mole/l NH$_3$ unchanged and will have produced $x$ moles/l NH$_4^+$ and $x$ moles/l OH$^-$.

[NH$_3$] = 0.55 − $x$; [NH$_4^+$] = $x$; [OH$^-$] = $x$.

NH$_3$ + H$_2$O $\rightleftharpoons$ NH$_4^+$ + OH$^-$.

$$K = \frac{[NH_4^+][OH^-]}{[NH_3]} = 1.81 \times 10^{-5} = \frac{(x)(x)}{0.55 - x}.$$

$$x = 3.2 \times 10^{-3} = [OH^-].$$

$$[H^+] = \frac{K_w}{[OH^-]} = \frac{1.00 \times 10^{-14}}{3.2 \times 10^{-3}} = 3.1 \times 10^{-12}.$$

$$pH = -\log(H^+) = -\log(3.1 \times 10^{-12}) = -(0.49 - 12) = 11.51$$

■ PROBLEM 636   A solution is made by dissolving 2.48 g $NH_3$ in enough water to make 1.00 l solution. Given that $K = 1.81 \times 10^{-5}$ for the equilibrium $NH_3 + H_2O \rightleftharpoons NH_4^+ + OH^-$ what will be the pH of the resulting solution?

ANSWER: 11.210

PROBLEM 637   You would like to have an aqueous ammonia solution with a pH of 11.111. Given that $K = 1.81 \times 10^{-5}$ for $NH_3 + H_2O \rightleftharpoons NH_4^+ + OH^-$, what molarity $NH_3$ solution would you take?

SOLUTION: You want the pH to be 11.111.

pH $= 11.111 = -\log[H^+]$.

$\log[H^+] = -11.111 = -12 + 0.889$.

$[H^+] = 7.74 \times 10^{-12}$.

Use $K_w = [H^+][OH^-]$ to find out what $[OH^-]$ this corresponds to.

$$[OH^-] = \frac{K_w}{[H^+]} = \frac{1.00 \times 10^{-14}}{7.74 \times 10^{-12}} = 1.29 \times 10^{-3} M$$

According to the reaction $NH_3 + H_2O \rightarrow NH_4^+ + OH^-$, there is produced one $NH_4^+$ for each $OH^-$. Therefore, the concentration of $NH_4^+$ in the solution must also be $1.29 \times 10^{-3} M$. We can use $K$ for the $NH_3$ "dissociation" to find the actual concentration of $NH_3$ needed for equilibrium with the above values of $NH_4^+$ and $OH^-$.

$NH_3 + H_2O \rightleftharpoons NH_4^+ + OH^-$.

$$K = \frac{[NH_4^+][OH^-]}{[NH_3]} = 1.81 \times 10^{-5} = \frac{(1.29 \times 10^{-3})(1.29 \times 10^{-3})}{[NH_3]}.$$

$$[NH_3] = \frac{(1.29 \times 10^{-3})^2}{1.81 \times 10^{-5}} = 0.0919 M.$$

The molarity of the $NH_3$ solution to be prepared needs to be great enough to supply the 0.0919 $M$ of free $NH_3$ plus $1.29 \times 10^{-3} M$ to take care of that part that converts to $NH_4^+$. So, total $NH_3$ needed $= 0.0919 + 1.29 \times 10^{-3} = 0.0932 M$.

■ P R O B L E M 638 What molarity $NH_3$ solution should you take to get a pH of 12.00? Use $K = 1.81 \times 10^{-5}$ for $NH_3 + H_2O \rightleftharpoons NH_4^+ + OH^-$.

ANSWER: **5.5 $M$ $NH_3$**

P R O B L E M 639 Suppose you dissolve 1.00 g $NH_3$ and 1.00 g $NH_4NO_3$ in enough water to make 0.250 l solution. Given that $K = 1.81 \times 10^{-5}$ for $NH_3 + H_2O \rightleftharpoons NH_4^+ + OH^-$, what pH would you get for this solution?

SOLUTION: (The only new point here is to note that the solution already has $NH_4^+$ from the $NH_4NO_3$ and this must be allowed for when calculating the $NH_3$ dissociation.)

$NH_4NO_3$ is a strong electrolyte and is 100% dissociated into $NH_4^+$ and $NO_3^-$.

1.00 g $NH_4NO_3 = \dfrac{1.00 \text{ g}}{80.04 \text{ g/mole}} = 0.0125$ mole $NH_4NO_3$, which gives 0.0125 mole $NH_4^+$. In a volume of 0.250 l, this gives an ammonium-ion concentration of $\dfrac{0.0125 \text{ mole}}{0.250 \text{ l}} = 0.0500 \; M$.

1.00 g $NH_3 = \dfrac{1.00 \text{ g}}{17.03 \text{ g/mole}} = 0.0587$ mole $NH_3$. In a volume of 0.250 l, this gives $\dfrac{0.0587 \text{ mole}}{0.250 \text{ l}} = 0.235 \; M \; NH_3$.

Let $x =$ moles/l of the $NH_3$ that react $NH_3 + H_2O \rightarrow NH_4^+ + OH^-$. This will give at equilibrium

$[NH_3] = 0.235 - x$; $[NH_4^+] = 0.0500 + x$; $[OH^-] = x$

$NH_3 + H_2O \rightleftharpoons NH_4^+ + OH^-$

$$K = \frac{[NH_4^+][OH^-]}{[NH_3]} = 1.81 \times 10^{-5} = \frac{(0.0500 + x)(x)}{0.235 - x}$$

Solve, using the very good approximation that $x$ is small enough to be neglected when added to 0.0500 or subtracted from 0.235. The result is $x = 8.51 \times 10^{-5} = [OH^-]$.

$[H^+] = \dfrac{K_w}{[OH^-]} = \dfrac{1.00 \times 10^{-14}}{8.51 \times 10^{-5}} = 1.18 \times 10^{-10} \; M$.

pH $= -\log [H^+] = -\log (1.18 \times 10^{-10}) = -(0.072 - 10) = $ **9.928.**

■ PROBLEM 640  If you mix 10.0 ml of 0.250 $M$ $NH_3$ with 30.0 ml of 0.100 $M$ $NH_4NO_3$, what will be the pH of the resulting solution? Assume volumes are additive, and use $K = 1.81 \times 10^{-5}$ for the equilibrium $NH_3 + H_2O \rightleftharpoons NH_4^+ + OH^-$.

ANSWER: 9.179

■■ PROBLEM 641  How many ml of 0.250 $M$ $NH_3$ must you add to the solution resulting from Problem 640 in order to make the pH go to 9.379? Assume volumes additive.

ANSWER: 5.8 ml

## Solutions of salts

The influence of an added salt on the pH of water depends on what effect the added salt has on the water dissociation equilibrium, $H_2O \rightleftharpoons H^+ + OH^-$. In general, cations that come from strong bases (e.g., $Na^+$, $K^+$, $Ba^{++}$) will not affect the water equilibrium, nor will anions that come from strong acids (e.g., $ClO_4^-$, $Cl^-$, $NO_3^-$). The reason for this is that such cations have no tendency to associate with $OH^-$ and such anions have no tendency to associate with $H^+$. Hence, the water equilibrium in such salt solutions is considered to stay unchanged from what it is in pure water.

PROBLEM 642  What is the pH of 0.10 $M$ $KNO_3$ solution?

SOLUTION: The equilibrium is $H_2O \rightleftharpoons H^+ + OH^-$.
Let $x$ = moles/l $H_2O$ that dissociate.
Then $x = [H^+] = [OH^-]$.
$K_w = [H^+][OH^-] = 1.00 \times 10^{-14} = (x)(x)$.
$x = 1.00 \times 10^{-7}$.
pH $= - \log [H^+] = - \log (1.00 \times 10^{-7}) = -(0.000 - 7) = 7.000$.

■ PROBLEM 643  What would be the pH of a solution made by dissolving 1.86 g $BaCl_2$ in 1.00 l water?

ANSWER: pH $= 7.000$

Cations of weak bases *do* influence the $H_2O \rightleftharpoons H^+ + OH^-$ by tying up some of the $OH^-$ ion. Similarly, anions of weak acids perturb the equilibrium $H_2O \rightleftharpoons H^+ + OH^-$ by tying up some $H^+$. In the first case (e.g., $NH_4^+$), the pH of the solution drops below 7; in the second case (e.g., $CO_3^=$), the pH rises above 7. Salts that produce such action are said to undergo hydrolysis. The computation of pH in hydrolysis is taken up in detail in Chapter 18.

A special kind of situation occurs with certain salts in which the anion can act as an acid. This occurs, for example, with $NaHSO_4$, where $HSO_4^-$ is a moderately strong acid ($K_{diss} = 1.26 \times 10^{-2}$). We are carefully avoiding at this time such cases as $NaHCO_3$, where $HCO_3^-$ can also act as an acid but where the situation is extensively complicated by its simultaneous ability to act as a base. $NaHSO_4$ does not have this complication, since $HSO_4^-$ has no tendency to pick up $H^+$ to form $H_2SO_4$.

PROBLEM 644 What is the pH of 0.168 $M$ $NaHSO_4$ solution, given that $K_{diss}$ is $1.26 \times 10^{-2}$?

SOLUTION: $NaHSO_4$ is a strong electrolyte and is taken to be 100% dissociated to $Na^+$ and $HSO_4^-$. Therefore, 0.168 $M$ $NaHSO_4$ can be considered 0.168 $M$ $Na^+$ and 0.168 $M$ $HSO_4^-$.

Suppose we let $x$ = moles per liter of $HSO_4^-$ that are dissociated.
$[HSO_4^-] = 0.168 - x$; $[H^+] = x$; $[SO_4^=] = x$.
$HSO_4^- \rightleftharpoons H^+ + SO_4^=$.

$$K = \frac{[H^+][SO_4^=]}{[HSO_4^-]} = 1.26 \times 10^{-2} = \frac{(x)(x)}{0.168 - x}.$$

This solves by the quadratic formula to give $x = 0.0401 = [H^+]$.
pH $= -\log [H^+] = -\log (0.0401) = -\log (4.01 \times 10^{-2})$
    $= -(0.603 - 2) = +1.397$

■ PROBLEM 645 If you dissolve 1.00 g $KHSO_4$ in enough water to make 25.0 ml solution, what would be the pH of the resulting solution? $K_{diss}$ for $HSO_4^-$ is $1.26 \times 10^{-2}$.
ANSWER: pH $= 1.260$

■ PROBLEM 646 What molarity $NaHSO_4$ solution would you need to take to get a pH of 1.500? $K_{diss} = 1.26 \times 10^{-2}$ for $HSO_4^-$.
ANSWER: 0.111 $M$ $NaHSO_4$

# 15

## BUFFER
## SOLUTIONS

A BUFFER SOLUTION is one to which either acid or base can be added without drastically changing the pH. In general, a buffer solution consists of a weak acid plus one of its salts, a weak base plus one of its salts, or a combination of weak acids and bases. The efficiency of the buffering action against added acid or base depends on the concentrations of the ingredients and is most effective when they are present in roughly equal amounts. Most of the discussion and computations that follow apply to buffers consisting of an acid HX and a salt NaX, since this is the type commonly encountered in freshman chemistry and qualitative analysis. However, we shall also do some computations for the $NH_3 - NH_4^+$ system, an important and practical buffer in the basic region. Some of the more complicated aspects of buffer calculations are postponed.

### The acetic acid–sodium acetate buffer

Acetic acid is one of the common, easy-to-work-with weak acids with a dissociation constant of $1.8 \times 10^{-5}$ for the reaction

$$HOAc \rightleftharpoons H^+ + OAc^-$$

(where the symbol Ac stands for the acetyl grouping $CH_3CO$). Any solution containing an appreciable amount of HOAc and of OAc⁻ provides buffering action against added $H^+$ (which would be picked up by free OAc⁻) or against added OH⁻ (which would be neutralized by HOAc).  Neither of these actions is 100% perfect, so the question is: How "constant" can the pH be held?

PROBLEM 647    What would be the pH of a buffer solution made by adding 0.350 mole HOAc and 0.350 mole NaOAc to enough water to make 0.600 l solution?

SOLUTION:

$$\frac{0.350 \text{ mole HOAc}}{0.600 \text{ l}} = 0.583 \ M \text{ HOAc.}$$

$$\frac{0.350 \text{ mole NaOAc}}{0.600 \text{ l}} = 0.583 \ M \text{ NaOAc.}$$

But sodium acetate, NaOAc, is a strong electrolyte, as most sodium salts are.  So, we can assume that the NaOAc is completely dissociated into $Na^+$ and OAc⁻.  From 0.583 $M$ NaOAc, we would then have 0.583 $M$ $Na^+$ and 0.583 $M$ OAc⁻.

Let $x$ = moles/l of the HOAc that is dissociated.  This will mean that the equilibrium concentration of HOAc has been reduced from 0.583 to 0.583 − $x$.  Likewise, the OAc⁻ concentration has been increased from 0.583 to 0.583 + $x$.

[HOAc] = 0.583 − $x$; [$H^+$] = $x$; [OAc⁻] = 0.583 + $x$.

HOAc ⇌ $H^+$ + OAc⁻.

$$K = \frac{[H^+][\text{OAc}^-]}{[\text{HOAc}]} = 1.8 \times 10^{-5} = \frac{(x)(0.583 + x)}{0.583 - x}$$

Solve this equation for $x$, noting that $x$ is small enough to be neglected when added to or subtracted from 0.583.

$$x \cong \frac{0.583}{0.583}(1.8 \times 10^{-5}) = 1.8 \times 10^{-5} = [H^+].$$

pH = − log [$H^+$] = − log (1.8 × 10⁻⁵) = −(0.26 − 5) = 4.74.

■ PROBLEM 648    What would be the pH of a buffer solution made by adding 0.225 mole HOAc and 0.225 mole NaOAc to enough water to make 0.600 l solution?

ANSWER: pH = 4.74

The two preceding problems illustrate one important point: The pH of a buffer solution is fixed by the $K_{diss}$ of the weak acid involved and, in fact, is equal to $- \log K_{diss}$ for all buffer solutions in which acid and salt are present in *equal* concentrations. What happens if they are not present in equal concentrations?

PROBLEM 649    What would be the pH of a buffer solution made by adding 0.350 mole HOAc and 0.225 mole NaOAc to enough water to make 0.600 l solution?

SOLUTION:

$$\frac{0.350 \text{ mole HOAc}}{0.600 \text{ l}} = 0.583 \ M \text{ HOAc}.$$

$$\frac{0.225 \text{ mole NaOAc}}{0.600 \text{ l}} = 0.375 \ M \text{ NaOAc}.$$

The 0.375 $M$ NaOAc will be dissociated 100% into 0.375 $M$ $Na^+$ and 0.375 $M$ $OAc^-$. Let $x$ = moles/l HOAc that are dissociated. This will give at equilibrium:

$$[HOAc] = 0.583 - x; \quad [H^+] = x; \quad [OAc^-] = 0.375 + x.$$

$$HOAc \rightleftharpoons H^+ + OAc^-.$$

$$K = \frac{[H^+][OAc^-]}{[HOAc]} = 1.8 \times 10^{-5} = \frac{(x)(0.375 + x)}{0.583 - x}.$$

$$x \cong \frac{0.583}{0.375}(1.8 \times 10^{-5}) = 2.8 \times 10^{-5} = [H^+].$$

$$pH = - \log [H^+] = - \log (2.8 \times 10^{-5}) = -(0.45 - 5) = 4.55.$$

■PROBLEM 650    What would be the pH of a buffer solution made by adding 0.225 mole HOAc and 0.350 mole NaOAc to enough water to make 0.600 l solution?

ANSWER: pH = 4.94

It should be evident at this stage that a buffer problem is nothing more than a weak electrolyte problem with the added complication that one of the dissociation products is already present in the solution. For rapid calculation of buffer hydrogen-ion concentration, it might be noted that the expression for a dissociation constant of weak acid HX

$$K_{\text{diss}} = \frac{[H^+][X^-]}{[HX]}$$

can be rewritten in the more convenient form

$$[H^+] = \frac{[HX]}{[X^-]} K_{\text{diss}}$$

This states that the hydrogen-ion concentration equals the ratio of weak acid-to-salt concentration times the dissociation constant. This form of the equation is particularly useful when other acid or base is added to the buffer solution.

PROBLEM 651 Suppose you have 0.250 l of a buffer solution which contains acetic acid at 0.350 $M$ concentration and sodium acetate at 0.350 $M$ concentration. What would be the pH change if 30.0 ml of 0.100 $M$ HCl is added to this buffer? Assume volumes additive. $K_{\text{diss}} = 1.8 \times 10^{-5}$ for HOAc.

SOLUTION: (First calculate the initial solution. Then add the acid.) In the initial solution, let $x =$ moles/l HOAc that dissociate.
$[HOAc] = 0.350 - x$; $[H^+] = x$; $[OAc^-] = 0.350 + x$.
$$x = [H^+] = \frac{[HOAc]}{[OAc^-]} K_{\text{diss}} = \frac{0.350 - x}{0.350 + x} (1.8 \times 10^{-5}) \cong 1.8 \times 10^{-5}$$
where we have neglected the $x$ as being small compared to 0.350.
pH $= -\log [H^+] = -\log (1.8 \times 10^{-5}) = -(0.26 - 5) = 4.74$.
Now add the 30.0 ml of 0.100 $M$ HCl. Since HCl is a strong electrolyte, we are effectively adding 30.0 ml of 0.100 $M$ H$^+$, or
$$(0.0300 \text{ l}) \left( 0.100 \frac{\text{mole H}^+}{\text{l}} \right) = 0.00300 \text{ mole H}^+.$$
Let us assume that all of this H$^+$ is picked up by OAc$^-$ to form HOAc. What will this do to the OAc$^-$ and HOAc in the buffer? The buffer initially contains
$$(0.250 \text{ l}) \left( 0.350 \frac{\text{mole HOAc}}{\text{l}} \right) = 0.0875 \text{ mole HOAc}$$
and
$$(0.250 \text{ l}) \left( 0.350 \frac{\text{mole OAc}^-}{\text{l}} \right) = 0.0875 \text{ mole OAc}^-$$

The effect of the added 0.00300 mole of $H^+$ would be to decrease the moles of $OAc^-$ by 0.00300 and increase the moles of HOAc by 0.00300 by the reaction

$$H^+ + OAc^- \rightarrow HOAc$$

Assuming 100% conversion, this will give us $0.0875 - 0.00300 = 0.0845$ mole $OAc^-$ and $0.0875 + 0.00300 = 0.0905$ mole HOAc. The total volume of the solution is now 0.280 l, made up of the 0.250 l original buffer plus the 30.0 ml added solution. So far as concentration is concerned, we now have

$$\frac{0.0845 \text{ mole } OAc^-}{0.280 \text{ l}} = 0.302 \ M \ OAc^-$$

and

$$\frac{0.0905 \text{ mole HOAc}}{0.280 \text{ l}} = 0.323 \ M \ HOAc$$

But this does not allow for any dissociation to give $H^+$.
Let $y =$ moles/l of the HOAc that dissociate.
$[HOAc] = 0.323 - y$; $[H^+] = y$; $[OAc^-] = 0.302 + y$.
$$y = H^+ = \frac{[HOAc]}{[OAc^-]} K_{diss} = \frac{0.323 - y}{0.302 + y} (1.8 \times 10^{-5}) \cong 1.9 \times 10^{-5}.$$
where, again, we take advantage of the fact that $y$ is small enough to neglect compared to 0.323 or 0.302.
$pH = - \log [H^+] = - \log (1.9 \times 10^{-5}) = -(0.28 - 5) = 4.72$.
So, the pH changes from 4.74 to 4.72 .

■PROBLEM 652   Suppose you have 0.250 l of a buffer solution which contains acetic acid at 0.225 $M$ concentration and sodium acetate at 0.225 $M$ concentration. What would be the pH change if 30.0 ml of 0.100 $M$ HCl is added to this buffer? Assume volumes additive. $K_{diss} = 1.8 \times 10^{-5}$ for HOAc.
ANSWER: pH changes from 4.74 to 4.70

Comparison of Problems 651 and 652 shows they are identical except that the former has higher concentrations of the buffer ingredients and suffers a smaller pH change when acid is added. This is generally true. The more concentrated a buffer is, the more efficient it is at keeping pH constant.

■ PROBLEM 653  Suppose you have 0.125
l of a buffer solution which contains acetic acid at 0.225 $M$ concentration and sodium acetate at 0.225 $M$ concentration. What would be the
pH change if 30.0 ml of 0.100 $M$ HCl is added to this buffer? Assume
volumes are additive. $K_{diss} = 1.8 \times 10^{-5}$ for HOAc.

ANSWER: pH changes **from 4.74 to 4.65**


Comparison of Problems 652 and 653 shows they are identical except that the former has a higher volume of buffer solution and suffers
a smaller pH change when acid is added. This is an example of the
general rule that the more of a buffer solution you take, the more efficient it is at keeping the pH constant.


■ PROBLEM 654  Just  for  comparison
with Problem 653, if you had 0.125 l pure water to which you added
30.0 ml of 0.100 $M$ HCl, what would the pH change be? This is an
example of an unbuffered solution. Assume additive volumes.

ANSWER: pH changes **from 7.000 to 1.713**


The preceding problems involve addition of acid to a buffer. True
buffering action requires that the same system be equally good at resisting change of pH on addition of base.


PROBLEM 655  (compare  to  Problem
651)  Suppose you have 0.250 l of a buffer solution which contains
acetic acid at 0.350 $M$ and sodium acetate at 0.350 $M$. What would be
the pH change if 30.0 ml of 0.100 $M$ NaOH is added? Assume volumes
are additive. $K_{diss} = 1.8 \times 10^{-5}$ for HOAc.

SOLUTION: The initial buffer has a pH of 4.74 as calculated in Problem 651. Now we add 30.0 ml of 0.100 $M$ NaOH. Since NaOH
is a strong electrolyte, it is taken to be 100% dissociated into
$Na^+$ and $OH^-$. From the 30.0 ml of 0.100 $M$ $OH^-$ we would get

$$(0.0300 \text{ l}) \left( 0.100 \frac{\text{mole}}{\text{l}} \right) = 0.00300 \text{ mole } OH^- \text{ added.}$$ The effect

of the added $OH^-$ is to convert HOAc to $OAc^-$ via the net reaction $OH^- + HOAc \rightarrow H_2O + OAc^-$.

The initial buffer has

$$(0.250 \text{ l}) \left( 0.350 \frac{\text{mole HOAc}}{\text{liter}} \right) = 0.0875 \text{ mole HOAc}$$

$$(0.250 \text{ l}) \left( 0.350 \frac{\text{mole OAc}^-}{\text{liter}} \right) = 0.0875 \text{ mole OAc}^-$$

Assuming all 0.00300 mole of the $OH^-$ reacts with HOAc to form more $OAc^-$, we would get $0.0875 - 0.00300 = 0.0845$ mole HOAc left along with, $0.0875 + 0.00300 = 0.0905$ mole $OAc^-$. In a total solution volume of $0.250 + 0.030 = 0.280$ l, we would have

$$\frac{0.0845 \text{ mole HOAc}}{0.280 \text{ l}} = 0.302 \ M \text{ HOAc}$$

$$\frac{0.0905 \text{ mole OAc}^-}{0.280 \text{ l}} = 0.323 \ M \text{ OAc}^-$$

Let $y$ = moles/l of this HOAc that is dissociated.
$[HOAc] = 0.302 - y$; $[H^+] = y$; $[OAc^-] = 0.323 + y$.

$$y = [H^+] = \frac{[HOAc]}{[OAc^-]} K_{\text{diss}} = \frac{(0.302 - y)}{(0.323 + y)} (1.8 \times 10^{-5}) \cong 1.7 \times 10^{-5}.$$

$$pH = -\log [H^+] = -\log (1.7 \times 10^{-5}) = -(0.23 - 5) = 4.77.$$

So, pH changes from 4.74 to 4.77.

## ■ PROBLEM 656

Given 0.250 l of a solution that is 0.225 $M$ HOAc and 0.225 $M$ NaOAc. What will be the pH change on addition of 30.0 ml of 0.100 $M$ NaOH? Assume additive volumes. $K_{\text{diss}} = 1.8 \times 10^{-5}$ for HOAc.

ANSWER: pH goes from 4.74 to 4.79

## ■ PROBLEM 657

Given 0.125 l of a solution that is 0.225 $M$ HOAc and 0.225 $M$ NaOAc. What will be the pH change on addition of 30.0 ml of 0.100 $M$ NaOH? Assume additive volumes. $K_{\text{diss}} = 1.8 \times 10^{-5}$ for HOAc.

ANSWER: pH goes from 4.74 to 4.84

## ■ PROBLEM 658 For comparison with

the preceding problem, what will be the pH change if 30.0 ml of 0.100 $M$ NaOH is added to 0.125 l pure water? Assume additive volumes.

ANSWER: pH goes from 7.000 to 12.287

## *The ammonia–ammonium salt buffer*

A buffer solution is most effective at keeping the pH constant at about the value that is given by $(- \log K_{\text{diss}})$ for the appropriate weak electrolyte. Thus, if we want to buffer around pH = 5, we select an acid with $K_{\text{diss}} = 10^{-5}$ and make up a solution of this acid and its sodium salt. If we want to buffer around pH = 7 we look for an acid with $K_{\text{diss}} = 10^{-7}$. What about the basic side? Suppose we want to buffer around pH = 9. We could do the same thing. Look for a weak acid with $K_{\text{diss}} = 10^{-9}$ and make up a solution containing equal concentrations of this weak acid and its sodium salt. There is an alternative method, however. We could select a weak base with $K_{\text{diss}} = 10^{-5}$ and make up a solution containing equal concentrations of this weak base and one of its salts. The $OH^-$ concentration would be buffered at $10^{-5} M$, which, of course, would be the same as keeping the pH constant at 9.

The ammonia "dissociation," which can be written

$$NH_3 + H_2O \rightleftharpoons NH_4^+ + OH^-$$

and which has

$$K_{\text{diss}} = \frac{[NH_4^+][OH^-]}{[NH_3]} = 1.81 \times 10^{-5}$$

is frequently used to buffer in this basic range.

PROBLEM 659   What will be the pH of a buffer solution consisting of 0.150 mole $NH_3$ plus 0.250 mole $NH_4Cl$ in enough water to make 0.750 l solution? $K_{\text{diss}} = 1.81 \times 10^{-5}$ for $NH_3$ in water.

SOLUTION:

$$\frac{0.150 \text{ mole } NH_3}{0.750 \text{ l}} = 0.200 \ M \ NH_3.$$

$NH_4Cl$ is a strong electrolyte and is 100% dissociated into $NH_4^+$ and $Cl^-$.

$$\frac{0.250 \text{ mole } NH_4^+}{0.750 \text{ l}} = 0.333 \ M \ NH_4^+.$$

[*Note:* There is no absolute requirement that the components of a buffer be present in equal concentrations. Equal concentrations are usually chosen so as to maximize the efficiency of the buffer to resisting pH change on addition of acid *or* base.]

Let $x$ = moles/l $NH_3$ that react via $NH_3 + H_2O \rightarrow NH_4^+ + OH^-$. This will give us $x$ moles $OH^-$ and will raise $NH_4^+$ from 0.333 to $0.333 + x$, at the same time decreasing $NH_3$ from 0.200 to $0.200 - x$.

$[NH_3] = 0.200 - x$; $[NH_4^+] = 0.333 + x$; $[OH^-] = x$.

$NH_3 + H_2O \rightleftharpoons NH_4^+ + OH^-$.

$$K = \frac{[NH_4^+][OH^-]}{[NH_3]} = 1.81 \times 10^{-5} = \frac{(0.333 + x)(x)}{0.200 - x}.$$

Neglecting $x$ where it adds or subtracts, we get $x = 1.09 \times 10^{-5}$. But this is the $OH^-$ concentration. To get $H^+$, we need to use $K_w$.

$$[H^+] = \frac{K_w}{[OH^-]} = \frac{1.00 \times 10^{-14}}{1.09 \times 10^{-5}} = 9.17 \times 10^{-10}.$$

$pH = - \log [H^+] = - \log (9.17 \times 10^{-10}) = -(0.962 - 10) = 9.038$.

■PROBLEM 660    What would be the pH of a buffer solution containing ammonia and ammonium ion at equal concentrations?

ANSWER: pH = 9.258

PROBLEM 661    Suppose you have 80.0 ml of a buffer solution consisting of 0.169 $M$ $NH_3$ and 0.183 $M$ $NH_4Cl$. If you add 10.0 ml of 0.100 $M$ HCl, what will be the pH change? $K_{diss} = 1.81 \times 10^{-5}$. Assume additive volumes.

SOLUTION: Initial solution has 0.169 $M$ $NH_3$ and 0.183 $M$ $NH_4^+$.

Let $x$ = moles/l $NH_3$ that react $NH_3 + H_2O \rightarrow NH_4^+ + OH^-$. This will give at equilibrium:

$[NH_3] = 0.169 - x$; $[NH_4^+] = 0.183 + x$; $[OH^-] = x$.

$NH_3 + H_2O \rightleftharpoons NH_4^+ + OH^-$.

$$K = \frac{[NH_4^+][OH^-]}{[NH_3]} = 1.81 \times 10^{-5} = \frac{(0.183 + x)(x)}{0.169 - x}.$$

$$x \cong \frac{0.169}{0.183} (1.81 \times 10^{-5}) = 1.67 \times 10^{-5} = [OH^-].$$

$$[H^+] = \frac{K_w}{[OH^-]} = \frac{1.00 \times 10^{-14}}{1.67 \times 10^{-5}} = 5.99 \times 10^{-10} \ M.$$

$$pH = - \log [H^+] = - \log (5.99 \times 10^{-10})$$
$$= -(0.777 - 10) = 9.223.$$

Now add the 10.0 ml of 0.100 $M$ HCl, which, being a strong electrolyte, gives $(0.0100 \text{ l}) \left( 0.100 \dfrac{\text{mole } H^+}{\text{liter}} \right) = 0.00100$ mole $H^+$. This $H^+$ will effectively be neutralized by the base $NH_3$. We assume the reaction $NH_3 + H^+ \rightarrow NH_4^+$ goes 100%. This converts the 0.00100 mole $H^+$ into 0.00100 mole $NH_4^+$ and uses up 0.00100 mole $NH_3$. The initial solution contained

$$(0.0800 \text{ l}) \left( 0.169 \dfrac{\text{mole } NH_3}{\text{liter}} \right) = 0.0135 \text{ mole } NH_3$$

and

$$(0.0800 \text{ l}) \left( 0.183 \dfrac{\text{mole } NH_4^+}{\text{liter}} \right) = 0.0146 \text{ mole } NH_4^+$$

These will now be decreased and increased, respectively, to give $0.0135 - 0.00100 = 0.0125$ mole $NH_3$ and $0.0146 + 0.00100 = 0.0156$ mole $NH_4^+$. The total volume of the solution has gone from 80.0 ml to $80.0 + 10.0 = 90.0$ ml, so the concentrations are

$$\frac{0.0125 \text{ mole } NH_3}{0.0900 \text{ l}} = 0.139 \ M \ NH_3$$

and

$$\frac{0.0156 \text{ mole } NH_4^+}{0.0900 \text{ l}} = 0.173 \ M \ NH_4^+$$

Let $y = \text{moles}/\text{l } NH_3$ that "dissociate" via the reaction $NH_3 + H_2O \rightarrow NH_4^+ + OH^-$ to give

$$[NH_3] = 0.139 - y; \quad [NH_4^+] = 0.173 + y; \quad [OH^-] = y.$$

$$NH_3 + H_2O \rightleftharpoons NH_4^+ + OH^-.$$

$$K = \frac{[NH_4^+][OH^-]}{[NH_3]} = 1.81 \times 10^{-5} = \frac{(0.173 + y)(y)}{0.139 - y}.$$

$$y \cong \frac{0.139}{0.173} (1.81 \times 10^{-5}) = 1.45 \times 10^{-5} \ M = [OH^-].$$

$$[H^+] = \frac{K_w}{[OH^-]} = \frac{1.00 \times 10^{-14}}{1.45 \times 10^{-5}} = 6.90 \times 10^{-10} \ M.$$

$$\text{pH} = -\log [\text{H}^+] = -\log (6.90 \times 10^{-10})$$
$$= -(0.839 - 10) = 9.161.$$

So, the pH goes **from 9.223 to 9.161.**

■ PROBLEM 662   What will be the pH change that occurs when 20.0 ml of 0.100 $M$ HCl is added to 80.0 ml of a buffer solution consisting of 0.169 $M$ NH$_3$ and 0.183 $M$ NH$_4$Cl? Assume additive volumes.   $K_{\text{diss}} = 1.81 \times 10^{-5}$ for NH$_3$ + H$_2$O $\rightleftharpoons$ NH$_4^+$ + OH$^-$.

ANSWER: pH goes **from 9.223 to 9.098**

PROBLEM 663   What will be the pH change that occurs when 20.0 ml of 0.100 $M$ NaOH is added to 80.0 ml of a buffer solution consisting of 0.169 $M$ NH$_3$ and 0.183 $M$ NH$_4$Cl? Assume additive volumes.   $K_{\text{diss}} = 1.81 \times 10^{-5}$ for NH$_3$ + H$_2$O $\rightleftharpoons$ NH$_4^+$ + OH$^-$.

SOLUTION: The pH of the initial buffer is 9.223, as calculated in Problem 661.   When 20.0 ml of 0.100 $M$ NaOH is added, the following happens: NaOH is a strong electrolyte and is taken to be 100% dissociated.   Thus, the 20.0 ml of 0.100 $M$ NaOH furnishes (0.0200 l) $\times \left( 0.100 \dfrac{\text{mole OH}^-}{\text{liter}} \right) = 0.00200$ mole OH$^-$.   This OH$^-$ will be largely sponged up by the NH$_4^+$ present.   We assume that 100% of the OH$^-$ is so used to convert some NH$_4^+$ into NH$_3$ via the reaction   NH$_4^+$ + OH$^-$ $\rightarrow$ NH$_3$ + H$_2$O.   The initial solution was 80.0 ml of 0.169 $M$ NH$_3$ and 0.183 $M$ NH$_4$Cl.   This would give

$$(0.0800 \text{ l}) \left( 0.169 \frac{\text{mole NH}_3}{\text{liter}} \right) = 0.0135 \text{ mole NH}_3$$

and

$$(0.0800 \text{ l}) \left( 0.183 \frac{\text{mole NH}_4^+}{\text{liter}} \right) = 0.0146 \text{ mole NH}_4^+$$

The reaction NH$_4^+$ + OH$^-$ $\rightarrow$ NH$_3$ + H$_2$O to consume the OH$^-$ reduces the moles of NH$_4^+$ from 0.0146 to 0.0146 $-$ 0.00200 = 0.0126 mole NH$_4^+$ and increases the moles of NH$_3$ from 0.0135 to 0.0135 + 0.00200 = 0.0155 mole NH$_3$.   The total volume of the solution is 80.0 ml + 20.0 ml = 0.100 l.   Therefore, the concentrations will be

$$\frac{0.0126 \text{ mole NH}_4^+}{0.100 \text{ l}} = 0.126 \text{ M NH}_4^+$$

$$\frac{0.0155 \text{ mole NH}_3}{0.100 \text{ l}} = 0.155 \text{ M NH}_3$$

Let $x$ = moles/l $NH_3$ that "dissociate" to form $NH_4^+$ and $OH^-$. This will give at equilibrium:

$[NH_3] = 0.155 - x$;  $[NH_4^+] = 0.126 + x$;  $[OH^-] = x$.

$NH_3 + H_2O \rightleftharpoons NH_4^+ + OH^-$.

$$K = \frac{[NH_4^+][OH^-]}{[NH_3]} = 1.81 \times 10^{-5} = \frac{(0.126 + x)(x)}{0.155 - x}.$$

$$x \cong \frac{0.155}{0.126}(1.81 \times 10^{-5}) = 2.23 \times 10^{-5} M = [OH^-].$$

$$[H^+] = \frac{K_w}{[OH^-]} = \frac{1.00 \times 10^{-14}}{2.23 \times 10^{-5}} = 4.48 \times 10^{-10} M.$$

$$pH = -\log[H^+] = -\log(4.48 \times 10^{-10})$$
$$= -(0.651 - 10) = 9.349.$$

So, the pH changes **from 9.223 to 9.349.**

■ PROBLEM 664  What pH change will occur when 20.0 ml of 0.100 $M$ NaOH is added to 230.0 ml of a buffer solution consisting of 0.169 $M$ $NH_3$ and 0.183 $M$ $NH_4Cl$? Assume volumes are additive.  $K_{diss} = 1.81 \times 10^{-5}$ for $NH_3 + H_2O \rightleftharpoons NH_4^+ + OH^-$.

ANSWER: pH changes **from 9.223 to 9.266**

■■ PROBLEM 665  You are given 0.250 l of 1.00 $M$ $NH_3$ and 0.250 l of 1.00 $M$ $NH_4Cl$. You are told to make up, working only with these two solutions, a buffer which has a pH of 9.200 and which will not change more than 0.010 pH unit when 10.0 ml of 0.100 $M$ NaOH or 10.0 ml of 0.100 $M$ HCl is added. What is the minimal recipe? Assume additive volumes.  $K_{diss} = 1.81 \times 10^{-5}$ for $NH_3 + H_2O \rightleftharpoons NH_4^+ + OH^-$.

ANSWER: **93.3 ml of 1.00 $M$ $NH_4Cl$ and 81.7 ml of 1.00 $M$ $NH_3$**

## The sulfate–hydrogen sulfate buffer

The buffer solution containing $SO_4^=$ and $HSO_4^-$ is an important one for several schemes of identifying cations by precipitation procedures. The buffer is a little out of ordinary because its effect is primarily in the fairly acid region around pH = 1.9. Calculations concerning it are somewhat more difficult than in the two preceding sections because the quadratic formula needs to be used here, whereas obvious approximations could be made in the HOAc-NaOAc and $NH_3$-$NH_4^+$ cases.

PROBLEM 666  Given a buffer solution made by dissolving 0.150 mole $NaHSO_4$ and 0.150 mole $Na_2SO_4$ in enough water to make 0.250 l solution. What is the pH of this buffer? $K_{diss} = 1.26 \times 10^{-2}$ for $HSO_4^- \rightleftharpoons H^+ + SO_4^=$.

SOLUTION: $NaHSO_4$ is a strong electrolyte; 0.150 mole $NaHSO_4$ gives 0.150 mole $Na^+$ and 0.150 mole $HSO_4^-$. $Na_2SO_4$ is also a strong electrolyte; 0.150 mole $Na_2SO_4$ gives 0.300 mole $Na^+$ and 0.150 mole $SO_4^=$. Not allowing for any dissociation of $HSO_4^-$, we would have in the solution

$$\frac{0.150 \text{ mole } HSO_4^-}{0.250 \text{ l}} = 0.600 \ M \ HSO_4^-$$

and

$$\frac{0.150 \text{ mole } SO_4^=}{0.250 \text{ l}} = 0.600 \ M \ SO_4^=$$

Now, let $x$ = moles/l $HSO_4^-$ that are dissociated. This will cut down the $HSO_4^-$ from 0.600 to $0.600 - x$ and will increase the $SO_4^=$ from 0.600 to $0.600 + x$, at the same time releasing $x$ moles/l $H^+$ into the solution. At equilibrium, we would have:

$[HSO_4^-] = 0.600 - x;$   $[SO_4^=] = 0.600 + x;$   $[H^+] = x.$

$HSO_4^- \rightleftharpoons H^+ + SO_4^=.$

$$K = \frac{[H^+][SO_4^=]}{[HSO_4^-]} = 1.26 \times 10^{-2} = \frac{(x)(0.600 + x)}{0.600 - x}$$

$x = 1.21 \times 10^{-2} = [H^+].$

$pH = -\log [H^+] = -\log (1.21 \times 10^{-2})$
$= -(0.083 - 2) = 1.917 .$

■ P R O B L E M  667   What will be the pH of a buffer solution made by mixing equal volumes of 0.150 $M$ $NaHSO_4$ and 0.150 $M$ $Na_2SO_4$?  $K_{diss} = 1.26 \times 10^{-2}$.

ANSWER: pH = 2.013

P R O B L E M  668   Given 0.120 l of a buffer solution consisting of 0.150 $M$ $NaHSO_4$ and 0.150 $M$ $Na_2SO_4$. What pH change will be produced on addition of 10.0 ml of 0.100 $M$ NaOH to this solution? Assume volumes are additive. $K_{diss} = 1.26 \times 10^{-2}$.

SOLUTION: In the initial solution, we have 0.150 $M$ $HSO_4^-$ and 0.150 $M$ $SO_4^=$. Let $x$ = moles/l $HSO_4^-$ that are dissociated. This gives at equilibrium:

$[HSO_4^-] = 0.150 - x$; $[SO_4^=] = 0.150 + x$; $[H^+] = x$.

$HSO_4^- \rightleftharpoons H^+ + SO_4^=$.

$$K = \frac{[H^+][SO_4^=]}{[HSO_4^-]} = 1.26 \times 10^{-2} = \frac{(x)(0.150 + x)}{0.150 - x}.$$

$x = 1.09 \times 10^{-2} = [H^+]$.

$$pH = -\log[H^+] = -\log(1.09 \times 10^{-2})$$
$$= -(0.037 - 2) = 1.963.$$

Now we add the 10.0 ml of 0.100 $M$ NaOH. Inasmuch as NaOH is a strong electrolyte and is 100% dissociated into $Na^+$ and $OH^-$, this will give us $(0.0100 \text{ l}) \left( 0.100 \dfrac{\text{mole } OH^-}{\text{liter}} \right) = 0.00100$ mole $OH^-$, which will convert $HSO_4^-$ to $SO_4^=$ by neutralization. As a first approximation, we assume 100% conversion via the reaction

$HSO_4^- + OH^- \rightarrow H_2O + SO_4^=$

From 0.00100 mole $OH^-$, we will get 0.00100 mole $SO_4^=$ and use up 0.00100 mole $HSO_4^-$.

The initial solution is 0.120 l of 0.150 $M$ $NaHSO_4$ and 0.150 $M$ $Na_2SO_4$. Therefore, we have initially

$(0.120 \text{ l}) \left( 0.150 \dfrac{\text{mole } HSO_4^-}{\text{liter}} \right) = 0.0180$ mole $HSO_4^-$

and

$(0.120 \text{ l}) \left( 0.150 \dfrac{\text{mole } SO_4^=}{\text{liter}} \right) = 0.0180$ mole $SO_4^=$

By adding 0.00100 mole $OH^-$, we raise $SO_4^=$ from 0.0180 to 0.0180 + 0.0010 = 0.0190 mole and decrease $HSO_4^-$ from 0.0180 to 0.0180 − 0.0010 = 0.0170 mole. The total volume of solution is 0.120 l + 0.010 l = 0.130 l. Concentrations are

$$\frac{0.0190 \text{ mole } SO_4^=}{0.130 \text{ l}} = 0.146 \ M \ SO_4^=$$

$$\frac{0.0170 \text{ mole } HSO_4^-}{0.130 \text{ l}} = 0.131 \ M \ HSO_4^-$$

Let $y$ = moles/l $HSO_4^-$ that are dissociated.
$[HSO_4^-] = 0.131 - y$; $[SO_4^=] = 0.146 + y$; $[H^+] = y$.
$HSO_4^- \rightleftharpoons H^+ + SO_4^=$.
$$K = \frac{[H^+][SO_4^=]}{[HSO_4^-]} = 1.26 \times 10^{-2} = \frac{(y)(0.146 + y)}{0.131 - y}.$$
$y = 9.80 \times 10^{-3} = [H^+]$.
pH = $- \log [H^+] = - \log (9.80 \times 10^{-3}) = -(0.991 - 3) = 2.009$.
So, pH changes **from 1.963 to 2.009.**

■ PROBLEM 669   Given 0.120 l of a buffer solution consisting of 0.150 $M$ $NaHSO_4$ and 0.150 $M$ $Na_2SO_4$. What pH change will be produced on addition of 10.0 ml of 0.100 $M$ HCl to this solution? Assume volumes are additive. $K_{diss} = 1.26 \times 10^{-2}$.

ANSWER: pH changes **from 1.963 to 1.927**

■■ PROBLEM 670   Given 0.120 l of a buffer solution consisting of 0.150 $M$ $NaHSO_4$ and 0.150 $M$ $Na_2SO_4$. What pH change will be produced on addition of 10.0 ml of 0.100 $M$ $H_2SO_4$ to this solution? Assume volumes are additive. $K_{diss} = 1.26 \times 10^{-2}$.

ANSWER: pH changes **from 1.963 to 1.906**

# 16

## ACID-BASE
## TITRATION CURVES

TITRATION is a process whereby a solution of one reagent—say, an acid—is gradually added to a solution of another reagent—say, a base. In acid-base titration, the extent of reaction can be monitored by following the pH as a function of the volume of added reagent. In oxidation-reduction titration, the reaction can be followed by noting the intensity of color of one of the reagents; alternatively, in what is called potentiometric titration, one might measure the voltage of an appropriate electrode reaction in which one of the ions is involved. In this chapter we shall confine ourselves to acid-base titration and look specifically at pH vs. ml of added base.

The general course of a pH vs. added base curve looks like that shown in Figure 64. There is first a slow rise, followed by a steep rise, followed again by a slow rise. This is a logarithmic representation of the hydrogen-ion concentration (since pH is $- \log [H^+]$) and is indispensable because the $[H^+]$ frequently decreases by a factor of $10^{12}$. A logarithmic plot is the only way to get all the hydrogen-ion information on the same graph.

This chapter takes up the computation of some typical pH curves: (1) strong acid plus strong base, (2) weak acid plus strong base, (3) strong acid plus weak base, (4) weak acid plus weak base, and (5) poly-

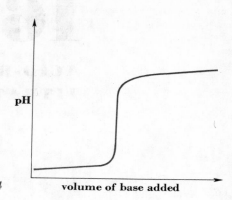

*Figure 64*    **volume of base added**

protic acids plus strong base.   The emphasis will be on the reasoning behind the calculation rather than the development of algebraic equations to substitute into.

### Strong acid plus strong base

What happens to the pH when a solution of a strong base (e.g., NaOH) is added stepwise to a solution of a strong acid (e.g., HCl)?   This problem is the simplest of the titration-curve problems since both NaOH and HCl are strong electrolytes, taken to be 100% dissociated, and, therefore, we are effectively adding a solution of $OH^-$ to a solution of $H^+$.   The result, obviously, will be neutralization via $OH^- + H^+ \rightarrow H_2O$.

To simplify the problem, we first consider a "constant-volume" system, where we add *solid* NaOH stepwise to a solution of HCl, assuming there is no increase in the volume.   In reality, when NaOH *solution* is added to a solution of HCl, there is an increase in the volume of the system, which produces a dilution effect that needs to be allowed for.

PROBLEM 671   Given 25.0 ml of 0.100 $M$ HCl.   What is its pH?

SOLUTION: HCl is a strong electrolyte, so is 100% dissociated to $H^+$ and $Cl^-$.   This means 0.100 $M$ HCl is 0.100 $M$ $H^+$ and 0.100 $M$ $Cl^-$.

$$pH = -\log[H^+] = -\log(0.100) = -\log(1.00 \times 10^{-1})$$
$$= -(0.000 - 1) = \mathbf{1.000}.$$

PROBLEM 672   Given 25.0 ml of 0.100 $M$ HCl.  To this solution you add $5.0 \times 10^{-4}$ mole NaOH.  Assuming no change in volume, calculate the pH of the resulting solution.

SOLUTION: (Figure out how much $H^+$ you have initially, then how much $OH^-$ you are adding.  Let react.  Calculate $H^+$ left.)

25.0 ml of 0.100 $M$ HCl provides $(0.0250 \text{ l})\left(0.100\ \dfrac{\text{mole } H^+}{\text{liter}}\right) = 0.00250$ mole $H^+$.  The added $5.0 \times 10^{-4}$ mole NaOH provides $5.0 \times 10^{-4}$ mole $OH^-$.  $H^+$ and $OH^-$ react via $H^+ + OH^- \to H_2O$.  We have 0.00250 mole $H^+$ and 0.00050 mole $OH^-$.  The $H^+$ is in excess and the reaction is limited by the $OH^-$.  0.00050 mole $OH^-$ will use up 0.00050 mole $H^+$.  This leaves $0.00250 - 0.00050 = 0.00200$ mole $H^+$.  The volume of the solution is 0.0250 l.  So, the final concentration of $H^+$ is $\dfrac{0.00200 \text{ mole } H^+}{0.0250 \text{ l}} = 0.0800\ M\ H^+$.

$$pH = -\log[H^+] = -\log(8.00 \times 10^{-2})$$
$$= -(0.903 - 2) = \mathbf{1.097}.$$

■ PROBLEM 673   Given 25.0 ml of 0.100 $M$ HCl.  To this solution you add two $5.0 \times 10^{-4}$ mole portions of NaOH.  Assuming no change in volume, calculate the pH of the resulting solution.

ANSWER: pH = **1.222**

■ PROBLEM 674   What would happen to the pH after a third and then a fourth $5.0 \times 10^{-4}$ mole portion of NaOH were added to the solution resulting from Problem 673?  Assume no volume change.

ANSWER: after third portion, pH = **1.398**; after fourth portion, pH = **1.70**

PROBLEM 675   Given 25.0 ml of 0.100 $M$ HCl.  What would be the pH of the resulting solution after five $5.0 \times 10^{-4}$ mole portions of NaOH have been added to this solution?  Assume no volume change.

SOLUTION: Five $5.0 \times 10^{-4}$ mole portions of NaOH would be $25.0 \times 10^{-4}$ mole of NaOH. The initial solution has

$$(0.0250 \text{ l}) \left( 0.100 \frac{\text{mole HCl}}{\text{liter}} \right) = 0.00250 \text{ mole HCl}.$$

At this stage in the titration, we have mixed equal moles of NaOH $(25.0 \times 10^{-4})$ and of HCl $(25.0 \times 10^{-4})$. These are equivalent amounts, in the stoichiometric sense, and the point is called the "equivalence point." Neither NaOH nor HCl is in excess and the neutralization of $H^+ + OH^- \rightarrow H_2O$ is complete. The solution has only $Na^+$ and $Cl^-$ in it and its pH is the same as that in pure water—namely, **7.000**.

This same result will be found whenever equimolar quantities of strong acid and strong base have been mixed. Note, also, that, whereas the preceding additions of $5.0 \times 10^{-4}$ mole NaOH portions have produced relatively modest changes in pH (Problems 671 to 674), this last portion boosts the pH from 1.70 to 7.000.

P R O B L E M   676   Suppose we add a sixth portion of $5.0 \times 10^{-4}$ mole of NaOH to the solution resulting from Problem 675. Still assuming no volume change, what happens to the pH?

SOLUTION: By this time the solution of HCl has been neutralized, so there is no $H^+$ left to worry about. In fact, we can consider the problem of further addition of NaOH as simply the addition of NaOH to water. If we add $5.0 \times 10^{-4}$ mole NaOH to 25.0 ml of a neutralized solution, we will get $5.0 \times 10^{-4}$ mole $OH^-$ spread out over the 0.0250 l. The concentration of $OH^-$ will be

$$\frac{5.0 \times 10^{-4} \text{ mole } OH^-}{0.0250 \text{ l}} = 2.0 \times 10^{-2} \, M \, OH^-$$

$$[H^+] = \frac{K_w}{[OH^-]} = \frac{1.00 \times 10^{-14}}{2.0 \times 10^{-2}} = 5.0 \times 10^{-13} \, M.$$

$$pH = -\log [H^+] = -\log (5.0 \times 10^{-13}) = -(0.70 - 13) = \mathbf{12.30}.$$

■ P R O B L E M   677   Suppose you add a seventh, eighth, ninth, and tenth portion of $5.0 \times 10^{-4}$ mole NaOH successively to the solution resulting from Problem 676. Assuming constant volume, what does the pH respectively become?

ANSWER:  **12.60; 12.78; 12.90; 13.00**

[*Note:* If you plot the pH results obtained in Problems
671 to 677 against the amount of added NaOH, you get
the solid graph shown in Figure 65.]

As indicated above, the actual performance of a titration experiment usually involves the addition of one *solution* to another *solution*.
The natural result will be an increase in the volume of the system, an
effect that was removed in the above computations.   What do we have
to do to take the volume expansion into account?   Actually, the procedure is most simple.   When converting excess moles of $H^+$ left un-
neutralized or excess moles of $OH^-$ added, simply divide by the ob-

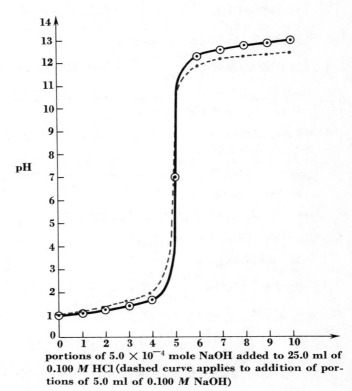

portions of $5.0 \times 10^{-4}$ mole NaOH added to 25.0 ml of
0.100 *M* HCl (dashed curve applies to addition of portions of 5.0 ml of 0.100 *M* NaOH)

*Figure 65*

served total volume of the solution as it gradually increases throughout the experiment.

PROBLEM 678    Given 25.0 ml of 0.100 $M$ HCl.  Suppose you add to it gradually 50.0 ml of 0.100 $M$ NaOH. Calculate the pH after each successive addition of 5.0 ml of the base. Assume volumes of solution are additive.

SOLUTION:

(a) The *initial solution* is 0.100 $M$ HCl, which gives $[H^+] = 0.100$ $M$.

$$pH = - \log [H^+] = - \log (0.100) = - \log (1.00 \times 10^{-1})$$
$$= -(0.000 - 1) = 1.000$$

(b) *after adding 5.0 ml of 0.100 M NaOH:*

Initial solution gives

$$(0.0250 \ l) \left( 0.100 \ \frac{mole \ H^+}{liter} \right) = 0.00250 \ mole \ H^+.$$

Added 5.0 ml of 0.100 $M$ NaOH gives

$$(0.0050 \ l) \left( 0.100 \ \frac{mole \ OH^-}{liter} \right) = 0.00050 \ mole \ OH^-.$$

0.00250 mole $H^+$ + 0.00050 mole $OH^-$ react via $H^+ + OH^- \rightarrow$ $H_2O$ to leave 0.00200 mole $H^+$.

Volume of final solution is the sum of initial 25.0 ml plus added 5.0 ml = 0.0300 l.

$$\text{Concentration of hydrogen ion} = \frac{0.00200 \ mole \ H^+}{0.0300 \ l}$$
$$= 0.0667 \ M \ H^+.$$

$$pH = - \log (6.67 \times 10^{-2}) = -(0.824 - 2) = 1.176.$$

(c) *after adding 10.0 ml of 0.100 M NaOH:*

Initial solution gives

$$(0.0250 \ l) \left( 0.100 \ \frac{mole \ H^+}{liter} \right) = 0.00250 \ mole \ H^+.$$

10.0 ml of 0.100 $M$ NaOH gives

$$(0.100 \ l) \left( 0.100 \ \frac{mole \ OH^-}{liter} \right) = 0.00100 \ mole \ OH^-.$$

0.00250 mole $H^+$ + 0.00100 mole $OH^- \rightarrow$ 0.00150 mole $H^+$ in excess.

Total volume of solution = 25.0 ml + 10.0 ml = 0.0350 l.

$$[H^+] = \frac{0.00150 \text{ mole } H^+}{0.0350 \text{ l}} = 0.0429 \ M \ H^+.$$

$$pH = - \log (4.29 \times 10^{-2}) = -(0.632 - 2) = 1.368$$

(d) *after adding 15.0 ml of 0.100 M NaOH:*

Initial solution gives

$$(0.0250 \text{ l}) \left( 0.100 \frac{\text{mole } H^+}{\text{liter}} \right) = 0.00250 \text{ mole } H^+.$$

15.0 ml of 0.100 $M$ NaOH gives

$$(0.0150 \text{ l}) \left( 0.100 \frac{\text{mole } OH^-}{\text{liter}} \right) = 0.00150 \text{ mole } OH^-.$$

0.00250 mole $H^+$ + 0.00150 mole $OH^- \rightarrow$ 0.00100 mole $H^+$ in excess.

Total volume of solution = 25.0 ml + 15.0 ml = 0.0400 l.

$$[H^+] = \frac{0.00100 \text{ mole } H^+}{0.0400 \text{ l}} = 0.0250 \ M \ H^+.$$

$$pH = - \log (2.50 \times 10^{-2}) = -(0.398 - 2) = 1.602.$$

(e) *after adding 20.0 ml of 0.100 M NaOH:*

Initial solution gives

$$(0.0250 \text{ l}) \left( 0.100 \frac{\text{mole } H^+}{\text{liter}} \right) = 0.00250 \text{ mole } H^+.$$

20.0 ml of 0.100 $M$ NaOH gives

$$(0.0200 \text{ l}) \left( 0.100 \frac{\text{mole } OH^-}{\text{liter}} \right) = 0.00200 \text{ mole } OH^-.$$

0.00250 mole $H^+$ + 0.00200 mole $OH^- \rightarrow$ 0.00050 mole $H^+$ in excess.

Total volume of solution = 25.0 ml + 20.0 ml = 0.0450 l.

$$[H^+] = \frac{0.00050 \text{ mole } H^+}{0.0450 \text{ l}} = 0.011 \ M \ H^+.$$

$$pH = - \log [H^+] = - \log (1.1 \times 10^{-2}) = -(0.04 - 2) = 1.96.$$

(f) *after adding 25.0 ml of 0.100 M NaOH:*

Initial solution gives

$$(0.0250 \text{ l}) \left(0.100 \, \frac{\text{mole H}^+}{\text{liter}}\right) = 0.00250 \text{ mole H}^+.$$

25.0 ml of 0.100 *M* NaOH gives

$$(0.0250 \text{ l}) \left(0.100 \, \frac{\text{mole OH}^-}{\text{liter}}\right) = 0.00250 \text{ mole OH}^-.$$

0.00250 mole H$^+$ + 0.00250 mole OH$^-$ → water only.

Solution is "neutralized"; its pH = **7.000.**

(g) *after adding 30.0 ml of 0.100 M NaOH:*

Initial solution gives

$$(0.0250 \text{ l}) \left(0.100 \, \frac{\text{mole H}^+}{\text{liter}}\right) = 0.00250 \text{ mole H}^+.$$

30.0 ml of 0.100 *M* NaOH gives

$$(0.0300 \text{ l}) \left(0.100 \, \frac{\text{mole OH}^-}{\text{liter}}\right) = 0.00300 \text{ mole OH}^-.$$

0.00250 mole H$^+$ + 0.00300 mole OH$^-$ → 0.00050 mole OH$^-$ in excess.

Total volume of solution = 25.0 ml + 30.0 ml = 55.0 ml.

$$\text{Concentration of OH}^- = \frac{0.00050 \text{ mole OH}^-}{0.0550 \text{ l}} = 0.0091 \, M.$$

$$\text{Concentration of H}^+ = \frac{K_w}{[\text{OH}^-]} = \frac{1.00 \times 10^{-14}}{9.1 \times 10^{-3}} = 1.1 \times 10^{-12}.$$

$$\begin{aligned} \text{pH} &= -\log{[\text{H}^+]} = -\log{(1.1 \times 10^{-12})} \\ &= -(0.04 - 12) = \mathbf{11.96.} \end{aligned}$$

(h) *after adding 35.0 ml of 0.100 M NaOH:*

25.0 ml of 0.100 *M* HCl gives

$$(0.0250 \text{ l}) \left(0.100 \, \frac{\text{mole H}^+}{\text{liter}}\right) = 0.00250 \text{ mole H}^+.$$

35.0 ml of 0.100 $M$ NaOH gives

$$(0.0350 \text{ l}) \left( 0.100 \, \frac{\text{mole OH}^-}{\text{liter}} \right) = 0.00350 \text{ mole OH}^-.$$

0.00250 mole $H^+$ + 0.00350 mole $OH^-$ → 0.00100 mole $OH^-$ in excess.

Total volume of solution = 25.0 ml + 35.0 ml = 0.0600 l.

$$\text{Concentration of OH}^- = \frac{0.00100 \text{ mole OH}^-}{0.0600 \text{ l}} = 0.0167 \, M \text{ OH}^-.$$

$$\text{Concentration of H}^+ = \frac{K_w}{[\text{OH}^-]} = \frac{1.00 \times 10^{-14}}{1.67 \times 10^{-2}}$$
$$= 5.99 \times 10^{-13} \, M \text{ H}^+.$$

$$\text{pH} = -\log [\text{H}^+] = -\log (5.99 \times 10^{-13})$$
$$= -(0.777 - 13) = \mathbf{12.223}.$$

($i$) *after adding 40.0 ml of 0.100 M NaOH:*

25.0 ml of 0.100 $M$ HCl gives

$$(0.0250 \text{ l}) \left( 0.100 \, \frac{\text{mole H}^+}{\text{liter}} \right) = 0.00250 \text{ mole H}^+.$$

40.0 ml of 0.100 $M$ NaOH gives

$$(0.0400 \text{ l}) \left( 0.100 \, \frac{\text{mole OH}^-}{\text{liter}} \right) = 0.00400 \text{ mole OH}^-.$$

0.00250 mole $H^+$ + 0.00400 mole $OH^-$ → 0.0015 mole $OH^-$ in excess.

Total volume of solution = 25.0 + 40.0 ml = 0.0650 l.

$$\text{Concentration of OH}^- = \frac{0.00150 \text{ mole OH}^-}{0.0650 \text{ l}} = 0.0231 \, M \text{ OH}^-.$$

$$\text{Concentration of H}^+ = \frac{K_w}{[\text{OH}^-]} = \frac{1.00 \times 10^{-14}}{2.31 \times 10^{-2}}$$
$$= 4.33 \times 10^{-13} \, M \text{ H}^+.$$

$$\text{pH} = -\log [\text{H}^+] = -\log (4.33 \times 10^{-13})$$
$$= -(0.636 - 13) = \mathbf{12.364}.$$

(*j*) *after adding 45.0 ml of 0.100 M NaOH:*

25.0 ml of 0.100 $M$ HCl gives

$$(0.0250 \text{ l}) \left( 0.100 \frac{\text{mole H}^+}{\text{liter}} \right) = 0.00250 \text{ mole H}^+.$$

45.0 ml of 0.100 $M$ NaOH gives

$$(0.0450 \text{ l}) \left( 0.100 \frac{\text{mole OH}^-}{\text{liter}} \right) = 0.00450 \text{ mole OH}^-.$$

0.00250 mole H$^+$ + 0.00450 mole OH$^-$ → 0.00200 mole OH$^-$ in excess.

Total volume of solution = 25.0 ml + 45.0 ml = 0.0700 l.

$$\text{Concentration of OH}^- = \frac{0.00200 \text{ mole OH}^-}{0.0700 \text{ l}} = 0.0286 \ M.$$

$$\text{Concentration of H}^+ = \frac{K_w}{[\text{OH}^-]} = \frac{1.00 \times 10^{-14}}{2.86 \times 10^{-2}}$$
$$= 3.50 \times 10^{-13} \ M \ \text{H}^+.$$

$$\text{pH} = -\log [\text{H}^+] = -\log (3.50 \times 10^{-13})$$
$$= -(0.544 - 13) = 12.456 \ .$$

(*k*) *after adding 50.0 ml of 0.100 M NaOH:*

25.0 ml of 0.100 $M$ HCl gives

$$(0.0250 \text{ l}) \left( 0.100 \frac{\text{mole H}^+}{\text{liter}} \right) = 0.00250 \text{ mole H}^+.$$

50.0 ml of 0.100 $M$ NaOH gives

$$(0.0500 \text{ l}) \left( 0.100 \frac{\text{mole OH}^-}{\text{liter}} \right) = 0.00500 \text{ mole OH}^-.$$

0.00250 mole H$^+$ + 0.00500 mole OH$^-$ → 0.00250 mole OH$^-$ in excess.

Total volume of solution = 25.0 ml + 50.0 ml = 0.0750 l.

$$\text{Concentration of OH}^- = \frac{0.00250 \text{ mole OH}^-}{0.0750 \text{ l}} = 0.0333 \ M \ \text{OH}^-.$$

$$\text{Concentration of H}^+ = \frac{K_w}{[\text{OH}^-]} = \frac{1.00 \times 10^{-14}}{3.33 \times 10^{-2}} = 3.00 \times 10^{-13}.$$

$$pH = -\log[H^+] = -\log(3.00 \times 10^{-13})$$
$$= -(0.477 - 13) = 12.523.$$

So, in summary, when 5.0-ml increments of 0.100 $M$ NaOH are added to 25.0 ml of 0.100 $M$ HCl, the pH changes successively in the following sequence: 1.000, 1.176, 1.368, 1.602, 1.96, 7.000, 11.96, 12.223, 12.364, 12.456, 12.523. The dashed curve in Figure 65 shows this in graphical representation, where it is compared to the constant volume case.

■ PROBLEM 679    Given 25.0 ml of 0.200 $M$ NaOH. Suppose you add to it gradually 50.0 ml of 0.200 $M$ HCl. Calculate the pH of the initial solution and after each successive addition of 5.00 ml of the acid. Assume additive volumes.

ANSWER: 13.301; 13.125; 12.933; 12.699; 12.347; 7.000; 1.740; 1.477; 1.336; 1.243; 1.176

■ PROBLEM 680    Calculate the pH at 10.0-ml intervals as 50.0 ml of 0.150 $M$ KOH is added gradually to 20.0 ml of 0.250 $M$ HNO$_3$. Assume volumes are additive.

ANSWER: 0.602; 0.933; 1.301; 2.00; 12.222; 12.553

## Weak acid plus strong base

The pH change that characterizes neutralization of a weak acid such as acetic acid, HOAc, by a strong base such as NaOH is considerably more complicated than that just considered for strong acid plus strong base. Two obvious points of difference and sources of complication are: (1) HOAc is only slightly dissociated whereas HCl is totally broken up into ions; (2) the product at the equivalence point, NaOAc, is not a "neutral" salt as is NaCl. The question of salt hydrolysis, which is involved in point (2), is taken up in detail in Chapter 18, but we shall have to make use of some of the results in this section.

The following sequence of problems illustrates how the pH changes in a typical titration of a weak acid with a strong base. You will find it instructive to make a problem-to-problem comparison with the sequence of problems worked out in the preceding section.

## PROBLEM 681

Given 25.0 ml of 0.100 $M$ HOAc. What will be the pH of this solution, taking $K_{diss}$ to be $1.8 \times 10^{-5}$?

SOLUTION: Let $x$ = moles/l HOAc that dissociate.
$[HOAc] = 0.100 - x$; $[OAc^-] = x$; $[H^+] = x$.
$HOAc \rightleftharpoons H^+ + OAc^-$.
$$K_{diss} = \frac{[H^+][OAc^-]}{[HOAc]} = 1.8 \times 10^{-5} = \frac{(x)(x)}{0.100 - x} \ .$$
$x = 1.3 \times 10^{-3} = [H^+]$.
$pH = -\log [H^+] = -\log (1.3 \times 10^{-3}) = -(0.11 - 3) = 2.89$.

## PROBLEM 682

Given 25.0 ml of 0.100 $M$ HOAc. To this solution you add $5.0 \times 10^{-4}$ mole solid NaOH. Assuming no change in volume has occurred, calculate the pH of the resulting solution. $K_{diss} = 1.8 \times 10^{-5}$.

SOLUTION: The NaOH is a strong electrolyte and is taken to be 100% dissociated.

The HOAc is a weak electrolyte and, on first approximation, is taken to be nondissociated.

$5.0 \times 10^{-4}$ mole NaOH gives $5.0 \times 10^{-4}$ mole $OH^-$.

25.0 ml of 0.100 $M$ HOAc gives

$$(0.0250 \text{ l}) \left( 0.100 \ \frac{\text{mole HOAc}}{\text{liter}} \right) = 0.00250 \text{ mole HOAc}.$$

This acid and base react according to the net equation

$$HOAc + OH^- \rightarrow H_2O + OAc^-.$$

From $5.0 \times 10^{-4}$ mole $OH^-$ plus $25.0 \times 10^{-4}$ mole HOAc we would get enough reaction to use up $5.0 \times 10^{-4}$ mole HOAc, leaving $20.0 \times 10^{-4}$ mole HOAc and forming $5.0 \times 10^{-4}$ mole $OAc^-$.

The volume of the solution is 25.0 ml.

$$\text{Concentration of HOAc} = \frac{20.0 \times 10^{-4} \text{ mole HOAc}}{0.0250 \text{ l}}$$
$$= 0.0800 \ M \text{ HOAc}.$$

$$\text{Concentration of OAc}^- = \frac{5.0 \times 10^{-4} \text{ mole OAc}^-}{0.0250 \text{ l}}$$
$$= 0.020 \ M \text{ OAc}^-.$$

However, these were calculated on the assumption no HOAc was dissociated. We now take care of this by letting $x$ = moles/l HOAc that dissociate.  This will give

$[HOAc] = 0.0800 - x$;   $[OAc^-] = 0.020 + x$;   $[H^+] = x$.

$HOAc \rightleftharpoons H^+ + OAc^-$.

$$K_{diss} = \frac{[H^+][OAc^-]}{[HOAc]} = 1.8 \times 10^{-5} = \frac{(x)(0.020 + x)}{0.0800 - x}$$

$$x \cong \frac{0.0800}{0.020}(1.8 \times 10^{-5}) = 7.2 \times 10^{-5} = [H^+].$$

$pH = -\log[H^+] = -\log(7.2 \times 10^{-5}) = -(0.86 - 5) = \mathbf{4.14}$.

### ■ PROBLEM 683

Given 25.0 ml of 0.100 $M$ HOAc.  To this solution you add two $5.0 \times 10^{-4}$ mole portions of NaOH.  Assuming no volume change and taking $K_{diss} = 1.8 \times 10^{-5}$, calculate the pH of the resulting solution.
ANSWER: **4.57**

### ■ PROBLEM 684

What would happen to the pH after a third and then a fourth $5.0 \times 10^{-4}$ mole portion of NaOH were added to the solution resulting from Problem 683?  Assume no volume change.
ANSWER: after third portion pH = **4.92**; after fourth portion pH = **5.35**

### PROBLEM 685

Given 25.0 ml of 0.100 $M$ HOAc.  What would be the pH of the resulting solution after five $5.0 \times 10^{-4}$ mole portions of NaOH have been added to the solution?  Assume no volume change.

SOLUTION: Five $5.0 \times 10^{-4}$ mole portions of NaOH would be $25.0 \times 10^{-4}$ mole NaOH.  This has been added to

$$(0.0250 \text{ l}) \left( 0.100 \frac{\text{mole HOAc}}{\text{liter}} \right) = 25.0 \times 10^{-4} \text{ mole HOAc}.$$

It is evident that by this stage of the titration we have mixed stoichiometrically equivalent amounts of NaOH and HOAc.  Since the same equilibrium

$$OH^- + HOAc \rightleftharpoons H_2O + OAc^-$$

can be approached from either side, we should have the same system as if we had simply placed $25.0 \times 10^{-4}$ mole NaOAc in

0.0250 l solution.   The only catch is that such a solution of NaOAc is not "neutral" in the same sense that a solution of NaCl would be—i.e., pH ≠ 7.   Because of hydrolysis, solutions of NaOAc are slightly basic.   Detailed computations for hydrolysis are given in Chapter 18, but we can easily arrive at a suitable answer for this particular case.   We treat the equivalence-point solution as if it were $\dfrac{25.0 \times 10^{-4} \text{ mole NaOAc}}{0.0250 \text{ l}} = 0.100\ M$ NaOAc.

What is the pH of such a solution? The NaOAc, being a sodium salt, is a strong electrolyte and is 100% dissociated, so we have 0.100 $M$ $Na^+$ and 0.100 $M$ $OAc^-$.   But $OAc^-$ has a tendency to pick up $H^+$ to form HOAc.   Suppose we let $x$ = moles/l $OAc^-$ that succeed in picking off an $H^+$ from the $H_2O \rightleftharpoons H^+ + OH^-$. This will mean that $x$ moles/l HOAc will be formed and also $x$ moles/l $OH^-$ will be set free in the solution.   At equilibrium, then, we would have

$$[OAc^-] = 0.100 - x; \quad [HOAc] = x; \quad [OH^-] = x$$

We know also that for any aqueous solution $K_w = [H^+][OH^-] = 1.00 \times 10^{-14}$, so if $[OH^-] = x$, then

$$[H^+] = \frac{K_w}{[OH^-]} = \frac{1.00 \times 10^{-14}}{x}.$$

We thus have

$$[OAc^-] = 0.100 - x; \quad [HOAc] = x; \quad [H^+] = \frac{1.00 \times 10^{-14}}{x}.$$

With these concentrations we must satisfy the equilibrium

$$HOAc \rightleftharpoons H^+ + OAc^-$$

for which

$$K_{diss} = \frac{[H^+][OAc^-]}{[HOAc]} = \frac{\left(\dfrac{1.00 \times 10^{-14}}{x}\right)(0.100 - x)}{x}$$

$$= 1.8 \times 10^{-5}$$

Neglecting the $x$ where it is subtracted from 0.100, we get the equation

$$\frac{(1.00 \times 10^{-14})(0.100)}{x^2} \cong 1.8 \times 10^{-5}$$

which solves to $x = 7.4 \times 10^{-6}$. This gives us the $OH^-$ concentration, but we want the $H^+$.

$$[H^+] = \frac{K_w}{[OH^-]} = \frac{1.00 \times 10^{-14}}{x} = \frac{1.00 \times 10^{-14}}{7.4 \times 10^{-6}} = 1.4 \times 10^{-9} \ M.$$

$pH = -\log [H^+] = -\log (1.4 \times 10^{-9}) = -(0.15 - 9) = 8.85.$

So, in summary, $0.100 \ M$ NaOAc is not neutral, but has a $pH = 8.85$, which is definitely on the basic side.

## PROBLEM 686

Suppose we add a sixth portion of $5.0 \times 10^{-4}$ mole NaOH to the solution resulting from Problem 685. Still assuming no volume change, what happens to the pH?

SOLUTION: We are adding $5.0 \times 10^{-4}$ mole NaOH to 25.0 ml of $0.100$ $M$ NaOAc. The solution, as calculated above, is essentially all $Na^+$ and $OAc^-$, with the merest trace of HOAc and $OH^-$ due to hydrolysis. There is so little $OH^-$ present compared to what we are adding that we can forget about it and simply regard this problem as the addition of $5.0 \times 10^{-4}$ mole $OH^-$ to a volume of $0.0250$ l.

$$[OH^-] = \frac{5.0 \times 10^{-4} \text{ mole } OH^-}{0.0250 \text{ l}} = 2.0 \times 10^{-2} \ M.$$

$$[H^+] = \frac{K_w}{[OH^-]} = \frac{1.00 \times 10^{-14}}{2.0 \times 10^{-2}} = 5.0 \times 10^{-13}.$$

$pH = -\log [H^+] = -\log (5.0 \times 10^{-13}) = -(0.70 - 13) = 12.30.$

## ■PROBLEM 687 Suppose you add a

seventh, eighth, ninth, and tenth portion of $5.0 \times 10^{-4}$ mole NaOH successively to the solution resulting from Problem 686. Assuming constant volume, what are the respective values of the pH?

ANSWER: 12.60; 12.78; 12.90; 13.00

[*Note:* Figure 66 summarizes the calculations of Problems 681 to 687 and compares the results with those found for adding NaOH to HCl.]

## PROBLEM 688 Given 25.0 ml of 0.100

$M$ HOAc ($K_{diss} = 1.8 \times 10^{-5}$). Suppose you add to it gradually 50.0 ml of $0.100 \ M$ NaOH. Calculate the pH after each successive addition of 5.0 ml of the base. Assume volumes of solution are additive.

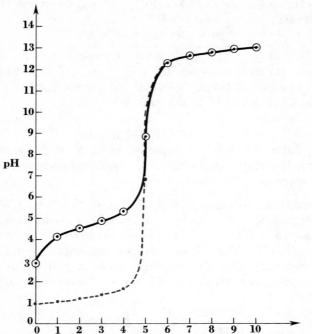

portions of $5.0 \times 10^{-4}$ mole solid NaOH added to 25.0 ml of 0.100 $M$ HOAc (dashed curve shows what happens when NaOH is added to 25.0 ml of 0.100 $M$ HCl)

*Figure 66*

SOLUTION:

(a) *initial solution 25.0 ml of 0.100 M HOAc:*

[HOAc] = 0.100 − $x$; [H$^+$] = $x$; [OAc$^-$] = $x$.

HOAc $\rightleftharpoons$ H$^+$ + OAc$^-$.

$$K_{\text{diss}} = \frac{[\text{H}^+][\text{OAc}^-]}{[\text{HOAc}]} = 1.8 \times 10^{-5} = \frac{(x)(x)}{0.100 - x}.$$

$x = 1.3 \times 10^{-3} = [\text{H}^+]$.

pH = $- \log [\text{H}^+] = - \log (1.3 \times 10^{-3}) = -(0.11 - 3) = \mathbf{2.89}$.

(b) *after adding 5.0 ml of 0.100 M NaOH:*

25.0 ml of 0.100 $M$ HOAc gives

$$(0.0250 \text{ l}) \left( 0.100 \frac{\text{mole HOAc}}{\text{liter}} \right) = 0.00250 \text{ mole HOAc.}$$

5.0 ml of 0.100 $M$ NaOH gives

$$(0.0050 \text{ l}) \left( 0.100 \frac{\text{mole OH}^-}{\text{liter}} \right) = 0.00050 \text{ mole OH}^-.$$

0.00250 mole HOAc + 0.00050 mole $OH^-$ react to give 0.00200 mole HOAc + 0.00050 mole $OAc^-$ by the reaction HOAc + $OH^- \rightarrow H_2O + OAc^-$.

Total volume of solution = 25.0 ml + 5.0 ml = 0.0300 l.

First we calculate without allowing for any dissociation of the HOAc.

$$\text{Concentration of HOAc} = \frac{0.00200 \text{ mole HOAc}}{0.0300 \text{ l}}$$
$$= 0.0667 \ M \text{ HOAc.}$$

$$\text{Concentration of OAc}^- = \frac{0.00050 \text{ mole OAc}^-}{0.0300 \text{ l}} = 0.017 \ M \text{ OAc}^-.$$

Then, let $x$ moles/l of this HOAc be dissociated.

$[\text{HOAc}] = 0.0667 - x$;   $[\text{H}^+] = x$;   $[\text{OAc}^-] = 0.017 + x$.

$$K_{\text{diss}} = \frac{[\text{H}^+][\text{OAc}^-]}{[\text{HOAc}]} = 1.8 \times 10^{-5} = \frac{(x)(0.017 + x)}{0.0667 - x}.$$

$$x \cong \frac{0.0667}{0.017} (1.8 \times 10^{-5}) = 7.1 \times 10^{-5} = [\text{H}^+].$$

pH = $- \log [\text{H}^+] = - \log (7.1 \times 10^{-5}) = -(0.85 - 5) = $ **4.15**.

(c) *after adding 10.0 ml of 0.100 M NaOH:*

25.0 ml of 0.100 $M$ HOAc gives

$$(0.0250 \text{ l}) \left( 0.100 \frac{\text{mole HOAc}}{\text{liter}} \right) = 0.00250 \text{ mole HOAc.}$$

10.0 ml of 0.100 $M$ NaOH gives

$$(0.0100 \text{ l}) \left( 0.100 \frac{\text{mole OH}^-}{\text{liter}} \right) = 0.00100 \text{ mole OH}^-.$$

$HOAc + OH^- \rightarrow H_2O + OAc^-$.

0.00250 mole HOAc + 0.00100 mole $OH^- \rightarrow$ 0.00150 mole HOAc + 0.00100 mole $OAc^-$.

Total volume of solution = 25.0 ml + 10.0 ml = 0.0350 l.

Concentration of HOAc = $\dfrac{0.00150 \text{ mole HOAc}}{0.0350 \text{ l}}$
   = 0.0429 $M$ HOAc.

Concentration of $OAc^-$ = $\dfrac{0.00100 \text{ mole } OH^-}{0.0350 \text{ l}}$ = 0.0286 $M$ $OAc^-$.

Let $x$ = moles/l of this HOAc that is dissociated.

$[HOAc] = 0.0429 - x$; $[H^+] = x$; $[OAc^-] = 0.0286 + x$.

$$K_{\text{diss}} = \frac{[H^+][OAc^-]}{[HOAc]} = 1.8 \times 10^{-5} = \frac{(x)(0.0286 + x)}{0.0429 - x}.$$

$$x \cong \frac{0.0429}{0.0286}(1.8 \times 10^{-5}) = 2.7 \times 10^{-5} = [H^+].$$

$$pH = -\log[H^+] = -\log(2.7 \times 10^{-5}) = -(0.43 - 5) = 4.57.$$

(d) *after adding 15.0 ml of 0.100 M NaOH:*

0.00250 mole HOAc + 0.00150 mole $OH^- \rightarrow$ 0.00100 mole HOAc + 0.00150 mole $OAc^-$.

Total volume of solution = 25.0 ml + 15.0 ml = 0.0400 l.

Concentration of HOAc = $\dfrac{0.00100 \text{ mole HOAc}}{0.0400 \text{ l}}$
   = 0.0250 $M$ HOAc.

Concentration of $OAc^-$ = $\dfrac{0.00150 \text{ mole } OAc^-}{0.0400 \text{ l}}$ = 0.0375 $M$ $OAc^-$.

Let $x$ = moles/l HOAc that are dissociated.

$[HOAc] = 0.0250 - x$; $[H^+] = x$; $[OAc^-] = 0.0375 + x$.

$$K_{\text{diss}} = \frac{[H^+][OAc^-]}{[HOAc]} = 1.8 \times 10^{-5} = \frac{(x)(0.0375 + x)}{0.0250 - x}.$$

$$x \cong \frac{0.0250}{0.0375} \ (1.8 \times 10^{-5}) = 1.2 \times 10^{-5} = [\text{H}^+].$$

$$\text{pH} = -\log [\text{H}^+] = -\log (1.2 \times 10^{-5}) = -(0.08 - 5) = 4.92.$$

(e) *after adding 20.0 ml of 0.100 M NaOH:*
    0.00250  mole  HOAc + 0.00200  mole  $\text{OH}^-$ → 0.00050  mole
    HOAc + 0.00200 mole $\text{OAc}^-$.

Total volume of solution = 25.0 ml + 20.0 ml = 0.0450 l.

$$\text{Concentration of HOAc} = \frac{0.00050 \text{ mole HOAc}}{0.0450 \text{ l}}$$
$$= 0.011 \ M \text{ HOAc}.$$

$$\text{Concentration of OAc}^- = \frac{0.00200 \text{ mole OAc}^-}{0.0450 \text{ l}} = 0.0444 \ M \text{ OAc}^-.$$

Let $x$ = moles/l HOAc actually dissociated.

$[\text{HOAc}] = 0.011 - x; \quad [\text{H}^+] = x; \quad [\text{OAc}^-] = 0.0444 + x.$

$$K_{\text{diss}} = \frac{[\text{H}^+][\text{OAc}^-]}{[\text{HOAc}]} = 1.8 \times 10^{-5} = \frac{(x)(0.044 + x)}{0.011 - x}.$$

$$x \cong \frac{0.011}{0.0444} \ (1.8 \times 10^{-5}) = 4.5 \times 10^{-6} = [\text{H}^+].$$

$$\text{pH} = -\log [\text{H}^+] = -\log (4.5 \times 10^{-6}) = -(0.65 - 6) = 5.35.$$

(f) *after adding 25.0 ml of 0.100 M NaOH:*

25.0 ml of 0.100 $M$ HOAc gives
$$(0.0250 \text{ l}) \left( 0.100 \ \frac{\text{mole HOAc}}{\text{liter}} \right) = 0.00250 \text{ mole HOAc}.$$

25.0 ml of 0.100 $M$ NaOH gives
$$(0.0250 \text{ l}) \left( 0.100 \ \frac{\text{mole OH}^-}{\text{liter}} \right) = 0.00250 \text{ mole OH}^-.$$

$\text{HOAc} + \text{OH}^- \rightarrow \text{OAc}^- + \text{H}_2\text{O}.$

0.00250 mole HOAc + 0.00250 mole $\text{OH}^- \rightarrow$ 0.00250 mole $\text{OAc}^-$.

Total volume of solution = 25.0 ml + 25.0 ml = 0.0500 l.

$$\text{Concentration of OAc}^- = \frac{0.00250 \text{ mole OAc}^-}{0.0500 \text{ l}}$$
$$= 0.0500 \; M \text{ OAc}^-.$$

As previously noted in Problem 685, some of this $OAc^-$ will hydrolyze—that is, it will pick up $H^+$ from the water to form some HOAc and liberate some $OH^-$.

Let $x$ = moles/l of $OAc^-$ that will so react.

This will give us at equilibrium

$$[OAc^-] = 0.0500 - x; \; [HOAc] = x; \; [OH^-] = x$$

But, again, we can say $[H^+] = \dfrac{K_w}{[OH^-]} = \dfrac{1.00 \times 10^{-14}}{x}$, so as to be able to substitute in

$$K_{\text{diss}} = \frac{[H^+][OAc^-]}{[HOAc]} = 1.8 \times 10^{-5}$$

$$= \frac{\left(\dfrac{1.00 \times 10^{-14}}{x}\right)(0.0500 - x)}{x}$$

Since $x$ is small compared to 0.0500, we can approximate

$$1.8 \times 10^{-5} \cong \frac{(1.00 \times 10^{-14})(0.0500)}{x^2}$$

which solves to $x = 5.3 \times 10^{-6} = [OH^-]$.

$$[H^+] = \frac{K_w}{[OH^-]} = \frac{1.00 \times 10^{-14}}{5.3 \times 10^{-6}} = 1.9 \times 10^{-9}.$$

$$pH = -\log [H^+] = -\log (1.9 \times 10^{-9}) = -(0.28 - 9) = 8.72.$$

[*Note*· If you compare the results of Problems 681 to 685 with what we have just calculated in solutions (a) to (f) of Problem 688, you see an interesting result.   The pH values are the same in the latter case, where dilution occurs as in the former constant volume case, except for the last solution, where we find 0.050 $M$ NaOAc has pH = 8.72 compared to pH = 8.85 for 0.10 $M$ NaOAc.   The reason for the preceding constancy of pH is that we are dealing with a buffer solution, where dilution has little effect on pH.   However, in the last solution *all* the HOAc has been neutralized, so that the buffer action is largely killed.]

(g) *after adding 30.0, 35.0, 40.0, 45.0, and 50.0 ml of 0.100 M NaOH:*

Subsequent addition of 0.100 $M$ NaOH simply adds $OH^-$ to a solution in which all the HOAc has been used up. To calculate the pH we take the added volume of 0.100 $M$ NaOH, subtract out 25.0 ml to take care of neutralizing the 25.0 ml of 0.100 $M$ HOAc, and regard the rest of the 0.100$M$ NaOH as being diluted to the total volume of solution. For example:

25.0 ml of 0.100 $M$ HOAc + 30.0 ml of 0.100 $M$ NaOH gives us 5.0 ml of 0.100 $M$ NaOH in excess over that required for the neutralization.

$$(0.0050 \text{ l}) \left( 0.100 \ \frac{\text{mole OH}^-}{\text{liter}} \right) = 0.00050 \text{ mole OH}^- \text{ in excess.}$$

Total volume is 25.0 ml + 30.0 ml = 0.0550 l.

$$\text{Concentration of OH}^- = \frac{0.00050 \text{ mole}}{0.0550 \text{ l}} = 9.1 \times 10^{-3} \ M.$$

$$[H^+] = \frac{K_w}{[OH^-]} = \frac{1.00 \times 10^{-14}}{9.1 \times 10^{-3}} = 1.1 \times 10^{-12} \ M.$$

$$\begin{aligned} pH &= -\log [H^+] = -\log (1.1 \times 10^{-12}) \\ &= -(0.04 - 12) = 11.96. \end{aligned}$$

Added 35.0 ml of 0.100 $M$ NaOH corresponds to 10.0 ml of 0.100 $M$ NaOH in excess, which leads to $[OH^-] = 0.0167 \ M$ and pH = 12.223.

Added 40.0 ml of 0.100 $M$ NaOH corresponds to 15.0 ml of 0.100 $M$ NaOH in excess, which leads to $[OH^-] = 0.0231 \ M$ and pH = 12.364.

Added 45.0 ml of 0.100 $M$ NaOH corresponds to 20.0 ml of 0.100 $M$ NaOH in excess, which leads to $[OH^-] = 0.0286 \ M$ and pH = 12.456.

Added 50.0 ml of 0.100 $M$ NaOH corresponds to 25.0 ml of 0.100 $M$ NaOH in excess in a total volume of 0.0750 l, which leads to $[OH^-] = 0.0333 \ M$ and pH = 12.523.

In summary, when 5.0-ml increments of 0.100 $M$ NaOH are added to 25.0 ml of 0.100 $M$ HOAc, the pH changes successively in the following sequence: **2.89, 4.15, 4.57, 4.92, 5.35, 8.72, 11.96, 12.223, 12.364, 12.456, 12.523.**

■ PROBLEM 689    Given 25.0 ml of 0.200 $M$ NaOH. Suppose you add to it gradually 50.0 ml of 0.200 $M$ HOAc ($K_{diss} = 1.8 \times 10^{-5}$). Calculate the pH of the initial solution and after each successive addition of 5.00 ml of the acid. Assume additive volumes.

ANSWER: **13.301; 13.125; 12.933; 12.699; 12.347; 8.85; 5.44; 5.14; 4.97; 4.84; 4.74**

## Strong acid plus weak base

We found that addition of NaOH to HOAc ran into complications because as soon as some OAc$^-$ has been produced in the solution by neutralization the subsequent pH change is largely dominated by the buffering action of the HOAc-OAc$^-$ system. The same kind of complication is to be expected when a weak base, BOH, is gradually added to a strong acid solution. As soon as some BOH has reacted with H$^+$ to form B$^+$, the subsequent pH change is largely controlled by the BOH-B$^+$ buffer. In this section we look at the specific case of adding aqueous NH$_3$ to a solution of HCl. Ammonia as a base has its own peculiar complications, but the system is important enough to warrant study of how to make calculations for it.

PROBLEM 690    We propose to carry out a titration using 0.120 $M$ HCl and 0.120 $M$ NH$_3$ solutions. Given that $K = 1.81 \times 10^{-5}$ for NH$_3$ + H$_2$O $\rightleftharpoons$ NH$_4^+$ + OH$^-$, what will be the pH of these two starting solutions?

SOLUTION: HCl is strong electrolyte and is taken to be 100% dissociated. 0.120 $M$ HCl $\rightarrow$ 0.120 $M$ H$^+$ and 0.120 $M$ Cl$^-$.
pH = $-\log[\text{H}^+]$ = $-\log(0.120)$ = $-\log(1.20 \times 10^{-1})$
    = $-(0.079 - 1)$ = **0.921.**
NH$_3$ is a weak electrolyte. Let $x$ = moles/l NH$_3$ that react via
    NH$_3$ + H$_2$O $\rightarrow$ NH$_4^+$ + OH$^-$.
[NH$_3$] = 0.120 $- x$; [NH$_4^+$] = $x$; [OH$^-$] = $x$.

$$K = \frac{[NH_4^+][OH^-]}{[NH_3]} = 1.81 \times 10^{-5} = \frac{(x)(x)}{0.120 - x}.$$

$$x = 1.47 \times 10^{-3} = [OH^-].$$

$$[H^+] = \frac{K_w}{[OH^-]} = \frac{1.00 \times 10^{-14}}{1.47 \times 10^{-3}} = 6.80 \times 10^{-12}.$$

$$pH = -\log [H^+] = -\log (6.80 \times 10^{-12})$$
$$= -(0.833 - 12) = 11.167.$$

PROBLEM 691    Given 25.0 ml of 0.120 $M$ HCl. You add to it 5.00 ml of 0.120 $M$ NH$_3$. What does the pH become? Assume volumes additive.

SOLUTION: 25.0 ml of 0.120 $M$ HCl gives

$$(0.0250 \text{ l}) \left( 0.120 \frac{\text{mole H}^+}{\text{liter}} \right) = 0.00300 \text{ mole H}^+.$$

5.00 ml of 0.120 $M$ NH$_3$ gives

$$(0.00500 \text{ l}) \left( 0.120 \frac{\text{mole NH}_3}{\text{liter}} \right) = 0.000600 \text{ mole NH}_3.$$

H$^+$ represents the acid; NH$_3$, the base. They react to neutralize each other via the reaction H$^+$ + NH$_3$ → NH$_4^+$. Let us assume neutralization is complete.

0.00300 mole H$^+$ + 0.000600 mole NH$_3$ → 0.00240 mole H$^+$ left in excess plus 0.00060 mole NH$_4^+$ formed.

We might expect NH$_4^+$ to dissociate somewhat, consistent with the reverse of the above reaction—viz., H$^+$ + NH$_3$ ← NH$_4^+$. However, in the presence of excess H$^+$ this "back-dissociation" cannot amount to much. We can assume it to be negligible.

The hydrogen-ion concentration is primarily fixed by the 0.00240 mole H$^+$ left in excess. The volume of the solution is equal to the 25.0 ml of initial 0.120 $M$ HCl plus 5.00 ml of added 0.120 $M$ NH$_3$ = 0.0300 l.

$$[H^+] = \frac{0.00240 \text{ mole H}^+}{0.0300 \text{ l}} = 0.0800 \text{ } M \text{ H}^+.$$

$$pH = -\log [H^+] = -\log (8.00 \times 10^{-2}) = -(0.903 - 2) = 1.097.$$

■PROBLEM 692    Given 25.0 ml of 0.120 $M$ HCl. You add to it 10.0 ml of 0.120 $M$ NH$_3$. What does the pH become? Assume volumes additive.

ANSWER: pH = 1.289

■PROBLEM 693    Given 25.0 ml of 0.120
$M$ HCl.   What does the pH become after addition of 15.0 ml of 0.120 $M$
$NH_3$?  What does the pH become after addition of 20.0 ml of 0.120 $M$
$NH_3$?  Assume additive volumes.

ANSWER: pH $= 1.523$ ; pH $= 1.88$

PROBLEM 694    What will be the pH of
a solution made by adding 25.0 ml of 0.120 $M$ $NH_3$ to 25.0 ml of 0.120
$M$ HCl?  Assume total volume is 50.0 ml.   $K = 1.81 \times 10^{-5}$ for
$NH_3 + H_2O \rightleftharpoons NH_4^+ + OH^-$.

SOLUTION: This mixture corresponds to the equivalence point.
25.0 ml of 0.120 $M$ HCl furnishes

$$(0.0250 \text{ l}) \left( 0.120 \frac{\text{mole H}^+}{\text{liter}} \right) = 0.00300 \text{ mole H}^+.$$

25.0 ml of 0.120 $M$ $NH_3$ furnishes

$$(0.0250 \text{ l}) \left( 0.120 \frac{\text{mole NH}_3}{\text{liter}} \right) = 0.00300 \text{ mole NH}_3.$$

$H^+ + NH_3 \rightarrow NH_4^+$.

0.00300 mole $H^+$ + 0.00300 mole $NH_3 \rightarrow$ 0.00300 mole $NH_4^+$.

The total volume of the solution is 0.0500 l, so (not allowing for any
"back-reaction") we can calculate the effective concentration of
$NH_4^+$ as $\dfrac{0.00300 \text{ mole}}{0.0500 \text{ l}} = 0.0600$ $M$ $NH_4^+$.   But, unlike the
preceding cases where excess $H^+$ repressed the "back-reaction"
($H^+ + NH_3 \leftarrow NH_4^+$), we have no excess $H^+$ nor $NH_3$ to pre-
vent some dissociation of $NH_4^+$, which is actually quite appreciable.
How can we calculate the equilibrium concentration of $H^+$ in a
solution that is 0.0600 $M$ $NH_4^+$?  There are two methods:

(a)  *NH$_4^+$ can be treated as a weak acid:*

For the dissociation reaction $NH_4^+ \rightleftharpoons NH_3 + H^+$ the equilibrium
constant is $5.52 \times 10^{-10}$.   If we let $x =$ moles/l $NH_4^+$ that
are dissociated this way, we would get $x$ moles/l $NH_3$ and $x$
moles/l $H^+$, leaving $0.0600 - x$ moles/l $NH_4^+$.

$[NH_4^+] = 0.0600 - x$; $[NH_3] = x$; $[H^+] = x$.

$NH_4^+ \rightleftharpoons NH_3 + H^+$.

$$K = \frac{[NH_3][H^+]}{[NH_4^+]} = 5.52 \times 10^{-10} = \frac{(x)(x)}{0.0600 - x}.$$

$x = 5.76 \times 10^{-6} = [H^+].$

$pH = -\log [H^+] = -\log (5.76 \times 10^{-6})$
$\quad = -(0.760 - 6) = \textbf{5.240.}$

(b) *$NH_4^+$ can be treated as the $B^+$ of a weak base BOH:*

This is considered in greater detail under hydrolysis, but we can get a numerical answer here by using a method analogous to the one we used to calculate $[OH^-]$ in NaOAc solution. Just as acetate ion disturbs the water equilibrium, $H_2O \leftrightarrows H^+ + OH^-$, by picking up $H^+$ to form HOAc, we can regard the ammonium ion as disturbing the water equilibrium by picking up $OH^-$ to form $NH_3 + H_2O$.

We had 0.0600 $M$ $NH_4^+$ to start with. Suppose we let $x$ moles/l of this $NH_4^+$ latch on to $OH^-$ to react via $NH_4^+ + OH^- \rightarrow NH_3 + H_2O$. The net effect would be to reduce the $NH_4^+$ concentration from 0.0600 to $0.0600 - x$, increase the $NH_3$ concentration from zero to $x$, and set free $x$ moles/l $H^+$ in the solution. The last-mentioned process can be visualized this way: Each time an ammonium ion swipes an $OH^-$ from the $H_2O$, it leaves an $H^+$ behind. At equilibrium, then, we would have

$[NH_4^+] = 0.0600 - x; \quad [NH_3] = x; \quad [H^+] = x$

Since $[H^+][OH^-] = K_w$, we could also write $[OH^-] = \dfrac{K_w}{[H^+]} = \dfrac{1.00 \times 10^{-14}}{x}$. But all along we have been working with the knowledge that $K = 1.81 \times 10^{-5}$ for $NH_3 + H_2O \rightleftharpoons NH_4^+ + OH^-$. All we need do is substitute.

$$K = \frac{[NH_4^+][OH^-]}{[NH_3]} = 1.81 \times 10^{-5}$$
$$= \frac{(0.0600 - x)\left(\dfrac{1.00 \times 10^{-14}}{x}\right)}{x}$$

Since $x$ is small compared to 0.0600, we can write approximately

$$1.81 \times 10^{-5} \cong \frac{(0.0600)(1.00 \times 10^{-14})}{x^2}$$

which solves to give $x = 5.76 \times 10^{-6} = [\text{H}^+]$.

$$\text{pH} = -\log[\text{H}^+] = -\log(5.76 \times 10^{-6})$$
$$= -(0.760 - 6) = \textbf{5.240}.$$

So, either method (a) or (b) gives pH = 5.240 for 0.0600 $M$ $\text{NH}_4{}^+$.

PROBLEM 695    Given 25.0 ml of 0.120 $M$ HCl.   You add to it 30.0 ml of 0.120 $M$ $\text{NH}_3$.   What does the pH become?   Assume additive volumes.   $K = 1.81 \times 10^{-5}$ for $\text{NH}_3 + \text{H}_2\text{O} \rightleftharpoons \text{NH}_4{}^+ + \text{OH}^-$.

SOLUTION: (This is a buffer solution containing $\text{NH}_3$ and $\text{NH}_4{}^+$.   Refer to Section 18.2.)

25.0 ml of 0.120 $M$ HCl gives

$$(0.0250 \text{ l})\left(0.120 \frac{\text{mole H}^+}{\text{liter}}\right) = 0.00300 \text{ mole H}^+.$$

30.0 ml of 0.120 $M$ $\text{NH}_3$ gives

$$(0.0300 \text{ l})\left(0.120 \frac{\text{mole NH}_3}{\text{liter}}\right) = 0.00360 \text{ mole NH}_3.$$

$\text{H}^+ + \text{NH}_3 \rightarrow \text{NH}_4{}^+$.

0.00300 mole $\text{H}^+$ + 0.00360 mole $\text{NH}_3 \rightarrow$ 0.00300 mole $\text{NH}_4{}^+$ + 0.00060 mole $\text{NH}_3$ in excess.

Total volume of solution = 25.0 ml + 30.0 ml = 0.0550 l.

Allowing for no "dissociation," we would have

$$\text{concentration of NH}_4{}^+ = \frac{0.00300 \text{ mole NH}_4{}^+}{0.0550 \text{ l}} = 0.0545 \ M \ \text{NH}_4{}^+$$

$$\text{concentration of NH}_3 = \frac{0.00060 \text{ mole NH}_3}{0.0550 \text{ l}} = 0.011 \ M \ \text{NH}_3$$

We are given $K$ for the reaction $\text{NH}_3 + \text{H}_2\text{O} \rightleftharpoons \text{NH}_4{}^+ + \text{OH}^-$. Let $x$ = moles/l $\text{NH}_3$ that get "dissociated" to $\text{NH}_4{}^+$ this way.
$[\text{NH}_3] = 0.011 - x$; $[\text{NH}_4{}^+] = 0.0545 + x$; $[\text{OH}^-] = x$.

$$K = \frac{[\text{NH}_4{}^+][\text{OH}^-]}{[\text{NH}_3]} = 1.81 \times 10^{-5} = \frac{(0.0545 + x)(x)}{0.011 - x}.$$

$$x \cong \frac{0.011}{0.0545} \ (1.81 \times 10^{-5}) = 3.7 \times 10^{-6} = [\text{OH}^-].$$

$$[\text{H}^+] = \frac{K_w}{[\text{OH}^-]} = \frac{1.00 \times 10^{-14}}{3.7 \times 10^{-6}} = 2.7 \times 10^{-9}.$$

$$\text{pH} = - \log \ [\text{H}^+] = - \log \ (2.7 \times 10^{-9}) = -(0.43 - 9) = \textbf{8.57}.$$

■ P R O B L E M  696   Given 25.0 ml of 0.120 $M$ HCl.  You add to it 35.0 ml of 0.120 $M$ NH$_3$.  What does the pH become?  Assume additive volumes.  $K = 1.81 \times 10^{-5}$ for NH$_3$ + H$_2$O $\rightleftharpoons$ NH$_4{}^+$ + OH$^-$.

ANSWER: pH = **8.860**

■ P R O B L E M  697   Given 25.0 ml of 0.120 $M$ HCl.  What will the pH become after adding 40.0 ml of 0.120 $M$ NH$_3$?  After adding 45.0 ml of 0.120 $M$ NH$_3$?  Assume additive volumes.  $K = 1.81 \times 10^{-5}$ for NH$_3$ + H$_2$O $\rightleftharpoons$ NH$_4{}^+$ + OH$^-$.

ANSWER: pH = **9.036**; pH = **9.161**

■ P R O B L E M  698   If you mix 25.0 ml of 0.120 $M$ HCl with 50.0 ml of 0.120 $M$ NH$_3$, what will be the pH of the resulting solution?  Assume additive volumes.  $K = 1.81 \times 10^{-5}$ for NH$_3$ + H$_2$O $\rightleftharpoons$ NH$_4{}^+$ + OH$^-$.

ANSWER: pH = **9.258**

Summarizing the results of Problems 690 to 698, we can get the titration curve for the progressive addition of 0.120 $M$ NH$_3$ to 25.0 ml of 0.120 $M$ HCl.  The pH changes successively, on each addition of 5.00 ml of 0.120 $M$ NH$_3$, as follows: 0.921, 1.097, 1.289, 1.523, 1.88, 5.240, 8.57, 8.860, 9.036, 9.161, and 9.258.  The graph representing the pH vs. volume of added NH$_3$ solution is shown in Figure 67.

■ P R O B L E M  699   Compute the pH for stepwise addition of 5.00-ml portions of 0.100 $M$ HCl to 25.0 ml of 0.100 $M$ NH$_3$ until 50.0 ml of 0.100 $M$ HCl has been added.  Assume additive volumes.  $K = 1.81 \times 10^{-5}$ for NH$_3$ + H$_2$O $\rightleftharpoons$ NH$_4{}^+$ + OH$^-$.

ANSWER: 11.127; 9.860; 9.434; 9.082; 8.656; 5.280; 2.04; 1.777; 1.636; 1.544; 1.478

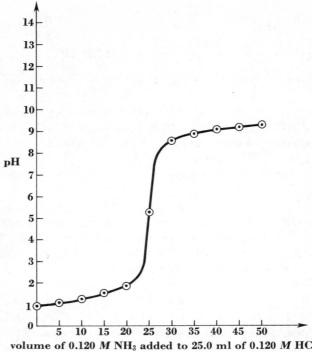

volume of 0.120 *M* NH₃ added to 25.0 ml of 0.120 *M* HCl

*Figure 67*

## Weak acid plus weak base

The titration curve for the neutralization of a weak acid by a weak base has three complications: (1) in the acidic region, the pH tends to be kept constant by an HX-X⁻ buffer; (2) in the basic region, the pH tends to be kept constant by a BOH-B⁺ buffer; and (3) at the equivalence point, there is extensive hydrolysis of the equivalent salt, which may, however, in some cases lead to a neutral (pH = 7) or near-neutral solution. The whole problem, especially point (3), fits into the category of complex equilibria as discussed in Chapter 18, but for comparison with the other cases we have just considered it is advantageous to make some preliminary computations here. As our model system, we consider the addition of aqueous ammonia to acetic acid solution. This system is a bit unusual because the $K_{diss}$ of aqueous ammonia ($1.81 \times 10^{-5}$) happens to be about the same as the $K_{diss}$ of HOAc ($1.8 \times 10^{-5}$).

PROBLEM 700  Given 25.0 ml of 0.100 $M$ HOAc. If you add to this solution 5.00 ml of 0.100 $M \cdot NH_3$, what change in pH will occur? Assume additive volumes.

SOLUTION: The initial solution has HOAc only slightly dissociated.
$HOAc \rightleftharpoons H^+ + OAc^-$.
$[HOAc] = 0.100 - x$; $[H^+] = x$; $[OAc^-] = x$.
$$K_{diss} = \frac{[H^+][OAc^-]}{[HOAc]} = 1.8 \times 10^{-5} = \frac{(x)(x)}{0.100 - x}.$$
$x = 1.3 \times 10^{-3} = [H^+]$.
$pH = -\log[H^+] = -\log(1.3 \times 10^{-3}) = -(0.11 - 3) = $ **2.89.**
When we add $NH_3$, we will get reaction between the acid HOAc and the base $NH_3$ via the net reaction

$$HOAc + NH_3 \rightarrow NH_4^+ + OAc^-$$

25.0 ml of 0.100 $M$ HOAc gives
$$(0.0250 \text{ l}) \left( 0.100 \frac{\text{mole HOAc}}{\text{liter}} \right) = 0.00250 \text{ mole HOAc.}$$
5.00 ml of 0.100 $M$ $NH_3$ gives
$$(0.00500 \text{ l}) \left( 0.100 \frac{\text{mole } NH_3}{\text{liter}} \right) = 0.000500 \text{ mole } NH_3.$$

As a first approximation, we assume 100% conversion via the above reaction.
0.00250 mole HOAc + 0.000500 mole $NH_3 \rightarrow$ 0.00200 mole HOAc left + 0.000500 mole $OAc^-$ formed + 0.00500 mole $NH_4^+$ formed.
Since both HOAc and $OAc^-$ are present in substantial quantities, the $H^+$ will be fixed by this buffer. (Although there is $NH_4^+$ present, there is not enough $NH_3$ so as to make the $NH_4^+$-$NH_3$ buffer important.)
The total volume of solution is 25.0 ml + 5.0 ml = 0.0300 l.
$$\text{Concentration of HOAc} = \frac{0.00200 \text{ mole}}{0.0300 \text{ l}} = 0.0667 \text{ } M \text{ HOAc.}$$
$$\text{Concentration of } OAc^- = \frac{0.000500 \text{ mole}}{0.0300 \text{ l}} = 0.0167 \text{ } M \text{ } OAc^-.$$
Let $x$ = moles/l HOAc that dissociate.

$[HOAc] = 0.0667 - x$; $[H^+] = x$; $[OAc^-] = 0.0167 + x$.

$$K_{diss} = \frac{[H^+][OAc^-]}{[HOAc]} = 1.8 \times 10^{-5} = \frac{(x)(0.0167 + x)}{0.0667 - x}.$$

$$x \cong \frac{0.0667}{0.0167} (1.8 \times 10^{-5}) = 7.2 \times 10^{-5} = [H^+].$$

pH $= - \log [H^+] = - \log (7.2 \times 10^{-5}) = -(0.86 - 5) = 4.14$.

So, pH changes **from 2.89 to 4.14**.

■ PROBLEM 701  Given 25.0 ml of 0.100 $M$ HOAc. What will be the pH after addition of 10.0 ml of 0.100 $M$ $NH_3$? After addition of 15.0 ml? After addition of 20.0 ml? Assume additive volumes. Assume also that the approximations made in Problem 700 still hold. These approximations get progressively worse as we approach neutralization.

ANSWER: **4.57; 4.92; 5.35**

PROBLEM 702  Suppose you mix 25.0 ml of 0.100 $M$ HOAc with 25.0 ml of 0.100 $M$ $NH_3$. What will be the pH of the resulting solution? Assume additive volumes.

SOLUTION: At this stage of the titration we have mixed equimolar quantities of HOAc and $NH_3$. We have been assuming they react 100%, via HOAc + $NH_3$ → $NH_4^+$ + $OAc^-$ and we have been able to get away with this assumption because, so far, we have always had some excess HOAc to help drive the reaction to "completion." But now this is no longer the case, so we have to allow for an appreciable amount of "back-reaction." In other words, we are up against the following equilibrium problem:

$$HOAc + NH_3 \rightleftharpoons NH_4^+ + OAc^-$$

How shall we handle it? We can approach the problem either from the left side or from the right side.

*(a) from the left:*

25.0 ml of 0.100 $M$ HOAc gives 0.00250 mole HOAc.

25.0 ml of 0.100 $M$ $NH_3$ gives 0.00250 mole $NH_3$.

Total volume of solution is 25.0 ml + 25.0 ml = 0.0500 l.

So, without allowing any reaction between HOAc and $NH_3$, we would calculate

$$\text{concentration of HOAc} = \frac{0.00250 \text{ mole HOAc}}{0.0500 \text{ l}} = 0.0500 \ M \text{ HOAc}$$

$$\text{concentration of NH}_3 = \frac{0.00250 \text{ mole NH}_3}{0.0500 \text{ l}} = 0.0500 \ M \text{ NH}_3$$

Now, we let $x$ moles/l HOAc react with $x$ moles/l $NH_3$ to establish equilibrium via the reaction $NH_3 + HOAc \rightarrow NH_4{}^+ + OAc^-$. This will give us the following equilibrium concentrations:

$[NH_3] = 0.0500 - x$; $[HOAc] = 0.0500 - x$; $[NH_4{}^+] = x$; $[OAc^-] = x$

These concentrations should satisfy the constant for the equilibrium $NH_3 + HOAc \rightleftharpoons NH_4{}^+ + OAc^-$:

$$K = \frac{[NH_4{}^+][OAc^-]}{[NH_3][HOAc]} = \frac{(x)(x)}{(0.0500 - x)(0.0500 - x)}$$

If we only knew the numerical value of $K$, we could solve the equation for $x$. Here we resort to a trick frequently employed by chemists when they need to get a $K$ value not listed in the literature. Take the $K$ expression desired and multiply its numerator and denominator by a concentration of an appropriate species so that the expression takes on a recognizable form. For example, if we multiply the above expression by $[H^+]$ in numerator and denominator, we get the following:

$$\frac{[NH_4{}^+][OAc^-]}{[NH_3][HOAc]} \frac{[H^+]}{[H^+]} = \frac{[NH_4{}^+]}{[NH_3][H^+]} \frac{[OAc^-][H^+]}{[HOAc]}$$

where we have shuffled the placing of the terms in order to emphasize the recognizable grouping $\dfrac{[OAc^-][H^+]}{[HOAc]}$. This grouping has the numerical value $1.8 \times 10^{-5}$, no matter where it occurs.

Similarly, we can multiply the numerator and denominator next by $[OH^-]$. This will give us $\dfrac{[NH_4{}^+][OH^-]}{[NH_3]}$ and $\dfrac{1}{[H^+][OH^-]}$, both of which we also know numerically. Thus, we have

$$\frac{[NH_4{}^+][OAc^-]}{[NH_3][HOAc]} \frac{[H^+]}{[H^+]} \frac{[OH^-]}{[OH^-]}$$

$$= \frac{[NH_4{}^+][OH^-]}{[NH_3]} \frac{[H^+][OAc^-]}{[HOAc]} \frac{1}{[H^+][OH^-]}$$

or, alternatively,

$$K \times 1 \times 1 = (1.81 \times 10^{-5})(1.8 \times 10^{-5}) \frac{1}{1.00 \times 10^{-14}}$$

Thus, $K = 3.2_6 \times 10^4$, where we have dropped the 6 below the line to signify it as a dubious digit going beyond the two significant figures we are allowed here.

Using this numerical value for $K$, we get the equation

$$\frac{(x)(x)}{(0.0500 - x)(0.0500 - x)} = 3.2_6 \times 10^4$$

We can solve this equation by taking the square root of each side, giving

$$\frac{x}{(0.0500 - x)} = \sqrt{3.2_6 \times 10^4} = 1.8_{06} \times 10^2$$

which solves to give $x = 0.049_7$.

Substituting this $x$ back into our original expressions for the various equilibrium concentrations, we get

$$[NH_3] = 0.0500 - x = 0.0500 - 0.049_7 = 0.000_3 \, M$$

$$[HOAc] = 0.0500 - x = 0.0500 - 0.049_7 = 0.000_3 \, M$$

$$[NH_4^+] = x = 0.049_7 \, M$$

$$[OAc^-] = x = 0.049_7 \, M$$

Our question originally asked for the pH; we can get at it by using either the $K_{diss}$ of HOAc or of $NH_3$. For the former, we substitute as follows:

$$K_{diss} = \frac{[H^+][OAc^-]}{[HOAc]} = 1.8 \times 10^{-5} = \frac{[H^+](0.049_7)}{0.000_3}$$

Solving for the hydrogen-ion concentration, we get

$$[H^+] = \frac{0.000_3}{0.049_7} (1.8 \times 10^{-5}) = 10^{-7}$$

This gives us a pH of 7, but, alas, there are *no* significant figures in the answer, not if we follow our simple rules of significant figures. (The troubles with the significant figures arise because we have unfortunately chosen to approach equilibrium from the unfavorable direction.)

(b) *from the right:*

25.0 ml of 0.100 $M$ HOAc gives 0.00250 mole HOAc.

25.0 ml of 0.100 $M$ $NH_3$ gives 0.00250 mole $NH_3$.

This time we let these two reagents react 100% by the reaction

$$HOAc + NH_3 \rightarrow NH_4^+ + OAc^-$$

0.00250 mole HOAc + 0.00250 mole $NH_3$ → 0.00250 mole $NH_4^+$ + 0.00250 mole $OAc^-$.

Total volume of solution is 0.0500 l.

So, without allowing any "back-reaction," we would calculate

$$\text{concentration of } NH_4^+ = \frac{0.00250 \text{ mole } NH_4^+}{0.0500 \text{ l}} = 0.0500 \ M \ NH_4^+$$

$$\text{concentration of } OAc^- = \frac{0.00250 \text{ mole } OAc^-}{0.0500 \text{ l}} = 0.0500 \ M \ OAc^-$$

Now we let $y$ moles/l of $NH_4^+$ and of $OAc^-$ react back to establish the equilibrium

$$NH_3 + HOAc \rightleftharpoons NH_4^+ + OAc^-$$

Equilibrium concentrations will be as follows:

$[NH_4^+] = 0.0500 - y$; $[OAc^-] = 0.0500 - y$; $[NH_3] = y$; $[HOAc) = y$

These should satisfy the constant $K$ as calculated in (a).

$$K = \frac{[NH_4^+][OAc^-]}{[NH_3][HOAc]} = \frac{(0.0500 - y)(0.0500 - y)}{(y)(y)} = 3.2_6 \times 10^4$$

The easiest way to solve this equation is to take the square root of each side. This gives

$$\frac{0.0500 - y}{y} = 1.8 \times 10^2$$

which solves to give $y = 2.8 \times 10^{-4}$. Substituting this value of $y$ in the equilibrium concentrations as defined above, we get

$[NH_4^+] = 0.0500 - y = 0.0500 - 2.8 \times 10^{-4} = 0.0497 \ M$

$[OAc^-] = 0.0500 - y = 0.0500 - 2.8 \times 10^{-4} = 0.0497 \ M$

$[NH_3] = y = 2.8 \times 10^{-4} \ M$

$[HOAc] = y = 2.8 \times 10^{-4} \ M$

To get $[H^+]$, we can use $K_{diss}$ for HOAc.

$$K_{diss} = \frac{[H^+][OAc^-]}{[HOAc]} = \frac{[H^+](0.0497)}{2.8 \times 10^{-4}} = 1.8 \times 10^{-5}$$

$$[H^+] = \frac{2.8 \times 10^{-4}}{0.0497}(1.8 \times 10^{-5}) = 1.0 \times 10^{-7}$$

$$pH = -\log[H^+] = -\log(1.0 \times 10^{-7}) = -(0.00 - 7) = 7.00$$

[*Note:* This result, which is free of the monkey-business on significant figures, should not be surprising. The fact that $K_{diss}$ for HOAc is the same as the $K_{diss}$ for $NH_3 + H_2O$ indicates that $OAc^-$ has about the same affinity for protons as $NH_4^+$ does for $OH^-$. In a solution containing equal amounts of $NH_4^+$ and $OAc^-$, the pickup from $H_2O$ of $OH^-$ by the former is just cancelled by the pickup from $H_2O$ of $H^+$ by the latter.]

PROBLEM 703    Given 25.0 ml of 0.100 $M$ HOAc. If you add to this solution 30.0 ml of 0.100 $M$ $NH_3$, what will be the pH of the resulting solution? Assume additive volumes.

SOLUTION: 25.0 ml of 0.100 $M$ HOAc gives

$$(0.0250 \text{ l})\left(0.100 \frac{\text{mole HOAc}}{\text{liter}}\right) = 0.00250 \text{ mole HOAc.}$$

30.0 ml of 0.100 $M$ $NH_3$ gives

$$(0.0300 \text{ l})\left(0.100 \frac{\text{mole } NH_3}{\text{liter}}\right) = 0.00300 \text{ mole } NH_3.$$

$HOAc + NH_3 \rightarrow NH_4^+ + OAc^-.$

0.00250 mole HOAc + 0.00300 mole $NH_3$ → 0.00250 mole $NH_4^+$ + 0.00250 mole $OAc^-$ + 0.00050 mole $NH_3$ in excess.

If we assume the above reaction goes 100% to the right, which is a circumstance favored by having excess $NH_3$ present, we get a system in which the $OH^-$ is controlled by the $NH_4^+$-$NH_3$ buffer.

Total volume of the solution is 25.0 ml + 30.0 ml = 0.0550 l.

$$\text{Concentration of } NH_4^+ = \frac{0.00250 \text{ mole } NH_4^+}{0.0550 \text{ l}} = 0.0455 \ M \ NH_4^+.$$

$$\text{Concentration of } NH_3 = \frac{0.00050 \text{ mole } NH_3}{0.0550 \text{ l}} = 0.0091 \ M \ NH_3.$$

Given that $K = 1.81 \times 10^{-5}$ for $NH_3 + H_2O \rightleftharpoons NH_4^+ + OH^-$.

$$K = \frac{[NH_4^+][OH^-]}{[NH_3]} = 1.81 \times 10^{-5}.$$

$$[OH^-] = \frac{[NH_3]}{[NH_4^+]} (1.81 \times 10^{-5}) \cong \frac{0.0091}{0.0455} (1.81 \times 10^{-5})$$
$$= 3.6 \times 10^{-6}.$$

$$[H^+] = \frac{K_w}{[OH^-]} = \frac{1.00 \times 10^{-14}}{3.6 \times 10^{-6}} = 2.8 \times 10^{-9}.$$

$$pH = -\log[H^+] = -\log(2.8 \times 10^{-9}) = -(0.45 - 9) = 8.55.$$

■ P R O B L E M   704   Given 25.0 ml of 0.100 $M$ HOAc.  What will be the pH after addition of 35.0 ml of 0.100 $M$ $NH_3$?  After addition of 40.0 ml?  Of 45.0 ml?  Of 50.0 ml?  Assume volumes are additive.

ANSWER: **8.860; 9.036; 9.161; 9.258**

Summarizing these results, when we add 0.100 $M$ $NH_3$ in 5.00-ml increments to 25.0 ml of 0.100 $M$ HOAc, the pH successively changes as follows: 2.89, 4.14, 4.57, 4.92, 5.35, 7.00, 8.55, 8.860, 9.036, 9.161, 9.258.   In the acid region, the hydrogen-ion concentration is controlled by the HOAc-OAc$^-$ buffer; in the basic region, the hydroxide-ion concentration is controlled by the $NH_4^+$-$NH_3$ buffer.   The pH titration curve is shown in Figure 68, where it is compared with the one for addition of a strong base to a strong acid.

## Polyprotic acids

When a base is added gradually to a solution of a polyprotic acid, the pH titration curve generally shows several steeply rising portions instead of just one, as in each of the cases we have just discussed.  Each of the rising portions (called inflection points) corresponds to pulling off another proton.  Only in the case of $H_2SO_4$, where the first dissociation is already complete, do we lose this inflection point corresponding to removal of the first proton.

The computation of the pH change as more base is added is quite complicated, because several equilibria need to be managed simultaneously.  The general problem is discussed in Chapter 18.  Here we

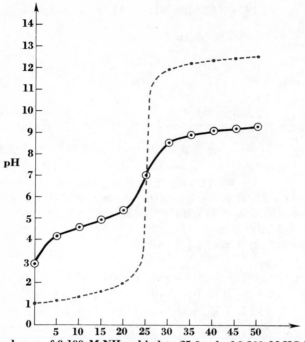

volume of 0.100 $M$ NH₃ added to 25.0 ml of 0.100 $M$ HOAc
(dashed curve shows what happens when 0.100 $M$ NaOH is
added to 25.0 ml of 0.100 $M$ HCl)

*Figure 68*

simply give a few "easy" calculations to illustrate the nature of the
problem.

PROBLEM 705   Sulfurous acid, $H_2SO_3$,
is a diprotic acid with $K_I = 1.25 \times 10^{-2}$ and $K_{II} = 5.6 \times 10^{-8}$. Suppose you had 25.0 ml of 0.100 $M$ $H_2SO_3$, what would be its pH?

SOLUTION: We can afford to ignore the second dissociation, while we
work only with the first.

$$H_2SO_3 \rightleftharpoons H^+ + HSO_3^-$$

Let $x$ = moles/l $H_2SO_3$ that are dissociated.

$[H_2SO_3] = 0.100 - x$; $[H^+] = x$; $[HSO_3^-] = x$.

$$K_I = \frac{[H^+][HSO_3^-]}{[H_2SO_3]} = 1.25 \times 10^{-2} = \frac{(x)(x)}{0.100 - x}.$$

Using the quadratic formula, we get $x = 0.0296 = [H^+]$.

pH $= -\log [H^+] = -\log (2.96 \times 10^{-2}) = -(0.471 - 2) = 1.529$.

PROBLEM 706 Given 25.0 ml of 0.100 $M$ $H_2SO_3$. What will be the pH after addition of 5.0 ml of 0.100 $M$ NaOH? Assume additive volumes. $K_I = 1.25 \times 10^{-2}$.

SOLUTION: 25.0 ml of 0.100 $M$ $H_2SO_3$ gives 0.00250 mole $H_2SO_3$.
5.0 ml of 0.100 $M$ NaOH gives 0.00050 mole $OH^-$.
So long as we have excess $H_2SO_3$ present, only the first proton needs to be considered and the net reaction will be

$H_2SO_3 + OH^- \rightarrow HSO_3^- + H_2O$

0.00250 mole $H_2SO_3$ + 0.00050 mole $OH^- \rightarrow$ 0.00050 mole $HSO_3^-$ + 0.00200 mole $H_2SO_3$ in excess.
Total volume is 25.0 ml + 5.0 ml = 0.0300 l.
Not allowing for any dissociation of the excess $H_2SO_3$, we would get after the above neutralization:

$$\text{concentration of } H_2SO_3 = \frac{0.00200 \text{ mole}}{0.0300 \text{ l}} = 0.0667 \ M \ H_2SO_3$$

$$\text{concentration of } HSO_3^- = \frac{0.00050 \text{ mole}}{0.0300 \text{ l}} = 0.017 \ M \ HSO_3^-$$

Now we allow $x$ moles/l $H_2SO_3$ to dissociate.
$[H_2SO_3] = 0.0667 - x$; $[H^+] = x$; $[HSO_3^-] = 0.017 + x$.

$$K_I = \frac{[H^+][HSO_3^-]}{[H_2SO_3]} = \frac{(x)(0.017 + x)}{0.0667 - x} = 1.25 \times 10^{-2}.$$

Using the quadratic formula, we get $x = 0.018 = [H^+]$.
pH $= -\log [H^+] = -\log (1.8 \times 10^{-2}) = -(0.26 - 2) = 1.74$.

■■PROBLEM 707 Assuming that only the first dissociation of $H_2SO_3$ needs to be considered, calculate the pH after addition to 25.0 ml of 0.100 $M$ $H_2SO_3$ of: (a) 10.0 ml of 0.100 $M$ NaOH; (b) 15.0 ml of 0.100 $M$ NaOH; (c) 20.0 ml of 0.100 $M$ NaOH. $K_I = 1.25 \times 10^{-2}$. Assume additive volumes.

ANSWER: 1.983; 2.250; 2.63

PROBLEM 708   What would be the pH
of a solution made by mixing 25.0 ml of 0.100 $M$ $H_2SO_3$ and 25.0 ml of
0.100 $M$ NaOH? Assume volumes are additive.   $K_I = 1.25 \times 10^{-2}$;
$K_{II} = 5.6 \times 10^{-8}$.

SOLUTION: 25.0 ml of 0.100 $M$ $H_2SO_3$ gives 0.00250 mole $H_2SO_3$.
25.0 ml of 0.100 $M$ NaOH gives 0.00250 mole $OH^-$.
$H_2SO_3 + OH^- \rightarrow HSO_3^- + H_2O$.
0.00250 mole $H_2SO_3$ + 0.00250 mole $OH^- \rightarrow$ 0.00250 mole $HSO_3^-$.
Total volume is 25.0 ml + 25.0 ml = 0.0500 l.
If the neutralization reaction went 100% to the right we would have

$$\text{concentration of } HSO_3^- = \frac{0.00250 \text{ mole}}{0.0500 \text{ l}} = 0.0500 \ M \ HSO_3^-$$

Now the complication comes in, because $HSO_3^-$ cannot only pick up
protons to re-form $H_2SO_3$ but it can also give off protons to form
$SO_3^=$. We have been ignoring the second of these processes because it is not likely to occur in solutions with excess acid present.
We no longer have that excuse, so we must consider both reactions:

$HSO_3^- \rightarrow H^+ + SO_3^=$

$HSO_3^- + H^+ \rightarrow H_2SO_3$

It turns out that these reactions help each other because $H^+$ liberated
in the first can be picked up in the second.   Let us assume that
the amount of $H^+$ liberated just equals the amount of $H^+$ picked
up.   This means we can add the above two equations and cancel
the $H^+$.   We get for the net reaction.

$2HSO_3^- \rightarrow SO_3^= + H_2SO_3$

When chemical equations are added, the respective equilibrium constants multiply together.   The $K$ for $HSO_3^- \rightarrow H^+ + SO_3^=$ is just
$K_{II}$; the $K$ for $HSO_3^- + H^+ \rightarrow H_2SO_3$ is $1/K_I$.
Consequently, for

$2HSO_3^- \rightleftharpoons SO_3^= + H_2SO_3$

$$K = (K_{II})\left(\frac{1}{K_I}\right) = (5.6 \times 10^{-8})\left(\frac{1}{1.25 \times 10^{-2}}\right) = 4.5 \times 10^{-6}$$

Now we can solve the problem of 0.0500 $M$ $HSO_3^-$.

Let $2x$ moles/l $HSO_3^-$ react by the above net equation. This will form $x$ moles/l $SO_3^=$ and $x$ moles/l $H_2SO_3$, while reducing the $HSO_3^-$ concentration from 0.0500 to $0.0500 - 2x$.

$[HSO_3^-] = 0.0500 - 2x$; $[SO_3^=] = x$; $[H_2SO_3] = x$.

$$K = \frac{[SO_3^=][H_2SO_3]}{[HSO_3^-]^2} = 4.5 \times 10^{-6} = \frac{(x)(x)}{(0.0500 - 2x)^2}.$$

The equation can easily be solved by taking the square root of each side. The final result is $x = 1.1 \times 10^{-4}$. Substituting this value of $x$ in the above concentration expressions, we get

$$[HSO_3^-] = 0.0500 - 2x = 0.0500 - 2(1.1 \times 10^{-4}) = 0.0498 \ M$$

$$[SO_3^=] = x = 1.1 \times 10^{-4} \ M$$

$$[H_2SO_3] = x = 1.1 \times 10^{-4} \ M$$

We can now calculate $[H^+]$ by substituting these values either in $K_I$ or in $K_{II}$.

$$K_I = \frac{[H^+][HSO_3^-]}{[H_2SO_3]} = 1.25 \times 10^{-2} = \frac{[H^+](0.0498)}{1.1 \times 10^{-4}}$$

$$[H^+] = \frac{1.1 \times 10^{-4}}{0.0498} (1.25 \times 10^{-2}) = 2.8 \times 10^{-5}.$$

$$pH = -\log[H^+] = -\log(2.8 \times 10^{-5}) = -(0.45 - 5) = 4.55.$$

PROBLEM 709 Given 25.0 ml of 0.100 $M$ $H_2SO_3$. You add to it 30.0 ml of 0.100 $M$ NaOH. What does the the pH become? Assume additive volumes. $K_{II} = 5.6 \times 10^{-8}$.

SOLUTION: 25.0 ml of 0.100 $M$ $H_2SO_3$ gives 0.00250 mole $H_2SO_3$.

30.0 ml of 0.100 $M$ NaOH gives 0.00300 mole $OH^-$.

We have reached now a stage in the titration where we have added more than enough $OH^-$ to chew up all the $H_2SO_3$ via the reaction $H_2SO_3 + OH^- \rightarrow HSO_3^- + H_2O$. In other words, all the $H_2SO_3$ is gone. But there is still 0.00050 mole $OH^-$ left over. What does it do? It proceeds to chew up the $HSO_3^-$ via the reaction $HSO_3^- + OH^- \rightarrow SO_3^= + H_2O$.

0.00250 mole $HSO_3^-$ + 0.00050 mole $OH^- \rightarrow$ 0.00050 mole $SO_3^=$.

Assuming all the extra $OH^-$ reacts this way, we will get 0.00050 mole $SO_3^=$ and we will reduce the $HSO_3^-$ from 0.00250 mole (resulting from the $H_2SO_3 + OH^-$ neutralization) to 0.00200 mole.

Total volume of solution = 25.0 ml + 30.0 ml = 0.0550 l.

Concentration of $SO_3^= = \dfrac{0.00050 \text{ mole}}{0.0550 \text{ l}} = 0.0091\ M\ SO_3^=.$

Concentration of $HSO_3^- = \dfrac{0.00200 \text{ mole}}{0.0550 \text{ l}} = 0.0364\ M\ HSO_3^-.$

We are now dealing with the $HSO_3^-$-$SO_3^=$ buffer, which is describable by $K_{II}$.

$[H^+] = \dfrac{[HSO_3^-]}{[SO_3^=]} K_{II} = \dfrac{0.0364 - x}{0.0091 + x}\ (5.6 \times 10^{-8})$

where $x$ represents the moles/l $HSO_3^-$ we allow to dissociate to establish this equilibrium. Since $x$, which is equal to the hydrogen-ion concentration, is very small, we can neglect it when added or subtracted. We get finally $[H^+] \cong 2.2 \times 10^{-7}$.

$pH = -\log [H^+] = -\log (2.2 \times 10^{-7}) = -(0.34 - 7) = \mathbf{6.66.}$

■■ P R O B L E M 710    Compute the pH for addition to 25.0 ml of 0.100 $M$ $H_2SO_3$ of the following: (a) 35.0 ml of 0.100 $M$ NaOH; (b) 40.0 ml of 0.100 $M$ NaOH; (c) 45.0 ml of 0.100 $M$ NaOH. Assume additive volumes and use the approximations made in Problem 709.

ANSWER: **7.08; 7.43; 7.85**

P R O B L E M 711    What will be the pH of the solution made by mixing 25.0 ml of 0.100 $M$ $H_2SO_3$ and 50.0 ml of 0.100 $M$ NaOH? Assume additive volumes.

SOLUTION: By this stage enough $OH^-$ has been added to neutralize both protons of $H_2SO_3$. So, allowing for the dilution, the mixture is equivalent to 0.0333 $M$ $Na_2SO_3$. We can see this as follows.

25.0 ml of 0.100 $M$ $H_2SO_3$ gives 0.00250 mole $H_2SO_3$.

50.0 ml of 0.100 $M$ NaOH gives 0.00500 mole $OH^-$.

We allow first: $H_2SO_3 + OH^- \rightarrow HSO_3^- + H_2O$.

Then we follow by: $HSO_3^- + OH^- \rightarrow SO_3^= + H_2O$.

This will give us 0.00250 mole $SO_3^=$ in 0.075 l, which is 0.0333 $M$, as stated above.

This, however, allows for no hydrolysis

Let $x$ = moles/l $SO_3^=$ that succeed in swiping a proton from the water, thereby forming $HSO_3^-$ and setting free an $OH^-$.

$[SO_3^=] = 0.0333 - x$; $[HSO_3^-] = x$; $[OH^-] = x$.

We are interested in $[H^+]$, which can be obtained as

$$\frac{K_w}{[OH^-]} = \frac{1.00 \times 10^{-14}}{x}.$$

Using the equilibrium $HSO_3^- \rightleftharpoons H^+ + SO_3^=$ we have

$$K_{II} = \frac{[H^+][SO_3^=]}{[HSO_3^-]} = 5.6 \times 10^{-8} = \frac{\left(\dfrac{1.00 \times 10^{-14}}{x}\right)(0.0333 - x)}{x}$$

Neglecting the $x$ where it subtracts from 0.0333, we get

$$5.6 \times 10^{-8} \cong \frac{(1.00 \times 10^{-14})(0.0333)}{x^2}$$

which solves to give $x = 7.7 \times 10^{-5} = [OH^-]$.

$$[H^+] = \frac{K_w}{[OH^-]} = \frac{1.00 \times 10^{-14}}{7.7 \times 10^{-5}} = 1.3 \times 10^{-10}.$$

$$pH = -\log[H^+] = -\log(1.3 \times 10^{-10}) = -(0.11 - 10) = 9.89.$$

PROBLEM 712 What is the pH after addition of 55.0 ml of 0.100 $M$ NaOH to 25.0 ml of 0.100 $M$ $H_2SO_3$? Assume additive volumes.

SOLUTION: 50.0 ml of the 55.0 ml 0.100 $M$ NaOH will be used to neutralize the $H_2SO_3$.

The remaining 5.0 ml of 0.100 $M$ NaOH simply serves to increase the $OH^-$ concentration of the solution.

5.0 ml of 0.100 $M$ NaOH gives 0.00050 mole $OH^-$.

Total volume of solution is 25.0 ml + 55.0 ml = 0.0800 l.

$$[OH^-] = \frac{0.00050 \text{ mole}}{0.080 \text{ l}} = 0.0062 \ M.$$

$$[H^+] = \frac{K_w}{[OH^-]} = \frac{1.00 \times 10^{-14}}{0.0062} = 1.6 \times 10^{-12}.$$

$$pH = -\log[H^+] = -\log(1.6 \times 10^{-12}) = -(0.20 - 12) = 11.80.$$

■ PROBLEM 713 Add successively four more 5.0-ml increments of 0.100 $M$ NaOH to the solution resulting from Problem 712. What does the pH become in the respective solutions?

ANSWER: 12.07; 12.22; 12.32; 12.40

In summary, when we add 0.100 $M$ NaOH stepwise to 25.0 ml of 0.100 $M$ $H_2SO_3$, the pH changes in the following sequence: 1.529, 1.74, 1.983, 2.250, 2.63, 4.55, 6.66, 7.08, 7.43, 7.85, 9.89, 11.80, 12.07, 12.22, 12.32, 12.40.    These results are presented graphically in Figure 69. Note particularly the first slow rise corresponding to the buffer $H_2SO_3$-$HSO_3^-$; then there is a sharp rise just when all the $H_2SO_3$ is exhausted. Next comes another gentle rise, which corresponds to the buffer $HSO_3^-$-$SO_3^=$; then there is a sharp rise when all the $HSO_3^-$ is exhausted. Finally, there is a slow gentle rise as more base gets added to an already quite basic solution.

In their titration behavior, triprotic acids are more complicated.

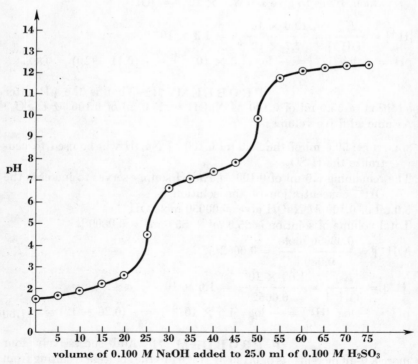

volume of 0.100 $M$ NaOH added to 25.0 ml of 0.100 $M$ $H_2SO_3$

*Figure 69*

# 17

# SOLUBILITY PRODUCTS

IN THIS CHAPTER we turn our attention to the problem of making calculations for a system consisting of excess solid salt in contact with its saturated solution—for example, solid $BaSO_4$ in contact with saturated $BaSO_4$ solution. We shall limit ourselves to cases of *slightly soluble* salts, because highly soluble salts would involve high concentrations of ions, which produce significant departures from ideal behavior. Furthermore, we shall limit ourselves to strong electrolytes (which covers most salts) so that we shall not have to worry about other equilibria, as would be involved, for example, with weak salts.

With many insoluble salts—for example, the carbonates—there is a complication in that the anions interact with the water equilibrium $(H_3O \rightleftharpoons H^+ + OH^-)$ in the process of hydrolysis. This means that we again would be faced with the problem of simultaneous equilibria, which is discussed in Chapter 18. To avoid too many complications at this time, we restrict ourselves to cases where hydrolysis can be neglected. Thus, in this chapter, we confine ourselves to equilibria of the following types:

$$AB_{(s)} \rightleftharpoons A^+ + B^-$$
$$AB_{2(s)} \rightleftharpoons A^{++} + 2B^-$$
$$A_2B_{(s)} \rightleftharpoons 2A^+ + B^=$$

## *Evaluation of the solubility product*

The equilibrium

$$AB_{(s)} \rightleftharpoons A^+ + B^-$$

can be described by the equilibrium condition $K_{s.p.} = [A^+][B^-]$, where $K_{s.p.}$ (usually read "kay-ess-pee" and sometimes called the "ion-product") is a conventional equilibrium constant except that there is no concentration term in the denominator corresponding to the left side of the chemical equation. The rationale behind leaving this term out is that the concentration of $AB_{(s)}$ in the solid state is a constant, no matter how much of the solid AB we take; and if we set a reference state as $AB_{(s)}$ we can regard solid AB as permanently staying at unit activity.

What $K_{s.p.} = [A^+][B^-]$ means is that the concentration of $A^+$ in the solution times the concentration of $B^-$ in that same solution is equal numerically to the characteristic number $K_{s.p.}$, and this must be true for any equilibrium system involving solid AB, $A^+$, and $B^-$. Usually $K_{s.p.}$ can be evaluated by noting how much AB dissolves in giving a saturated solution. (All of our following computations are for 25°C, which needs to be mentioned, since $K_{s.p.}$ generally changes with temperature.)

PROBLEM 714   When you try to dissolve barium sulfate in water, you find that only 0.0017 g $BaSO_4$ will dissolve in 187 ml $H_2O$. What is the $K_{s.p.}$ for $BaSO_4$?

SOLUTION: The equilibrium for the saturated solution is

$$BaSO_{4(s)} \rightleftharpoons Ba^{++} + SO_4^{=}$$

and the $K_{s.p.}$ has the form

$$K_{s.p.} = [Ba^{++}][SO_4^{=}]$$

so we need to know the concentration of $Ba^{++}$ and of $SO_4^{=}$ in the saturated solution.

One mole $BaSO_4$ weighs 233.4 g.

$$0.0017 \text{ g } BaSO_4 = \frac{0.0017 \text{ g}}{233.4 \text{ g/mole}} = 7.3 \times 10^{-6} \text{ mole.}$$

The volume of the solution is 0.187 l. (Strictly speaking we should worry about the volume after mixing 0.187 l water plus $7.3 \times 10^{-6}$

mole $BaSO_4$.  But the latter is such a trifling amount that it contributes a negligible change of volume.)

$$\text{Concentration of dissolved } BaSO_4 = \frac{7.3 \times 10^{-6} \text{ mole}}{0.187 \text{ l}} = 3.9 \times 10^{-5} \text{ M}.$$

$BaSO_4$, like most salts. is a strong electrolyte, so we can assume that all the $BaSO_4$ that goes into solution is dissociated into $Ba^{++}$ and $SO_4^{=}$ ions.  From $3.9 \times 10^{-5}$ M $BaSO_4$ completely dissociated we would have $3.9 \times 10^{-5}$ M $Ba^{++}$ and $3.9 \times 10^{-5}$ M $SO_4^{=}$.  Substitute these values in the expression for $K_{s.p.}$

$$K_{s.p.} = [Ba^{++}][SO_4^{=}] = (3.9 \times 10^{-5})(3.9 \times 10^{-5}) = 1.5 \times 10^{-10}.$$

■PROBLEM 715 What would be the $K_{s.p.}$ of AgCl corresponding to the observation that $3.5 \times 10^{-4}$ g AgCl dissolves in 187 ml water to give a saturated solution?

ANSWER: $1.7 \times 10^{-10}$

PROBLEM 716 To produce a saturated solution of calcium fluoride, $CaF_2$, you need to dissolve 0.0068 g $CaF_2$ per 0.250 l.  What is the $K_{s.p.}$ for $CaF_2$?

SOLUTION: The equilibrium for the saturated solution is

$$CaF_{2(s)} \rightleftharpoons Ca^{++} + 2F^-$$

and the equilibrium condition is given by

$$K_{s.p.} = [Ca^{++}][F^-]^2$$

Note that the concentration of fluoride ion is taken to the second power in conformance with the coefficient 2 in the above chemical equation.  All we need to know now is what is the concentration of calcium ion and what is the concentration of fluoride ion in the saturated solution.

One mole $CaF_2$ weighs 78.08 g.

$$0.0068 \text{ g } CaF_2 \text{ is } \frac{0.0068 \text{ g}}{78.08 \text{ g/mole}} = 8.7 \times 10^{-5} \text{ mole.}$$

The volume of the solution is 0.250 l.

$$\text{Concentration of dissolved } CaF_2 \text{ is } \frac{8.7 \times 10^{-5} \text{ mole}}{0.250 \text{ mole}} = 3.5 \times 10^{-4} \text{ M}$$

We assume that $CaF_2$, being a strong electrolyte, is 100% dissociated into $Ca^{++}$ and $F^-$.  This means that, conforming to the chemical equation $CaF_{2(s)} \rightarrow Ca^{++} + 2F^-$, the dissolving of $3.5 \times 10^{-4}$ mole/l $CaF_2$ will produce $3.5 \times 10^{-4}$ mole/l $Ca^{++}$ and (2) $\times$ $(3.5 \times 10^{-4})$, or $7.0 \times 10^{-4}$, mole/l $F^-$.

$[Ca^{++}] = 3.5 \times 10^{-4} M$; $[F^-] = 7.0 \times 10^{-4} M$.

$K_{s.p.} = [Ca^{++}][F^-]^2 = (3.5 \times 10^{-4})(7.0 \times 10^{-4})^2 = 1.7 \times 10^{-10}$.

■ PROBLEM 717   If it takes 0.048 g $BaF_2$ to saturate 15.0 ml water, what is the $K_{s.p.}$ of $BaF_2$?

ANSWER: $2.4 \times 10^{-5}$

PROBLEM 718   Suppose you are told that a given solution in equilibrium with solid $Ag_2CrO_4$ contains, besides other things, $Ag^+$ at a concentration of $4.4 \times 10^{-6}$ mole/l and $CrO_4^=$ at a concentration of 0.100 $M$. What would be the corresponding $K_{s.p.}$ of $Ag_2CrO_4$?

SOLUTION: We are told there is an equilibrium between solid $Ag_2CrO_4$ and $Ag^+$ and $CrO_4^=$ in solution. We can write this as follows:

$Ag_2CrO_{4(s)} \rightleftharpoons 2Ag^+ + CrO_4^=$

The requirement for equilibrium is given by

$K_{s.p.} = [Ag^+]^2[CrO_4^=]$

We are told that equilibrium exists when

$[Ag^+] = 4.4 \times 10^{-6} M$;  $[CrO_4^=] = 0.100 \ M$

so we simply substitute these values in the expression for $K_{s.p.}$:

$K_{s.p.} = [Ag^+]^2[CrO_4^=] = (4.4 \times 10^{-6})^2(0.100) = 1.9 \times 10^{-12}$

PROBLEM 719   You are given an equilibrium system consisting of solid $Mg(OH)_2$ and solid $MgF_2$ in contact with a saturated solution containing $Mg^{++}$, $OH^-$, and $F^-$. Analysis of the solution shows that it contains $Mg^{++}$ at a concentration of 0.0027 $M$, $OH^-$ at $5.75 \times 10^{-5} M$, and $F^-$ at 0.0054 $M$. Calculate the $K_{s.p.}$ for $Mg(OH)_2$ and for $MgF_2$.

SOLUTION: Both equilibria exist simultaneously.

$Mg(OH)_{2(s)} \rightleftharpoons Mg^{++} + 2OH^-$

$MgF_{2(s)} \rightleftharpoons Mg^{++} + 2F^-$

The equilibrium requirements are

$$K_{s.p.} \text{ of } Mg(OH)_2 = [Mg^{++}][OH^-]^2$$

$$K_{s.p.} \text{ of } MgF_2 = [Mg^{++}][F^-]^2$$

We are told what some typical equilibrium concentrations are:

$$[Mg^{++}] = 0.0027 \ M; \ [OH^-] = 5.75 \times 10^{-5} \ M; \ [F^-] = 0.0054 \ M$$

All we need do is substitute these values in the above expressions:

$$K_{s.p.} \text{ of } Mg(OH)_2 = [Mg^{++}][OH^-]^2 = (0.0027)(5.75 \times 10^{-5})^2$$
$$= 8.9 \times 10^{-12}$$

$$K_{s.p.} \text{ of } MgF_2 = [Mg^{++}][F^-]^2 = (0.0027)(0.0054)^2 = 7.9 \times 10^{-8}$$

The important point to be learned from all the above problems is that the concentration of ion that feeds into the $K_{s.p.}$ expression is the concentration of ion in solution, no matter what that particular concentration happens to be. So long as it is an equilibrium concentration, it satisfies $K_{s.p.}$.

## Calculations from $K_{s.p.}$

Once the numerical value of $K_{s.p.}$ of a given salt has been determined, it can be used from there on to describe any equilibrium system in which the same ions in solution coexist with excess solid phase. Extensive tabulations of $K_{s.p.}$'s may be found in the chemistry handbooks as well as in the book *Oxidation Potentials* by W. M. Latimer (Prentice-Hall, 1952). The one special point that deserves emphasizing is that the $K_{s.p.}$ puts a restriction only on the combined product of ionic concentrations, not on what the individual values must be.

Two principal calculations involving $K_{s.p.}$ are: (1) the prediction of how much salt can dissolve in a given amount of water (or of solution containing a common-ion) and (2) the prediction of whether precipitation will occur when two solutions are mixed. $K_{s.p.}$ also enables us to calculate one ionic concentration if the other one is specified.

First we consider the simple case where a solid dissolves in water to give the same number of positive ions as negative ions.

PROBLEM 720    Given that the $K_{s.p.}$ of $BaSO_4$ is $1.5 \times 10^{-9}$, how many g barium sulfate can you dissolve in 1000 l water?

SOLUTION: The equilibrium will be

$$BaSO_{4(s)} \rightleftharpoons Ba^{++} + SO_4^{=}$$

for which the equilibrium requirement is

$$K_{s.p.} = [Ba^{++}][SO_4^{=}] = 1.5 \times 10^{-9}$$

This means that the concentration of barium ion, whatever it is, times the concentration of sulfate ion, whatever it is, must come out to equal $1.5 \times 10^{-9}$.

There is, however, another requirement in this case. We are dissolving $BaSO_4$ in pure water—that is, in water containing no $Ba^{++}$ and no $SO_4^{=}$ to start. The dissolving reaction is $BaSO_{4(s)} \rightarrow Ba^{++} + SO_4^{=}$ and it indicates that we get one $Ba^{++}$ for each $SO_4^{=}$. In other words, we have here also the requirement that the $Ba^{++}$ concentration be equal to the $SO_4^{=}$ concentration. This is not part of the $K_{s.p.}$ requirement; it comes about because of the way we are making our saturated solution.

Let $x$ = moles/l solid $BaSO_4$ that dissolves.
This will give $x$ moles/l $Ba^{++}$ and $x$ moles/l $SO_4^{=}$.
$[Ba^{++}] = x$; $[SO_4^{=}] = x$.
$K_{s.p.} = [Ba^{++}][SO_4^{=}] = 1.5 \times 10^{-9} = (x)(x)$.
Solving for $x$ gives $3.9 \times 10^{-5}$.
This gives the moles of $BaSO_4$ that can dissolve per liter.
One mole $BaSO_4$ weighs 233.4 g, so we can dissolve per liter

$$(3.9 \times 10^{-5} \text{ mole}) \left( 233.4 \ \frac{g}{mole} \right) = 9.1 \times 10^{-3} \text{ g.}$$

In 1000 l, this amounts to $\left( 9.1 \times 10^{-3} \ \frac{g}{liter} \right) (1000 \text{ l}) = \mathbf{9.1 \ g}$

■ PROBLEM 721    Given that the $K_{s.p.}$ of thallous iodide, TlI, is $8.9 \times 10^{-8}$, calculate how many g TlI can be dissolved in 1.26 l water.

ANSWER: **0.12 g**

Next we consider a case where a salt dissolves in a solution already containing a common-ion.

PROBLEM 722 Given that the $K_{s.p.}$
of $BaSO_4$ is $1.5 \times 10^{-9}$, how many g $BaSO_4$ can you dissolve in 1000 l
of 0.100 $M$ $Na_2SO_4$ solution?

SOLUTION: When you have added enough $BaSO_4$ to saturate the solution, the equilibrium will be

$$BaSO_{4(s)} \rightleftharpoons Ba^{++} + SO_4^{=}$$

for which the equilibrium condition requires that

$$K_{s.p.} = [Ba^{++}][SO_4^{=}] = 1.5 \times 10^{-9}$$

Let $x$ = moles/l $BaSO_4$ that dissolve. This will put into the solution $x$
moles/l $Ba^{++}$ and $x$ moles/l $SO_4^{=}$. But the solution already contains 0.100 $M$ $Na_2SO_4$ before you dissolved in any $BaSO_4$. Furthermore, since $Na_2SO_4$ is a strong electrolyte, 0.100 $M$ $Na_2SO_4$ corresponds to 0.100 $M$ $SO_4^{=}$. If we add $x$ moles/l $SO_4^{=}$ to the 0.100 $M$
already there, we will have at equilibrium:

$$[SO_4^{=}] = 0.100 + x; \ [Ba^{++}] = x$$

[*Note:* $[Ba^{++}]$ is *not* equal to $SO_4^{=}$, as was true in Problem 720.]
Substitute these values in $K_{s.p.}$ and solve for $x$.
$K_{s.p.} = [Ba^{++}][SO_4^{=}] = 1.5 \times 10^{-9} = (x)(0.100 + x)$.
No point to solving the quadratic for $x$ since $x$ is obviously small compared to 0.100, so we assume that $(0.100 + x) \cong 0.100$. This
leads to $1.5 \times 10^{-9} \cong 0.100x$, which solves to $x = 1.5 \times 10^{-8}$
for the moles/l $BaSO_4$ that can be dissolved.
One mole $BaSO_4$ weighs 233.4 g and we are working with 1000 l.

$$\text{Total } BaSO_4 \text{ dissolved} = \left(1.5 \times 10^{-8} \frac{\text{mole}}{\text{liter}}\right)\left(233.4 \frac{\text{g}}{\text{mole}}\right)(1000 \text{ l})$$

$$= \textbf{0.0035 g}$$

■ PROBLEM 723 Given that the $K_{s.p.}$ of
strontium sulfate, $SrSO_4$, is $7.6 \times 10^{-7}$, how many g $SrSO_4$ can you dissolve in 1000 l of 0.100 $M$ $Sr(NO_3)_2$?
ANSWER: **1.4 g**

■ PROBLEM 724 Given that the $K_{s.p.}$ of
silver acetate, AgOAc, is $2.3 \times 10^{-3}$, how many g AgOAc can you dissolve in 1.26 l of 0.150 $M$ $AgNO_3$? Recall that Ac stands for $CH_3CO$.
ANSWER: **2.9 g**

The above cases correspond to salts dissolving to give an equal number of positive and negative ions.  What do we do if the dissolving produces twice as many of one ion as of the other?

PROBLEM 725    Given that the $K_{\text{s.p.}}$ of $MgF_2$ is $8 \times 10^{-8}$, how many g $MgF_2$ can you dissolve in 0.250 l water?

SOLUTION: The equilibrium will be

$$MgF_{2(s)} \rightleftharpoons Mg^{++} + 2F^-$$

and the requirement for equilibrium is that

$$K_{\text{s.p.}} = [Mg^{++}][F^-]^2 = 8 \times 10^{-8}$$

Let $x$ = moles/l $MgF_2$ that dissolve in water.

When $x$ moles/l $MgF_2$ dissolve, then according to the reaction $MgF_{2(s)} \rightarrow Mg^{++} + 2F^-$, we would get $x$ moles/l $Mg^{++}$ and $2x$ moles/l $F^-$.  This gives us at equilibrium:

$$[Mg^{++}] = x; [F^-] = 2x$$

Substitute these in the $K_{\text{s.p.}}$ expression:

$$K_{\text{s.p.}} = [Mg^{++}][F^-]^2 = (x)(2x)^2 = 8 \times 10^{-8}$$

*Note:* The square bracket indicates moles per liter of that species.  The exponent 2 on $[F^-]^2$ means we have to square whatever goes inside the bracket—that is, whatever the fluoride-ion concentration happens to be.  The way we have defined $x$, the fluoride-ion concentration is $2x$, and we shall have to square that whole business.  This appearance of the 2 in two places causes students a great deal of trouble, usually because they forget the meaning of the square brackets and also because they resort to dangerous shortcuts such as putting $2F^-$ inside the square brackets.  You can save yourself much grief if you stick to the notation as used above.

We need to solve $4x^3 = 8 \times 10^{-8}$, which can be done by dividing both sides by 4 and taking the cube root

$$x = (2 \times 10^{-8})^{1/3} = (20 \times 10^{-9})^{1/3} = 3 \times 10^{-3}$$

where we round off to stick with the only-one-allowed significant figure.  This gives us how many moles of $MgF_2$ can dissolve per liter.  To get grams per 0.250 l, we need to multiply by the weight of one mole, 62.31 g, and 0.250 l.

Total $MgF_2$ dissolved $= \left( 3 \times 10^{-3} \dfrac{\text{mole}}{\text{liter}} \right) \left( 62.31 \dfrac{\text{g}}{\text{mole}} \right) (0.250 \text{ l})$

$= 0.05 \text{ g}.$

Now we complicate it a bit. Still working with the case where the dissolving introduces twice as many of one kind of ion as the other, what do we do if the solution already contains a common-ion?

## PROBLEM 726

Given that the $K_{\text{s.p.}}$ of $MgF_2$ is $8 \times 10^{-8}$, how many g $MgF_2$ can you dissolve in 0.250 l of 0.100 $M$ $Mg(NO_3)_2$?

SOLUTION: Let $x =$ moles/l $MgF_2$ that dissolve to establish equilibrium. This will produce $x$ moles/l $Mg^{++}$ and $2x$ moles/l $F^-$ via the reaction $MgF_2 \rightarrow Mg^{++} + 2F^-$.

But there is already some $Mg^{++}$ in the solution, corresponding to 0.100 $M$ $Mg(NO_3)_2$. $Mg(NO_3)_2$ is a strong electrolyte, and 0.100 $M$ $Mg(NO_3)_2$ is the same as 0.100 $Mg^{++}$ and 0.200 $M$ $NO_3^-$.

Therefore, the total $Mg^{++}$ concentration at equilibrium will be $0.100 + x$; the total $F^-$ concentration will be $2x$.

$[Mg^{++}] = 0.100 + x$; $[F^-] = 2x$.

The equilibrium

$$MgF_{2(s)} \rightleftharpoons Mg^{++} + 2F^-$$

requires that

$$K_{\text{s.p.}} = [Mg^{++}][F^-]^2 = 8 \times 10^{-8}$$

Substituting the above concentrations, we get

$$[Mg^{++}][F^-]^2 = (0.100 + x)(2x)^2 = 8 \times 10^{-8}$$

Nominally, this is a cubic equation which can be solved exactly. However, since only one significant figure is allowed in the answer, we can make do with an approximate solution. Since $x$ has to be small compared to 0.100, we can assume $0.100 + x \cong 0.100$. This gives us the approximate equation $(0.100)(2x)^2 = 8 \times 10^{-8}$, which quickly solves to $x = 4 \times 10^{-4}$ as the number of moles $MgF_2$ that can be dissolved per liter of 0.100 $M$ $Mg(NO_3)_2$. To get grams per 0.250 l,

$$\left( 4 \times 10^{-4} \dfrac{\text{mole}}{\text{liter}} \right) (0.250 \text{ l}) \left( 62.31 \dfrac{\text{g } MgF_2}{\text{mole}} \right) = 0.006 \text{ g}.$$

## PROBLEM 727

Given that $K_{s.p.}$ of $MgF_2$ is $8 \times 10^{-8}$, how many g $MgF_2$ can you dissolve in 0.250 l of 0.100 $M$ NaF?

SOLUTION: Let $x$ = moles/l $MgF_2$ that can dissolve. This will give $x$ moles/l $Mg^{++}$ and $2x$ moles/l $F^-$ via the reaction $MgF_2 \rightarrow Mg^{++} + 2F^-$.

But the solution already contains 0.100 $M$ $F^-$.

At equilibrium

$$[Mg^{++}] = x; [F^-] = 2x + 0.100$$

$$K_{s.p.} = [Mg^{++}][F^-]^2 = (x)(2x + 0.100)^2 = 8 \times 10^{-8}$$

Again, $x$ looks to be small, so we assume $2x + 0.100 \cong 0.100$.

This gives $(x)(0.100)^2 \cong 8 \times 10^{-8}$, which solves to $x = 8 \times 10^{-6}$ mole/l $MgF_2$ that can be dissolved in 0.100 $M$ NaF. For grams in 0.250 l,

$$\left( 8 \times 10^{-6} \frac{\text{mole } MgF_2}{\text{liter}} \right) (0.250 \text{ l}) \left( 62.31 \frac{\text{g } MgF_2}{\text{mole}} \right) = 1 \times 10^{-4} \text{ g}$$

It would pay to spend some extra time studying the preceding three problems to see how they compare with each other. In all three cases, the equilibrium condition for saturation is the same: $K_{s.p.} = [Mg^{++}][F^-]^2 = 8 \times 10^{-8}$. The only difference has been in what goes inside the brackets. For dissolving $MgF_2$ in pure water, what goes in the $F^-$ bracket is just twice what goes in for $Mg^{++}$. For dissolving $MgF_2$ in 0.100 $M$ $Mg(NO_3)_2$, we need to allow for an additional 0.100 $M$ $Mg^{++}$, so $[Mg^{++}]$ becomes $(x + 0.100)$. For dissolving $MgF_2$ in 0.100 $M$ NaF, we need to allow for an additional 0.100 $M$ $F^-$, so $[F^-]$ becomes $(2x + 0.100)$. The values of $x$ will thus come out to be different in the three cases.

■ PROBLEM 728 Given that the $K_{s.p.}$ of $Ag_2CrO_4$ is $1.9 \times 10^{-12}$, calculate how many g $Ag_2CrO_4$ can be dissolved in 5.6 l water.

ANSWER: **0.14 g**

■ PROBLEM 729 Given that the $K_{s.p.}$ of $Ag_2Cro_4$ is $1.9 \times 10^{-12}$, calculate how many g $Ag_2CrO_4$ can be dissolved

in 5.6 l of (a) 0.125 $M$ AgNO$_3$ solution and (b) 0.125 $M$ Na$_2$CrO$_4$ solution.
ANSWER: (a) $2.3 \times 10^{-7}$ g; (b) $3.6 \times 10^{-3}$ g

■■ PROBLEM 730 Radium nitrate, Ra(NO$_3$)$_2$, is rather unusual in being a slightly soluble nitrate, whereas most nitrates are soluble to a large extent. Given that $K_{s.p.}$ of Ra(NO$_3$)$_2$ is $6.3 \times 10^{-3}$, calculate how many moles/l Ra(NO$_3$)$_2$ will dissolve in (a) pure water, (b) 0.100 $M$ NaNO$_3$, and (c) 0.100 $M$ Ra(OH)$_2$. Assume Ra(OH)$_2$ to be a strong electrolyte.
ANSWER: (a) 0.12; (b) 0.085; (c) 0.091 moles/l

## Precipitation reactions

In the preceding section, we approached equilibrium by adding a slightly soluble salt, such as AB, to water or to a common-ion solution and letting enough AB dissolve to give equilibrium concentrations of A$^+$ and B$^-$. We could just as well approach equilibrium from the other side by mixing solutions of A$^+$ and B$^-$ and letting AB precipitate until equilibrium concentrations of A$^+$ and B$^-$ are left. The two major difficulties that students encounter in the latter type of calculation are: (a) proper allowance for the dilution of one solution by the other; (b) proper setting up of the equations so that difficult algebraic computations are avoided.

A practical point to consider is that the calculations will generally tell only whether precipitation is expected. In actual laboratory manipulation, other factors need to be considered such as how fast does the reaction come to equilibrium, how much extra solid needs to be allowed for in order to make a precipitate "visible," etc.

PROBLEM 731 Given that the $K_{s.p.}$ of BaSO$_4$ is $1.5 \times 10^{-9}$, would you expect a precipitate to form if 10.0 ml of 0.0100 $M$ BaCl$_2$ solution were mixed with 30.0 ml of 0.0050 $M$ Na$_2$SO$_4$ solution?

SOLUTION: The condition for the equilibrium

$$BaSO_{4(s)} \rightleftharpoons Ba^{++} + SO_4^=$$

is that

$$K_{s.p.} = [Ba^{++}][SO_4^=] = 1.5 \times 10^{-9}$$

If the product of the barium-ion concentration times the sulfate concentration is greater than $1.5 \times 10^{-9}$, $BaSO_4$ should precipitate so as to reduce the ion concentrations to equilibrium values.

Because $BaCl_2$ and $Na_2SO_4$ are strong electrolytes, they will be 100% dissociated.

10.0 ml of 0.0100 $M$ $BaCl_2$ gives

$$(0.0100 \text{ l}) \left( 0.0100 \, \frac{\text{mole } Ba^{++}}{\text{liter}} \right) = 0.000100 \text{ mole } Ba^{++}$$

30.0 ml of 0.0050 $M$ $Na_2SO_4$ gives

$$(0.0300 \text{ l}) \left( 0.00500 \, \frac{\text{mole } SO_4^=}{\text{liter}} \right) = 1.5 \times 10^{-4} \text{ mole } SO_4^=$$

Total volume of the solution is 10.0 ml + 30.0 ml = 0.0400 l.

Therefore, *if no reaction occurred* when solutions are mixed, we could calculate the concentrations as follows:

$$\text{concentration of } Ba^{++} = \frac{0.000100 \text{ mole } Ba^{++}}{0.0400 \text{ l}}$$
$$= 2.50 \times 10^{-3} \, M \, Ba^{++}$$

$$\text{concentration of } SO_4^- = \frac{1.5 \times 10^{-4} \text{ mole } SO_4^=}{0.0400 \text{ l}}$$
$$= 3.8 \times 10^{-3} \, M \, SO_4^=$$

If no $BaSO_4$ precipitates, $[Ba^{++}][SO_4^=]$ would equal

$$(2.50 \times 10^{-3})(3.8 \times 10^{-3}) = 9.5 \times 10^{-6}.$$

This ion product would be considerably higher than the value of $K_{s.p.}$ (which is $1.5 \times 10^{-9}$), so it would not correspond to an equilibrium situation and **precipitation should occur**.

■ PROBLEM 732    The $K_{s.p.}$ of $SrSO_4$ is $7.6 \times 10^{-7}$. Should precipitation occur when 25.0 ml of $1.0 \times 10^{-3}$ $M$ $SrCl_2$ solution is mixed with 15.0 ml of $2.0 \times 10^{-3}$ $M$ $Na_2SO_4$?

ANSWER: **no**; $[Sr^{++}][SO_4^=] = 4.7 \times 10^{-7}$, which is less than $K_{s.p.}$

PROBLEM 733    Would you expect $BaF_2$ to precipitate if 20.0 ml of 0.010 $M$ $BaCl_2$ is mixed with 30.0 ml of 0.010 $M$ $NaF$? The $K_{s.p.}$ of $BaF_2$ is $2.4 \times 10^{-5}$.

SOLUTION: $BaCl_2$ and $NaF$ are strong electrolytes, 100% dissociated. 20.0 ml of 0.010 $M$ $BaCl_2$ would give

$$(0.0200 \text{ l}) \left( 0.010 \frac{\text{mole Ba}^{++}}{\text{liter}} \right) = 2.0 \times 10^{-4} \text{ mole Ba}^{++}.$$

30.0 ml of 0.010 $M$ NaF would give

$$(0.0300 \text{ l}) \left( 0.010 \frac{\text{mole F}^-}{\text{liter}} \right) = 3.0 \times 10^{-4} \text{ mole F}^-.$$

If no reaction occurs, the concentrations in the final solution would be as follows, taking into account that the total volume is now 0.0500 l:

$$\text{concentration of Ba}^{++} = \frac{2.0 \times 10^{-4} \text{ mole}}{0.0500 \text{ l}}$$
$$= 4.0 \times 10^{-3} \ M \text{ Ba}^{++}$$

$$\text{concentration of F}^- = \frac{3.0 \times 10^{-4} \text{ mole}}{0.0500 \text{ l}} = 6.0 \times 10^{-3} \ M \text{ F}^-$$

To get precipitation would mean setting up the equilibrium

$$\text{BaF}_{2(s)} \rightleftharpoons \text{Ba}^{++} + 2\text{F}^-$$

for which the equilibrium requirement is

$$K_{\text{s.p.}} = [\text{Ba}^{++}][\text{F}^-]^2 = 2.4 \times 10^{-5}$$

How does our mixture compare with this equilibrium requirement? Calculate $[\text{Ba}^{++}][\text{F}^-]^2$ to find out.

$$[\text{Ba}^{++}][\text{F}^-]^2 = (4.0 \times 10^{-3})(6.0 \times 10^{-3})^2 = 1.4 \times 10^{-7}$$

Since this ion-product is appreciably less than $K_{\text{s.p.}}$, it means we do **not** have enough concentration of $\text{Ba}^{++}$ and $\text{F}^-$ to form a saturated solution. In other words, we do **not** expect precipitation to occur.

■ PROBLEM 734 The $K_{\text{s.p.}}$ of $\text{Ca(OH)}_2$ is $1.3 \times 10^{-6}$. Would you expect $\text{Ca(OH)}_2$ to precipitate when 2.00 l of 0.0500 $M$ $\text{CaCl}_2$ is mixed with 0.50 l of 0.50 $M$ NaOH?

ANSWER: yes; ion-product $[\text{Ca}^{++}][\text{OH}^-]^2 = 4 \times 10^{-4}$ exceeds $K_{\text{s.p.}}$.

■ PROBLEM 735 The $K_{\text{s.p.}}$ of AgOAc is $2.3 \times 10^{-3}$. Should you get precipitation on mixing 20.0 ml of 1.2 $M$ $\text{AgNO}_3$ with 30.0 ml of 1.4 $M$ HOAc?

SOLUTION: You have to be careful here since $\text{AgNO}_3$ is a strong electrolyte 100% dissociated into $\text{Ag}^+$ and $\text{NO}_3{}^-$, but HOAc is a weak electrolyte, only slightly dissociated to $\text{H}^+$ and $\text{OAc}^-$.

Calculate first as if no precipitation occurs.

20.0 ml of 1.2 $M$ AgNO$_3$ gives

$$(0.0200 \text{ l}) \left( 1.2 \frac{\text{mole Ag}^+}{\text{liter}} \right) = 0.024 \text{ mole Ag}^+.$$

30.0 ml of 1.4 $M$ HOAc gives

$$(0.0300 \text{ l}) \left( 1.4 \frac{\text{mole HOAc}}{\text{liter}} \right) = 0.042 \text{ mole HOAc}.$$

Total volume of solution is 0.0500 l.

Concentration of Ag$^+$ would be $\dfrac{0.024 \text{ mole}}{0.0500 \text{ l}} = 0.48 \; M \text{ Ag}^+.$

Concentration of HOAc would be $\dfrac{0.042 \text{ mole}}{0.0500 \text{ l}} = 0.84 \; M \text{ HOAc}.$

If we get a precipitate of AgOAc, the equilibrium we are interested in would be

$$\text{AgOAc}_{(s)} \rightleftharpoons \text{Ag}^+ + \text{OAc}^-$$

$$K_{\text{s.p.}} = [\text{Ag}^+][\text{OAc}^-] = 2.3 \times 10^{-3}$$

So we don't really care what the concentration of HOAc is but what the concentration of free OAc$^-$ would be. We need, therefore, to calculate the concentration of OAc$^-$ in 0.84 $M$ HOAc.

Let $x$ = moles/l HOAc that dissociate.

$$\text{HOAc} \rightleftharpoons \text{H}^+ + \text{OAc}^-$$

$$K_{\text{diss}} = \frac{[\text{H}^+][\text{OAc}^-]}{[\text{HOAc}]} = 1.8 \times 10^{-5} = \frac{(x)(x)}{0.84 - x}$$

$$[\text{OAc}^-] = x = 3.9 \times 10^{-3} \; M$$

If now we look at the ion-product [Ag$^+$][OAc$^-$], we get $(0.48)(3.9 \times 10^{-3}) = 1.9 \times 10^{-3}$, which is smaller than $K_{\text{s.p.}}$, so **no precipitation** of AgOAc is expected.

■ PROBLEM 736 If you mix 40.0 ml of 1.5 $M$ NH$_3$ with 10.0 ml of 0.10 $M$ CaCl$_2$, do you expect Ca(OH)$_2$ to precipitate? The $K_{\text{s.p.}}$ of Ca(OH)$_2$ is $1.3 \times 10^{-6}$; $K_{\text{diss}}$ of NH$_3$ is $1.81 \times 10^{-5}$.

ANSWER: **no**; the ion-product [Ca$^{++}$][OH$^-$]$^2$ is $4.3 \times 10^{-7}$, which is less than $K_{\text{s.p.}}$.

The foregoing problems are not very complicated and in fact are not much more than exercises in calculating concentrations. For this purpose, it is useful to develop short cuts for speeding up the computations. One of the most obvious is to recognize the dilution factor, whereby the concentration in the final mixture is figured as the initial concentration times a fraction which describes what portion of the final volume is contributed by each solution. For example, in Problem 736, where 10.0 ml of 0.10 $M$ $CaCl_2$ is mixed with 40.0 ml of 1.5 $M$ $NH_3$, the final concentration of $CaCl_2$ is 1/5 of 0.10 $M$, since 10.0 ml is 10.0/50.0 of the total volume; similarly, the final concentration of $NH_3$ is 4/5 of 1.5 $M$, since 40.0 ml is 40.0/50.0 of the total volume. The other point to be especially careful about is to note that the "ion-product" which is to be compared with the $K_{s.p.}$ value must be calculated by taking each concentration to the proper power as shown by the coefficients in the chemical equation for the equilibrium.

A more complex problem appears when we look at a precipitation reaction and try to calculate what concentration of ions should be left in solution after precipitation occurs. There are two different cases: (1) the ions are mixed in the molar ratio that corresponds to their consumption in the chemical equation for precipitation (e.g., mix $Mg^{++}$ and $F^-$ in a ratio of 1 to 2); (2) one of the ions is in excess over what the stoichiometry requires.

PROBLEM 737 If you mix 10.0 ml of 0.100 $M$ $BaCl_2$ with 40.0 ml of 0.0250 $M$ $Na_2SO_4$, what should be the concentration of $Ba^{++}$ and of $SO_4^=$ in solution after precipitation has occurred? $K_{s.p.}$ of $BaSO_4$ is $1.5 \times 10^{-9}$.

SOLUTION: 10.0 ml of 0.100 $M$ $BaCl_2$ gives

$$(0.0100 \text{ l}) \left( 0.100 \frac{\text{mole } Ba^{++}}{\text{liter}} \right) = 0.00100 \text{ mole } Ba^{++}.$$

40.0 ml of 0.0250 $M$ $Na_2SO_4$ gives

$$(0.0400 \text{ l}) \left( 0.0250 \frac{\text{mole } SO_4^=}{\text{liter}} \right) = 0.00100 \text{ mole } SO_4^=.$$

We thus have equal numbers of moles of $Ba^{++}$ and of $SO_4^=$. When they react via the equation $Ba^{++} + SO_4^= \rightarrow BaSO_{4(s)}$ neither $Ba^{++}$ nor $SO_4^=$ will be left in excess. This means solid $BaSO_4$ is precipitated until equilibrium is established, one in which $Ba^{++}$

and $SO_4^=$ are left in solution in equal concentrations. But that would be the same problem as dissolving $BaSO_4$ in pure water. The resulting solution there also has $Ba^{++}$ and $SO_4^=$ in equal concentration. (In the present case, there is also $Cl^-$ and $Na^+$ in solution but neither of these is involved in the $BaSO_4$ equilibrium.) So, the simplest way to solve the above problem of mixing $Ba^{++}$ and $SO_4^=$ in equal quantities is to approach equilibrium from the other side—namely, add $BaSO_4$ to saturate a solution.

$$BaSO_{4(s)} \rightleftharpoons Ba^{++} + SO_4^=$$

$$[Ba^{++}] = x; \ [SO_4^=] = x$$

$$K_{s.p.} = [Ba^{++}][SO_4^=] = 1.5 \times 10^{-9} = (x)(x)$$

$$x = 3.9 \times 10^{-5} M = [Ba^{++}] = [SO_4^=]$$

■ PROBLEM 738 Suppose you mix 2.0 l of 0.10 $M$ $SrCl_2$ solution with 0.25 l of 0.80 $M$ $Na_2SO_4$. What should be the concentration of $Sr^{++}$ and of $SO_4^=$ in the final solution? $K_{s.p.}$ of $SrSO_4$ is $7.6 \times 10^{-7}$.

ANSWER: $8.7 \times 10^{-4}$ $M$ $Sr^{++}$   and   $8.7 \times 10^{-4}$ $M$ $SO_4^=$

The same procedure applies when the stoichiometry of the precipitation reaction requires two of one ion per one of the other. Again, assuming you mix enough to cause precipitation, the easiest thing to do is to approach equilibrium from the other side.

PROBLEM 739 Suppose you mix 10.0 ml of 0.25 $M$ $Mg(NO_3)_2$ and 25.0 ml of 0.20 $M$ $NaF$. What should be the concentration of $Mg^{++}$ and of $F^-$ in the final solution? $K_{s.p.}$ of $MgF_2$ is $8 \times 10^{-8}$.

SOLUTION: First you should see whether precipitation occurs. Just after mixing, before any reaction occurs, the

concentration of $Mg^{++}$ would be $\left(\dfrac{10.0}{35.0}\right)$ (0.25 $M$), or 0.071 $M$;

concentration of $F^-$ would be $\left(\dfrac{25.0}{35.0}\right)$ (0.20 $M$), or 0.14 $M$.

The ion-product $[Mg^{++}][F^-]^2$, which equals $(0.071)(0.14)^2 = 1.4 \times 10^{-3}$, exceeds $K_{s.p.}$, so precipitation to form solid $MgF_2$ should occur.

Now we note that $Mg^{++}$ and $F^-$ are being added together in a 1-to-2 ratio, the same as required in the chemical equation $Mg^{++} + 2F^- \rightleftharpoons MgF_{2(s)}$. The equilibrium system will thus be the same as if approached from the other side—that is, by adding solid $MgF_2$ to water.

Hence, all we need to do is to solve the regular solubility problem.

$$MgF_{2(s)} \rightleftharpoons Mg^{++} + 2F^-$$

$$[Mg^{++}] = x; \ [F^-] = 2x$$

$$K_{s.p.} = [Mg^{++}][F^-]^2 = 8 \times 10^{-8} = (x)(2x)^2$$

$$x = 3 \times 10^{-3}$$

$$[Mg^{++}] = x = 3 \times 10^{-3} \ M; \ [F^-] = 2x = 6 \times 10^{-3} \ M$$

[*Note:* There is another way to solve these problems which may on first sight look more straightforward.   Given a solution where you put together 0.071 $M$ $Mg^{++}$ and 0.14 $M$ $F^-$, let $y$ = moles/l $MgF_2$ that precipitate.   According to the reaction $Mg^{++} + 2F^- \rightarrow MgF_{2(s)}$, this would use up $y$ moles/l $Mg^{++}$ and $2y$ moles/l $F^-$. Hence at equilibrium, the concentration of $Mg^{++}$ would be $(0.071 - y)$ $M$ and the concentration of $F^-$ would be $(0.14 - 2y)$ $M$.   Substitute these as usual:

$$MgF_{2(s)} \rightleftharpoons Mg^{++} + 2F^-$$

$$K_{s.p.} = [Mg^{++}][F^-]^2 = 8 \times 10^{-8} = (0.071 - y)(0.14 - 2y)^2$$

What's wrong with such a method?   Nothing.   The only objection is that it gets you into some nasty algebra—a cubic equation and a situation where $y$ cannot be neglected.   The reason you get into this mess is that you are approaching equilibrium from the unfavorable side and defining an unknown which is a relatively large number.   Always try to rig your calculations so you are calculating a small effect—e.g., a trace of solid dissolving—instead of a big effect—e.g., lots of precipitate forming.   If you are clever, the approximations will be clearly evident and the algebra will be simple, but only *if you set up the problem right.*]

■ P R O B L E M  740  Suppose you dissolve 5.1 g $AgNO_3$ and 2.9 g $K_2CrO_4$ in enough water to make 225 ml solution.   Should $Ag_2CrO_4$ precipitate?   What should be the concentration of $Ag^+$ and $CrO_4^=$ in the final solution? $K_{s.p.}$ of $Ag_2CrO_4$ is $1.9 \times 10^{-12}$.

ANSWER: **precipitation should occur**, because the ion-product, $[Ag^+]^2[CrO_4^=]$, comes out to be $1.2 \times 10^{-3}$, which exceeds $K_{s.p.}$; $[Ag^+] = 1.6 \times 10^{-4}$ $M$; $[CrO_4^=] = 7.8 \times 10^{-5}$ $M$

What happens if one of the ions in a precipitation reaction is in excess over what stoichiometry requires? Then, some of that ion will be left in solution in appreciable quantity and its concentration will effectively control how much of the other ion can be in solution at the same time. The computation is a "common-ion" problem.

PROBLEM 741    Suppose you mix 40.0 ml of 0.10 $M$ $AgNO_3$ and 10.0 ml of 0.15 $M$ NaBr. What should be the final concentrations of $Ag^+$ and $Br^-$, given that the $K_{s.p.}$ of AgBr is $5.0 \times 10^{-13}$?

SOLUTION: 40.0 ml of 0.10 $M$ $AgNO_3$ gives

$$(0.0400 \text{ l}) \left( 0.10 \frac{\text{mole } Ag^+}{\text{liter}} \right) = 0.0040 \text{ mole } Ag^+$$

10.0 ml of 0.15 $M$ NaBr gives

$$(0.0100 \text{ l}) \left( 0.15 \frac{\text{mole } Br^-}{\text{liter}} \right) = 0.0015 \text{ mole } Br^-.$$

Total volume of final solution is 50.0 ml.
If no precipitation occurred, there would be:

$$\text{concentration of } Ag^+ = \frac{0.0040 \text{ mole}}{0.050 \text{ l}} = 0.080 \text{ } M \text{ } Ag^+$$

$$\text{concentration of } Br^- = \frac{0.0015 \text{ mole}}{0.050 \text{ l}} = 0.030 \text{ } M \text{ } Br^-$$

The precipitation reaction $Ag^+ + Br^- \rightarrow AgBr_{(s)}$ requires a 1-to-1 molar ratio, so $Ag^+$ is evidently in excess. Let us assume that the excess $Ag^+$ drives all the $Br^-$ out of solution. This means that 0.080 $M$ $Ag^+$ reacts with 0.030 $M$ $Br^-$ to produce AgBr while leaving 0.050 $M$ $Ag^+$ in excess.

Let us now let as much AgBr dissolve as needed to establish the AgBr saturation equilibrium—let us say, $x$ moles/l. This will raise the

$Ag^+$ concentration to $0.050 + x$ and will make the $Br^-$ concentration equal to $x$.

$$AgBr_{(s)} \rightleftharpoons Ag^+ + Br^-$$

$$K_{s.p.} = [Ag^+][Br^-] = 5.0 \times 10^{-13} = (0.050 + x)(x)$$

Since $x$ is small compared to 0.050, we can estimate $0.050 + x \cong 0.050$. This gives us the approximate equation $5.0 \times 10^{-13} \cong (0.050)(x)$, which solves to $x = 1.0 \times 10^{-11}$. The final concentrations would be

$$[Ag^+] = 0.050 + x \cong 0.050 \ M$$

$$[Br^-] = x = 1.0 \times 10^{-11} \ M$$

■ **PROBLEM** 742 The $K_{s.p.}$ for $AgBrO_{3(s)}$ $\rightleftharpoons Ag^+ + BrO_3^-$ is $5.4 \times 10^{-5}$. What should be the final concentrations of $Ag^+$ and $BrO_3^-$ in a solution made by mixing 25.0 ml of 0.10 $M$ $AgNO_3$ and 45.0 ml of 0.10 $M$ $NaBrO_3$?

ANSWER: $[Ag^+] = 1.8 \times 10^{-3} \ M$; $[BrO_3^-] = 0.030 \ M$

**PROBLEM** 743 The $K_{s.p.}$ for $Ag_2MoO_4$ $\rightleftharpoons 2Ag^+ + MoO_4^=$ is $2.6 \times 10^{-11}$. What should be the final concentration of $Ag^+$ and of $MoO_4^=$ in a solution made by mixing 25.0 ml of 0.10 $M$ $AgNO_3$ and 45.0 ml of 0.10 $M$ $Na_2MoO_4$?

SOLUTION: On mixing, the concentrations, without precipitation, become:

$$\text{concentration of } Ag^+ = \left(\frac{25.0 \ ml}{70.0 \ ml}\right)(0.10 \ M) = 0.036 \ M$$

$$\text{concentration of } MoO_4^= = \left(\frac{45.0 \ ml}{70.0 \ ml}\right)(0.10 \ M) = 0.064 \ M$$

The precipitation reaction $2Ag^+ + MoO_4^= \rightarrow Ag_2MoO_{4(s)}$ requires two moles $Ag^+$ per one mole $MoO_4^=$, so the $MoO_4^=$ is present in large excess. If we assume it drives all the $Ag^+$ out of solution, then to remove 0.036 $M$ $Ag^+$ out of solution we will use up 0.018 $M$ $MoO_4^=$. This will leave $0.064 - 0.018 = 0.046 \ M \ MoO_4^=$.

Let $x$ = moles/l of the solid $Ag_2MoO_4$ that will redissolve to set up the $Ag_2MoO_4$ saturation equilibrium. This will give $2x$ moles/l $Ag^+$ and $x$ moles/l $MoO_4^=$ additional to the 0.046 $M$ there already.

$$[Ag^+] = 2x; \quad [MoO_4^=] = 0.046 + x$$

$$Ag_2MoO_{4(s)} \rightleftharpoons 2Ag^+ + MoO_4^=$$

$$K_{s.p.} = [Ag^+]^2[MoO_4^=] = 2.6 \times 10^{-11}$$

$$(2x)^2(0.046 + x) = 2.6 \times 10^{-11}$$

Neglecting the $x$ where it adds to 0.046, we get the approximate equation $(2x)^2(0.046) \cong 2.6 \times 10^{-11}$, which solves to give $x = 1.2 \times 10^{-5}$. Final concentrations will be

$$[Ag^+] = 2x = 2.4 \times 10^{-5}\ M$$

$$[MoO_4^=] = 0.046 + x = 0.046\ M$$

■PROBLEM 744   The $K_{s.p.}$ for $Ag_2$-$MoO_{4(s)} \rightleftharpoons 2Ag^+ + MoO_4^=$ is $2.6 \times 10^{-11}$. Suppose you mix 45.0 ml of 0.10 $M$ $AgNO_3$ and 25.0 ml of 0.10 $M$ $Na_2MoO_4$. What should be the final concentration of $Ag^+$ and of $MoO_4^=$?

ANSWER: $[Ag^+] = 8.4 \times 10^{-5}\ M$; $[MoO_4^=] = 3.6 \times 10^{-3}\ M$

■■PROBLEM 745   The $K_{s.p.}$ of $Ra(NO_3)_2$ is $6.3 \times 10^{-3}$. What should be the final concentration of $Ra^{++}$ and of $NO_3^-$ in a solution made by mixing 32.0 ml of 0.90 $M$ $NaNO_3$ and 28.0 ml of 0.24 $M$ $Ra(OH)_2$? Assume $Ra(OH)_2$ is a strong electrolyte.

ANSWER: $[Ra^{++}] = 0.049\ M$; $[NO_3^-] = 0.36\ M$

## Mixing problems

One of the most common problems in freshman chemistry is to mix several reagents in a solution, decide what species are present in the final solution, and at what concentrations. To handle these problems successfully it is necessary to be systematic in collecting the information given, taking care of any reactions that occur, and calculating final concentrations with due allowance for dilution effects. If any reactions occur, they can usually be calculated easily if one or more of the reactants is present in excess. If a reactant is left over in excess, then in general its residual concentration can be used as a departure point for calculating the concentrations of other species in equilibrium with it.

In this section we consider primarily "mixing problems" in which precipitation and neutralization reactions are involved. We have already done several of these in preceding sections but not with all the ions in question.

PROBLEM 746 Suppose you mix 25.0
ml of 0.012 $M$ $BaCl_2$ with 50.0 ml of 0.010 $M$ $Ag_2SO_4$. What will be the
final concentrations of the ions in solution? $K_{s.p.}$ of AgCl is 1.7 ×
$10^{-10}$; $K_{s.p.}$ of $BaSO_4$ is 1.5 × $10^{-9}$.

SOLUTION: One of the most efficient ways to solve a mixing problem
such as this is to make a table showing which ions are involved,
how many moles of each are available for reaction, how much
change occurs due to reaction, what moles are left after reaction,
and what the final concentrations will be.

| (1) Ion | (2) Moles available | (3) Change | (4) Moles after | (5) Concentration |
|---------|---------------------|------------|-----------------|-------------------|
| $Ba^{++}$ | 0.00030 | −0.00030 | ∼0 | 5.6 × $10^{-7}$ $M$ |
| $Cl^-$ | 0.00060 | −0.00060 | ∼0 | 3 × $10^{-8}$ $M$ |
| $Ag^+$ | 0.0010 | −0.00060 | 0.0004 | 0.005 $M$ |
| $SO_4^=$ | 0.00050 | −0.00030 | 0.00020 | 0.0027 $M$ |

In collecting our information for this table we note that $BaCl_2$ is a
strong electrolyte, which is taken to be 100% dissociated into $Ba^{++}$
and $Cl^-$. Similarly, $Ag_2SO_4$ is considered 100% dissociated into
$Ag^+$ and $SO_4^=$. For calculating column 2, "moles available," we
proceed in the usual way of multiplying the volume in liters of each
solution by the concentration in moles per liter it provides of each
ion.
25.0 ml of 0.012 $M$ $BaCl_2$ gives

$$(0.0250 \text{ l}) \left( 0.012 \frac{\text{mole } Ba^{++}}{\text{liter}} \right) = 0.00030 \text{ mole } Ba^{++} \text{ and}$$

$$(0.0250 \text{ l}) \left( 0.024 \frac{\text{mole } Cl^-}{\text{liter}} \right) = 0.00060 \text{ mole } Cl^-.$$

50.0 ml of 0.010 $M$ $Ag_2SO_4$ gives

$$(0.0500 \text{ l}) \left( 0.020 \frac{\text{mole } Ag^+}{\text{liter}} \right) = 0.0010 \text{ mole } Ag^+ \text{ and}$$

$$(0.0500 \text{ l}) \left( 0.010 \frac{\text{mole } SO_4^=}{\text{liter}} \right) = 0.00050 \text{ mole } SO_4^=.$$

For column 3, labeled "change," we need to know how many moles of each species will be used up in reaction. Two reactions occur here and we consider them independently.

$$Ag^+ + Cl^- \rightarrow AgCl_{(s)}$$

$$Ba^{++} + SO_4^= \rightarrow BaSO_{4(s)}$$

For the silver chloride precipitation, where we need to use up equimolar amounts of $Ag^+$ and $Cl^-$, we note from column 2 that we have available 0.00060 mole $Cl^-$ and 0.0010 mole $Ag^+$—in other words, an excess of $Ag^+$. We assume as a first approximation that the excess $Ag^+$ drives all the $Cl^-$ out of solution. (We will correct later for the small amount of $Cl^-$ left.) To precipitate 0.00060 mole $Cl^-$ out of solution requires 0.00060 mole $Ag^+$. We have 0.0010 mole $Ag^+$ available, and we use up 0.00060; that leaves us 0.0004 mole $Ag^+$, which we can enter in column 4, labeled "moles after." Since we are assuming all the $Cl^-$ has been driven out of solution, we put $\sim 0$ (approximately zero) in column 4 for $Cl^-$.

Similarly, for the barium sulfate precipitation we assume that the excess $SO_4^=$ drives out all the $Ba^{++}$. Starting with 0.00030 mole $Ba^{++}$ and 0.00050 mole $SO_4^=$ (column 2), we see that we need to use up 0.00030 mole of each (column 3), leaving approximately zero moles $Ba^{++}$ and 0.00020 mole $SO_4^=$ (column 4).

To get the values in column 5, labeled "concentration," we simply note that the moles (column 4) are in a total volume of 25.0 ml + 50.0 ml = 0.0750 l solution. So each value in column 4 gets divided by 0.0750 l to go into column 5. This will give us a pretty good idea of the $Ag^+$ and $SO_4^=$ concentrations—viz., **0.005 $M$** and **0.0027 $M$**, respectively (note the difference in significant figures)—but it does not help for the $\sim 0$ of $Ba^{++}$ and $Cl^-$. There, however, we can quickly calculate $[Cl^-]$ from the $K_{s.p.}$ of AgCl once we know that $[Ag^+] = 0.005$ $M$. Similarly, we can use the $[SO_4^=] = 0.0027$ $M$ to fix the concentration of $Ba^{++}$ via the $K_{s.p.}$ of $BaSO_4$.

Let $x$ = moles/l AgCl that dissolve in the presence of 0.005 $M$ $Ag^+$.

$$K_{s.p.} = [Ag^+][Cl^-] = 1.7 \times 10^{-10}$$

$$(0.005 + x)(x) = 1.7 \times 10^{-10}$$

$$x \cong \frac{1.7 \times 10^{-10}}{0.005} = 3 \times 10^{-8} \; M = [Cl^-]$$

Let $z$ = moles/l $BaSO_4$ that can dissolve in the presence of 0.0027 $M$ $SO_4^=$.

$$K_{s.p.} = [Ba^{++}][SO_4^=] = 1.5 \times 10^{-9}$$

$$(z)(z + 0.0027) = 1.5 \times 10^{-9}$$

$$z \cong \frac{1.5 \times 10^{-9}}{0.0027} = 5.6 \times 10^{-7} \, M = [Ba^{++}]$$

■ PROBLEM 747  Suppose you mix 2.50 l of 0.0100 $M$ $BaBr_2$ solution with 2.00 l of 0.0150 $M$ $Ag_2SO_4$. What will be the final concentrations of the ions in solution? $K_{s.p.}$ of $BaSO_4$ is $1.5 \times 10^{-9}$; $K_{s.p.}$ of AgBr is $5.0 \times 10^{-13}$.

ANSWER: **0.00222 $M$ $Ag^+$; 0.0011 $M$ $SO_4^=$; $1.4 \times 10^{-6}$ $M$ $Ba^{++}$; $2.3 \times 10^{-10}$ $M$ $Br^-$**

PROBLEM 748  What will be the final concentrations of the ions in a solution made by mixing $1.50 \times 10^{-2}$ mole $Sr(NO_3)_2$ and $3.0 \times 10^{-3}$ mole NaF in enough water to make 0.200 l solution? The $K_{s.p.}$ of $SrF_2$ is $7.9 \times 10^{-10}$.

SOLUTION:

| Ion | Moles available | Change | Moles after | Concentration |
|---|---|---|---|---|
| $Sr^{++}$ | 0.0150 | −0.0015 | 0.0135 | 0.0675 $M$ |
| $NO_3^-$ | 0.0300 | no | 0.0300 | 0.150 $M$ |
| $Na^+$ | 0.0030 | no | 0.0030 | 0.015 $M$ |
| $F^-$ | 0.0030 | −0.0030 | ∼0 | $1.1 \times 10^{-4}$ $M$ |

The "change" is the precipitation of $SrF_{2(s)}$ via the reaction $Sr^{++} + 2F^- \rightarrow SrF_{2(s)}$. We have available 0.0150 mole $Sr^{++}$ and 0.0030 mole $F^-$—in other words, a large excess of $Sr^{++}$. Reaction is limited by the $F^-$. If all the fluoride ion is chased out of solution, 0.0030 mole $F^-$ requires 0.0015 mole $Sr^{++}$, corresponding to the $2F^-$-to-$1Sr^{++}$ stoichiometry. This will leave 0.0150 − 0.0015 mole, or 0.0135 mole, of $Sr^{++}$. In a volume of 0.200 l, it corresponds to a concentration of $\dfrac{0.0135 \text{ mole } Sr^{++}}{0.200 \text{ l}} = 0.0675 \, M$ .

The equilibrium between solid $SrF_2$ precipitate and the saturated solution is

$$SrF_{2(s)} \rightleftharpoons Sr^{++} + 2F^-$$

$$K_{s.p.} = [Sr^{++}][F^-]^2 = 7.9 \times 10^{-10}$$

If the concentration of $Sr^{++}$ is 0.0675 $M$ (plus a small trace due to some dissolved $SrF_2$), we can calculate the fluoride-ion concentration by substituting 0.0675 $M$ for $[Sr^{++}]$.

$$(0.0675)\,[F^-]^2 = 7.9 \times 10^{-10}$$

$$[F^-] = 1.1 \times 10^{-4}\,M$$

[*Note:* An easy way to get a quick check on these problems is to see if the concentration of positive charge equals the concentration of negative charge.  For positive charge, we have a total of (2) × (0.0675) $M$ from the $Sr^{++}$ plus 0.015 $M$ from the $Na^+ = 0.150\,M$; for negative charge, we have 0.150 $M$ from the $NO_3^-$ and a negligible amount from the $F^-$.]

■ PROBLEM 749  Suppose you mix 2.00 g $AgNO_3$ and 3.00 g $K_2CrO_4$ in enough water to make 50.0 ml solution. What will be the concentrations of the ions in the final solution? $K_{s.p.}$ of $Ag_2CrO_4$ is $1.9 \times 10^{-12}$.

ANSWER: $[Ag^+] = 3.2 \times 10^{-6}\,M$; $[NO_3^-] = 0.236\,M$; $[K^+] = 0.618\,M$; $[CrO_4^=] = 0.19\,M$

PROBLEM 750  If you mix 10.0 ml of 0.10 $M$ $CaCl_2$ with 20.0 ml of 0.10 $M$ $AgNO_3$, what will be the concentrations of the ions in the final solution? $K_{s.p.}$ of $AgCl$ is $1.7 \times 10^{-10}$.

SOLUTION:

| Ion | Moles available | Change | Moles after | Concentration |
|---|---|---|---|---|
| $Ca^{++}$ | 0.0010 | no | 0.0010 | 0.033 $M$ |
| $Cl^-$ | 0.0020 | −0.0020 | ∼0 | $1.3 \times 10^{-5}\,M$ |
| $Ag^+$ | 0.0020 | −0.0020 | ∼0 | $1.3 \times 10^{-5}\,M$ |
| $NO_3^-$ | 0.0020 | no | 0.0020 | 0.067 $M$ |

[*Note:* This problem differs from the preceding ones in that the precipitating ions, $Ag^+$ and $Cl^-$, are present in stoichiometric amounts. Neither is in excess, so the final solution is the same as if $AgCl_{(s)}$ were dissolved in pure water.

$$[Ag^+] = [Cl^-] = \text{square root of } 1.7 \times 10^{-10} = 1.3 \times 10^{-5} \; M$$

PROBLEM 751  What will be the final concentrations in the solution resulting from the mixing of 0.100 l of 0.150 $M$ $H_2SO_4$ with 0.300 l of 0.200 $M$ $Ba(OH)_2$? $K_{s.p.}$ of $BaSO_4$ is $1.5 \times 10^{-9}$.

SOLUTION:

| Ion | Moles available | Change | Moles after | Concentration |
|---|---|---|---|---|
| $H^+$ | 0.0300 | −0.0300 | ∼0 | $4.3 \times 10^{-14} \; M$ |
| $SO_4^=$ | 0.0150 | −0.0150 | ∼0 | $1.3 \times 10^{-8} \; M$ |
| $Ba^{++}$ | 0.0600 | −0.0150 | 0.0450 | 0.113 $M$ |
| $OH^-$ | 0.120 | −0.0300 | 0.090 | 0.23 $M$ |

There are two reactions here:

$$H^+ + OH^- \rightarrow H_2O$$

$$Ba^{++} + SO_4^= \rightarrow BaSO_{4(s)}$$

There is more $OH^-$ available than $H^+$, so all the acid will be neutralized. This means we do not have to worry about $HSO_4^-$ in the solution. Once the acid-base neutralization has occurred, we can calculate the residual $OH^-$ concentration and get from that the concentration of $H^+$.

$$[H^+] = \frac{K_w}{[OH^-]} = \frac{1.00 \times 10^{-14}}{0.23} = 4.3 \times 10^{-14} \; M$$

The excess $Ba^{++}$ drives most of the $SO_4^=$ out of the solution; the trace that is left can be computed from the residual $Ba^{++}$ concentration and the $K_{s.p.}$ of $BaSO_4$.

■ PROBLEM 752 What will be the concentrations of $Ag^+$, $NO_3^-$, $H^+$, $Cl^-$, and $OH^-$ in a solution made by adding 0.500 g $AgNO_3$ to 25.0 ml of 0.100 $M$ HCl? $K_{s.p.} = 1.7 \times 10^{-10}$ for AgCl.

ANSWER: 0.018 $M$ $Ag^+$; 0.118 $M$ $NO_3^-$; 0.100 $M$ $H^+$; 9.4 $\times$ $10^{-9}$ $M$ $Cl^-$; $1.00 \times 10^{-13}$ $M$ $OH^-$

PROBLEM 753 A solution is made by mixing 0.10 l of 0.12 $M$ NaCl, 0.20 l of 0.14 $M$ NaBr, and 0.30 l of 0.10 $M$ $AgNO_3$. What will be the concentration of each ion in the final solution? The $K_{s.p.}$ of AgCl is $1.7 \times 10^{-10}$; the $K_{s.p.}$ of AgBr is $5.0 \times 10^{-13}$.

SOLUTION:

| (1) Ion | (2) Moles available | (3) Change | (4) Moles after | (5) Concentration |
|---|---|---|---|---|
| $Na^+$ | $0.012 + 0.028$ | no | 0.040 | 0.067 $M$ |
| $Cl^-$ | 0.012 | $-0.002$ | 0.010 | 0.017 $M$ |
| $Br^-$ | 0.028 | $-0.028$ | $\sim 0$ | $5.0 \times 10^{-5}$ $M$ |
| $Ag^+$ | 0.030 | $-0.030$ | $\sim 0$ | $1.0 \times 10^{-8}$ $M$ |
| $NO_3^-$ | 0.030 | no | 0.030 | 0.050 $M$ |

In working up the data, we note for column 2 that $Na^+$ is contributed from two sources: 0.012 mole from 0.10 l of 0.12 $M$ NaCl plus 0.028 mole from 0.20 l of 0.14 $M$ NaBr.

In deciding on the change for column 3, we note that two possible reactions can occur:

$$Ag^+ + Cl^- \rightarrow AgCl_{(s)}$$

$$Ag^+ + Br^- \rightarrow AgBr_{(s)}$$

We do not have enough $Ag^+$ to complete both of these reactions; only 0.030 mole $Ag^+$ is available, but 0.12 mole $Cl^-$ plus 0.28 mole $Br^-$ would need 0.040 mole $Ag^+$ for complete precipitation. The question is which reaction is preferred. As a rule, the least soluble substance is the one most likely to be produced. (You can justify this by noting that if the more soluble salt deposited first, then it would have in equilibrium with itself a *higher* concentration of $Ag^+$ than the less soluble salt. With a *higher* $Ag^+$ concentration in solution we would be more likely to exceed the $K_{s.p.}$ of the less soluble salt and therefore preferentially drive the less soluble salt out of solution.)

Since the $K_{s.p.}$ of AgBr is smaller than the $K_{s.p.}$ of AgCl we expect AgBr to precipitate first. Starting with the initially available moles, we would have 0.030 mole $Ag^+$ + 0.028 mole $Br^-$ → 0.028 mole AgBr precipitated and 0.002 mole $Ag^+$ left over.

Then, the remainder of the $Ag^+$ can operate on the $Cl^-$.

0.002 mole $Ag^+$ + 0.012 mole $Cl^-$ → 0.002 mole AgCl precipitated and 0.010 mole $Cl^-$ left over.

The net result is to use up all the available $Ag^+$, drive out of solution all the available $Br^-$, and part of the available $Cl^-$.

Knowing how many moles of $Cl^-$ are left in the final solution (column 4), we can calculate the final concentration of $Cl^-$ as $\dfrac{0.010 \text{ mole}}{0.60 \text{ l}}$ = 0.017 $M$ (column 5).

Once we have $[Cl^-]$ = 0.017 $M$, we can calculate $[Ag^+]$.

$$[Ag^+] = \frac{K_{s.p.} \text{ of AgCl}}{[Cl^-]} = \frac{1.7 \times 10^{-10}}{0.017} = 1.0 \times 10^{-8} \, M$$

Once we have the $[Ag^+]$, we can calculate the trace of $Br^-$ that is left in solution.

$$[Br^-] = \frac{K_{s.p.} \text{ of AgBr}}{[Ag^+]} = \frac{5.0 \times 10^{-13}}{1.0 \times 10^{-8}} = 5.0 \times 10^{-5} \, M$$

■ PROBLEM 754    A solution is made by mixing 0.10 l of 0.12 $M$ $Na_2CO_3$, 0.20 l of 0.14 $M$ $Na_2SO_4$, and 0.20 l of 0.15 $M$ $Pb(NO_3)_2$. What will be the concentration of each ion in the final solution? $K_{s.p.}$ of $PbSO_4$ is 1.3 × $10^{-8}$; $K_{s.p.}$ of $PbCO_3$ is 1.5 × $10^{-13}$. Neglect hydrolysis.

ANSWER:0.16 $M$ $Na^+$; 2.3 × $10^{-7}$ $M$ $CO_3^=$; 0.020 $M$ $SO_4^=$; 6.5 × $10^{-7}$ $M$ $Pb^{++}$; 0.12 $M$ $NO_3^-$

# 18

## HYDROLYSIS AND OTHER CASES OF SIMULTANEOUS EQUILIBRIA

IN THE LAST SEVERAL CHAPTERS we have been flirting with the rather complex problem of handling several equilibria at the same time. So far, we have been able to avoid serious difficulties by introducing appropriate approximations when necessary. Now we need to look more closely at what approximations can be made and why they can be made. There is nothing wrong with a procedure based on valid approximations and, in fact, the chemist normally approaches his systems of study with a highly developed sense of what is the important process in a given system, and what can be ignored. It takes considerable training to develop such a feeling for what can be neglected, and frequently it comes only after extensive experience in carrying through hundreds of laborious calculations. The purpose of working out the preceding problems of this book was largely to acquire such an experience.

### *Hydrolysis of NaOAc*

Sodium acetate is typical of a salt that is derived from a strong base (NaOH) and a weak acid (HOAc). When NaOAc is placed in water, we get a basic solution and the problem is to account for this basicity in a quantitative fashion. The qualitative reason why NaOAc gives a basic solution is this: The added $OAc^-$ disturbs the water equilibrium $H_2O \rightleftharpoons H^+ + OH^-$ by tying up some $H^+$ and thereby reducing the concentration of hydrogen ion below the concentration of hydroxide ion.

PROBLEM 755 The dissociation constant of HOAc is $1.8 \times 10^{-5}$. Calculate the species concentrations and the pH of $1.00$ $M$ NaOAc solution.

SOLUTION: There are three ways we can solve this problem.

(a) *Method I*

Let us try to solve the problem exactly. When we put $1.00$ $M$ NaOAc in water, we get $1.00$ $M$ $Na^+$ and $1.00$ $M$ $OAc^-$. The $Na^+$ remains free, but some of the $OAc^-$ will combine with $H^+$ to form HOAc. Thus we will have in the solution two equilibria to worry about:

$$H_2O \rightleftharpoons H^+ + OH^- \qquad \text{for which } K_w = [H^+][OH^-]$$

$$HOAc \rightleftharpoons H^+ + OAc^- \qquad \text{for which } K_{diss} = \frac{[H^+][OAc^-]}{[HOAc]}$$

Let the concentrations at equilibrium be represented as follows:

$[H^+] = w$

$[OH^-] = x$

$[OAc^-] = y$

$[HOAc] = z$

What relations must exist between these four unknowns?

First, we need to satisfy $K_w = [H^+][OH^-] = 1.00 \times 10^{-14}$. This gives us the equation $(w)(x) = 1.00 \times 10^{-14}$.

Second, we need to satisfy the dissociation constant.

$$K_{diss} = \frac{[H^+][OAc^-]}{[HOAc]} = 1.8 \times 10^{-5}$$

This gives us the equation $\frac{(w)(y)}{(z)} = 1.8 \times 10^{-5}$.

Third, the solution must remain electrically neutral. This requires that the sum of the positive charge concentrations equals the sum of the negative charge concentrations. The positive species in the solution are $Na^+$ and $H^+$; the negative, $OAc^-$ and $OH^-$. This means that the sum of the $Na^+$ and $H^+$ concentrations equals the sum of the $OAc^-$ and $OH^-$ concentrations.

$$[Na^+] + [H^+] = [OAc^-] + [OH^-]$$

or

$$1.00 + w = y + x$$

Fourth, we need to maintain conservation of mass. There can be no loss or gain as equilibrium gets established. So far as we are concerned, this means that the total acetate we put into the solution must show up as HOAc or $OAc^-$. We put in 1.00 mole/l, so we have to account for that much.

$$[HOAc] + [OAc^-] = 1.00$$

or

$$z + y = 1.00$$

That is all we need. We have four unknowns $w$, $x$, $y$, and $z$ and we have four independent relations between them:

$$(w)(x) = 1.00 \times 10^{-14}$$

$$\frac{(w)(y)}{(z)} = 1.8 \times 10^{-5}$$

$$1.00 + w = y + x$$

$$z + y = 1.00$$

All we need to do is to solve these four simultaneous equations. It is messy and tedious but it can be done to give the following results:

$$w = 4.2 \times 10^{-10}\ M = [H^+]$$

$$x = 2.4 \times 10^{-5}\ M = [OH^-]$$

$$y = 1.00\ M = [OAc^-]$$

$$z = 2.4 \times 10^{-5}\ M = [HOAc]$$

Try the method from scratch and you will see that this is obviously not a method to use when you are in a hurry.

## (b) Method II

This is a method where we introduce the approximation that for each
$OAc^-$ that takes an $H^+$ from $H_2O$, an $OH^-$ is released into the
solution. This means that if $x$ moles/1 $OAc^-$ pick up $H^+$ to form
HOAc, we will get $x$ moles/1 HOAc and $x$ moles/1 $OH^-$, as well as
reduce the $OAc^-$ concentration from 1.00 to $1.00 - x$.

At equilibrium, we would have

$$[OAc^-] = 1.00 - x; [HOAc] = x; [OH^-] = x$$

We know that we must satisfy $K_{diss}$:

$$K_{diss} = \frac{[H^+][OAc^-]}{[HOAc]} = 1.8 \times 10^{-5}$$

If we express $[H^+] = \dfrac{K_w}{[OH^-]} = \dfrac{1.00 \times 10^{-14}}{x}$, which simply amounts

to relating $x$ moles/1 $OH^-$ via the water constant to $\left(\dfrac{1.00 \times 10^{-14}}{x}\right)$

moles/1 $H^+$, then on substituting in $K_{diss}$, we get

$$K_{diss} = \frac{[H^+][OAc^-]}{[HOAc]} = \frac{\left(\dfrac{1.00 \times 10^{-14}}{x}\right)(1.00 - x)}{x} = 1.8 \times 10^{-5}$$

Rewriting, we get

$$\frac{(1.00 \times 10^{-14})(1.00 - x)}{x^2} = 1.8 \times 10^{-5}$$

This can easily be solved for $x$, since $x$ can be neglected when subtracted
from 1.00 and we can assume $1.00 - x \cong 1.00$.
The approximate equation

$$\frac{(1.00 \times 10^{-14})(1.00)}{x^2} \cong 1.8 \times 10^{-5}$$

solves to give $x = 2.4 \times 10^{-5}$. This leads to the following equilibrium concentrations:

$$[HOAc] = x = 2.4 + 10^{-5} \, M$$

$$[OAc^-] = 1.00 - x = 1.00 \, M$$

$$[OH^-] = x = 2.4 + 10^{-5} \, M$$

$$[H^+] = \frac{K_w}{[OH^-]} = \frac{1.00 \times 10^{-14}}{2.4 \times 10^{-5}} = 4.2 \times 10^{-10} \, M$$

which answers are the same as those obtained, more tediously, in method I.

(c) Method III (recommended)
When OAc$^-$ is put in water, it picks up H$^+$ to form HOAc. We can write this reaction

$$OAc^- + H^+ \rightarrow HOAc$$

But as soon as some H$^+$ is withdrawn from the solution this way, the H$_2$O dissociates some more to try to replace that H$^+$. The reaction would be

$$H_2O \rightarrow H^+ + OH^-$$

If we assume that the H$_2$O thus furnishes all the H$^+$ used up in converting OAc$^-$ to HOAc, then we can add the two above reactions to get the net reaction

$$OAc^- + H_2O \rightleftharpoons HOAc + OH^-$$

We have cancelled the H$^+$ from both sides of the equation and have put in the double arrows to emphasize that this net reaction, as well as the individual steps, must come to equilibrium. This is the so-called *hydrolysis reaction*, and its equilibrium constant, sometimes designated $K_h$ (called the *hydrolysis constant*), can be written as follows:

$$K_h = \frac{[HOAc][OH^-]}{[OAc^-]}$$

We leave out the water from the denominator because as usual its activity stays constant.
The numerical value of $K_h$ can be shown to be equal to $K_w/K_{diss}$ by the simple expedient of multiplying the numerator and the denominator by [H$^+$].

$$K_h = \frac{[HOAc][OH^-]}{[OAc^-]} \frac{[H^+]}{[H^+]} = \frac{[H^+][OH^-]}{[H^+][OAc^-]/[HOAc]} = \frac{K_w}{K_{diss}}$$

To solve our problem, we now compute as with any equilibrium situation.

Let $x$ = moles/l $OAc^-$ that hydrolyze by the net reaction

$$OAc^- + H_2O \rightleftharpoons HOAc + OH^-$$

This will give us at equilibrium $x$ moles/l HOAc and $x$ moles/l $OH^-$ while reducing the concentration of $OAc^-$ from 1.00 $M$ to $(1.00 - x)$ $M$.

$$[HOAc] = x; [OH^-] = x; [OAc^-] = 1.00 - x$$

$$K_h = \frac{[HOAc][OH^-]}{[OAc^-]} = \frac{(x)(x)}{1.00 - x} = \frac{K_w}{K_{diss}} = \frac{1.00 \times 10^{-14}}{1.8 \times 10^{-5}}$$

$$= 5.6 \times 10^{-10}$$

If we solve the equation

$$\frac{(x)(x)}{1.00 - x} = 5.6 \times 10^{-10}$$

we get $x = 2.4 \times 10^{-5}$, which leads to the following:

$$[HOAc] = x = 2.4 \times 10^{-5} M$$

$$[OH^-] = x = 2.4 \times 10^{-5} M$$

$$[OAc^-] = 1.00 - x = 1.00 M$$

$$[H^+] = \frac{K_w}{[OH^-]} = \frac{1.00 \times 10^{-14}}{2.4 \times 10^{-5}} = 4.2 \times 10^{-10} M$$

These values are the same as those obtained by method I or II.

$$pH = -\log [H^+] = -\log (4.2 \times 10^{-10}) = -(0.62 - 10)$$
$$= 9.38$$

■ PROBLEM 756   Calculate the pH of 0.25 $M$ NaOAc solution.
ANSWER: pH = 9.08

■ PROBLEM 757   Calculate the pH of 0.025 $M$ NaOAc solution.
ANSWER: pH = 8.57

PROBLEM 758  How concentrated a solution of NaOAc must you take in order to have 0.015% of the acetate ion in the "hydrolyzed" state?

SOLUTION: Let $c$ be the over-all concentration of the desired solution. This will give us $c$ moles/l $Na^+$ and $c$ moles/l $OAc^-$. But 0.015% of $c$, or $0.00015c$, will be converted to HOAc and $OH^-$ by the reaction

$$OAc^- + H_2O \rightarrow HOAc + OH^-$$

This will leave 99.985% of $c$, or $0.99985c$, in the unhydrolyzed state. So, at equilibrium we can write the concentrations as follows:

$$[OAc^-] = 0.99985c; \quad [HOAc] = 0.00015c; \quad [OH^-] = 0.00015c$$

Substitute these values in the equilibrium condition for the hydrolysis equilibrium:

$$OAc^- + H_2O \rightleftharpoons HOAc + OH^-$$

$$K_h = \frac{[HOAc][OH^-]}{[OAc^-]} = \frac{K_w}{K_{diss}} = \frac{1.00 \times 10^{-14}}{1.8 \times 10^{-5}} = 5.6 \times 10^{-10}$$

$$\frac{(0.00015c)(0.00015c)}{0.99985c} = 5.6 \times 10^{-10}$$

$$c = 2.5 \times 10^{-2} \text{ mole/l}$$

When can we expect the above approximation, as outlined in methods II and III, to break down? The assumption we are making is that the $H^+$ picked up by the $OAc^-$ is just matched by dissociation of $H_2O \rightarrow H^+ + OH^-$. This leads to the net equation $OAc^- + H_2O \rightarrow HOAc + OH^-$, which shows that HOAc and $OH^-$ are produced in equal amounts. Under what circumstances will we *not* be able to say that the concentration of HOAc equals the concentration of $OH^-$? The answer: when the solution is very dilute. Given a very dilute solution of NaOAc—say, $10^{-7}$ $M$—then the amount of $OH^-$ produced by the hydrolysis is actually less than the amount of $OH^-$ produced by the normal water dissociation, and we cannot assume that $[HOAc] = [OH^-]$. In fact, the normal $H_2O \rightleftharpoons H^+ + OH^-$ equilibrium would be the dominant equilibrium and would set $[H^+] \cong 10^{-7}$ $M$ to which the $[OAc^-]/[HOAc]$ would have to conform. To solve the problem exactly, we would need to follow the procedure as outlined in method I with all its tedious algebra.  Fortunately, freshman chemistry problems routinely avoid asking for precise hydrolysis calculations in very dilute solutions.  The following problem illustrates the kind of troubles you can get into.

■■ PROBLEM 759  Calculate the concentration of $H^+$, $OH^-$, HOAc, and $OAc^-$ in $1.00 \times 10^{-6}$ $M$ NaOAc solution.

ANSWER: $[H^+] = 9.7_1 \times 10^{-8} M$; $[OH^-] = 1.0_3 \times 10^{-7} M$; $[HOAc] = 5.4 \times 10^{-9}$ $M$; $[OAc^-] = 9.9_4 \times 10^{-7}$ $M$ (recall that the digits dropped below the line are uncertain and go beyond what is allowed by our rules of significant figures)

## Hydrolysis of $NH_4Cl$

Ammonium chloride is typical of the salts derived from a weak base ($NH_3$) and a strong acid (HCl).   There is the minor additional complication that the weak base is not of the general type BOH, although all the following computations can be done just as well assuming that $NH_3$ in $H_2O$ is $NH_4OH$.   However, we shall try to stick to modern thinking on ammonia solutions as much as possible and avoid postulating presence of $NH_3OH$.

When ammonium chloride is added to water, we get 100% dissociation into $NH_4^+$ and $Cl^-$, as is generally assumed for any strong electrolyte.  The $Cl^-$ does not affect the water equilibrium $H_2O \rightleftharpoons H^+ + OH^-$ but the $NH_4^+$ does, because some of it can combine with $OH^-$ to produce $NH_3$ and $H_2O$ by the reaction

$$NH_4^+ + OH^- \rightarrow NH_3 + H_2O$$

If we again make the assumption that $H_2O$ dissociation furnishes all the $OH^-$ used in this reaction, we can add the equation

$$H_2O \rightarrow H^+ + OH^-$$

and get a total equation

$$NH_4^+ + \cancel{OH^-} + \cancel{H_2O} \rightarrow NH_3 + \cancel{H_2O} + H^+ + \cancel{OH^-}$$

from which, cancelling the duplication of $OH^-$ and $H_2O$ which appear on both sides, we get the net reaction

$$NH_4^+ \rightarrow NH_3 + H^+$$

This looks like a simple dissociation of a protonic acid and in fact you have a choice of considering $NH_4Cl$ solutions as representing hydrolysis of $NH_4^+$ or dissociation of $NH_4^+$, provided you use the right equilibrium constants and interpret them correctly. This illustrates, incidentally, the very fundamental point that *hydrolysis is not really a phenomenon separate from dissociation but that it represents a special way of looking at the competition between $H_2O$ and other proton-donating or proton-accepting species.*

What is the equilibrium constant for

$$NH_4^+ \rightleftharpoons NH_3 + H^+?$$

It has the form

$$K = \frac{[NH_3][H^+]}{[NH_4^+]}$$

If we multiply numerator and denominator by $[OH^-]$, which does not change any numerical values, because we are multiplying the whole business by one, we get

$$K = \frac{[NH_3][H^+]}{[NH^+]}\frac{[OH^-]}{[OH^-]} = \frac{[H^+][OH^-]}{[NH_4^+][OH^-]/[NH_3]}$$

The terms have been rearranged to emphasize certain groupings and we see immediately that $[H^+][OH^-]$ is just $K_w$ and the denominator $[NH_3^+][OH^-]/[NH_3]$ is just what we have been calling the "dissociation constant of aqueous ammonia". Putting in the numerical values $K_w = 1.00 \times 10^{-14}$ and $K_{diss} = 1.81 \times 10^{-5}$, we get $K = 5.52 \times 10^{-10}$. This is frequently called the hydrolysis constant of ammonium ion but it could just as well be called the "dissociation constant of ammonium ion."

PROBLEM 760    Compute the pH of 1.00 $M$ $NH_4Cl$.

SOLUTION: $NH_4Cl$ is a strong electrolyte; we take it to be 100% dissociated into $NH_4^+$ and $Cl^-$. Of the 1.00 $M$ $NH_4^+$ introduced into the solution, let $x$ moles/l convert by the reaction

$$NH_4^+ \rightarrow NH_3 + H^+$$

to give $x$ moles/l $NH_3$, $x$ moles/l $H^+$, and leave $(1.00 - x)$ moles/l $NH_4^+$.

$$[NH_4^+] = 1.00 - x; \ [NH_3] = x; \ [H^+] = x$$

$$NH_4^+ \rightleftharpoons NH_3 + H^+$$

$$K = \frac{[NH_3][H^+]}{[NH_4^+]} = 5.52 \times 10^{-10} = \frac{(x)(x)}{1.00 - x}$$

$$x = 2.35 \times 10^{-5}$$

$$[NH_4^+] = 1.00 \ M; \ [NH_3] = 2.35 \times 10^{-5} \ M; \ [H^+] = 2.35 \times 10^{-5} \ M$$

$$pH = -\log [H^+] = -\log (2.35 \times 10^{-5}) = -(0.371 - 5)$$
$$= 4.629$$

■ **PROBLEM 761** Compute the pH of 0.25 $M$ $NH_4Cl$ solution.

ANSWER: pH = **4.93**

■ **PROBLEM 762** Compute the pH of 0.025 $M$ $NH_4Cl$ solution.

ANSWER: pH = **5.43**

**PROBLEM 763** How many g $NH_4Cl$ would you need to dissolve in 0.200 l water to provide a solution having a pH of 4.75?

SOLUTION:

$$pH = 4.75 = -\log [H^+]$$
$$\log [H^+] = -4.75 = -5.00 + 0.25$$
$$[H^+] = (10^{-5})(10^{0.25}) = 1.8 \times 10^{-5}$$

If this $H^+$ is to come from $NH_4^+$ dissociation, there must be an equal concentration of $NH_3$ in solution.

$$[H^+] = 1.8 \times 10^{-5} \ M; \ [NH_3] = 1.8 \times 10^{-5} \ M$$

What must be the concentration of ammonium ion to be consistent with these? We substitute in $K$ to find out.

$$K = \frac{[NH_3][H^+]}{[NH_4^+]} = 5.52 \times 10^{-10} = \frac{(1.8 \times 10^{-5})(1.8 \times 10^{-5})}{[NH_4^+]}$$

$$[NH_4^+] = \frac{(1.8 \times 10^{-5})(1.8 \times 10^{-5})}{5.52 \times 10^{-10}} = 0.59 \, M$$

Total concentration needed is 0.59 $M$ (to take care of $NH_4^+$) plus 1.8 $\times 10^{-5}$ $M$ (to take care of $NH_3$), or 0.59 $M$.

To answer the question of how many g per 0.200 l, we need to multiply molarity by the number of liters and by the weight of one mole $NH_4Cl$ (53.49 g).

$$\text{grams needed} = \left(0.59 \, \frac{\text{mole}}{\text{liter}}\right) (0.200 \, \text{l}) \left(53.49 \, \frac{\text{g}}{\text{mole}}\right)$$

$$= 6.3 \, g$$

As in any salt solution, the degree of hydrolysis can be repressed by having some of the weak electrolyte added to the solution. Thus, we can diminish the extent of $NH_4^+$ hydrolysis by having some additional $NH_3$ in the solution. Then of course, the problem becomes similar to the buffer problems.

PROBLEM 764   Suppose you have 1.00 l of 1.50 $M$ $NH_4Cl$ solution and 1.00 l of 1.50 $M$ $NH_3$ solution. You wish to make 0.200 l of a solution that has pH = 7.00. What is the recipe?

SOLUTION:

pH = 7.00 = $- \log [H^+]$

$\log [H^+] = -7.00 = 0.00 - 7$

$[H^+] = (10^{0.00})(10^{-7}) = 1.0 \times 10^{-7} \, M$

Use this $[H^+]$ to fix the ratio of $NH_3$ to $NH_4^+$ needed.

The equilibrium is

$$NH_4^+ \rightleftharpoons NH_3 + H^+$$

The requirement for equilibrium is

$$K = \frac{[NH_3][H^+]}{[NH_4^+]} = 5.52 \times 10^{-10} = \frac{[NH_3](1.0 \times 10^{-7})}{[NH_4^+]}$$

which leads to

$$\frac{[NH_3]}{[NH_4^+]} = \frac{5.52 \times 10^{-10}}{1.0 \times 10^{-7}} = 5.5 \times 10^{-3}$$

This fraction is so much less than one that we can be quite sure the solution is essentially all $NH_4^+$ with just a trace of $NH_3$.

Let $V_1$ = volume of 1.50 $M$ $NH_4Cl$ solution to be taken.

$V_2$ = volume of 1.50 $M$ $NH_3$ solution to be taken.

$V_1 + V_2$ = total volume = 0.200 l.

$V_1$ l of 1.50 $M$ $NH_4Cl$ will give $1.50V_1$ moles $NH_4^+$.

$V_2$ l of 1.50 $M$ $NH_3$ will give $1.50V_2$ moles $NH_3$.

Let $x$ = moles of $NH_4^+$ that will dissociate to $NH_3$ and $H^+$ to fix the final equilibrium. This will leave us with $(1.50V_1 - x)$ moles $NH_4^+$ and $(1.50V_2 + x)$ moles $NH_3$ in the final solution. Dividing by 0.200 l will give us concentrations. The ratio of the final concentrations must come out to be the number $5.5 \times 10^{-3}$ as figured above.

$$\frac{[NH_3]}{[NH_4^+]} = 5.5 \times 10^{-3} = \frac{(1.50V_2 + x) \text{ moles } NH_3/0.200 \text{ l}}{(1.50V_1 - x) \text{ moles } NH_4^+/0.200 \text{ l}}$$

Since the 0.200 l divides into the numerator and into the denominator, it cancels out. We are left with

$$5.5 \times 10^{-3} = \frac{1.50V_2 + x}{1.50V_1 - x}$$

where $V_1 + V_2 = 0.200$ l. $x$ can be neglected, since it is a very small number, being equal to the number of moles of $H^+$ produced in the solution—namely, $(1.0 \times 10^{-7} M)(0.200 \text{ l}) = 2 \times 10^{-8}$.

Substituting $V_1 = 0.200 - V_2$ in the above equation gives us

$$5.5 \times 10^{-3} = \frac{1.50V_2}{(1.50)(0.200 - V_2)}$$

which solves to $V_2 = 1.1 \times 10^{-3}$ l and $V_1 = 0.199$ l.

So, to make our solution we need to add **1.1 ml of 1.50 $M$ $NH_3$ solution** to **0.199 l of 1.50 $M$ $NH_4Cl$ solution.**

■ PROBLEM 765 How much 1.50 $M$ $NH_3$ solution do you have to add to 0.200 l of 1.50 $M$ $NH_4Cl$ to obtain a solution which has pH = 7.500.

ANSWER: **3.50 ml**

When will these equations for calculating the hydrolysis of $NH_4^+$ break down? Again the answer is: in dilute solution. At first sight, this may be surprising, since the $NH_4^+$ hydrolysis looks like a dissociation ($NH_4^+ \leftrightharpoons NH_3 + H^+$) and in Chapter 13 we did not encounter any troubles with dissociation of weak acids. True, but it is also true that we did not consider any very dilute solutions. If we had, we would have been in trouble, because it stands to reason that in a very dilute solution of HX the amount of $H^+$ coming from $HX \rightarrow H^+ + X^-$ may be comparable or even less than that which comes from $H_2O \leftrightharpoons H^+ + OH^-$. In such a case, we cannot just work with $K_{diss} = \frac{[H^+][X^-]}{[HX]}$ but most also consider $K_w = [H^+][OH^-]$ as a simultaneous equilibrium. The quantitative calculations again get to be very tedious, requiring an exact method such as method I for NaOAc solutions. Fortunately, we run into this kind of trouble only with very dilute solutions—e.g., more dilute than $10^{-5}$ $M$ $NH_4^+$.

■■ P R O B L E M  766  Calculate the concentration of $H^+$, $OH^-$, $NH_4^+$, and $NH_3$ in $1.00 \times 10^{-6}$ $M$ $NH_4Cl$ solution. $K_w = 1.00 \times 10^{-14}$ and $K_{diss} = 5.52 \times 10^{-10}$ for $NH_4^+ \rightleftharpoons NH_3 + H^+$.

SOLUTION: Set up four unknowns for the four species mentioned.

$$[H^+] = w; \quad [OH^-] = x; \quad [NH_4^+] = y; \quad [NH_3] = z$$

Then set up the four equations that relate these concentrations.
(a)  water equilibrium: $H_2O \rightleftharpoons H^+ + OH^-$

$$K_w = [H^+][OH^-] = 1.00 \times 10^{-14} = (w)(x)$$

(b)  ammonium dissociation: $NH_4^+ \rightleftharpoons NH_3 + H^+$

$$K = \frac{[NH_3][H^+]}{[NH_4^+]} = 5.52 \times 10^{-10} = \frac{(z)(w)}{y}$$

(c)  neutrality condition:

$$[NH_4^+] + [H^+] = [Cl^-] + [OH^-]$$

$$y + w = 1.00 \times 10^{-6} + x$$

(*d*) mass conservation:

$$[NH_4^+] + [NH_3] = 1.00 \times 10^{-6}$$
$$y + z = 1.00 \times 10^{-6}$$

Solving these four simultaneous equations gives the following results:

$$[H^+] = 1.03 \times 10^{-7}\ M;\ [OH^-] = 9.75 \times 10^{-8}\ M;$$
$$[NH_4^+] = 9.95 \times 10^{-7}\ M;\ [NH_3] = 5.35 \times 10^{-9}\ M$$

[*Note:* You may have some trouble solving the third-order equation here. If an unknown apparently comes out to be zero, then you have selected the wrong unknown to start with. Re-do your calculation by combining the four above equations in such a way as to eliminate the unknown that comes out to be zero. In other words, re-cast your third-order equation in terms of one of the variables that does not come out to be zero.]

## *Hydrolysis of NH₄OAc*

Ammonium acetate represents a salt derived from a weak base ($NH_3$) and a weak acid (HOAc), with the added twist that the constant for the hydrolysis of $NH_4^+$ just matches the constant for the hydrolysis of $OAc^-$. Therefore, it should be no surprise that the solutions of $NH_4OAc$ come out to be neutral, because the pick-up of $H^+$ by $OAc^-$ just matches the pick-up of $OH^-$ by $NH_4^+$. What is surprising is the large extent to which the ions get hydrolyzed in this solution—much more so than if the other ion were not present. The problem then is to calculate the extent of hydrolysis of $NH_4^+$ (or of $OAc^-$) in a solution of $NH_4OAc$.

The hydrolysis of $NH_4^+$ can be written, in the following way:

$$NH_4^+ \rightarrow NH_3 + H^+$$

The hydrolysis of $NH_4^+$ can be written in the following way:

$$OAc^- + H_2O \rightarrow HOAc + OH^-$$

The point that is of interest in a solution of $NH_4OAc$ is that each of these reactions helps the other to go further to the right. This comes about because the $H^+$ from the first reaction gets neutralized by the $OH^-$ from the second reaction. The Le Chatelier principle says that if an ion is removed from an equilibrium, the system tends to readjust to re-form that ion. So, we get more $NH_4^+$ hydrolysis in the presence of $OAc^-$ than we would in its absence.

To handle this problem mathematically we make the same assumption as before as to the mechanism of hydrolysis and assume in addition that the $H^+$ from the first reaction just cancels the $OH^-$ from the second reaction by the reaction

$$H^+ + OH^- \rightarrow H_2O$$

This is a very good assumption here, because the constants for the two hydrolysis reactions are equal ($K = 5.5 \times 10^{-10}$ for each), but it turns out to be a rather good assumption even more generally when the $K$ of hydrolysis of the cation does not equal the $K$ of hydrolysis of the anion. What saves us is that neither of the hydrolysis reactions can predominate very much. If it did, it would generate an excess of $H^+$ (or $OH^-$), which would have the immediate effect of pulling the other reaction further to the right to compensate.

If we add up the three reactions

$$NH_4^+ \rightarrow NH_3 + H^+$$

$$OAc^- + H_2O \rightarrow HOAc + OH^-$$

$$H^+ + OH^- \rightarrow H_2O$$

and cancel duplications, we get a net reaction as follows:

$$NH_4^+ + OAc^- \rightarrow NH_3 + HOAc$$

The $K$ for this reaction is given by

$$K = \frac{[NH_3][HOAc]}{[NH_4^+][OAc^-]} = \frac{K_w}{K_{NH_3}K_{HOAc}}$$

and is called the hydrolysis constant of ammonium acetate. Its numerical value can be calculated from the dissociation constants of water, aqueous ammonia, and acetic acid. That this is so can be proved (see also Problem 702) by multiplying numerator and denominator by $[H^+]$ times $[OH^-]$ and regrouping the terms.

$$K = \frac{[NH_3][HOAc]}{[NH_4^+][OAc^-]} \frac{[H^+]}{[H^+]} \frac{[OH^-]}{[OH^-]} = \frac{[H^+][OH^-]}{\dfrac{[NH_4^+][OH^-]}{[NH_3]} \dfrac{[H^+][OAc^-]}{[HOAc]}}$$

Since $K_{NH_3} = 1.81 \times 10^{-5}$ and $K_{HOAc} = 1.8 \times 10^{-5}$, we can calculate

$$K = \frac{K_w}{K_{NH_3}K_{HOAc}} = \frac{1.00 \times 10^{-14}}{(1.81 \times 10^{-5})(1.8 \times 10^{-5})} = 3.1 \times 10^{-5}$$

PROBLEM 767  Calculate the per cent hydrolysis of $OAc^-$ in $1.00$ $M$ $NH_4OAc$ and compare it to the per cent hydrolysis of $OAc^-$ in $1.00$ $M$ $NaOAc$.

SOLUTION: $NH_4OAc$ is a strong electrolyte and is taken to be 100% dissociated into $1.00$ $M$ $NH_4^+$ and $1.00$ $M$ $OAc^-$. Let $x = $ moles/l $OAc^-$ that hydrolyze by the reaction.

$$NH_4^+ + OAc^- \rightleftharpoons NH_3 + HOAc$$

Then according to the stoichiometry, $x$ also represents the moles/l $NH_4^+$ that are used up in the hydrolysis to form $x$ moles/l $NH_3$ and of HOAc.  At equilibrium, we have

$$[NH_4^+] = 1.00 - x; \quad [OAc^-] = 1.00 - x; \quad [NH_3] = x; \quad [HOAc] = x$$

$$K = \frac{[NH_3][HOAc]}{[NH_4^+][OAc^-]} = \frac{K_w}{K_{NH_3}K_{HOAc}} = 3.1 \times 10^{-5}$$

$$= \frac{(x)(x)}{(1.00 - x)(1.00 - x)}$$

The equation

$$3.1 \times 10^{-5} = \frac{x^2}{(1.00 - x)^2}$$

is simply solved by taking the square root of both sides of the equation.  The result is $x = 5.5 \times 10^{-3}$.

To calculate the per cent hydrolysis, we need to divide the amount actually hydrolyzed by the amount available.

$$\% \text{ hydrolysis} = \frac{5.5 \times 10^{-3}}{1.00} \times 100 = 0.55\%$$

In $1.00$ $M$ NaOAc, if we let $z$ moles/l hydrolyze by the reaction

$$OAc^- + H_2O \rightarrow HOAc + OH^-$$

We have at equilibrium:

$$[OAc^-] = 1.00 - z; \; [HOAc] = z; \; [OH^-] = z$$

$$K_{hyd} = \frac{[HOAc][OH^-]}{[OAc^-]} = \frac{(z)(z)}{1.00 - z}$$

$$K_{hyd} = \frac{K_w}{K_{HOAc}} = \frac{1.00 \times 10^{-14}}{1.8 \times 10^{-5}} = 5.6 \times 10^{-10} = \frac{z^2}{1.00 - z}$$

$$z = 2.4 \times 10^{-5}$$

$$\% \text{ hydrolysis} = \frac{\text{amount of } OAc^- \text{ hydrolyzed}}{\text{total } OAc^- \text{ available}}$$

$$= \frac{2.4 \times 10^{-5}}{1.00} \times 100$$

$$= 2.4 \times 10^{-3}\%$$

Thus, the per cent hydrolysis of $OAc^-$ in 1.00 $M$ $NH_4OAc$ is about 230 times as great as it is in 1.00 $M$ NaOAc.

■ P R O B L E M  768   Calculate the per cent hydrolysis of $OAc^-$ in 0.10 $M$ $NH_4OAc$.

ANSWER: **0.55%**

P R O B L E M  769   What will be the concentration of hydrogen ion in 0.15 $M$ $NH_4OAc$ solution?

SOLUTION: Let $x$ = moles/l $NH_4^+$ that hydrolyze by the reaction

$$NH_4^+ + OAc^- \rightarrow NH_3 + HOAc$$

Then, according to the equation, $x$ is also the moles/l $OAc^-$ that hydrolyze, giving $x$ $M$ $NH_3$ and $x$ $M$ HOAc.

$$[NH_4^+] = 0.15 - x; \; [OAc^-] = 0.15 - x; \; [NH_3] = x; \; [HOAc] = x$$

For the equilibrium:

$$NH_4^+ + OAc^- \rightleftharpoons NH_3 + HOAc$$

$$K = \frac{[NH_3][HOAc]}{[NH_4^+][OAc^-]} = \frac{(x)(x)}{(0.15 - x)(0.15 - x)}$$

$$K = \frac{K_w}{K_{NH_3}K_{HOAc}} = \frac{1.00 \times 10^{-14}}{(1.81 \times 10^{-5})(1.8 \times 10^{-5})} = 3.1 \times 10^{-5}$$

$$= \frac{x^2}{(0.15 - x)^2}$$

$$x = 8.3 \times 10^{-4} \, M$$

Substituting this in the above concentration expressions, we get

$[NH_4^+] = 0.15 \, M;$ $[OAc^-] = 0.15 \, M;$ $[NH_3] = 8.3 \times 10^{-4} \, M;$ $[HOAc] = 8.3 \times 10^{-4} \, M$

We can calculate the $[H^+]$ from the dissociation constant of acetic acid, since we know all but one of the concentration terms.

$$K_{HOAc} = \frac{[H^+][OAc^-]}{[HOAc]} = 1.8 \times 10^{-5}$$

$$\frac{[H^+](0.15)}{8.3 \times 10^{-4}} = 1.8 \times 10^{-5}$$

$$[H^+] = 1.0 \times 10^{-7} \, M$$

■ P R O B L E M  770  Calculate the hydrogen-ion concentration in a solution made by putting 0.77 g ammonium acetate in 250 ml water.

ANSWER: $[H^+] = 1.0 \times 10^{-7} \, M$

## Hydrolysis of $Na_2CO_3$ and $Na_2S$

Sodium carbonate and sodium sulfide represent salts in which dinegative anions, derived from diprotic acids, can hydrolyze to a considerable extent. The way of handling the problem mathematically is similar to that used for acetate ion except that the dissociation constant in question is $K_{II}$.

P R O B L E M  771  Calculate the pH of 0.150 $M$ $Na_2CO_3$ solution and the per cent hydrolysis. $K_{II} = 4.84 \times 10^{-11}$.

SOLUTION: The hydrolysis reaction can be written

$$CO_3^{=} + H_2O \rightarrow HCO_3^- + OH^-$$

corresponding to the pick-up of a proton from $H_2O$ by $CO_3^=$ to form $HCO_3^-$ and set free $OH^-$. The equilibrium constant for this reaction has the form

$$K_{hyd} = \frac{[HCO_3^-][OH^-]}{[CO_3^=]}$$

If we multiply numerator and denominator by $[H^+]$ we get

$$K_{hyd} = \frac{[HCO_3^-][OH^-]}{[CO_3^=]} \frac{[H^+]}{[H^+]} = \frac{[H^+][OH^-]}{[H^+][CO_3^=]/[HCO_3^-]} = \frac{K_w}{K_{II}}$$

where the numerator is $K_w$ and the denominator is the second dissociation constant of "carbonic acid." Thus, we can evaluate $K_{hyd} = 1.00 \times 10^{-14}/4.84 \times 10^{-11} = 2.07 \times 10^{-4}$.

To solve the problem of $0.150\ M\ Na_2CO_3$, let us put $x$ as the moles/l $CO_3^=$ that get hydrolyzed over to $HCO_3^-$ and $OH^-$. This will decrease the concentration of $CO_3^=$ from 0.150 to $(0.150 - x)$ and will raise the concentration of $HCO_3^-$ and $OH^-$ from zero to $x$. At equilibrium we will then have

$$[CO_3^=] = 0.150 - x;\ [HCO_3^-] = x;\ [OH^-] = x$$

$$K_{hyd} = \frac{[HCO_3^-][OH^-]}{[CO_3^=]} = \frac{K_w}{K_{II}} = \frac{1.00 \times 10^{-14}}{4.84 \times 10^{-11}} = 2.07 \times 10^{-4}$$

$$\frac{(x)(x)}{0.150 - x} = 2.07 \times 10^{-4}$$

In solving this equation, $x$ is not quite negligible compared to 0.150, but neither is it important enough to justify using the quadratic formula. Use successive approximations: first, estimate $(0.150 - x) \cong 0.150$ and solve the rest of the equation to get $x \cong 0.558 \times 10^{-2}$; then, estimate $(0.150 - x) \cong (0.150 - 0.558 \times 10^{-2}) = 0.144$ and solve the rest to get $x = 0.546 \times 10^{-2}$; finally, try $(0.150 - x) \cong (0.150 - 0.546 \times 10^{-2}) = 0.145$. We get $x = 5.48 \times 10^{-3}$. This gives us the concentration of hydroxide ion. We want the concentration of hydrogen ion.

$$[H^+] = \frac{K_w}{[OH^-]} = \frac{1.00 \times 10^{-14}}{5.48 \times 10^{-3}} = 1.82 \times 10^{-12}$$

$$pH = -\log[H^+] = -\log(1.82 \times 10^{-12}) = -(0.260 - 12)$$
$$= 11.740$$

The per cent hydrolysis is the amount hydrolyzed divided by what was available originally. The amount hydrolyzed is $5.48 \times 10^{-3}$ $M$; the amount available was $0.150$ $M$.

$$\% \text{ hydrolysis} = \frac{5.48 \times 10^{-3}}{0.150} \times 100 = 3.65\%$$

■ **P R O B L E M  772**  Calculate the pH of $0.100$ $M$ $Na_2CO_3$ and figure out the per cent hydrolysis.

ANSWER: pH = 11.650; $\%$ hydrolysis = 4.46$\%$

For the preceding problems, we might raise the question: How come we worry only about picking up one proton? Isn't it possible that a second proton will be picked up as well? The answer is: Although in principle a second proton can be picked up by a reaction such as

$$HCO_3^- + H_2O \rightarrow H_2O + CO_2 + OH^-$$

not much of this reaction will occur. There are two reasons for this: (1) there is not much $HCO_3^-$ to start with, only the small amount formed by the first stage of hydrolysis $CO_3^= + H_2O \rightleftharpoons HCO_3^- + OH^-$; (2) the dissociation $K$ of $H_2O + CO_2$ (which can also be written $H_2CO_3$) is relatively large, which means $HCO_3^-$ does not have nearly the affinity for protons that $CO_3^=$ does. Therefore, the second stage of hydrolysis is less likely to occur. We will generally ignore it in computing the $OH^-$. That is not to say, however, that we cannot compute the concentrations of the additional species involved. Once we have calculated the principal equilibrium, we can use the results to find out about the other equilibria in the same solution.

**P R O B L E M  773**  Given that the "first dissociation constant of carbonic acid" is $4.16 \times 10^{-7}$ for $H_2O + CO_2 \rightleftharpoons H^+ + HCO_3^-$ calculate the concentration of $CO_2$ in the $0.150$ $M$ $Na_2CO_3$ solution we examined in Problem 771.

SOLUTION: In Problem 771 we had

$$[CO_3^=] = 0.150 - x; \quad [HCO_3^-] = x; \quad [OH^-] = x$$

where $x$ turned out to be $5.48 \times 10^{-3}$ $M$. From this we calculated the hydrogen-ion concentration $[H^+] = K_w/[OH^-] = 1.82 \times 10^{-12}$ $M$. So, we know that in a solution of $0.150$ $M$ $Na_2CO_3$, we must have $[H^+] = 1.82 \times 10^{-12}\ M$ and $[HCO_3^-] = x = 5.48 \times 10^{-3}\ M$. But that is all we need to fix $[CO_2]$, since the equilibrium

$$CO_2 + H_2O \rightleftharpoons H^+ + HCO_3^-$$

requires

$$K_I = \frac{[H^+][HCO_3^-]}{[CO_2]} = 4.16 \times 10^{-7}$$

If we substitute into this expression $[H^+] = 1.82 \times 10^{-12}\ M$ and $[HCO_3^-] = 5.48 \times 10^{-3}\ M$, we get

$$\frac{(1.82 \times 10^{-12})(5.48 \times 10^{-3})}{[CO_2]} = 4.16 \times 10^{-7}$$

which leads to $[CO_2] = 2.40 \times 10^{-8}\ M$

PROBLEM 774    For the diprotic acid $H_2S$, the successive dissociation constants are $K_I = 1.1 \times 10^{-7}$ and $K_{II} = 1.0 \times 10^{-14}$. Calculate the concentrations of all species in 0.15 $M\ Na_2S$ solution.

SOLUTION: Take 0.15 $M\ Na_2S$ to be 100% dissociated into 0.30 $M\ Na^+$ and 0.15 $M\ S^=$.

Let $x$ = moles/l $S^=$ that hydrolyze

$$S^= + H_2O \rightleftharpoons HS^- + OH^-$$

This will give at equilibrium the following concentrations:

$[S^-] = 0.15 - x$; $[HS^-] = x$; $[OH^-] = x$

$$K_{hyd} = \frac{[HS^-][OH^-]}{[S^=]} = \frac{K_w}{K_{II}} = \frac{1.00 \times 10^{-14}}{1.0 \times 10^{-14}} = 1.0$$

$$\frac{(x)(x)}{0.15 - x} = 1.0$$

Solve this by the quadratic formula to give $x = 0.13$. The corresponding concentrations will be

$[S^=] = 0.15 - x = 0.15 - 0.13 = 0.02\ M$

$[HS^-] = x = 0.13\ M$

$[OH^-] = x = 0.13\ M$

We can also calculate the hydrogen-ion concentration:

$$[H^+] = \frac{K_w}{[OH^-]} = \frac{1.00 \times 10^{-14}}{0.13} = 7.7 \times 10^{-14} \; M$$

Furthermore, knowing both $[H^+]$ and $[HS^-]$, we can get $[H_2S]$ from the first dissociation constant corresponding to

$$H_2S \rightleftharpoons H^+ + HS^-$$

$$K_I = \frac{[H^+][HS^-]}{[H_2S]} = 1.1 \times 10^{-7}$$

$$[H_2S] = \frac{[H^+][HS^-]}{1.1 \times 10^{-7}} = \frac{(7.7 \times 10^{-14})(0.13)}{1.1 \times 10^{-7}} = 9.1 \times 10^{-8} \; M$$

Thus, we have, in summary:

$[Na^+] = 0.30 \; M$; $[HS^-] = 0.13 \; M$; $[OH^-] = 0.13 \; M$;
$[H^+] = 7.7 \times 10^{-14} \; M$; $[S^=] = 0.02 \; M$; $[H_2S] = 9.1 \times 10^{-8} \; M$

[Note the interesting point that according to the above calculation the major sulfur-containing species in $0.15 \; M$ $Na_2S$ is *not* sulfide ion but is actually $HS^-$.]

■ **PROBLEM 775** Calculate the concentration of all species in a solution made by dissolving $75.2$ g solid $Na_2S \cdot 9H_2O$ in enough water to make a liter of solution. $K_I = 1.1 \times 10^{-7}$; $K_{II} = 1.1 \times 10^{-14}$.

ANSWER: $[Na^+] = 0.626 \; M$; $[HS^-] = 0.25 \; M$; $[OH^-] = 0.25 \; M$; $[H^+] = 4.0 \times 10^{-14} \; M$; $[S^=] = 0.06 \; M$; $[H_2S] = 9.1 \times 10^{-8} \; M$

■ **PROBLEM 776** For the diprotic acid, sulfurous acid, $H_2SO_3$, the dissociation constants are: $K_I = 1.25 \times 10^{-2}$; $K_{II} = 5.6 \times 10^{-8}$. Calculate the concentration of all species in a solution made by dissolving $15.7$ g $Na_2SO_3$ per liter of solution.

ANSWER: $[Na^+] = 0.250 \; M$; $[HSO_3^-] = 1.5 \times 10^{-4} \; M$; $[OH^-] = 1.5 \times 10^{-4} \; M$; $[SO_3^=] = 0.125 \; M$; $[H^+] = 6.7 \times 10^{-11} \; M$; $[H_2SO_3] = 8.0 \times 10^{-13} \; M$

■■ **PROBLEM 777** Suppose you have $0.250$ l of the $0.15 \; M$ $Na_2S$ solution considered in Problem 774. If you drop into this solution 0.050 mole solid NaOH (assume no volume change), what will happen to the concentrations of all species?

ANSWER: $[Na^+] = 0.50\ M$ ; $[HS^-] = 0.11\ M$ ; $[OH^-] = 0.31\ M$ ;
$[H^+] = 3.2 \times 10^{-14}\ M$ ; $[S^=] = 0.04\ M$ ;
$[H_2S] = 3.2 \times 10^{-8}\ M$

## Hydrolysis of $(NH_4)_2CO_3$

Aqueous solutions of ammonium carbonate, $(NH_4)_2CO_3$, are important for two reasons: (1) they represent a typical case of complex simultaneous equilibria where both cation and anion undergo extensive hydrolysis; (2) when mixed with aqueous $NH_3$, they provide an important reagent for precipitating alkaline earth carbonates under buffered conditions.

PROBLEM 778    Given that $K_{NH_3} = 1.81 \times 10^{-5}$ for $NH_3 + H_2O \rightleftharpoons NH_4^+ + OH^-$ and $K_{II} = 4.84 \times 10^{-11}$ for $HCO_3^- \rightleftharpoons H^+ + CO_3^=$, calculate the concentrations of the species involved in 0.500 $M$ $(NH_4)_2CO_3$ solution.

SOLUTION: We assume that the 0.500 $M$ $(NH_4)_2CO_3$ is 100% dissociated into 1.000 $M$ $NH_4^+$ and 0.500 $M$ $CO_3^=$.

The $NH_4^+$ ion will hydrolyze by the reaction

$$NH_4^+ \rightarrow NH_3 + H^+$$

The $CO_3^=$ ion will hydrolyze according to the reaction

$$CO_3^= + H_2O \rightarrow HCO_3^- + OH^-$$

We assume that the $H^+$ created by the first reaction combines with $OH^-$ from the second reaction

$$H^+ + OH^- \rightarrow H_2O$$

The net reaction, obtained as the sum of these three equations, is

$$NH_4^+ + CO_3^= \rightarrow NH_3 + HCO_3^-$$

It assumes that $NH_3$ and $HCO_3^-$ are produced in about equal amounts, based on the reasoning that neither $H^+$ nor $OH^-$ can pile up in the solution in large excess.

Let $x$ = moles/l $NH_4^+$ that hydrolyze by this reaction. That will make the final equilibrium concentration of $NH_4^+$ equal to $(1.000 - x)\ M$ and will make the $CO_3^=$ go to $(0.500 - x)\ M$. At the same time, $NH_3$ and $HCO_3^-$ will be created in the solution to the extent of $x$ moles/l.

$[NH_4^+] = 1.000 - x$; $[CO_3^=] = 0.500 - x$; $[NH_3] = x$; $[HCO_3^-] = x$

These concentrations must satisfy the equilibrium condition for

$$NH_4^+ + CO_3^= \rightleftharpoons NH_3 + HCO_3^-$$

which is given by

$$K = \frac{[NH_3][HCO_3^-]}{[NH_4^+][CO_3^=]} = \frac{(x)(x)}{(1.000 - x)(0.500 - x)}$$

What is the numerical value of $K$? We can show that $K = [K_w]/(K_{NH_3}K_{II})$ by multiplying numerator and denominator by $[H^+] \times [OH^-]$ and regrouping the terms:

$$K = \frac{[NH_3][HCO_3^-]}{[NH_4^+][CO_3^=]} \frac{[H^+][OH^-]}{[H^+][OH^-]} = \frac{[H^+][OH^-]}{\underbrace{\frac{[NH_4^+][OH^-]}{[NH_3]}}\,\underbrace{\frac{[H^+][CO_3^=]}{[HCO_3^-]}}}$$

$$= \frac{K_w}{K_{NH_3}K_{II}}$$

Putting in $K_{NH_3} = 1.81 \times 10^{-5}$ and $K_{II} = 4.84 \times 10^{-11}$, we get $K = 11.4$. This gives us the equation

$$11.4 = \frac{(x)(x)}{(1.000 - x)(0.500 - x)}$$

which is best solved by the quadratic formula. It gives two roots, $x = 1.18$ or $0.465$. The former is physically impossible since it would lead to negative values of the $NH_4^+$ concentration (i.e., $1.000 - x$) and of the $CO_3^=$ concentration (i.e., $0.500 - x$). So, the root $x = 0.465$ must be the correct one. Substituting it in our expressions for concentrations above, we get

$[NH_4^+] = 0.535$ $M$; $[CO_3^=] = 0.035$ $M$; $[NH_3] = 0.465$ $M$; $[HCO_3^-] = 0.465$ $M$

We can calculate the hydrogen-ion concentration from $K_{II}$ by substituting in the values for $CO_3^=$ and $HCO_3^-$.

$$K_{II} = \frac{[H^+][CO_3^=]}{[HCO_3^-]} = 4.84 \times 10^{-11} = \frac{[H^+](0.035)}{0.465}$$

It gives us $[H^+] = 6.4 \times 10^{-10}$ $M$, which leads to $[OH^-] = K_w/[H^+]$ $= (1.00 \times 10^{-14})/(6.4 \times 10^{-10}) = 1.6 \times 10^{-5}$ $M$.

We could, of course, also calculate the hydroxide-ion concentration from $K_{NH_3}$ by substituting in the values for the concentrations of $NH_3$ and $NH_4^+$.

$$K_{NH_3} = \frac{[NH_4^+][OH^-]}{[NH_3]} = 1.81 \times 10^{-5} = \frac{(0.535)[OH^-]}{0.465}$$

It gives us $[OH^-] = 1.57 \times 10^{-5}$ $M$, agreeing with the above.

In summary, we have: $[H^+] = 6.4 \times 10^{-10}$ $M$; $[OH^-] = 1.57 \times 10^{-5}$ $M$; $[NH_4^+] = 0.535$ $M$; $[CO_3^=] = 0.035$ $M$; $[NH_3] = 0.465$ $M$; $[HCO_3^-] = 0.465$ $M$

■ P R O B L E M  779  How does the per cent hydrolysis of carbonate ion in 0.100 $M$ $(NH_4)_2CO_3$ compare to that in 0.100 $M$ $Na_2CO_3$?

ANSWER: 92.9% in 0.100 $M$ $(NH_4)_2CO_3$ compared to 4.46% in 0.100 $M$ $Na_2CO_3$

■ P R O B L E M  780  How does the per cent hydrolysis of ammonium ion in 0.250 $M$ $(NH_4)_2CO_3$ compare to that in 0.250 $M$ $NH_4Cl$?

ANSWER: 46.4% in 0.250 $M$ $(NH_4)_2CO_3$ compared to 0.00468% in 0.250 $M$ $NH_4Cl$

P R O B L E M  781  Suppose you make up a solution that is simultaneously 0.500 $M$ $(NH_4)_2CO_3$ and 1.00 $M$ $NH_3$. Calculate the equilibrium concentrations of $H^+$, $OH^-$, $NH_4^+$, $CO_3^=$, $NH_3$, and $HCO_3^-$, given $K_{NH_3} = 1.81 \times 10^{-5}$ for $NH_3 + H_2O \rightleftharpoons NH_4^+ + OH^-$ and $K_{II} = 4.84 \times 10^{-11}$ for $HCO_3^- \rightleftharpoons H^+ + CO_3^=$.

SOLUTION: Consider 0.500 $M$ $(NH_4)_2CO_3$ to be 100% dissociated into 1.000 $M$ $NH_4^+$ and 0.500 $M$ $CO_3^=$.

As in Problem 969, the net reaction will be taken to be

$$NH_4^+ + CO_3^= \rightarrow NH_3 + HCO_3^-$$

Let $x$ = moles/l $NH_4^+$ that hydrolyze this way. This will decrease the concentration of $NH_4^+$ from 1.000 to $(1.000 - x)$ $M$. It will also decrease the concentration of $CO_3^=$ from 0.500 to $(0.500 - x)$ $M$. At the same time, it will form $x$ moles $NH_3$ and $x$ moles $HCO_3^-$.

However, we start out with 1.00 $M$ $NH_3$, so the concentration of $NH_3$ goes from 1.00 to $(1.00 + x)$ $M$ while the concentration of $HCO_3^-$ goes from zero to $x$ $M$. At equilibrium, the concentrations will be $[NH_4^+] = 1.000 - x$; $[CO_3^=] = 0.500 - x$; $[NH_3] = 1.00 + x$; $[HCO_3^-] = x$

For the equilibrium:

$$NH_4^+ + CO_3^= \rightleftharpoons NH_3 + HCO_3^-$$

$$K = \frac{[NH_3][HCO_3^-]}{[NH_4^+][CO_3^=]} = \frac{K_w}{K_{NH_3}K_{II}} = \frac{1.00 \times 10^{-14}}{(1.81 \times 10^{-5})(4.84 \times 10^{-11})}$$

$$= 11.4$$

Substituting the above concentrations in the equilibrium condition gives

$$\frac{(1.00 + x)(x)}{(1.000 - x)(0.500 - x)} = 11.4$$

Solving this by the quadratic formula, we get $x = 0.413$, which leads to

$[NH_4^+] = 0.587$ $M$; $[CO_3^=] = 0.087$ $M$; $[NH_3] = 1.41$ $M$; $[HCO_3^-] = 0.413$ $M$

To get the hydrogen-ion concentration, we substitute these equilibrium concentrations of $CO_3^=$ and $HCO_3^-$ into $K_{II}$ for $HCO_3^- \rightleftharpoons H^+ + CO_3^=$:

$$K_{II} = \frac{[H^+][CO_3^=]}{[HCO_3^-]} = 4.84 \times 10^{-11} = \frac{[H^+](0.087)}{0.413}$$

$$[H^+] = 2.3 \times 10^{-10} \ M$$

from which

$$[OH^-] = \frac{K_w}{[H^+]} = \frac{1.00 \times 10^{-14}}{2.3 \times 10^{-10}} = 4.3 \times 10^{-5} \ M$$

The summary is: $[H^+] = 2.3 \times 10^{-10}$ $M$; $[OH^-] = 4.3 \times 10^{-5}$ $M$; $[NH_4^+] = 0.587$ $M$; $[CO_3^=] = 0.087$ $M$; $[NH_3] = 1.41$ $M$; $[HCO_3^-] = 0.413$ $M$

Comparing these numbers to those obtained in Problem 778, we see that the main effect of added $NH_3$ is to boost the carbonate concentration considerably and make the solution a bit more basic.

■ PROBLEM 782    Suppose you are given a solution that is 0.500 $M$ $(NH_4)_2CO_3$ and told to adjust its equilibrium carbonate concentration to a value of 0.050 $M$ by adding $NH_3$. How many moles $NH_3$ per liter would you need to add? [*Hint:* How much hydrolysis needs to occur to reduce 0.500 $M$ available $CO_3^=$ to 0.050 $M$ equilibrium concentration?]

ANSWER: **0.247 mole $NH_3/l$**

## Solutions of $NaHCO_3$

Solutions of sodium bicarbonate, $NaHCO_3$, are typical of those cases where the anion of a salt can act as an acid in dissociating off a proton $(HCO_3^- \rightarrow H^+ + CO_3^=)$ and simultaneously as a base in picking up a proton $(HCO_3^- + H^+ \rightarrow H_2O + CO_2)$. The same problem was raised on page 272 in connection with $NaHSO_4$, but there it was pointed out that $HSO_4^-$ has no appreciable tendency to pick up $H^+$, since $H_2SO_4$ is a strong electrolyte (100% dissociated) for the first step of dissociation. The exact mathematical analysis of $NaHCO_3$ solutions can be done by defining five unknowns for $H^+$, $OH^-$, $CO_2$, $HCO_3^-$, and $CO_3^=$ and writing five simultaneous equations (three from the three equilibrium conditions set by $K_I$, $K_{II}$, and $K_w$ and two from the electrical neutrality requirement and mass conservation condition). Solving these five simultaneous equations is extraordinarily difficult (more so than was the analogous case on page 386), so we cast about for some simplifying assumptions. We get a major assist from noting that

$$HCO_3^- \rightarrow H^+ + CO_3^=$$

cannot "go" much farther to the right than does the reaction

$$HCO_3^- + H^+ \rightarrow H_2O + CO_2$$

the reason being that we cannot greatly pile up excess $H^+$ in the solution (otherwise, the second reaction would sponge it up) or seriously deplete the solution of $H^+$ (otherwise, the first reaction would tend to replenish it).   The upshot is that these two reactions must go along to about the same extent—that is, the $H^+$ produced by the first is used up by the second reaction.   The situation is not unlike that encountered previously with the dual hydrolysis of $NH_4^+$ and $OAc^-$ (page 397), where the two reactions substantially cancel each other.   If we can assume that the over-all reaction is the sum of the two equations written above, then we can add the two equations to get the net reaction

$$2HCO_3^- \rightarrow CO_3^= + H_2O + CO_2$$

to describe the principal net equilibrium in a $NaHCO_3$ solution.   The reaction can be visualized as a transfer of a proton from one $HCO_3^-$ to another $HCO_3^-$, followed by immediate break-up of the $H_2CO_3$ formed into $H_2O$ and $CO_2$.

PROBLEM   783   Given that $K_I = 4.16 \times 10^{-7}$ for $CO_2 + H_2O \rightleftharpoons H^+ + HCO_3^-$ and $K_{II} = 4.84 \times 10^{-11}$ for $HCO_3^- \rightleftharpoons H^+ + CO_3^=$ calculate the $K$ for $2HCO_3^- \rightleftharpoons H_2O + CO_2 + CO_3^=$.

SOLUTION: For the equilibrium

$$2HCO_3^- \rightleftharpoons H_2O + CO_2 + CO_3^=$$

the equilibrium constant has the form

$$K = \frac{[CO_2][CO_3^=]}{[HCO_3^-]^2}$$

leaving out the water because its activity stays constant.
If we multiply the numerator and denominator by $[H^+]$ we get

$$K = \frac{[CO_2][CO_3^=]}{[HCO_3^-]^2} \frac{[H^+]}{[H^+]} = \frac{[H^+][CO_3^=]}{[HCO_3^-]} \frac{[CO_2]}{[H^+][HCO_3^-]}$$

The grouping $[H^+][CO_3^=]/[HCO_3^-]$ is just equal to $K_{II}$ for the equilibrium $HCO_3^- \rightleftharpoons H^+ + CO_3^=$.
The grouping $[CO_2]/[H^+][HCO_3^-]$ is equal to the inverse of $K_I$ for the equilibrium $CO_2 + H_2O \rightleftharpoons H^+ + HCO_3^-$.
We have, thus,

$$K = K_{II} \frac{1}{K_I} = \frac{K_{II}}{K_I} = \frac{4.84 \times 10^{-11}}{4.16 \times 10^{-7}} = 1.16 \times 10^{-4}$$

PROBLEM 784   Calculate the concentrations of the various species present in a solution that is labeled 0.500 $M$ NaHCO$_3$, using the constants given in Problem 783.

SOLUTION: The net reaction is $2HCO_3^- \rightarrow H_2O + CO_2 + CO_3^=$.
Let $x$ = moles/l $CO_2$ and $CO_3^=$ formed this way. Then $2x$ represents the moles/l $HCO_3^-$ that have disappeared in the process. This means the $HCO_3^-$ concentration has gone from 0.500 $M$ (which was put into the solution) to $(0.500 - 2x)$ $M$ at equilibrium. We can summarize the equilibrium concentrations as follows:

$$[HCO_3^-] = 0.500 - 2x; \; [CO_2] = x; \; [CO_3^=] = x$$

The condition for equilibrium for the system

$$2HCO_3^- \rightleftharpoons H_2O + CO_2 + CO_3^=$$

is that

$$K = \frac{[CO_2][CO_3^=]}{[HCO_3^-]^2} = \frac{K_{II}}{K_I} = \frac{4.84 \times 10^{-11}}{4.16 \times 10^{-7}} = 1.16 \times 10^{-4}$$

$$\frac{(x)(x)}{(0.500 - 2x)^2} = 1.16 \times 10^{-4}$$

Solving this equation by taking the square root of each side gives

$$\frac{x}{0.500 - 2x} = 1.08 \times 10^{-2}$$

or $x = 5.28 \times 10^{-3}$. Substituting in the equilibrium concentrations as summarized above, we get

$$[HCO_3^-] = 0.489 \; M; \; [CO_2] = 5.28 \times 10^{-3} \; M;$$
$$[CO_3^=] = 5.28 \times 10^{-3} \; M$$

The $[H^+]$ we can calculate either from $K_I$ or from $K_{II}$.

$$K_I = \frac{[H^+][HCO_3^-]}{[CO_2]} = 4.16 \times 10^{-7}$$

$$[H^+] = \frac{[CO_2]}{[HCO_3^-]} (4.16 \times 10^{-7}) = \frac{5.28 \times 10^{-3}}{0.489} (4.16 \times 10^{-7})$$

$$= 4.49 \times 10^{-9}$$

or

$$K_{II} = \frac{[H^+][CO_3^=]}{[HCO_3^-]} = 4.84 \times 10^{-11}$$

$$[H^+] = \frac{[HCO_3^-]}{[CO_3^=]}(4.84 \times 10^{-11}) = \frac{0.489}{5.28 \times 10^{-3}}(4.84 \times 10^{-11})$$

$$= 4.48 \times 10^{-9}$$

To get $[OH^-]$, we use the water constant $K_w$:

$$[OH^+] = \frac{K_w}{[H^+]} = \frac{1.00 \times 10^{-14}}{4.48 \times 10^{-9}} = 2.23 \times 10^{-6}\ M$$

So, in summary, we have for 0.500 $M$ NaHCO$_3$ solution:

$[Na^+] = 0.500\ M$ ; $[HCO_3^-] = 0.489\ M$ ; $[CO_2] = 5.28 \times 10^{-3}\ M$ ;
$[CO_3^=] = 5.28 \times 10^{-3}\ M$ ; $[H^+] = 4.48 \times 10^{-9}\ M$ ;
$[OH^-] = 2.23 \times 10^{-6}\ M$

■PROBLEM 785   Calculate the hydro-
gen-ion and hydroxide-ion concentrations in 0.250 $M$ NaHCO$_3$ solution.
ANSWER: $[H^+] = 4.49 \times 10^{-9}\ M$ ; $[OH^-] = 2.23 \times 10^{-6}\ M$

■PROBLEM 786   For   sulfurous   acid,
H$_2$SO$_3$, the two dissociation constants are $K_I = 1.25 \times 10^{-2}$ for
H$_2$SO$_3 \rightleftharpoons H^+ + HSO_3^-$ and $K_{II} = 5.6 \times 10^{-8}$ for HSO$_3^- \rightleftharpoons H^+ +$
SO$_3^=$.   Calculate the concentrations of all species in a solution that is
labeled 0.500 $M$ NaHSO$_3$.
ANSWER: $[Na^+] = 0.500\ M$ ; $[HSO_3^-] = 0.498\ M$ ; $[H_2SO_3] =$
1.1 $\times 10^{-3}\ M$ ; $[SO_3^=] = 1.1 \times 10^{-3}\ M$ ; $[H^+] = 2.6 \times$
$10^{-5}\ M$ ; $[OH^-] = 3.8 \times 10^{-10}\ M$

[Note: Comparing Problem 786 to Problem 784, we see
that 0.500 $M$ NaHSO$_3$ is on the acid side of neutral,
whereas 0.500 $M$ NaHCO$_3$ is on the basic.   Which side
it happens to be depends on which of the reactions pre-
dominates—the proton dissociation or the proton accept-
ance.   Incidentally, the excess moles of H$^+$ over OH$^-$,
or vice versa, gives a measure of how far off we are from
the perfect matching that we assumed in writing the net
reaction above as the sum of the two equations.]

## PROBLEM 787

Suppose you have 0.280 l of 0.500 $M$ $NaHCO_3$ and you add to it 24.0 ml of 0.500 $M$ NaOH. What happens to all the concentrations in the solution? $K_I = 4.16 \times 10^{-7}$; $K_{II} = 4.84 \times 10^{-11}$.

SOLUTION: 24.0 ml of 0.500 $M$ NaOH supplies 0.0120 mole $Na^+$ and 0.0120 mole $OH^-$.

0.280 l of 0.500 $M$ $NaHCO_3$ supplies 0.140 mole $Na^+$ and 0.140 mole $HCO_3^-$.

Let us assume as a first approximation that the $OH^-$ is completely used up by $HCO_3^-$ in the reaction

$$OH^- + HCO_3^- \rightarrow H_2O + CO_3^=$$

This will use up 0.0120 mole $HCO_3^-$, leaving 0.140 − 0.012, or 0.128, mole $HCO_3^-$; it will form 0.0120 mole $CO_3^=$.

The total volume of the solution is 0.304 l.

The following concentrations are available:

$$Na^+: \frac{0.0120 \text{ mole} + 0.140 \text{ mole}}{0.304 \text{ l}} = 0.500 \ M$$

$$HCO_3^-: \frac{0.128 \text{ mole}}{0.304 \text{ l}} = 0.421 \ M$$

$$CO_3^=: \frac{0.0120 \text{ mole}}{0.304 \text{ l}} = 0.0395 \ M$$

This, however, does not allow for the reaction

$$2HCO_3^- \rightleftharpoons H_2O + CO_2 + CO_3^=$$

Let $x = $ moles/l $CO_2$ formed this way. It will be accompanied by formation of $x$ moles/l more $CO_3^=$ and a decrease of $2x$ moles/l $HCO_3^-$. So, at equilibrium the concentrations will be

$$[HCO_3^-] = 0.421 - 2x; \quad [CO_3^=] = 0.0395 + x; \quad [CO_2] = x$$

Substitute these in the equilibrium condition:

$$K = \frac{[CO_2][CO_3^=]}{[HCO_3^-]^2} = \frac{K_{II}}{K_I} = \frac{4.84 \times 10^{-11}}{4.16 \times 10^{-7}} = 1.16 \times 10^{-4}$$

$$\frac{(x)(0.0395 + x)}{(0.421 - 2x)^2} = 1.16 \times 10^{-4}$$

This looks like a hard one to solve, except that we might guess $x$ to be small since the effect of added $CO_3^=$ will be to repress the tendency to form more. If we neglect the $x$ terms where added or subtracted, we get $x \cong 5.20 \times 10^{-4}$ as a first approximation. If we put this $x$ in place of the dropped terms, we get $x \cong 5.12 \times 10^{-4}$ as a second approximation. A third approximation gives also $x = 5.12 \times 10^{-4}$. Substituting this value of $x$ in the above equilibrium concentrations, we get

$$[HCO_3^-] = 0.420 \ M; \ [CO_3^=] = 0.0400 \ M; \ [CO_2] = 5.12 \times 10^{-4} \ M$$

To get $[H^+]$, we use $K_{II}$:

$$[H^+] = \frac{[HCO_3^-]}{[CO_3^=]} (4.84 \times 10^{-11}) = 5.08 \times 10^{-10} \ M$$

To get $[OH^-]$, we use $K_w$:

$$[OH^-] = \frac{K_w}{[H^+]} = \frac{1.00 \times 10^{-14}}{5.08 \times 10^{-10}} = 1.97 \times 10^{-5} \ M$$

So, for the final concentrations, we would have the following:

$$[Na^+] = 0.500 \ M; [HCO_3^-] = 0.420 \ M; [CO_2] = 5.12 \times 10^{-4} \ M;$$
$$[CO_3^=] = 0.0400 \ M; [H^+] = 5.08 \times 10^{-10} \ M;$$
$$[OH^-] = 1.97 \times 10^{-5} \ M$$

## ■ PROBLEM 788

Suppose you have 0.280 l of 0.500 $M$ $NaHSO_3$ and you add to it 24.0 ml of 0.500 $M$ NaOH. What happens to all the concentrations in the solution? $K_I = 1.25 \times 10^{-2}$; $K_{II} = 5.6 \times 10^{-8}$.

ANSWER: $[Na^+] = 0.500 \ M; \ [HSO_3^-] = 0.421 \ M;$
$[H_2SO_3] = 2.0 \times 10^{-5} \ M; \ [SO_3^=] = 0.0395 \ M;$
$[H^+] = 6.0 \times 10^{-7} \ M; \ [OH^-] = 1.7 \times 10^{-8} \ M$

## Hydrolysis of aluminum salts

Many of the cations of metals, especially the small-size and large-charge ones, tend to make solutions acidic because they again disturb the water equilibrium $H_2O \rightleftharpoons H^+ + OH^-$. The aluminum ion, $Al^{+3}$, is a good example of this. In aqueous solution it can be considered to react with water to form $AlOH^{++}$ and set free $H^+$ by the net reaction

$$Al^{+3} + H_2O \rightleftharpoons AlOH^{++} + H^+$$

**PROBLEM 789** The dissociation constant of $AlOH^{++} \rightleftharpoons Al^{+3} + OH^-$ has a value of $7.1 \times 10^{-10}$. Calculate the hydrolysis constant corresponding to $Al^{+3} + H_2O \rightleftharpoons AlOH^{++} + H^+$.

SOLUTION: The hydrolysis constant in this case has the usual form of species on the right in the numerator and species on the left in the denominator.

$$K_{hyd} = \frac{[AlOH^{++}][H^+]}{[Al^{+3}]}$$

If we multiply numerator and denominator by $[OH^-]$ we get

$$K_{hyd} = \frac{[AlOH^{++}][H^+]}{[Al^{+3}]} \frac{[OH^-]}{[OH^-]} = \frac{[H^+][OH^-]}{[Al^{+3}][OH^-]/[AlOH^{++}]}$$

The numerator is just $K_w$ and has the value $1.00 \times 10^{-14}$. The denominator is the equilibrium constant for the reaction $AlOH^{++} \rightleftharpoons Al^{+3} + OH^-$, which is the dissociation of hydroxyaluminum ion. Thus, the denominator has the value $7.1 \times 10^{-10}$, as given in the problem.

$$K_{hyd} = \frac{K_w}{K_{AlOH^{++}}} = \frac{1.00 \times 10^{-14}}{7.1 \times 10^{-10}} = 1.4 \times 10^{-5}$$

**PROBLEM 790** Assuming the main equilibrium is $Al^{+3} + H_2O \rightleftharpoons AlOH^{++} + H^+$, calculate the concentrations of the ions in a solution made by dissolving 6.37 g $Al(NO_3)_3 \cdot 9H_2O$ in enough water to make 0.250 l solution.

SOLUTION: One mole $Al(NO_3)_3 \cdot 9H_2O$ weighs 375.13 g.

$$6.37 \text{ g } Al(NO_3)_3 \cdot 9H_2O = \frac{6.37 \text{ g}}{375.13 \text{ g/mole}} = 0.0170 \text{ mole.}$$

Concentration would be $\dfrac{0.0170 \text{ mole}}{0.250 \text{ l}} = 0.0680 \; M.$

Aluminum nitrate is a strong electrolyte, so we assume that the 0.0680 $M$ $Al(NO_3)_3$ is 100% dissociated to give 0.0680 $M$ $Al^{+3}$ and 0.204 $M$ $NO_3^-$.

Let $x$ = moles/l $Al^{+3}$ that hydrolyze via the reaction

$$Al^{+3} + H_2O \rightleftharpoons AlOH^{++} + H^+$$

At equilibrium:

$$[Al^{+3}] = 0.0680 - x; \quad [AlOH^{++}] = x; \quad [H^+] = x$$

$$K_{hyd} = \frac{[AlOH^{++}][H^+]}{[Al^{+3}]} = \frac{K_w}{K_{AlOH^{++}}} = \frac{1.00 \times 10^{-14}}{7.1 \times 10^{-10}}$$

$$= 1.4 \times 10^{-5}$$

$$\frac{(x)(x)}{0.0680 - x} = 1.4 \times 10^{-5}$$

$$x = 9.7 \times 10^{-4}$$

Substituting this value of $x$ in the above equilibrium concentrations, we get

$$[Al^{+3}] = 0.0670 \ M; \quad [AlOH^{++}] = 9.7 \times 10^{-4} \ M;$$
$$[H^+] = 9.7 \times 10^{-4} \ M$$

Furthermore, we can solve for the hydroxide-ion concentration by using the water constant:

$$[OH^-] = \frac{K_w}{[H^+]} = \frac{1.00 \times 10^{-14}}{9.7 \times 10^{-4}} = 1.0 \times 10^{-11} \ M$$

Summarizing our results for all the species present, we have

$$[Al^{+3}] = 0.0670 \ M; \quad [NO_3^-] = 0.204 \ M;$$
$$[AlOH^{++}] = 9.7 \times 10^{-4} \ M; \quad [H^+] = 9.7 \times 10^{-4} \ M;$$
$$[OH^-] = 1.0 \times 10^{-11} \ M$$

■ PROBLEM 791 A solution was made by dissolving aluminum chloride, $Al_2Cl_6$, in water. Assuming that the only important equilibrium is $Al^{+3} + H_2O \rightleftharpoons AlOH^{++} + H^+$ for which $K_{hyd} = 1.4 \times 10^{-5}$, calculate how many g $Al_2Cl_6$ must have been dissolved in 0.450 l solution to account for an observed pH of 2.85.

ANSWER: 8.4 g

PROBLEM 792 Potassium alum is $KAl(SO_4)_2 \cdot 12H_2O$. As a strong electrolyte, it is considered to be 100% dissociated into $K^+$, $Al^{+3}$, and $SO_4^=$. The solutions are acidic because of the hydrolysis of $Al^{+3}$, but not so acidic as might be expected, because the sulfate ion can sponge up some of the hydrogen ion by forming $HSO_4^-$. Given a solution made by dissolving 11.4 g $KAl(SO_4)_2 \cdot$

$12H_2O$ in enough water to make 0.100 l solution, calculate its hydrogen-ion concentration: (a) just considering the hydrolysis $Al^{+3} + H_2O \rightleftharpoons AlOH^{++} + H^+$ with $K_{hyd} = 1.4 \times 10^{-5}$; and (b) allowing also for the equilibrium $HSO_4^- \rightleftharpoons H^+ + SO_4^=$ with $K_{II} = 1.26 \times 10^{-2}$.

SOLUTION:

(a) One mole $KAl(SO_4)_2 \cdot 12H_2O$ weighs 474.38 g.

$$11.4 \text{ g } KAl(SO_4)_2 \cdot 12H_2O = \frac{11.4 \text{ g}}{474.38 \text{ g/mole}} = 0.0240 \text{ mole.}$$

Dissolved in 0.100 l, this would give a concentration of $\dfrac{0.0240 \text{ mole}}{0.100 \text{ l}} = 0.240 \ M$.

Assuming 100% dissociation, 0.240 $M$ $KAl(SO_4)_2$ would correspond to 0.240 $M$ $K^+$, 0.240 $M$ $Al^{+3}$, 0.480 $M$ $SO_4^=$.

Considering only the hydrolysis of $Al^{+3}$ we can write

$$Al^{+3} + H_2O \rightleftharpoons AlOH^{++} + H^+$$

If $x$ = moles/l $Al^{+3}$ so converted to $AlOH^{++}$ we would have at equilibrium:

$$[Al^{+3}] = 0.240 - x; \quad [AlOH^{++}] = x; \quad [H^+] = x$$

Substituting into the hydrolysis constant, we get

$$K_{hyd} = \frac{[AlOH^{++}][H^+]}{[Al^{+3}]} = \frac{(x)(x)}{0.240 - x} = 1.4 \times 10^{-5}$$

This equation solves to give $x = 1.82 \times 10^{-3} \ M = [H^+]$.

(b) Now take into account that some of this $H^+$ just calculated will combine with $SO_4^=$ to form $HSO_4^-$. The simplest thing to do would be to assume that, because of the relatively large $SO_4^=$ concentration in the solution, all the $H^+$ set free by the $Al^{+3}$ hydrolysis gets picked up by $SO_4^=$. This means adding the two reactions:

$$Al^{+3} + H_2O \rightleftharpoons AlOH^{++} + H^+$$
$$\underline{H^+ + SO_4^= \rightleftharpoons HSO_4^-}$$
$$H_2O + Al^{+3} + SO_4^= \rightleftharpoons AlOH^{++} + HSO_4^-$$

The $K$ for this net reaction has the form

$$K = \frac{[AlOH^{++}][HSO_4^-]}{[Al^{+3}][SO_4^=]} = \frac{K_{hyd}}{K_{II}} = \frac{1.4 \times 10^{-5}}{1.26 \times 10^{-2}} = 1.1 \times 10^{-3}$$

Let $y$ = moles/l $Al^{+3}$ that convert to $AlOH^{++}$ in this new set-up.

This will produce $y$ moles/l $AlOH^{++}$ and $y$ moles/l $HSO_4^-$.
$[Al^{+3}] = 0.240 - y$; $[AlOH^{++}] = y$; $[SO_4^=] = 0.480 - y$;
$[HSO_4^-] = y$

$$K = \frac{[AlOH^{++}][HSO_4^-]}{[Al^{+3}][SO_4^=]} = \frac{(y)(y)}{(0.240 - y)(0.480 - y)} = 1.1 \times 10^{-3}$$

Solving this equation by successive approximation leads to $y = 1.1 \times 10^{-2}$, and substituting this $y$ in the concentration expressions leads to the following:

$[SO_4^=] = 0.480 - y = 0.480 - 1.1 \times 10^{-2} = 0.469\ M$

$[HSO_4^-] = y = 1.1 \times 10^{-2}\ M$

We can find the hydrogen-ion concentration by putting these values into $K_{II}$ for $HSO_4^- \rightleftharpoons H^+ + SO_4^=$:

$$K_{II} = \frac{[H^+][SO_4^=]}{[HSO_4^-]} = 1.26 \times 10^{-2}$$

$$[H^+] = \frac{[HSO_4^-]}{[SO_4^=]} (1.26 \times 10^{-2}) = \frac{1.1 \times 10^{-2}}{0.469} (1.26 \times 10^{-2})$$

$$[H^+] = 3.0 \times 10^{-4}\ M$$

Comparing this result with that obtained in part ($a$) we note that the presence of the $SO_4^=$ reduces the hydrogen-ion concentration to about one-sixth of the previous value.

■PROBLEM 793   Chromium ion, $Cr^{+3}$, hydrolyzes somewhat more extensively than does $Al^{+3}$. The $K_{hyd}$ for $Cr^{+3} + H_2O \rightleftharpoons CrOH^{++} + H^+$ is equal to $1.5 \times 10^{-4}$. Given a solution containing 24.4 g chrome alum, $KCr(SO_4)_2 \cdot 12H_2O$, per 0.100 l solution, calculate what its pH should be, taking into account the $SO_4^=$ interference. $K_{HSO_4^-} = 1.26 \times 10^{-2}$.

ANSWER: pH $= 3.03$

■PROBLEM 794   Mercuric ion, $Hg^{++}$, is also quite extensively hydrolyzed in aqueous solution, having a hydrolysis constant of $3.2 \times 10^{-3}$ for the reaction $Hg^{++} + H_2O \rightleftharpoons HgOH^+ + H^+$.   Calculate the per cent hydrolysis in 0.100 $M$

$Hg(NO_3)_2$ solution and figure out what concentration of $HNO_3$ would have to be established in the solution to limit the per cent hydrolysis to 5.0%.

ANSWER: 16% in the original solution; 0.056 $M$ $HNO_3$ needed

## Mixtures of weak acids

How do we handle the problem of two or more weak acids in the same solution? We have already worked on the problem in two of its applications: (1) any solution of a weak acid in water is really a two-electrolyte problem, because we have the dissociation $H_2O \rightleftharpoons H^+ + OH^-$ to consider as well as the dissociation $HX \rightleftharpoons H^+ + X^-$. In general, we have been able to assume that the water equilibrium is a subsidiary equilibrium which is fixed after the $HX \rightleftharpoons H^+ + X^-$ equilibrium has been computed. This procedure will break down for acids with $K_{diss}$ of the order of $10^{-12}$ or smaller and also in very dilute solutions of $HX$; (2) in the case of polyprotic acids, we have had several proton donors able to dissociate to give $H^+$ (e.g., $H_3PO_4$, $H_2PO_4^-$, $HPO_4^=$). We have avoided difficulties because in general the $K$'s for the successive dissociation steps usually go down by several orders of magnitude (e.g., $H_3PO_4$ has $K_I = 7.5 \times 10^{-3}$, $K_{II} = 6.2 \times 10^{-8}$, and $K_{III} = 1 \times 10^{-12}$), so that one of the proton donors is clearly dominant; furthermore, as a result of stepwise reaction, the concentration of each successive proton donor is much less than that of a preceding one (e.g., in a solution of $H_3PO_4$, $[H_3PO_4] > [H_2PO_4^-] > (HPO_4^=)$). Thus, we have taken the first dissociation step as the principal equilibrium and treated the second and third as subsidiary. This procedure will break down if the successive $K$'s are large and not very different from each other—for example, in the case of pyrophosphoric acid, $H_4P_2O_7$, where $K_I$ is $1.4 \times 10^{-1}$ and $K_{II}$ is $1.1 \times 10^{-2}$.

Now we have to face up to the general problem of several weak acids in equilibrium simultaneously in the same solution.

PROBLEM 795   Suppose you have a solution that is simultaneously 0.150 $M$ $HNO_2$ ($K_{diss} = 4.5 \times 10^{-4}$) and 0.200 $M$ HOAc ($K_{diss} = 1.8 \times 10^{-5}$). Calculate the concentrations of $H^+$, $NO_2^-$, and $OAc^-$ in the solution.

SOLUTION: We assume that the dissociation of water contributes a negligible concentration of hydrogen-ion and worry only about that which comes from $HNO_2$ and from HOAc.

Let $x$ = moles/l $HNO_2$ that dissociate. This will give $x$ moles/l $H^+$ and $x$ moles/l $NO_2^-$ and leave $(0.150 - x)$ moles/l undissociated $HNO_2$.

Let $y$ = moles/l HOAc that dissociate. This will give $y$ moles/l $H^+$ and $y$ moles/l $OAc^-$, leaving $(0.200 - y)$ moles/l undissociated HOAc.

The equilibrium concentration of hydrogen ion will be $x + y$—that is, the sum of what is contributed by each acid.

The equilibrium concentrations of all the species are as follows:

$[H^+] = x + y$; $[NO_2^-] = x$; $[OAc^-] = y$; $[HNO_2] = 0.150 - x$; $[HOAc] = 0.200 - y$

Both equilibria need to be satisfied:

$$HNO_2 \rightleftharpoons H^+ + NO_2^-$$

$$HOAc \rightleftharpoons H^+ + OAc^-$$

The conditions required for equilibrium are

$$K_{HNO_2} = \frac{[H^+][NO_2^-]}{[HNO_2]} = 4.5 \times 10^{-4} = \frac{(x + y)(x)}{0.150 - x}$$

$$K_{HOAc} = \frac{[H^+][OAc^-]}{[HOAc]} = 1.8 \times 10^{-5} = \frac{(x + y)(y)}{0.200 - y}$$

Obviously there is only one hydrogen-ion concentration characteristic of the whole solution, and it must satisfy each equilibrium condition.

The problem now boils down to solving the two simultaneous equations

$$4.5 \times 10^{-4} = \frac{(x + y)(x)}{0.150 - x} \quad \text{and} \quad 1.8 \times 10^{-5} = \frac{(x + y)(y)}{0.200 - y}$$

(Generally, $x$ or $y$ would be significantly smaller and could be neglected in the sum $x + y$. However, we have deliberately picked a case where this is not true.)

To solve, we first note that $x$ must be small compared to 0.150, so the denominator $(0.150 - x)$ can be approximated as 0.150. Similarly,

$y$ must be small compared to 0.200, so the denominator $(0.200 - y)$ can be approximated as 0.200. These substitutions give us

$$4.5 \times 10^{-4} \cong \frac{(x + y)(x)}{0.150} \quad \text{and} \quad 1.8 \times 10^{-5} \cong \frac{(x + y)(y)}{0.200}$$

Next, we get $y$ in terms of $x$ from one equation and substitute it in the other. From the equation on the left, we get

$$y = \frac{6.7_5 \times 10^{-5}}{x} - x$$

and substituting this into the equation on the right we get

$$x = 8.0_2 \times 10^{-3}$$

Putting this value of $x$ back into the equation on the left, we get

$$y = 0.40 \times 10^{-3}$$

We can improve the answers somewhat by using these values of $x$ and $y$ in a second approximation, where in the original equation the denominator $(0.150 - x)$ is approximated by $(0.150 - 8 \times 10^{-3})$, or 0.142. The other denominator, $0.200 - y$, was well estimated as 0.200. The second cycle of approximation leads to $x = 7.8 \times 10^{-3}$ and $y = 4.3 \times 10^{-4}$.

Substituting these numbers in our concentration expressions gives us the final equilibrium concentrations:

$$[H^+] = x + y = 7.8 \times 10^{-3} + 4.3 \times 10^{-4} = 8.2 \times 10^{-3} \; M$$

$$[NO_2^-] = x = 7.8 \times 10^{-3} \; M$$

$$[OAc^-] = y = 4.3 \times 10^{-4} \; M$$

■PROBLEM 796    In $H_2O$, propionic acid, $CH_3CH_2COOH$, and butyric acid, $CH_3CH_2CH_2COOH$, have almost the same constants for dissociating off the terminal proton. Given that $K_{diss}$ for propionic acid is $1.54 \times 10^{-5}$ and $K_{diss}$ for butyric acid is $1.51 \times 10^{-5}$, calculate the concentration of $H^+$, of propionate ion, and of butyrate ion in a solution that is simultaneously 0.100 $M$ $CH_3CH_2COOH$ and 0.100 $M$ $CH_3CH_2CH_2COOH$.

ANSWER: $[H^+] = 1.69 \times 10^{-3} \; M$;
$[CH_3CH_2COO^-] = 7.95 \times 10^{-4} \; M$;
$[CH_3CH_2CH_2COO^-] = 8.90 \times 10^{-4} \; M$

■■ P R O B L E M  797  Sulfuric acid, $H_2SO_4$, and selenic acid, $H_2SeO_4$, are strong electrolytes with 100% dissociation into $H^+$ and $HSO_4^-$ or into $H^+$ and $HSeO_4^-$. $K_{II}$ for $HSO_4^- \rightleftharpoons H^+ + SO_4^=$ is $1.26 \times 10^{-2}$ and $K_{II}$ for $HSeO_4^- \rightleftharpoons H^+ + SeO_4^=$ is $8.9 \times 10^{-3}$. What will be the concentrations of $H^+$, $SO_4^=$, and $SeO_4^=$ in a solution that is simultaneously 0.250 $M$ $NaHSO_4$ and 0.250 $M$ $NaHSeO_4$?

ANSWER: $[H^+] = 0.068\ M$; $[SO_4^=] = 0.039\ M$; $[SeO_4^=] = 0.029\ M$

P R O B L E M  798  What will be the concentrations of all the species present in a solution made by mixing 0.200 l of 0.400 $M$ HOAc and 0.600 l of 0.800 $M$ HCN? The dissociation constant of HOAc is $1.8 \times 10^{-5}$; the dissociation constant of HCN is $4 \times 10^{-10}$.

SOLUTION: Although HOAc and HCN are both weak acids, HOAc is so much stronger than HCN that its dissociation dominates the situation. In other words, the concentration of hydrogen ion coming from the dissociation of HCN is peanuts compared to what comes from the dissociation of HOAc.

First calculate the concentration of HOAc and HCN in the mixture. The HOAc gets diluted from 0.200 l to 0.800 l, so its concentration falls to (0.200/0.800) of 0.400 $M$, or 0.100 $M$. The HCN gets diluted from 0.600 l to 0.800 l, so its concentration goes to (0.600/0.800) of 0.800 $M$, or 0.600 $M$.

Let $x$ = moles/l HOAc that dissociate. This will give $x$ moles/l $H^+$ and $x$ moles/l $OAc^-$, leaving $(0.100 - x)$ moles/l undissociated HOAc.

$[H^+] = x$; $[OAc^-] = x$; $[HOAc] = 0.100 - x$

$HOAc \rightleftharpoons H^+ + OAc^-$

$$K = \frac{[H^+][OAc^-]}{[HOAc]} = \frac{(x)(x)}{0.100 - x} = 1.8 \times 10^{-5}$$

$x = 1.3 \times 10^{-3}\ M$

Let $y$ = moles/l HCN that dissociate. This will produce $y$ moles/l $H^+$ and $y$ moles/l $CN^-$, leaving $(0.600 - y)$ moles/l undissociated HCN. The $H^+$ adds on to the $1.3 \times 10^{-3}$ $M$ that comes from the HOAc to make $[H^+] = 1.3 \times 10^{-3} + y$, but $y$ is such a small number that it is negligible compared to $1.3 \times 10^{-3}$. Therefore, we can write for the equilibrium concentrations:

$[H^+] = 1.3 \times 10^{-3}$; $[CN^-] = y$; $[HCN] = 0.600 - y$

$HCN \rightleftharpoons H^+ + CN^-$

$$K = \frac{[H^+][CN^-]}{[HCN]} = \frac{(1.3 \times 10^{-3})(y)}{0.600 - y} = 4 \times 10^{-10}$$

$y = 2 \times 10^{-7}$

Collecting our results, we have

$[H^+] = x = \mathbf{1.3 \times 10^{-3}}$ $\mathbf{M}$

$[OAc^-] = x = \mathbf{1.3 \times 10^{-3}}$ $\mathbf{M}$

$[HOAc] = 0.100 - x = \mathbf{0.099}$ $\mathbf{M}$

$[CN^-] = y = \mathbf{2 \times 10^{-7}}$ $\mathbf{M}$

$[HCN] = 0.600 - y = \mathbf{0.600}$ $\mathbf{M}$

Finally, we can also calculate the hydroxide-ion concentration, once we know $[H^+]$:

$$[OH^-] = \frac{K_w}{[H^+]} = \frac{1.00 \times 10^{-14}}{1.3 \times 10^{-3}} = \mathbf{7.7 \times 10^{-12}}\ \mathbf{M}$$

■ **PROBLEM** 799    Formic acid, HCOOH, has a dissociation constant of $1.76 \times 10^{-4}$ for release of the terminal proton. What will be the concentration of $CN^-$ in a solution made by adding 0.150 mole HCOOH to 0.300 l of 0.200 $M$ HCN solution? Assume no volume change. $K_{diss}$ of HCN is $4 \times 10^{-10}$.

ANSWER: $\mathbf{9 \times 10^{-9}}$

In the above calculations, we have ignored the water equilibrium $H_2O \rightleftharpoons H^+ + OH^-$ except as an afterthought. However, as noted at the beginning of this section, it becomes important in very dilute solutions. The following problem illustrates how a simple calculation such as the dissociation of acetic acid can become enormously complicated when the solute is present in very low concentration.

**PROBLEM** 800    Calculate the concentration of $H^+$ and the per cent dissociation of acetic acid in $1.00 \times 10^{-7}$ $M$ HOAc.

SOLUTION: The first impulse is to set up the problem in the usual way: let $x$ = moles/l HOAc that dissociate to give $x$ moles/l $H^+$ and $x$ moles/l $OAc^-$, leaving $(1.00 \times 10^{-7} - x)$ moles/l undissociated HOAc. Substituting these concentrations in $K_{diss}$ would give

$$K_{diss} = \frac{[H^+][OAc^-]}{[HOAc]} = \frac{(x)(x)}{1.00 \times 10^{-7} - x} = 1.8 \times 10^{-5}$$

and the quadratic formula would lead to $x = 0.995 \times 10^{-7}$. We cannot accept this result because it would give us a hydrogen-ion concentration less than that of pure water. What happened to the added acetic acid, which appears to be 99.5% dissociated?

So now we start to worry about the water dissociation. We really ought to allow for some $H^+$ to come from $H_2O \rightleftharpoons H^+ + OH^-$ as well as from $HOAc \rightleftharpoons H^+ + OAc^-$. Perhaps we can set up the problem in the same way we handled two weak acids in Problem 795. Let $x$ = moles/l $H^+$ that come from $H_2O \rightleftharpoons H^+ + OH^-$ dissociation and let $y$ = moles/l $H^+$ that come from the $HOAc \rightleftharpoons H^+ + OAc^-$ dissociation. The total concentration of hydrogen ion would then be $(x + y)$ moles/l and the other concentrations would be as follows:

$$[OH^-] = x; \quad [OAc^-] = y; \quad [HOAc] = 1.00 \times 10^{-7} - y$$

Both equilibrium conditions must be satisfied simultaneously:

$$K_w = [H^+][OH^-] = 1.00 \times 10^{-14} = (x + y)(x)$$

$$K_{HOAc} = \frac{[H^+][OAc^-]}{[HOAc]} = 1.8 \times 10^{-5} = \frac{(x + y)(y)}{1.00 \times 10^{-7} - y}$$

With two independent equations for two unknowns, we should be able to solve for $x$ and $y$. Unfortunately, $y$ is almost certainly not negligible with respect to $1.00 \times 10^{-7}$, so we appear to have some difficult algebra in prospect. We can solve the two equations by getting $x$ in terms of $y$ from the second equation:

$$x = \left(\frac{1.8 \times 10^{-5}}{y}\right)(1.00 \times 10^{-7} - y) - y$$

and substituting the result for $x$ in the first equation. We get

$$0 = y^3 + 1.79 \times 10^{-5}y^2 - 3.60 \times 10^{-12}y + 1.8 \times 10^{-19}$$

Undaunted by the third-order equation, we try to solve it only to discover to our horror that its only acceptable root $y = 1.00 \times 10^{-7}$ is paired with $x = 1.00 \times 10^{-7}$. Since $x$ represents the hydroxide-ion concentration, we are faced with the awkward question of what means a negative hydroxide-ion concentration? Actually, the situation isn't all that bad, because we can repeat the calculation carrying through more digits—more than apparently allowed by significant figure rules. But it's still a mess, and we ask whether there might be another way to set up the problem.

There is one last hope. Let us set up the problem in the most general way possible. We have four species in solution: $H^+$, $OH^-$, $OAc^-$, and HOAc. Let us define these as our four unknowns:

$[H^+] = w;\ [OH^-] = x;\ [OAc^-] = y;\ (HOAc) = z$

We need four independent equations in order to be able to evaluate all four of these unknowns:

(a) The water equilibrium must be satisfied.

$H_2O \rightleftharpoons H^+ + OH^-$

$K_w = [H^+][OH^-] = 1.00 \times 10^{-14} = (w)(x)$

(b) The acetic acid dissociation equilibrium must also be satisfied.

$HOAc \rightleftharpoons H^+ + OAc^-$

$K_{diss} = \dfrac{[H^+][OAc^-]}{[HOAc]} = 1.8 \times 10^{-5} = \dfrac{(w)(y)}{z}$

(c) The solution must remain electrically neutral. This means the positive charge concentration must equal the negative charge concentration.

$[H^+] = [OH^-] + [OAc^-]$

$w = x + y$

(d) All the acetic acid put into the solution $(1.00 \times 10^{-7}$ mole/l) has to be accounted for. It must show up either as acetate ion or as undissociated acetic acid.

$1.00 \times 10^{-7} = [OAc^-] + [HOAc]$

$1.00 \times 10^{-7} = y + z$

So here we have our four equations:

(a) $(w)(x) = 1.00 \times 10^{-14}$

(b) $\dfrac{(w)(y)}{z} = 1.8 \times 10^{-5}$

(c) $w = x + y$

(d) $1.00 \times 10^{-7} = y + z$

All we need to do is to solve them as a simultaneous set. We will minimize our troubles if we try to solve for the most abundant species first. This will probably be the hydrogen ion, so we ought to combine our equations in such a way that we end up with only the one variable $w$. (In this way we will avoid the hassle we got into in the preceding method we tried, where we were trying to solve for acetate concentration, which is probably small.) The best way to tackle the problem is to solve equation (a) for $x$ in terms of $w$ and substitute the result in equation (c). Then solve equation (d) for $z$ in terms of $y$ and substitute the result in equation (b). Finally, combine the two resulting equations to eliminate $y$. We end up with a cubic equation for $w$:

$$0 = w^3 + 1.8 \times 10^{-5}w^2 - 1.81 \times 10^{-12}w - 1.8 \times 10^{-19}$$

Using the method for third-order equations, we get $w = 1.61 \times 10^{-7}$. Feeding $w$ back into equations (a), (b), (c), and (d) we can get values for $x$, $y$, and $z$. The final results look like this:

$[H^+] = w = 1.6 \times 10^{-7}\ M$

$[OH^-] = x = 6.2 \times 10^{-8}\ M$

$[OAc^-] = y = 9.9 \times 10^{-8}\ M$

$[HOAc] = z = 0.090 \times 10^{-8}\ M$

Thus, the acetic acid in $1.00 \times 10^{-7}\ M$ HOAc solution turns out to be **99% dissociated**

■■ P R O B L E M  801  Calculate what per cent of the acetic acid is dissociated in $1.00 \times 10^{-6}\ M$ HOAc.

ANSWER: **95%**

# APPENDIXES

# LOGARITHMS

| | 0 | 1 | 2 | 3 | 4 | 5 | 6 | 7 | 8 | 9 |
|---|---|---|---|---|---|---|---|---|---|---|
| 10 | 0000 | 0043 | 0086 | 0128 | 0170 | 0212 | 0253 | 0294 | 0334 | 0374 |
| 11 | 0414 | 0453 | 0492 | 0531 | 0569 | 0607 | 0645 | 0682 | 0719 | 0755 |
| 12 | 0792 | 0828 | 0864 | 0899 | 0934 | 0969 | 1004 | 1038 | 1072 | 1106 |
| 13 | 1139 | 1173 | 1206 | 1239 | 1271 | 1303 | 1335 | 1367 | 1399 | 1430 |
| 14 | 1461 | 1492 | 1523 | 1553 | 1584 | 1614 | 1644 | 1673 | 1703 | 1732 |
| 15 | 1761 | 1790 | 1818 | 1847 | 1875 | 1903 | 1931 | 1959 | 1987 | 2014 |
| 16 | 2041 | 2068 | 2095 | 2122 | 2148 | 2175 | 2201 | 2227 | 2253 | 2279 |
| 17 | 2304 | 2330 | 2355 | 2380 | 2405 | 2430 | 2455 | 2480 | 2504 | 2529 |
| 18 | 2553 | 2577 | 2601 | 2625 | 2648 | 2672 | 2695 | 2718 | 2742 | 2765 |
| 19 | 2788 | 2810 | 2833 | 2856 | 2878 | 2900 | 2923 | 2945 | 2967 | 2989 |
| 20 | 3010 | 3032 | 3054 | 3075 | 3096 | 3118 | 3139 | 3160 | 3181 | 3201 |
| 21 | 3222 | 3243 | 3263 | 3284 | 3304 | 3324 | 3345 | 3365 | 3385 | 3404 |
| 22 | 3424 | 3444 | 3464 | 3483 | 3502 | 3522 | 3541 | 3560 | 3579 | 3598 |
| 23 | 3617 | 3636 | 3655 | 3674 | 3692 | 3711 | 3729 | 3747 | 3766 | 3784 |
| 24 | 3802 | 3820 | 3838 | 3856 | 3874 | 3892 | 3909 | 3927 | 3945 | 3962 |
| 25 | 3979 | 3997 | 4014 | 4031 | 4048 | 4065 | 4082 | 4099 | 4116 | 4133 |
| 26 | 4150 | 4166 | 4183 | 4200 | 4216 | 4232 | 4249 | 4265 | 4281 | 4298 |
| 27 | 4314 | 4330 | 4346 | 4362 | 4378 | 4393 | 4409 | 4425 | 4440 | 4456 |
| 28 | 4472 | 4487 | 4502 | 4518 | 4533 | 4548 | 4564 | 4579 | 4594 | 4609 |
| 29 | 4624 | 4639 | 4654 | 4669 | 4683 | 4698 | 4713 | 4728 | 4742 | 4757 |
| 30 | 4771 | 4786 | 4800 | 4814 | 4829 | 4843 | 4857 | 4871 | 4886 | 4900 |
| 31 | 4914 | 4928 | 4942 | 4955 | 4969 | 4983 | 4997 | 5011 | 5024 | 5038 |
| 32 | 5051 | 5065 | 5079 | 5092 | 5105 | 5119 | 5132 | 5145 | 5159 | 5172 |
| 33 | 5185 | 5198 | 5211 | 5224 | 5237 | 5250 | 5263 | 5276 | 5289 | 5302 |
| 34 | 5315 | 5328 | 5340 | 5353 | 5366 | 5378 | 5391 | 5403 | 5416 | 5428 |
| 35 | 5441 | 5453 | 5465 | 5478 | 5490 | 5502 | 5514 | 5527 | 5539 | 5551 |
| 36 | 5563 | 5575 | 5587 | 5599 | 5611 | 5623 | 5635 | 5647 | 5658 | 5670 |
| 37 | 5682 | 5694 | 5705 | 5717 | 5729 | 5740 | 5752 | 5763 | 5775 | 5786 |
| 38 | 5798 | 5809 | 5821 | 5832 | 5843 | 5855 | 5866 | 5877 | 5888 | 5899 |
| 39 | 5911 | 5922 | 5933 | 5944 | 5955 | 5966 | 5977 | 5988 | 5999 | 6010 |
| 40 | 6021 | 6031 | 6042 | 6053 | 6064 | 6075 | 6085 | 6096 | 6107 | 6117 |
| 41 | 6128 | 6138 | 6149 | 6160 | 6170 | 6180 | 6191 | 6201 | 6212 | 6222 |
| 42 | 6232 | 6243 | 6253 | 6263 | 6274 | 6284 | 6294 | 6304 | 6314 | 6325 |
| 43 | 6335 | 6345 | 6355 | 6365 | 6375 | 6385 | 6395 | 6405 | 6415 | 6425 |
| 44 | 6435 | 6444 | 6454 | 6464 | 6474 | 6484 | 6493 | 6503 | 6513 | 6522 |
| 45 | 6532 | 6542 | 6551 | 6561 | 6571 | 6580 | 6590 | 6599 | 6609 | 6618 |
| 46 | 6628 | 6637 | 6646 | 6656 | 6665 | 6675 | 6684 | 6693 | 6702 | 6712 |
| 47 | 6721 | 6730 | 6739 | 6749 | 6758 | 6767 | 6776 | 6785 | 6794 | 6803 |
| 48 | 6812 | 6821 | 6830 | 6839 | 6848 | 6857 | 6866 | 6875 | 6884 | 6893 |
| 49 | 6902 | 6911 | 6920 | 6928 | 6937 | 6946 | 6955 | 6964 | 6972 | 6981 |
| 50 | 6990 | 6998 | 7007 | 7016 | 7024 | 7033 | 7042 | 7050 | 7059 | 7067 |
| 51 | 7076 | 7084 | 7093 | 7101 | 7110 | 7118 | 7126 | 7135 | 7143 | 7152 |
| 52 | 7160 | 7168 | 7177 | 7185 | 7193 | 7202 | 7210 | 7218 | 7226 | 7235 |
| 53 | 7243 | 7251 | 7259 | 7267 | 7275 | 7284 | 7292 | 7300 | 7308 | 7316 |
| 54 | 7324 | 7332 | 7340 | 7348 | 7356 | 7364 | 7372 | 7380 | 7388 | 7396 |

|    | 0 | 1 | 2 | 3 | 4 | 5 | 6 | 7 | 8 | 9 |
|----|------|------|------|------|------|------|------|------|------|------|
| 55 | 7404 | 7412 | 7419 | 7427 | 7435 | 7443 | 7451 | 7459 | 7466 | 7474 |
| 56 | 7482 | 7490 | 7497 | 7505 | 7513 | 7520 | 7528 | 7536 | 7543 | 7551 |
| 57 | 7559 | 7566 | 7574 | 7582 | 7589 | 7597 | 7604 | 7612 | 7619 | 7627 |
| 58 | 7634 | 7642 | 7649 | 7657 | 7664 | 7672 | 7679 | 7686 | 7694 | 7701 |
| 59 | 7709 | 7716 | 7723 | 7731 | 7738 | 7745 | 7752 | 7760 | 7767 | 7774 |
| 60 | 7782 | 7789 | 7796 | 7803 | 7810 | 7818 | 7825 | 7832 | 7839 | 7846 |
| 61 | 7853 | 7860 | 7868 | 7875 | 7882 | 7889 | 7896 | 7903 | 7910 | 7917 |
| 62 | 7924 | 7931 | 7938 | 7945 | 7952 | 7959 | 7966 | 7973 | 7980 | 7987 |
| 63 | 7993 | 8000 | 8007 | 8014 | 8021 | 8028 | 8035 | 8041 | 8048 | 8055 |
| 64 | 8062 | 8069 | 8075 | 8082 | 8089 | 8096 | 8102 | 8109 | 8116 | 8122 |
| 65 | 8129 | 8136 | 8142 | 8149 | 8156 | 8162 | 8169 | 8176 | 8182 | 8189 |
| 66 | 8195 | 8202 | 8209 | 8215 | 8222 | 8228 | 8235 | 8241 | 8248 | 8254 |
| 67 | 8261 | 8267 | 8274 | 8280 | 8287 | 8293 | 8299 | 8306 | 8312 | 8319 |
| 68 | 8325 | 8331 | 8338 | 8344 | 8351 | 8357 | 8363 | 8370 | 8376 | 8382 |
| 69 | 8388 | 8395 | 8401 | 8407 | 8414 | 8420 | 8426 | 8432 | 8439 | 8445 |
| 70 | 8451 | 8457 | 8463 | 8470 | 8476 | 8482 | 8488 | 8494 | 8500 | 8506 |
| 71 | 8513 | 8519 | 8525 | 8531 | 8537 | 8543 | 8549 | 8555 | 8561 | 8567 |
| 72 | 8573 | 8579 | 8585 | 8591 | 8597 | 8603 | 8609 | 8615 | 8621 | 8627 |
| 73 | 8633 | 8639 | 8645 | 8651 | 8657 | 8663 | 8669 | 8675 | 8681 | 8686 |
| 74 | 8692 | 8698 | 8704 | 8710 | 8716 | 8722 | 8727 | 8733 | 8739 | 8745 |
| 75 | 8751 | 8756 | 8762 | 8768 | 8774 | 8779 | 8785 | 8791 | 8797 | 8802 |
| 76 | 8808 | 8814 | 8820 | 8825 | 8831 | 8837 | 8842 | 8848 | 8854 | 8859 |
| 77 | 8865 | 8871 | 8876 | 8882 | 8887 | 8893 | 8899 | 8904 | 8910 | 8915 |
| 78 | 8921 | 8927 | 8932 | 8938 | 8943 | 8949 | 8954 | 8960 | 8965 | 8971 |
| 79 | 8976 | 8982 | 8987 | 8993 | 8998 | 9004 | 9009 | 9015 | 9020 | 9025 |
| 80 | 9031 | 9036 | 9042 | 9047 | 9053 | 9058 | 9063 | 9069 | 9074 | 9079 |
| 81 | 9085 | 9090 | 9096 | 9101 | 9106 | 9112 | 9117 | 9122 | 9128 | 9133 |
| 82 | 9138 | 9143 | 9149 | 9154 | 9159 | 9165 | 9170 | 9175 | 9180 | 9186 |
| 83 | 9191 | 9196 | 9201 | 9206 | 9212 | 9217 | 9222 | 9227 | 9232 | 9238 |
| 84 | 9243 | 9248 | 9253 | 9258 | 9263 | 9269 | 9274 | 9279 | 9284 | 9289 |
| 85 | 9294 | 9299 | 9304 | 9309 | 9315 | 9320 | 9325 | 9330 | 9335 | 9340 |
| 86 | 9345 | 9350 | 9355 | 9360 | 9365 | 9370 | 9375 | 9380 | 9385 | 9390 |
| 87 | 9395 | 9400 | 9405 | 9410 | 9415 | 9420 | 9425 | 9430 | 9435 | 9440 |
| 88 | 9445 | 9450 | 9455 | 9460 | 9465 | 9469 | 9474 | 9479 | 9484 | 9489 |
| 89 | 9494 | 9499 | 9504 | 9509 | 9513 | 9518 | 9523 | 9528 | 9533 | 9538 |
| 90 | 9542 | 9547 | 9552 | 9557 | 9562 | 9566 | 9571 | 9576 | 9581 | 9586 |
| 91 | 9590 | 9595 | 9600 | 9605 | 9609 | 9614 | 9619 | 9624 | 9628 | 9633 |
| 92 | 9638 | 9643 | 9647 | 9652 | 9657 | 9661 | 9666 | 9671 | 9675 | 9680 |
| 93 | 9685 | 9689 | 9694 | 9699 | 9703 | 9708 | 9713 | 9717 | 9722 | 9727 |
| 94 | 9731 | 9736 | 9741 | 9745 | 9750 | 9754 | 9759 | 9763 | 9768 | 9773 |
| 95 | 9777 | 9782 | 9786 | 9791 | 9795 | 9800 | 9805 | 9809 | 9814 | 9818 |
| 96 | 9823 | 9827 | 9832 | 9836 | 9841 | 9845 | 9850 | 9854 | 9859 | 9863 |
| 97 | 9868 | 9872 | 9877 | 9881 | 9886 | 9890 | 9894 | 9899 | 9903 | 9908 |
| 98 | 9912 | 9917 | 9921 | 9926 | 9930 | 9934 | 9939 | 9943 | 9948 | 9952 |
| 99 | 9956 | 9961 | 9965 | 9969 | 9974 | 9978 | 9983 | 9987 | 9991 | 9996 |

# TRIGONOMETRIC
# FUNCTIONS

| angle | sin | tan | cot | cos | |
|---|---|---|---|---|---|
| 0° | .0000 | .0000 | ∞ | 1.0000 | 90° |
| 1 | .0175 | .0175 | 57.29 | .9999 | 89 |
| 2 | .0349 | .0349 | 28.64 | .9994 | 88 |
| 3 | .0523 | .0524 | 19.08 | .9986 | 87 |
| 4 | .0698 | .0699 | 14.30 | .9976 | 86 |
| 5 | .0872 | .0875 | 11.43 | .9962 | 85 |
| 6 | .1045 | .1051 | 9.514 | .9945 | 84 |
| 7 | .1219 | .1228 | 8.144 | .9926 | 83 |
| 8 | .1392 | .1405 | 7.115 | .9903 | 82 |
| 9 | .1564 | .1584 | 6.314 | .9877 | 81 |
| 10 | .1737 | .1763 | 5.671 | .9848 | 80 |
| 11 | .1908 | .1944 | 5.145 | .9816 | 79 |
| 12 | .2079 | .2126 | 4.705 | .9782 | 78 |
| 13 | .2250 | .2309 | 4.332 | .9744 | 77 |
| 14 | .2419 | .2493 | 4.011 | .9703 | 76 |
| 15 | .2588 | .2680 | 3.732 | .9659 | 75 |
| 16 | .2756 | .2868 | 3.487 | .9613 | 74 |
| 17 | .2924 | .3057 | 3.271 | .9563 | 73 |
| 18 | .3090 | .3249 | 3.078 | .9511 | 72 |
| 19 | .3256 | .3443 | 2.904 | .9455 | 71 |
| 20 | .3420 | .3640 | 2.748 | .9397 | 70 |
| 21 | .3584 | .3839 | 2.605 | .9336 | 69 |
| 22 | .3746 | .4040 | 2.475 | .9272 | 68 |
| 23 | .3907 | .4245 | 2.356 | .9205 | 67 |
| 24 | .4067 | .4452 | 2.246 | .9136 | 66 |
| 25 | .4226 | .4663 | 2.145 | .9063 | 65 |
| 26 | .4384 | .4877 | 2.050 | .8988 | 64 |
| 27 | .4540 | .5095 | 1.963 | .8910 | 63 |
| 28 | .4695 | .5317 | 1.881 | .8830 | 62 |
| 29 | .4848 | .5543 | 1.804 | .8746 | 61 |
| 30 | .5000 | .5774 | 1.732 | .8660 | 60 |
| 31 | .5150 | .6009 | 1.664 | .8572 | 59 |
| 32 | .5299 | .6249 | 1.600 | .8481 | 58 |
| 33 | .5446 | .6494 | 1.540 | .8387 | 57 |
| 34 | .5592 | .6745 | 1.483 | .8290 | 56 |
| 35 | .5736 | .7002 | 1.428 | .8192 | 55 |
| 36 | .5878 | .7265 | 1.376 | .8090 | 54 |
| 37 | .6018 | .7536 | 1.327 | .7986 | 53 |
| 38 | .6157 | .7813 | 1.280 | .7880 | 52 |
| 39 | .6293 | .8098 | 1.235 | .7772 | 51 |
| 40 | .6428 | .8391 | 1.192 | .7660 | 50 |
| 41 | .6561 | .8693 | 1.150 | .7547 | 49 |
| 42 | .6691 | .9004 | 1.111 | .7431 | 48 |
| 43 | .6820 | .9325 | 1.072 | .7314 | 47 |
| 44 | .6947 | .9657 | 1.036 | .7193 | 46 |
| 45 | .7071 | 1.0000 | 1.000 | .7071 | 45 |
| | cos | cot | tan | sin | angle |

# C

## EQUILIBRIUM VAPOR PRESSURE OF H₂O

## EQUILIBRIUM VAPOR PRESSURE OF $H_2O$

| Temp., °C | Press., mm Hg | Temp., °C | Press., mm Hg | Temp., °C | Press., mm Hg | Temp., °C | Press., mm Hg |
|---|---|---|---|---|---|---|---|
| 0 | 4.579 | | | | | | |
| 1 | 4.926 | 26 | 25.209 | 51 | 97.20 | 76 | 301.4 |
| 2 | 5.294 | 27 | 26.739 | 52 | 102.09 | 77 | 314.1 |
| 3 | 5.685 | 28 | 28.349 | 53 | 107.20 | 78 | 327.3 |
| 4 | 6.101 | 29 | 30.043 | 54 | 112.51 | 79 | 341.0 |
| 5 | 6.543 | 30 | 31.824 | 55 | 118.04 | 80 | 355.1 |
| 6 | 7.013 | 31 | 33.695 | 56 | 123.80 | 81 | 369.7 |
| 7 | 7.513 | 32 | 35.663 | 57 | 129.82 | 82 | 384.9 |
| 8 | 8.045 | 33 | 37.729 | 58 | 136.08 | 83 | 400.6 |
| 9 | 8.609 | 34 | 39.898 | 59 | 142.60 | 84 | 416.8 |
| 10 | 9.209 | 35 | 42.175 | 60 | 149.38 | 85 | 433.6 |
| 11 | 9.844 | 36 | 44.563 | 61 | 156.43 | 86 | 450.9 |
| 12 | 10.518 | 37 | 47.067 | 62 | 163.77 | 87 | 468.7 |
| 13 | 11.231 | 38 | 49.692 | 63 | 171.38 | 88 | 487.1 |
| 14 | 11.987 | 39 | 52.442 | 64 | 179.31 | 89 | 506.1 |
| 15 | 12.788 | 40 | 55.324 | 65 | 187.54 | 90 | 525.8 |
| 16 | 13.634 | 41 | 58.34 | 66 | 196.09 | 91 | 546.0 |
| 17 | 14.530 | 42 | 61.50 | 67 | 204.96 | 92 | 567.0 |
| 18 | 15.477 | 43 | 64.80 | 68 | 214.17 | 93 | 588.6 |
| 19 | 16.477 | 44 | 68.26 | 69 | 223.73 | 94 | 610.9 |
| 20 | 17.535 | 45 | 71.88 | 70 | 233.7 | 95 | 633.9 |
| 21 | 18.650 | 46 | 75.65 | 71 | 243.9 | 96 | 657.6 |
| 22 | 19.827 | 47 | 79.60 | 72 | 254.6 | 97 | 682.1 |
| 23 | 21.068 | 48 | 83.71 | 73 | 265.7 | 98 | 707.3 |
| 24 | 22.377 | 49 | 88.02 | 74 | 277.2 | 99 | 733.2 |
| 25 | 23.756 | 50 | 92.51 | 75 | 289.1 | 100 | 760.0 |

# D

## OXIDATION POTENTIALS AT 25°C

| | |
|---|---|
| $Na_{(s)} \rightarrow Na^+ + e^-$ | $E° = +2.71$ v |
| $Mg_{(s)} \rightarrow Mg^{++} + 2e^-$ | $E° = +2.37$ v |
| $Al_{(s)} \rightarrow Al^{+3} + 3e^-$ | $E° = +1.66$ v |
| $Zn_{(s)} \rightarrow Zn^{++} + 2e^-$ | $E° = +0.76$ v |
| $Fe_{(s)} \rightarrow Fe^{++} + 2e^-$ | $E° = +0.44$ v |
| $Co_{(s)} \rightarrow Co^{++} + 2e^-$ | $E° = +0.28$ v |
| $Ni_{(s)} \rightarrow Ni^{++} + 2e^-$ | $E° = +0.25$ v |
| $Sn_{(s)} \rightarrow Sn^{++} + 2e^-$ | $E° = +0.14$ v |
| $Pb_{(s)} \rightarrow Pb^{++} + 2e^-$ | $E° = +0.13$ v |
| $H_{2(g)} \rightarrow 2H^+ + 2e^-$ | $E° = $ zero v |
| $Sn^{++} \rightarrow Sn^{+4} + 2e^-$ | $E° = -0.15$ v |
| $2I^- \rightarrow I_{2(s)} + 2e^-$ | $E° = -0.54$ v |
| $2H_2O + HAsO_2 \rightarrow H_3AsO_4 + 2H^+ + 2e^-$ | $E° = -0.56$ v |
| $H_2O_2 \rightarrow O_{2(g)} + 2H^+ + 2e^-$ | $E° = -0.68$ v |
| $Fe^{++} \rightarrow Fe^{+3} + e^-$ | $E° = -0.77$ v |
| $Ag_{(s)} \rightarrow Ag^+ + e^-$ | $E° = -0.80$ v |
| $2H_2O + NO \rightarrow NO_3^- + 4H^+ + 3e^-$ | $E° = -0.96$ v |
| $4Cl^- + Au_{(s)} \rightarrow AuCl_4^- + 3e^-$ | $E° = -1.00$ v |
| $2Br^- \rightarrow Br_2 + 2e^-$ | $E° = -1.07$ v |
| $6H_2O + I_2 \rightarrow 2IO_3^- + 12H^+ + 10e^-$ | $E° = -1.20$ v |
| $2H_2O \rightarrow O_{2(g)} + 4H^+ + 4e^-$ | $E° = -1.23$ v |
| $7H_2O + 2Cr^{+3} \rightarrow Cr_2O_7^= + 14H^+ + 6e^-$ | $E° = -1.33$ v |
| $2Cl^- \rightarrow Cl_{2(g)} + 2e^-$ | $E° = -1.36$ v |
| $4H_2O + Mn^{++} \rightarrow MnO_4^- + 8H^+ + 5e^-$ | $E° = -1.51$ v |

# E

## SOME GASEOUS EQUILIBRIUM CONSTANTS

| | |
|---|---|
| $N_2 + 3H_2 \rightleftharpoons 2NH_3$ | $K = 2.37 \times 10^{-3}$ at 1000°K |
| $NH_3 \rightleftharpoons \frac{1}{2}N_2 + \frac{3}{2}H_2$ | $K = 0.395$ at 600°K |
| $2H_2 + S_2 \rightleftharpoons 2H_2S$ | $K = 9.39 \times 10^5$ at 750°C |
| $2NO + O_2 \rightleftharpoons 2NO_2$ | $K = 6.45 \times 10^5$ at 500°K |
| $PCl_5 \rightleftharpoons PCl_3 + Cl_2$ | $K = 0.0224$ at 500°K |
| | $K = 33.3$ at 760°K |
| $I_2 \rightleftharpoons 2I$ | $K = 3.76 \times 10^{-5}$ at 1000°K |
| $H_2 + CO_2 \rightleftharpoons H_2O + CO$ | $K = 4.40$ at 2000°K |
| $COCl_2 \rightleftharpoons CO + Cl_2$ | $K = 0.329$ at 1000°K |
| | $K = 0.0820$ at 900°K |
| $2H_2O \rightleftharpoons 2H_2 + O_2$ | $K = 5.31 \times 10^{-10}$ at 2000°K |
| $2SO_2 + O_2 \rightleftharpoons 2SO_3$ | $K = 261$ at 1000°K |
| | $K_p = 3.18$ at 1000°K |
| $2CO + O_2 \rightleftharpoons 2CO_2$ | $K = 2.24 \times 10^{22}$ at 1000°K |
| | $K_p = 2.73 \times 10^{20}$ |
| $2O_3 \rightleftharpoons 3O_2$ | $K = 2.54 \times 10^{12}$ at 2000°K |
| | $K_p = 4.17 \times 10^{14}$ at 2000°K |

# F

## SOME AQUEOUS DISSOCIATION CONSTANTS AT 25°C

| | |
|---|---|
| $HF \rightleftharpoons H^+ + F^-$ | $K = 6.71 \times 10^{-4}$ |
| $HClO \rightleftharpoons H^+ + ClO^-$ | $K = 3.2 \times 10^{-8}$ |
| $HClO_2 \rightleftharpoons H^+ + ClO_2^-$ | $K = 1.1 \times 10^{-2}$ |
| $HBrO \rightleftharpoons H^+ + BrO^-$ | $K = 2.06 \times 10^{-9}$ |
| $H_2S \rightleftharpoons H^+ + HS^-$ | $K = 1.1 \times 10^{-7}$ |
| $HS^- \rightleftharpoons H^+ + S^=$ | $K = 1 \times 10^{-14}$ |
| $H_2SO_3 \rightleftharpoons H^+ + HSO_3^-$ | $K = 1.25 \times 10^{-2}$ |
| $HSO_3^- \rightleftharpoons H^+ + SO_3^=$ | $K = 5.6 \times 10^{-8}$ |
| $HSO_4^- \rightleftharpoons H^+ + SO_4^=$ | $K = 1.26 \times 10^{-2}$ |
| $H_2Se \rightleftharpoons H^+ + HSe^-$ | $K = 1.88 \times 10^{-4}$ |
| $HSe^- \rightleftharpoons H^+ + Se^=$ | $K = 1 \times 10^{-14}$ |
| $H_2SeO_3 \rightleftharpoons H^+ + HSeO_3^-$ | $K = 2.7 \times 10^{-3}$ |
| $HSeO_3^- \rightleftharpoons H^+ + SeO_3^=$ | $K = 2.5 \times 10^{-7}$ |
| $HSeO_4^- \rightleftharpoons H^+ + SeO_4^=$ | $K = 8.9 \times 10^{-3}$ |
| $NH_3 + H_2O \rightleftharpoons NH_4^+ + OH^-$ | $K = 1.81 \times 10^{-5}$ |
| $HNO_2 \rightleftharpoons H^+ + NO_2^-$ | $K = 4.5 \times 10^{-4}$ |
| $H_3PO_4 \rightleftharpoons H^+ + H_2PO_4^-$ | $K = 7.5 \times 10^{-3}$ |
| $H_2PO_4^- \rightleftharpoons H^+ + HPO_4^=$ | $K = 6.2 \times 10^{-8}$ |
| $HPO_4^= \rightleftharpoons H^+ + PO_4^{-3}$ | $K = 1 \times 10^{-12}$ |
| $CO_2 + H_2O \rightleftharpoons H^+ + HCO_3^-$ | $K = 4.16 \times 10^{-7}$ |
| $HCO_3^- \rightleftharpoons H^+ + CO_3^=$ | $K = 4.84 \times 10^{-11}$ |
| $HCN \rightleftharpoons H^+ + CN^-$ | $K = 4 \times 10^{-10}$ |
| $HCNO \rightleftharpoons H^+ + CNO^-$ | $K = 1.2 \times 10^{-4}$ |
| $H_3AsO_4 \rightleftharpoons H^+ + H_2AsO_4^-$ | $K = 2.5 \times 10^{-4}$ |
| $H_2AsO_4^- \rightleftharpoons H^+ + HAsO_4^=$ | $K = 5.6 \times 10^{-8}$ |
| $HAsO_4^= \rightleftharpoons H^+ + AsO_4^{-3}$ | $K = 3 \times 10^{-13}$ |

# NOTES

# NOTES

# NOTES